Instructor's Resource Manual

with Mini Lecture Notes and Tests

GALE BREWER
EDIE CARTER

Amarillo College

3RD EDITION

INTRODUCTORY & INTERMEDIATE ALGEBRA

for College Students

BLITZER

PEARSON

Prentice
Hall

Upper Saddle River, NJ 07458

Editorial Director, Mathematics: Christine Hoag
Editor-in-Chief: Paul Murphy
Editorial Project Manager: Dawn Nuttall
Assistant Editor: Christine Whitlock
Senior Managing Editor: Linda Mihatov Behrens
Associate Managing Editor: Bayani Mendoza de Leon
Project Manager: Barbara Mack
Art Director: Heather Scott
Supplement Cover Manager: Paul Gourhan
Supplement Cover Designer: Victoria Colotta
Operations Specialist: Ilene Kahn
Operations Supervisor: Diane Peirano

© 2009 Pearson Education, Inc.

Pearson Prentice Hall

Pearson Education, Inc.

Upper Saddle River, NJ 07458

Pearson Prentice Hall™ is a trademark of Pearson Education, Inc.

The author and publisher of this book have used their best efforts in preparing this book. These efforts include the development, research, and testing of the theories and programs to determine their effectiveness. The author and publisher make no warranty of any kind, expressed or implied, with regard to these programs or the documentation contained in this book. The author and publisher shall not be liable in any event for incidental or consequential damages in connection with, or arising out of, the furnishing, performance, or use of these programs.

Printed in the United States of America

10 9 8 7 6 5 4 3 2 1

ISBN-13:   978-0-13-603169-7

ISBN-10:   0-13-603169-2

Pearson Education Ltd., *London*
Pearson Education Singapore, Pte. Ltd.
Pearson Education Canada, Inc.
Pearson Education—*Japan*
Pearson Education Australia PTY, Limited
Pearson Education North Asia, Ltd., *Hong Kong*
Pearson Educación de Mexico, S.A. de C.V.
Pearson Education Malaysia, Pte. Ltd.
Pearson Education Upper Saddle River, New Jersey

Instructor's Resource Manual

Introductory & Intermediate Algebra for College Students, Third Edition
Robert Blitzer

TABLE OF CONTENTS

TEST FORMS

Mini Lecture 1.1
Introduction to Algebra: Variables and Mathematical Models

Learning Objectives:
1. Evaluate algebraic expressions.
2. Translate English phrases into algebraic expressions.
3. Determine whether a number is a solution of an equation.
4. Translate English sentences into algebraic equations.
5. Evaluate formulas.

Examples:
1. Evaluate each expression for $x = 5$.

   a. $4(x-3)$ b. $\dfrac{6x-15}{3x}$

2. Evaluate each expression for $x = 3$ and $y = 6$.

   a. $5(x+y)$ b. $\dfrac{2x+3y}{2y}$

3. Write each English phrase as an algebraic expression. Let x represent the number.
   a. the difference of a number and six
   b. eight more than four times a number
   c. four less than the quotient of a number and twelve

4. Determine whether the given number is a solution of the equation.
   a. $x-8=12$; 20   b. $4x-7=9$; 3   c. $3(y-5)=6$; 7

5. Write each English sentence as an equation. Let x represent the number.
   a. The product of a number and seven is twenty-one.
   b. The difference of twice a number and three is equal to twenty-seven.
   c. Six less than three times a number is the same as the number increased by twelve.

Teaching Notes:
- It may be helpful to draw students' attention to the word "evaluate". Help them see the letters $v - a - l - u$. This will help them remember that evaluate means to find the value of an expression.
- Students often make mistakes with the phrase "less than" so they should be cautioned about the order of the subtraction.
- Translating from English to algebra is an important skill that will be used often .

Answers: 1a. 8 b. 1 2a. 45 b. 2 3a. $x-6$ b. $4x+8$ c. $\dfrac{x}{12}-4$ 4a. yes b. not a solution c. yes 5a. $7x=21$ b. $2x-3=27$ c. $3x-6=x+12$

Learning Objectives:
1. Convert between mixed numbers and improper fractions.
2. Write the prime factorization of a composite number.
3. Reduce or simplify fractions.
4. Multiply fractions.
5. Divide fractions.
6. Add and subtract fractions with identical denominators.
7. Add and subtract fractions with unlike denominators.
8. Solve problems involving fractions in algebra.

Examples:

1. Convert each mixed number to an improper fraction.

a. $3\frac{7}{10}$　　　b. $8\frac{3}{7}$　　　c. $5\frac{2}{3}$　　　d. $9\frac{1}{4}$

2. Convert each improper fraction to a mixed number.

a. $\frac{13}{8}$　　　b. $\frac{12}{11}$　　　c. $\frac{25}{3}$　　　d. $\frac{37}{7}$

3. Give the prime factorization of each of the following composite numbers.
a. 24　　　b. 48　　　c. 90　　　d. 108

4. What makes a number a prime?

5. Reduce the following fractions to lowest terms by factoring each numerator and denominator and dividing out common factors.

a. $\frac{10}{12}$　　　b. $\frac{32}{48}$　　　c. $\frac{24}{50}$　　　d. $\frac{77}{98}$

6. Perform the indicated operation. Always reduce answer, if possible.

a. $\frac{3}{4} + \frac{1}{6}$　　　　　b. $8\frac{1}{8} + 3\frac{1}{3}$　　　　　c. $\frac{7}{10} - \frac{3}{8}$

d. $10\frac{11}{12} - 4\frac{1}{4}$　　　e. $\left(\frac{7}{9}\right)\left(\frac{18}{19}\right)$　　　f. $\left(6\frac{2}{3}\right)\left(2\frac{1}{4}\right)$

g. $\frac{7}{8} \div \frac{3}{4}$　　　　　h. $5\frac{3}{8} \div 2\frac{1}{4}$

Teaching Notes:
- When teaching factorization, it is often helpful to review divisibility rules.
- To add or subtract fractions, you must have a LCD.
- To divide fractions, multiply by the reciprocal of the divisor.
- To multiply or divide mixed numbers, change to improper fractions first.

Answers:　　　1. a. 37/10 b. 59/7 c. 17/3 d. 37/4 2. a. 1 5/8 b. 1 1/11 c. 8 1/3 d. 5 2/7
3. a. $2 \cdot 2 \cdot 2 \cdot 3$ b. $2 \cdot 2 \cdot 2 \cdot 2 \cdot 3$ c. $2 \cdot 3 \cdot 3 \cdot 5$ d. $2 \cdot 2 \cdot 3 \cdot 3 \cdot 3$
4. a number whose only factors are 1 and itself 5. a. 5/6 b. 2/3 c. 12/25 d. 11/14 6. a. 11/12
b. $\frac{275}{24}$ or 11 11/24 c. 13/40 d. $\frac{20}{3}$ or 6 2/3 e. 14/19 f. 15 g. 7/6 or 1 1/6 h. 43/18 or 2 7/18

Mini Lecture 1.3
The Real Numbers

Learning Objectives:

1. Define the sets of numbers that make up the set of real numbers.
2. Graph numbers on a number line.
3. Express rational numbers as decimals.
4. Classify numbers as belonging to one or more sets of real numbers.
5. Understand and use inequality symbols.
6. Find the absolute value of a real number.

Examples:

1. Answer the following questions about each number:

   Is it a natural number?   Is it rational?
   Is it a whole number?   Is it irrational?
   Is it an integer?   Is it a real number?

   a. 18   b. -3.5 c. $\sqrt{5}$ d. 0   e. $-\dfrac{3}{4}$ f. π g. -5 h. 0.45

2. Graph each number on the number line.

   a. 5.5   b. $-\dfrac{16}{4}$ c. $2\dfrac{1}{4}$ d. -3.2

   (number line from -6 to 6)

3. Express each rational number as a decimal.

   a. $\dfrac{7}{8}$ b. $\dfrac{9}{11}$ c. $\dfrac{5}{3}$ d. $\dfrac{1}{4}$

4. Use $>$ or $<$ to compare the numbers.

   a. 18 □ -20 b. -16 □ -13 c. -4.3 □ -6.2

   d. $\dfrac{4}{7}$ □ $\dfrac{8}{11}$ e. $-\dfrac{3}{5}$ □ $\dfrac{2}{3}$

5. Give the absolute value.

   a. $|8|$ b. $|-5|$ c. $|-3.2|$ d. $|22|$

Teaching Notes:

- Make sure the students have minimal understanding of square roots.
- Absolute value is ALWAYS POSITIVE because it measures distance from zero.
- A number cannot be rational and irrational.
- To change a rational number to a decimal, divide the numerator by the denominator.

Answers: 1. a. natural, whole, integer, rational , real   b. rational, real   c. irrational, real
d. whole, integer, rational, real   e. rational, real   f. irrational, real   g., integer, rational, real
h. rational, real   2. See below   3. a. 0.875   b. 0.81   c. 0.6   d. 0.25   4. a. >   b. <   c. >   d. <
e. <   5. a. 8   b. 5   c. 3.2   d. 22

(number line from -6 to 6 with points marked)

Mini Lecture 1.4
Basic Rules of Algebra

Learning Objectives:

1. Understand and use the vocabulary of algebraic expressions.
2. Use commutative properties.
3. Use associative properties.
4. Use distributive properties.
5. Combine like terms.
6. Simplify algebraic expressions.

Examples:

1. Fill in the blanks.

Algebraic Expression	# of terms	coefficients	like terms
a. $6y - 3x - 4y + 8$	____	____	____
b. $5x^2 + 2y - 2x^2 + 9 - 3y$	____	____	____
c. $6x^2 - 9y + 4x + 8 - y + 5$	____	____	____

2. Name the property being illustrated and then simplify if possible.

   a. $6(x + 2) = 6x + 12$ _____

   b. $(9 \cdot 12)5 = 9(12 \cdot 5)$ _____

   c. $(x + 4) + 8 = x + (4 + 8)$ _____

   d. $(2)(3.14)(5) = 2(5)(3.14)$ _____

3. Simplify.

   a. $6x - x + 2x =$ _____
   b. $3a - 8 + 2a + 10 =$ _____
   c. $6(x + 3) - 5 =$ _____
   d. $2(x - 4) - (x - 2) =$ _____
   e. $5(y - 2) + 3(4 - y) =$ _____

Teaching Notes:

- A coefficient is the number factor of a term.
- Like terms have the very same variables raised to the same exponents.
- When applying the commutative property, only the order changes.
- The commutative property holds for addition and multiplication only.
- When applying the associative property the grouping changes.
- The associative property holds for addition and multiplication only.
- When combining like terms, add or subtract the coefficients, the variable part remains the same.
- Always use parentheses when substituting a value for a variable.

Answers: 1 a. 4; 6, –3, –4, 8; $6y$ and $–4y$ b. 5; 5, 2, –2, 9, –3; $5x^2$ and $–2x^2$; $2y$ and $–3y$
c. 6; 6, –9, 4, 8, –1, 5; $9y$ and $–y$; 8 and 5   2. a. distributive   b. associative of multiplication
c. associative of addition   d. commutative of multiplication   3. a. $7x$ b. $5a + 2$ c. $6x + 13$
d. $x – 6$ e. $2y + 2$

Mini Lecture 1.5
Addition of Real Numbers

Learning Objectives:
1. Add numbers with a number line.
2. Find sums using identity and inverse properties.
3. Add numbers without a number line.
4. Use addition rules to simplify algebraic expressions.
5. Solve applied problems using a series of additions.

Examples:
1. Find the sum using a number line.

   a. $3 + -5$ b. $-4 + -6$ c. $-1 + 2$ d. $5 + 4$

2. Add without using a number line.

   a. $-7 + -11$ b. $-0.4 + -3.2$ c. $-\dfrac{4}{5} + -\dfrac{3}{10}$ d. $-15 + 4$

   e. $7.1 + 8.5$ f. $-8 + 25$ g. $-6.4 + 6.1$ h. $\dfrac{5}{8} + -\dfrac{3}{4}$

3. Simplify the following.

   a. $-30x + 5x$ b. $-2y + 5x + 8x + 3y$ c. $-2(3x + 5y) + 6(x + 2y)$

4. Write a sum of signed numbers that represents the following situation. Then, add to find the overall change.

   If the stock you purchased last week rose 2 points, then fell 4, rose 1, fell 2, and rose 1, what was the overall change for the week?

Teaching Notes:
- When adding numbers with like signs, add and take the sign.
- When adding unlike signs, subtract the smaller absolute value from the larger absolute value, and the answer will have the sign of the number with the larger absolute value.

Answers: 1. a. -2 b. -10 c. 1 d. 9   2. a. -18 b. -3.6 c. $-\dfrac{11}{10}$ or $-1\dfrac{1}{10}$ d. -11 e. 15.6
f. 17 g. -0.3 h. $-\dfrac{1}{8}$ 3. a. $-25x$ b. $13x + y$ c. $2y$
4. $2 + (-4) + 1 + (-2) + 1 = -2$; fell 2 points

Mini Lecture 1.6
Subtraction of Real Numbers

Learning Objectives:
1. Subtract real numbers.
2. Simplify a series of additions and subtractions.
3. Use the definition of subtraction to identify terms.
4. Use the subtraction definition to simplify algebraic expressions.
5. Solve problems involving subtraction.

Examples:
1. Subtract by changing each subtraction to addition of the opposite first.

   a. $6 - 12$ b. $-15 - 15$ c. $13 - 21$ d. $\dfrac{2}{5} - \dfrac{5}{6}$

   e. $4.2 - 6.8$ f. $25 - (-25)$ g. $-51 - (-13)$ h. $14 - (-13)$

2. Simplify.

   a. $-16 - 14 - (-10)$ b. $-20.3 - (-40.1) - 18$

   c. $15 - (-3) - 10 - 18$ d. $-11 - 21 - 31 - 41$

3. Identify the number of terms in each expression; then name the terms.

   a. $4x - 6y + 12 - 3y$ b. $16 - 2x - 15$

   c. $15a - 2ab + 3b - 6a + 18$ d. $5y - x + 3y - 14xy$

4. Simplify each algebraic expression.

   a. $8x + 7 - x$ b. $-11y - 14 + 2y - 10$

   c. $15a - 10 - 12a + 12$ d. $25 - (-3x) - 15 - (-2x)$

5. Applications.

   a. The temperature at dawn was -7 degrees but fortunately the sun came out and by 4:00 p.m. the temperature had reached 38 degrees. What was the difference in the temperature at dawn and 4:00 p.m.?

   b. Express 214 feet below sea level as a negative integer. Express 10,510 above sea level as a positive integer. What is the difference between the two elevations?

Teaching Notes:
- Say the problem to yourself. When you hear the word "minus", immediately make a "change-change". That means to "change" the subtraction to addition and "change" the sign of the number that follows to its opposite.
- Remember, the sign in front of a term goes with the term.
- The symbol "−"can have different meanings:
  1. subtract or "minus" only when it is between 2 terms
  2. the opposite of
  3. negative

Answers: 1. a. -6 b. -30 c. -8 d. $-\dfrac{13}{30}$ e. -2.6 f. 50 g. -38 h. 27 2. a. -20 b. 1.8 c. -10
d. -104 3. a. 4 terms; $4x, -6y, 12, -3y$ b. 3 terms; $16, -2x, -15$ c. 5 terms; $15a, -2ab, 3b, -6a, 18$
d. 4 terms; $5y, -x, 3y, -14xy$ 4. a. $7x + 7$ b. $-9y - 24$ c. $3a + 2$ d. $5x + 10$ 5. a. 45 degrees
b. -214 feet. 10,500 feet; 10, 724 feet

Mini Lecture 1.7
Multiplication and Division of Real Numbers

Learning Objectives:
1. Multiply real numbers.
2. Multiply more than two real numbers.
3. Find multiplicative inverses.
4. Use the definition of division.
5. Divide real numbers.
6. Simplify algebraic expressions involving multiplication.
7. Determine whether a number is a solution of an equation.
8. Use mathematical models involving multiplication and division.

Examples:
1. Multiply.

    a. $(3)(-4)$ b. $(-6)(-5)$ c. $(-8)(0)$ d. $(-3.2)(-1.1)$ e. $\left(-\dfrac{3}{4}\right)\left(\dfrac{2}{9}\right)$

    f. $(-5)(2)(-1)$ g. $(-2)(2)(-3)(-3)$

2. Find the multiplicative inverse of each number.

    a. -8 b. $\dfrac{2}{5}$ c. -7 d. $\dfrac{1}{4}$

3. Use the definition of division to find each quotient.

    a. $-49 \div 7$ b. $\dfrac{-24}{-4}$

4. Divide or state that the expression is undefined.

    a. $\dfrac{-18}{0}$ b. $-\dfrac{4}{5} \div \dfrac{20}{25}$ c. $-32.4 \div 8$ d. $0 \div -8$

5. Simplify.
    a. $-3(2x)$ b. $9x + x$ c. $-12a + 4a$ d. $-(5x - 3)$

    e. $-2(3y + 4)$ f. $2(3x + 4) - (4x - 6)$

Teaching Notes:
- The product of an even number of negative numbers is positive.
- The product of an odd number of negative numbers is negative.
- Any product using zero as a factor will equal zero.
- The quotient of two real numbers with different signs is negative.
- The quotient of two real numbers with same signs is positive.
- Division of a non-zero number by zero is undefined.
- Any non-zero number divided into 0 is 0.

Answers: 1. a. -12 b. 30 c. 0 d. 3.52 e. $-\dfrac{1}{6}$ f. 10 g. -36 2. a. $-\dfrac{1}{8}$ b. $\dfrac{5}{2}$ c. $-\dfrac{1}{7}$ d. $\dfrac{4}{1}$
3. a. -7 b. 6 4. a. undefined b. -1 c. -4.05 d. 0 5.a. $-6x$ b. $10x$ c. $-8a$ d. $-5x + 3$
e. $-6y - 8$ f. $2x + 14$

Mini Lecture 1.8
Exponents and Order of Operations

<u>**Learning Objectives:**</u>
1. Evaluate exponential expressions.
2. Simplify algebraic expressions with exponents.
3. Use order of operation agreement.
4. Evaluate mathematical models.

<u>**Examples:**</u>
1. Identify the base and the exponent, then evaluate.
   a. 3^4 b. $(-4)^3$ c. -8^2 d. $(-8)^2$

2. Evaluate.
   a. 13^2 b. 2^5 c. $(-3)^3$ d. 5^2

3. Simplify if possible.
   a. $6x^2 - x^2$ b. $5y^3 + 2y - 3y^3$ c. $6a^2 + 2a - 4a^2 - 6a$
   d. $10p^3 - 8p^2$

4. Simplify by using the order of operations.
   a. $30 \div 2 \cdot 3 - 52$
   b. $14 - (33 \div 11) + 4$
   c. $(5 + 2)^2$
   d. $10 - 7(32 \div 8) + 5 \cdot 3$
   e. $\left(\dfrac{1}{4}\right) + \left(\dfrac{1}{3}\right)^2$
   f. $15 - 3[8 - (-12 \div 2^2) - 4^2]$
   g. $\dfrac{16 + 4^2 \div 8}{-2 - (-5)}$
   h. $22 + 5(x + 7) - 3x - 10$

5. 5. Evaluate each expression for the given value.
   a. $-a - a^2$ if $a = -3$ b. $-a - a^2$ if $a = 3$ c. $4x^2 - x + 3x$ if $x = -1$

6. Use the formula for perimeter of a rectangle, $P = 2w + 2l$ to find the perimeter of a rectangle if the length is 28 cm and the width is 15 cm.

<u>**Teaching Notes:**</u>
- If the negative sign is part of the base, it will be inside the parentheses.
- **NEVER** multiply the base and the exponent together.
- The exponent tells how many times to write the base as a factor.
- Always use parentheses when substituting a value for a variable.
- The Order of Operations must be followed on every problem.

<u>Answers:</u> 1. a. 81 b. −64 c. −64 d. 64 2. a. 169 b. 32 c. −27 d. 25 3. a. $5x^2$ b. $2y^3 + 2y$
c. $2a^2 - 4a$ d. $10p^3 - 8p^2$ 4. a. −7 b. 15 c. 49 d. −3 e. $\dfrac{13}{36}$ f. 30 g. 6 h. $2x + 47$
5. a. −6 b. −12 c. 2 6. 86 cm

Mini Lecture 2.1
The Addition Property of Equality

Learning Objectives:
1. Identify linear equations in one variable.
2. Use the addition property of equality to solve equations.
3. Solve applied problems using formulas.

Examples:
1. Identify the linear equations in one variable.
   a. $x + 7 = 10$
   b. $x^2 - 2 = 7$
   c. $\dfrac{3}{x} = 5$
   d. $|x + 1| = 6$
2. Solve the following equations using the addition property of equality. Be sure to check your proposed solution.
   a. $x + 2 = 17$

   b. $-12 = x - 9$

   c. $x - \dfrac{1}{2} = 4$

   d. $3x - 2x = 8$

   e. $5x + 1 = 4(x - 2)$

   f. $x + 3.5 = 4.8$

   g. $2x + 5 = x - 2$

   h. $3x + 5 = 2x + 5$

3. If Sue is 2 years older than John then we will use S to represent Sue's age and J to represent John's age. Use the equation $S = J + 2$ to find John's age if Sue is 41.

Teaching Notes:
- Solving an equation is the process of finding the number (or numbers) that make the equation a true statement. These numbers are called the solutions, or roots, or the equation.
- To apply the addition property of equality, one must add the same number or expression to both sides of the equation.
- Equivalent equations are equations that have the same solution.

Answers: 1. a. linear b. not linear c. not linear d. not linear 2. a. 15 b. -3 c. $4\dfrac{1}{2}$ or $\dfrac{9}{2}$ d. 8
e. -9 f. 1.3 g. -7 h. 0 3. 39

Mini Lecture 2.2
The Multiplication Property of Equality

Learning Objectives:
1. Use multiplication property of equality to solve equations.
2. Solve equations in the form $-x = c$.
3. Use addition and multiplication properties to solve equations.

Examples:

1. Multiply both sides of the equation by the reciprocal of the coefficient of the variable to solve for the variable.

   a. $6x = 18$ b. $-2x = -14$ c. $15y = -10$ d. $24 = -3x$

2. Divide both sides of the equation by the coefficient of the variable to solve for the variable.

   a. $6x = 18$ b. $-2x = -14$ c. $15y = -10$ d. $24 = -3x$

Both of the above methods of isolating the variable are effective for solving equations.

3. Solve each equation by multiplying or dividing.

   a. $18y = -108$ b. $\dfrac{3}{5}x = 12$ c. $124 = \dfrac{x}{3}$ d. $-7x = -63$

4. Multiply or divide both sides of each equation by -1 to get a positive x.

   a. $-x = -7$ b. $82 = -x$ c. $-a = -\dfrac{3}{7}$ d. $14 = -x$

5. Solve each equation.

   a. $3x - 5 = 13$ b. $18 - 6x = 14 - 2x$ c. $23 = 2a - 7$

   d. $-6y - 21 = 21$ e. $33 - x = 3x - 11$ f. $\dfrac{2}{3}x - 6 = 12$

Teaching Notes:
- Remind students that reciprocals always have the same sign.
- When students see $-x$ they must realize the coefficient is -1.

Answers: 1. a. $x = 3$ b. $x = 7$ c. $y = -\dfrac{2}{3}$ d. $x = -8$ 2. a. $x = 3$ b. $x = 7$ c. $y = -\dfrac{2}{3}$ d. $x = -8$

3. a. $y = -6$ b. $x = 20$ c. $x = 372$ d. $x = 9$ 4. a. $x = 7$ b. $x = -82$ c. $a = \dfrac{3}{7}$ d. $x = -14$

5. a. $x = 6$ b. $x = 1$ c. $a = 15$ d. $y = -7$ e. $x = 11$ f. $x = 27$

Mini Lecture 2.3
Solving Linear Equations

Learning Objectives:
1. Solve linear equations.
2. Solve linear equations containing fractions.
3. Identify equations with no solution or infinitely many solutions.
4. Solve applied problems using formulas.

Examples:

1. $3x + 2x + 8 = -7 + x + 11$

2. $6x = 3(x + 9)$

3. $5(2x - 1) - 15 = 3(4x + 2) + 4$

4. $\dfrac{x}{5} = \dfrac{2x}{3} + \dfrac{7}{15}$

5. $2x + 9 = 2(x + 4)$

6. $4(x + 2) + 5 = 5(x + 1) + 8$

7. Use the formula $P = 4s$ to find the length of a side of a square whose perimeter is 32 in.

Teaching Notes:
- Simplify the algebraic expression on each side of the equal sign.
- Collect variable terms on one side of the equal sign and all constant terms on the other side of the equal sign.
- Isolate the variable and solve.
- Check your solution in the original expression.

Answers: 1. −1   2. 9   3. −15   4. −1   5. inconsistent, no solution   6. 0   7. 8 inches

Mini Lecture 2.4
Formulas and Percents

Learning Objectives:
1. Solve a formula for a variable.
2. Express decimals as percents and percents as decimals.
3. Solve applied problems involving percent.

Examples:
1. Solve the formula for the indicated variable by isolating the variable.

   a. $A = \dfrac{B_1 + B_2}{2}$ for B_1 b. $P = a + b + c$ for c

   c. $A = \pi r^2 h$ for h d. $4p + H = M$ for p

   e. $Ax + By = C$ for A f. $y = mx + b$ for b

2. Express each percent as a decimal.

   a. 42%   b. 4%   c. 0.8%   d. 56%   e. 310%   f. $\dfrac{3}{4}$%

3. Express each decimal as a percent.
   a. 0.47   b. 0.33   c. 0.05   d. 6.21   e. 110   f. 0.004

4. Translate each question into an equation using the percent formula, $A = PB$, then solve the equation.
   a. What is 15 percent of 60?   b. 62% of what number is 31?

   c. What percent of 132 is 33?   d. 60 is what percent of 500?

Teaching Notes:
- Many students have trouble solving formulas for a letter and need to be reminded the same steps are used when solving for a letter in a formula as are used when solving any equation for a variable.
- When changing a decimal to a percent, move the decimal point two places to the right and use the % symbol.
- When changing a percent to a decimal, move the decimal point two places to the left and drop the % symbol.
- When translating English into a mathematical equation, the word "is" translates to equals and the word "of" means multiply.

Answers: 1. a. $B_1 = 2A - B_2$ b. $c = P - a - b$ c. $h = \dfrac{A}{\pi r^2}$ d. $p = \dfrac{M - H}{4}$ e. $A = \dfrac{C - By}{x}$

f. $b = y - mx$ 2. a. 0.42   b. 0.04   c. 0.008   d. 0.56   e. 3.1   f. 0.0075   3. a. 47%   b. 33%   c. 5%
d. 621%   e. 11000%   f. 0.4%   4. a. $x = 0.15(60)$; 9   b. $0.62x = 31$; 50   c. $x \cdot 132 = 33$; 25%
d. $60 = x \cdot 500$; 12%

Mini Lecture 2.5
An Introduction to Problem Solving

Learning Objectives:
1. Translate English phrases into algebraic expressions.
2. Solve algebraic word problems using linear equations.

Examples:
1. Translate each English phrase into an algebraic expression. Let "x" represent the unknown.
   a. Three times a number decreased by 11.
   b. The product of seven and a number increased by 2.
   c. Eight more than a number.

2. Translate each sentence into an algebraic equation and then solve the equation.
   a. Twice a number less five is eleven.
   b. Five times the sum of a number and eight is 30.

3. Identify all unknowns, set up an equation, and then solve.
   a. Bill earns five dollars more per hour than Joe. Together their pay for one hour totals $21. How much does each man earn per hour?
   b. Two consecutive even integers equal 42. Find the integers.

Teaching Notes for solving algebraic equations:
- Make sure to familiarize all students with basic mathematical terms and the proper way to translate to algebraic terms.
- First, read the problem carefully and assign a variable for one of the unknown quantities.
- Write expressions if necessary for any other unknown quantities in terms of same variable.
- Write an equation for the stated problem.
- Solve the equation and answer the question.
- Check the solution in the original stated problem.

Answers: 1. a. $3x - 11$ 2. a. $2x - 5 = 11$
        b. $7x + 2$ $x = 8$
        c. $x + 8$ b. $5(x + 8) = 30$
                       $x = -2$

      3. a. $x =$ Joe   b. $x = 1^{st}$ even integer
          $x + 5 =$ Bill $x + 2 = 2^{nd}$ even integer
          $x + (x + 5) = 21$ $x + (x + 2) = 42$
          $x = \$8$ (Joe) $x = 20$
          $x + 5 = \$13$ (Bill) $x + 2 = 22$

Mini Lecture 2.6
Problem Solving in Geometry

Learning Objectives:

1. Solve problems using formulas for perimeter and area.
2. Solve problems using formulas for a circle's area and circumference.
3. Solve problems using formulas for volume.
4. Solve problems involving the angles of a triangle.
5. Solve problems involving complementary and supplementary angles.

Examples:

1. A triangular flower bed has an area of 48 square feet and a height of 12 feet. Find the base of the flower bed.

2. The diameter of a fish pond is 6 feet. Find the area and circumference of the fish pond. First express answer in terms of π, then round both answers to the nearest square foot and foot respectively.

3. Which is the better buy: a 3 liter bottle of soft drink for $2.99 or a 1.2 liter bottle for $1.10?

4. Find the volume of a cylinder with a radius of 2 inches and height of 6 inches. Give answer in π form and then round answer to nearest cubic inch.

5. A volleyball has a radius of 3 inches. Find how much air is needed to fill the ball. Give answer in π form and then round answer to nearest cubic inch.

6. Given a right triangle and knowing that the two acute angles are complementary, find the measure of each if one angle is twice the measure of the other.

Teaching Notes:

- Make sure to emphasize the formulas outlined in the section.
- Write formula, substitute the given values and solve for the unknown.

Answers: 1. base = 8 ft. 2. area = 9π ft^2, 28 ft^2; circumference = 6π ft., 19 ft. 3. 1.2 liter bottle 4. 24π in^3, 75 ft^3 5. 36π in^3, 113 in^3 6. 30°, 60°

Mini Lecture 2.7
Solving Linear Inequalities

Learning Objectives:
1. Graph inequality solutions on a number line.
2. Use set builder notation and interval notation.
3. Solve linear inequalities in one variable.

Examples:
1. Graph each inequality on the number line.

   a. $x \geq -4$ b. $x < 3$ c. $-1 \leq x < 5$

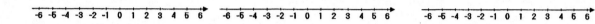

2. Solve each inequality. Write answers in set builder notation and interval notation.

   a. $4x - 3 \leq 5$ b. $6 - x \geq 3$ c. $6x - 12 < 8x - 14$

3. Solve each inequality and give the solution in set builder notation: Graph solution on a number line.

   a. $\dfrac{1}{5}x > -3$ b. $4(6 - 2x) \geq 12 - 4x$ c. $12x - 3 \geq 4(3x + 2)$

   d. $5(x - 3) \geq 5x - 15$ e. $20 < 3x + 5$ f. $2(x - 5) > 5x + 3$

Teaching Notes:
- When graphing the solution of an inequality:
  Use a solid dot when the end point is included in the solution. ($\geq$ or $\leq$)
- When graphing the solution of an inequality:
  Use an open dot when the end point is not included in the solution. ($>$ or $<$)
- When an inequality is multiplied or divided by a negative value, the inequality symbol must be reversed.

Answers: 1. a. b.

c.

2. a. $\{x \mid x \leq 2\}$ $(-\infty, 2]$ b. $\{x \mid x \leq 3\}$ $(-\infty, 3]$ c. $\{x \mid x > 1\}$ $(1, \infty)$

ML-15

3. a. $x > -15$ $\{x \mid x > -15\}$

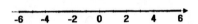

b. $x \leq 3$ $\{x \mid x \leq 3\}$

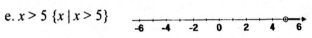

c. No Solution { } or ∅

d. All Real Numbers $\{x \mid x \text{ is a real number}\}$

e. $x > 5$ $\{x \mid x > 5\}$

f. $x > -\dfrac{13}{3}$ $\left\{x \mid x > -\dfrac{13}{3}\right\}$

Mini Lecture 3.1
Graphing Equations in Two Variables

Learning Objectives:
1. Plot ordered pairs in the rectangular coordinate system.
2. Find coordinates of points in the rectangular coordinate system.
3. Determine whether an ordered pair is a solution of an equation.
4. Find solutions of an equation in two variables.
5. Use point plotting to graph linear equations.
6. Use graphs of linear equations to solve problems.

Examples:
1. Plot the given points in a rectangular coordinate system. Indicate in which quadrant each point lies.
    a. $(-2, -4)$
    b. $(3, 1)$
    c. $(-2, 3)$
    d. $(5, -2)$
2. Give the ordered pairs that correspond to the points labeled.

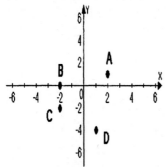

3. Determine if the ordered pair is a solution for the given equation.
    a. $2x + 3y = 10$ $(2, 2)$
    b. $3x - y = 5$ $(-1, 2)$

4. Find five solutions for $y = 2x - 1$ by completing the table of values.
    a.

x	$y = 2x - 1$	(x, y)
-2		
-1		
0		
1		
2		

    b. Plot the ordered pairs to graph the line $y = 2x - 1$.

5. Find five solutions for $y = -x + 1$ by completing the table of values.
    a.

x	$y = -x + 1$	(x, y)
-2		
-1		
0		
1		
2		

    b. Plot the ordered pairs to graph the quadratic equation $y = -x + 1$.

6. a. Your cell phone contract has a base charge of $10 per month and a $.03 per minute charge for nation-wide calling. Create a table of values for $y = .03x + 10$. Use 0, 60, 120, 180, 240 for x.

   b. Plot the ordered pairs to graph the above equation.

Teaching Notes:
- The basics for plotting ordered pairs comes from section 1.3.
- When graphing linear equations $(y = mx + b)$ on a coordinate plane, the ordered pairs will form a line when connected.
- Quadratic equations $y = ax^2 + bx + c$ when graphed on a coordinate plane form a parabola.

Answers: 1.

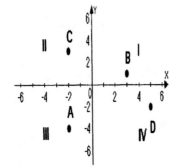

2.a. (2, 1) b. (–2, 0) c. (–1, –2) d. (1, –4)

3.a. yes b. no
b.

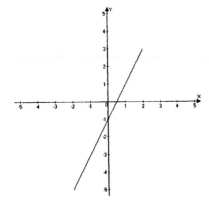

4. a. (–2, –5) (–1, –3) (0, –1) (1, 1) (2, 3)

5. a. (–2, 3) (–1, 2) (0, 1) (1, 0) (2, –1)

b.

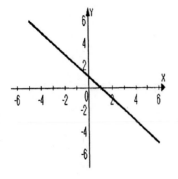

6. a.

x	$y = 0.03x + 10$	(x, y)
0	$y = 0 + 10$	(0, 10)
60	$y = 1.8 + 10$	(60, 11.80)
120	$y = 3.6 + 10$	(120, 13.60)
180	$y = 5.4 + 10$	(180, 15.40)
240	$y = 7.2 + 10$	(240, 17.20)

b.

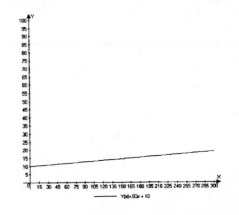

ML-18

Mini Lecture 3.2
Graphing Linear Equations Using Intercepts

Learning Objectives:
1. Use a graph to identify x and y intercepts.
2. Graph a linear equation in two variables using intercepts.
3. Graph horizontal and vertical lines.

Examples:
1. Identify the x and y-intercepts of each line.

   a.

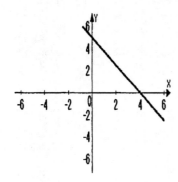

   b.

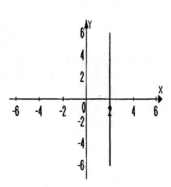

   c.

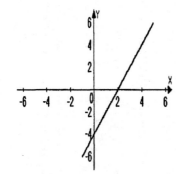

2. Find the x-intercept of the graphs of each of the following equations by substituting 0 in for y and solving for x.

   a. $4x + 7y = 12$ b. $y = 3x - 3$ c. $x - 2y = -8$

3. Find the y-intercept of the graphs of each of the following equations by substituting 0 in for the x and solving for y.

   a. $3x + 2y = -12$ b. $y = 2x + 7$ c. $5x - y = 3$

4. Graph each of the following equations by finding the x and y-intercepts and a check point. Label the intercepts.

   a. $2x - 4y = 12$ b. $5x + 3y = -15$ c. $y = 2x + 6$

5. Graph each equation on the coordinate plane.

   a. $y + 8 = 12$ b. $x = -3$

Teaching Notes:
- Intercepts are <u>points</u> not just numbers.
- The *x*-intercept is the point where a graph crosses the *x* axis. The value of *y* is always zero at the *x*-intercept.
- The *y*-intercept is the point where a graph crosses the *y* axis. The value of *x* is always zero at the *y*-intercept.
- When an equation is in standard form and *a* and *b* are factors of *c*, then finding intercepts is a good method to choose for graphing.
- A table is often useful to find intercepts.
- A vertical line has no *y*-intercept, unless it <u>is</u> the *y*-axis ($x = 0$).
- A horizontal line has no *x*-intercept, unless it <u>is</u> the *x*-axis ($y = 0$).

<u>Answers:</u> 1. a. *x*-intercept (4,0); *y*-intercept (0,5) b. *x*-intercept (2,0); *y*-intercept (none)
c. *x*-intercept (2,0); *y*-intercept (0, –4) 2. a. (3,0) b. (1,0) c. (–8,0) 3. a. (0, –6) b. (0,7) c. (0, –3)

4. a.
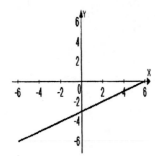

b.
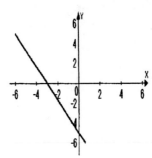

c.
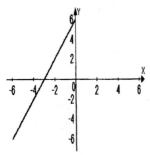

5. a.
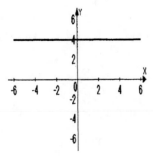

b.
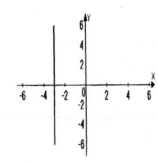

Mini Lecture 3.3
Slope

Learning Objectives:
1. Compute a line's slope.
2. Use slope to show that lines are parallel.
3. Use slope to show that lines are perpendicular.
4. Calculate rate of change in applied situations.

Examples:

1. Using the formula for slope $m = \dfrac{y_2 - y_1}{x_2 - x_1}$, find the slope of the line passing through each pair of points.

   a. $(2, 4)\,(-3, 1)$

   b. $(-4, 2)\,(3, -1)$

   c. $(1, 5)\,(2, 5)$

   d. $(-8, 3)\,(-8, 1)$

2. Determine which lines are parallel.

A $(5, 2)$	B $(3, 4)$	Slope of $\overline{AB}$ _____ .
C $(3, 1)$	D $(5, 3)$	Slope of $\overline{CD}$ _____ .
E $(-3, 5)$	F $(-1, 3)$	Slope of $\overline{EF}$ _____ .

   Line _____ is parallel to line _____ .

3. Determine which lines are perpendicular.

S $(1, 4)$	T $(5, 6)$	Slope of $\overline{ST}$ _____ .
U $(3, 2)$	V $(1, 1)$	Slope of $\overline{UV}$ _____ .
W $(1, -5)$	X $(0, -3)$	Slope of $\overline{WX}$ _____ .

   Line _____ is perpendicular to line _____ .

4 Property taxes have continued to increase year after year. Given that in 1980 a home's taxes were $1200 and that same home's taxes were $2300 in 2002. If x represents the year and y the real estate tax, calculate the slope and explain the meaning of your answer.

Teaching Notes:

- Slope is defined as $\dfrac{rise}{run}\left(\dfrac{horizontal\ change}{vertical\ change}\right)$.

- $m = \dfrac{y_2 - y_1}{x_2 - x_1}$, where m represents slope and comes from the French verb "*monter*" meaning to rise or ascend.

- Four slope possibilities:
    1. $m > 0$, positive slope, rises from left to right
    2. $m < 0$, negative slope, falls from left to right
    3. $m = 0$, line is horizontal
    4. m is undefined, line is vertical

Answers: 1.a. $\dfrac{3}{5}$ b. $-\dfrac{3}{7}$ c. 0 d. undefined 2. $\overline{AB}$, $m = -1$ $\overline{CD}, m = 1$ $\overline{EF}, m = -1$; $\overline{AB} \parallel \overline{EF}$

3. $\overline{ST}$, $m = \dfrac{1}{2}$ $\overline{UV}$, $m = -\dfrac{1}{2}$ $\overline{WX}$, $m = -2$; $\overline{ST} \perp \overline{WX}$

4. slope is $\dfrac{50}{1}$; taxes went up \$50 per year.

Mini Lecture 3.4
The Slope-Intercept Form of the Equation of a Line

<u>**Learning Objectives:**</u>
1. Identify the slope and y-intercept of a line from its equation.
2. Graph lines in slope-intercept form.
3. Change an equation from standard form to slope-intercept form.

<u>**Examples:**</u>
1. Find the slope and y-intercept of each line with the following equations: (Write the y-intercept as a point.)

   a. $y = \dfrac{2}{3}x - 4$ b. $y = -3x + 2$ c. $y = -1$

   d. $y = \dfrac{1}{2}x$ e. $y = 4x - 5$ f. $y = -\dfrac{3}{4}x + 8$

2. Put each equation in slope-intercept form by solving for y. (Isolate y) Then name the slope and y-intercept.
   a. $2x + y = -6$ b. $-4x - 3y = 6$ c. $x - 2y = 8$
   d. $5y = 10x + 4$ e. $x + y = 10$ f. $3x - 4y = 7$

3. Graph each equation using the slope and the y-intercept.
   a. $4x - 2y = 6$ b. $6y = -3x + 12$ c. $3x - y = -3$

<u>**Teaching Notes:**</u>
- In an equation in the form $y = mx + b$, m is the slope of line and b is the y-coordinate of the y-intercept.
- To graph: use the y-intercept as the starting point. Then use the slope to plot at least two more points.
- Remember, the slope must be in fraction form, $\dfrac{rise}{run}$. If the slope is an integer, it can be put over 1 to form a fraction.

<u>Answers:</u> 1. a. slope $\dfrac{2}{3}$; y-intercept $(0, -4)$ b. slope -3; y-intercept $(0, 2)$ c. slope 0; y-intercept $(0, -1)$

d. slope $\dfrac{1}{2}$; y-intercept $(0, 0)$ e. slope 4, y-intercept $(0, -5)$ f. slope $-\dfrac{3}{4}$; y-intercept $(0, 8)$

2. a. $y = -2x - 6$; slope -2; y-intercept $(0, -6)$ b. $y = -\dfrac{4}{3}x - 2$; slope $-\dfrac{4}{3}$; y-intercept $(0, -2)$

c. $y = \dfrac{1}{2}x - 4$; slope $\dfrac{1}{2}$; y-intercept $(0, -4)$ d. $y = 2x + \dfrac{4}{5}$; slope 2; y-intercept $(0, \dfrac{4}{5})$

e. $y = -x + 10$; slope -1, y-intercept $(0, 10)$ f. $y = \dfrac{3}{4}x - \dfrac{7}{4}$; slope $\dfrac{3}{4}$, y-intercept $\left(0, -\dfrac{7}{4}\right)$

3. a.

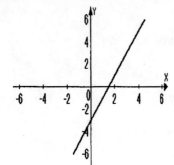

b.

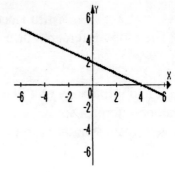

c.

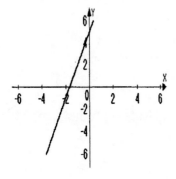

Mini Lecture 3.5
The Point-Slope Form of the Equation of a Line

Learning Objectives:

1. Use the point-slope form to write equations of a line.
2. Find slopes and equations of parallel and perpendicular lines.
3. Write linear equations that model data and make predictions.

Examples:

1. Write the point-slope form and the slope-intercept form of the equation of the line with slope 3 that passes through the point $(-1, 4)$.
2. Write the point-slope form and the slope-intercept form of the equation of the line through the points $(1, 4)$ $(-2, 3)$.
3. Given $x + 2y = 6$. Find the slope of a line that is parallel to the given. Then find the slope of a line that is perpendicular to the given.
4. Write the equation of a line in point-slope and slope-intercept that is parallel to the line whose equation is $y = 3x + 4$ and passes through $(2, 5)$.
5. Write the equation of a line in point-slope and slope-intercept that is perpendicular to the line whose equation is $2x + 4y = 10$ and passes through $(-2, 4)$.
6. The cost of graphing calculators over time has decreased. In 1990, one particular brand sold for $110, in 2004 that same calculator sold for $82. Use the coordinates of the two points $(1990, 110)$ $(2004, 82)$ to write the equation in point-slope and slope-intercept form.

Teaching Notes:

- Distinguish between 2 forms of an equation of a line: point-slope and slope-intercept.
- Point-slope equation with the slope of m and passing through point (x_1, y_1) is $y - y_1 = m(x - x_1)$.
- Use the point-slope equation when given at least one point and the slope.
- If given two points and asked to find the equation of the line, one must first find the slope, and then use the slope and one of the given points in the point-slope equation.

Answers: 1. $y - 4 = 3(x + 1)$; $y = 3x + 7$ 2. $y - 4 = \dfrac{1}{3}(x - 1)$; $y = \dfrac{1}{3}x + \dfrac{11}{3}$

3. $-\dfrac{3}{2}$; $\dfrac{2}{3}$ 4. $y - 5 = 3(x - 2)$; $y = 3x - 1$ 5. $y - 4 = -\dfrac{1}{2}(x + 2)$; $y = -\dfrac{1}{2}x + 3$

6. $y - 110 = -2(x - 1990)$; $y = -2x + 4090$ or $y - 82 = -2(x - 2004)$; $y = -2x + 4090$

Mini Lecture 4.1
Solving Systems of Linear Equations by Graphing

Learning Objectives:
1. Decide whether an ordered pair is a solution of a linear system.
2. Solve systems of linear equations by graphing.
3. Use graphing to identify systems with no solution or infinitely many solutions.
4. Use graphs of linear systems to solve problems.

Examples:
1. Consider the system.
$$x + y = -3$$
$$2x + y = 1$$

   Determine if each ordered pair is a solution of the system.
   a. $(4, 7)$ b. $(4, -7)$

2. Solve the following systems by graphing. State the solution (the intersection point) as an ordered pair (x, y) or state if there is no solution, or state if there are an infinite number of solutions.

   a. $2x + y = -3$
      $y = -2x - 3$

   b. $2x + y = 3$
      $3x - 2y = 8$

   c. $x + 2y = 6$
      $x + 2y = 2$

Teaching Notes:
- When graphing a system of linear equations, there are three possible outcomes:
  1. The two lines can intersect at one point, meaning there is one solution to the system.
  2. The two lines can be parallel to one another, meaning there is no solution to the system.
  3. The two lines are identical or coincide, meaning there are infinitely many solutions to the system.
- When two lines are parallel the system is inconsistent and has no solution.
- When two lines are coinciding, they are called dependent equations and have infinitely many solutions.

Answers:
1. a. not a solution b. yes, a solution 2. a. infinitely many solutions b. $(2, -1)$ c. lines parallel, no solution

Mini Lecture 4.2
Solving Systems of Linear Equations by the Substitution Method

Learning Objectives:
1. Solve linear systems by the substitution method.
2. Use the substitution method to identify systems with no solution or infinitely many solutions.
3. Solve problems using the substitution method.

Examples:
Solve each system using the substitution method. If there is no solution or an infinite number of solutions, so state.

1. a. $x + y = 3$
   $y = x + 5$

   b. $3x - 2y = 5$
   $x = 4y - 5$

   c. $7x + 6y = -9$
   $y = -2x + 1$

   d. $5x - 6y = -4$
   $x = y$

2. a. $x + 3y = 4$
   $x - 2y = -1$

   b. $-2x - y = -3$
   $3x + y = 0$

   c. $8x - y = 15$
   $3x + 4y = 10$

   d. $3x - 5y = 12$
   $x + 2y = 4$

3. a. $3x + 5y = -3$
   $x - 5y = -5$

   b. $2x - 4y = -4$
   $x + 2y = 8$

   c. $7x - 6y = -1$
   $x - 2y = -1$

   d. $2x - y = 1$
   $4x + y = 8$

4. a. $6x + 3y = 1$
   $y = -2x - 5$

   b. $4x - 4y = 8$
   $x - y = 2$

   c. $4x - 2y = 8$
   $2x - y = 4$

   d. $y = -3x + 2$
   $6x + 2y = 1$

Teaching Notes:
- Students like to follow specific steps so give them a list of steps to use for solving systems by substitution. Begin with: Isolate a variable with a coefficient of 1 first.
- Many students think they must solve for y. Stress that it does not matter whether the variable solved for is x or y.
- Use colored pens or markers to underline in one equation what will be substituted in the other equation.
- If a graphing calculator is being used in the class, graphing on the calculator is a good way to <u>check</u> solutions.

Answers: 1. a. $(-1, 4)$ b. $(3, 2)$ c. $(3, -5)$ D. $(4, 4)$ 2. a. $(1, 1)$ b. $(-3, 9)$ c. $(2, 1)$ d. $(4, 0)$
3. a. $(-2, \frac{3}{5})$ b. $(3, \frac{5}{2})$ c. $(\frac{1}{2}, \frac{3}{4})$ d. $(\frac{3}{2}, 2)$ 4. a. No solution b. Infinite solutions
c. Infinite solutions d. No solution

Mini Lecture 4.3
Solving Systems of Linear Equations by the Addition Method

Learning Objectives:
1. Solving linear systems by the addition method.
2. Use the addition method to identify systems with no solution or infinitely many solutions.
3. Determine the most efficient method for solving a linear system.

Examples:
Solve the following systems by the addition method.

1. $x + y = 10$
   $x - y = 8$

2. $4x + 3y = 7$
   $-4x + y = 5$

3. $3x - y = 8$
   $x + 2y = 5$

4. $2w - 3z = -1$
   $3w + 4z = 24$

5. $4x - 5y = 8$
   $-4x + 5y = -8$

6. $2x = 5y + 4$
   $2x - 5y = 6$

Teaching Notes:
- When solving a system of linear equations there are three methods:
  Graphing (5.1)
  Substitution (5.2)
  Addition (5.3)
- Any of the three methods will work when solving a system and produce the correct answer.
- Teach students how to determine which of the three methods is the most efficient when solving a system of equations.

Answers: 1. $(9, 1)$ 2. $\left(-\dfrac{1}{2}, 3\right)$ 3. $(3, 1)$ 4. $(4, 3)$ 5. infinitely many solutions 6. no solution

Problem Solving Using Systems of Equations

Learning Objectives:
   1. Solve problems using linear systems.

Examples:

Use variables to represent unknown quantities. Write a: Let $x =$ and $y =$ statement for each problem. (Do not solve).

   1. The sum of two numbers is 14. One number is six times larger than the other. Find the two numbers.
   2. Three pairs of socks and two pairs of mitten cost $42. One pair of the same kind of socks and four pair of the mittens cost $24. Find out how much one pair of socks and one pair of mittens cost.
   3. John has $5 bills and $10 bills in his wallet. He has a total of $80. He has twice as many $5 bills as $10 bills. How many $5 bills and how many $10 bills does he have?

Now, for problems 4 – 6, write a system of equations that models the conditions of each problem. (Do not solve).
   4.
   5.
   6.

Solve each of the following using a system of equations.
   7. The sum of two numbers is 11. The second number is 1 less than twice the first number. Find the two numbers.
   8. Alexis has $1.65 in nickels and quarters. She has 9 coins altogether. How many coins of each kind does she have?
   9. Paul invested $12,000 in two accounts. One account paid 4% interest and one account paid 5% interest. At the end of the year his money had earned $560 in interest. How much did he invest in each account?
   10. A department store receives 2 shipments of bud vases and picture frames. The first shipment of 5 bud vases and 4 picture frames costs $62. The second shipment of 10 bud vases and 3 picture frames cost $84. Find the cost of a vase and a picture frame.

Teaching Notes:
   *   Stress the importance of reading the problem several times before beginning. Reading aloud really helps.
   *   Have students write a Let $x=$ and $y =$ statements for each word problem before trying to write the system of equations.
   *   Help students look at the system they have created and determine which method of solving will work best.
   *   Remind students to make sure their answers make sense for the given situation.
   *   Try to build confidence with word problems.

Answers: 1. Let $x =$ one number; let $y =$ the other number. 2. Let $x =$ cost of 1 pair of socks; let $y =$ cost of 1 pair of mittens. 3. Let $x =$ number of $5 bills; let $y =$ number of $10 bills
4. $x + y = 14$ 5. $3x + 2y = 42$ 6. $5x + 10y = 80$
   $x = 6y$ $x + 4y = 24$ $x = 2y$
7. The numbers are 4 and 7 8. 3 nickels, 6 quarters 9. $4000 invested @ 4% and $8000 invested @ 5%
10. bud vases $6, picture frames $8

Mini Lecture 4.5
Systems of Linear Equations in Three Variables

Learning Objectives:
1. Verify the solution of a system of linear equations in three variables.
2. Solve systems of linear equations in three variables.
3. Identify inconsistent and dependent systems.
4. Solve problems using systems in three variables.

Examples

1. Show that the ordered triple (1, 2, 3) is a solution of the system:
$$x + y + z = 6$$
$$2x - y + z = 3$$
$$x + 2y - 3z = -4$$

2. Solve the system:
$$x + y + z = 4$$
$$x - y - z = 2$$
$$2x + 2y - z = 2$$

3. Solve the system:
$$-x + 4y - 3z = 2$$
$$2x - 8y + 6z = 1$$
$$3x - y + z = 0$$

4. Solve the system:
$$2x + 3y - z = 5$$
$$4x + 6y - 2z = 10$$
$$x - 4y + 3z = 5$$

5. Create three equations from the stated problem and then solve.
   The sum of the three numbers is 14. The largest is 4 times the smallest, while the sum of the smallest and twice the largest is 18.

Teaching Notes:
- A system of linear equations is three variables represents three planes.
- A linear system that intersects at one point is called a <u>consistent system</u> and has an ordered triple as an answer (x, y, z).
- A linear system that intersects at infinitely many points is also called a <u>consistent system</u> and is also called <u>dependent.</u>
- A linear system that has no common point(s) of intersection represents an <u>inconsistent system</u> and has no solution.

Answers: 1. $1+2+3=6$, $2-2+3=3$, $1+4-9=-4$ 2. $(3,-1,2)$ 3. No Solution , Inconsistent system.
4. infinitely many solutions, dependant equations 5. $x + y + z = 14$, $z = 4x$, $x + 2z = 18$. The numbers are 2, 4 and 8.

Mini Lecture 5.1
Adding and Subtracting Polynomials

Learning Objectives:
1. Understand the vocabulary used to describe polynomials.
2. Add polynomials.
3. Subtract polynomials.
4. Graph equations defined by polynomials of degree 2.

Examples:

1. Identify each polynomial as a monomial, a binomial, or a trinomial. Give the degree of the polynomial.
   a. $5x - 1$
   b. $9x^2$
   c. 8
   d. $3x^2 - 2x + 1$

2. Add: $\left(5x^3 + 3x^2 - 5x + 4\right) + \left(-2x^3 + 4x^2 - 8x - 2\right)$

3. Add: $\begin{aligned} -9x^3 + 4x^2 - 5x + 3 \\ \underline{2x^3 \qquad\quad + 3x - 7} \end{aligned}$

4. Subtract: $\left(4x^4 + 3x^3 + 2x - 7\right) - \left(-2x^3 + x^2 - 4x + 5\right)$

5. Subtract: $3x^2 + 5x + 4$ from $8x^2 - 2x - 1$

6. Subtract: $\begin{aligned} 10x^4 + 3x^3 - 4x^2 \qquad + 5 \\ \underline{(\qquad 2x^3 + 3x^2 + 4x \qquad)} \end{aligned}$

7. Find seven solutions for $y = x^2 + 2$ by completing the table of values.
   a.

x	$y = x^2 + 2$	y
-3		
-2		
-1		
0		
1		
2		
3		

   b. Plot the ordered pairs to graph the quadratic equation $y = x^2 + 2$.

- Vocabulary terms are very important when teaching/learning about polynomials. Example: monomial, degree of polynomial, coefficient, exponent.
- When adding or subtracting polynomials either the horizontal or vertical format may be used.
- When using the vertical format, if a particular term is missing, leave a vacant space making sure to line up like terms in columns.
- When subtracting, make sure to change the sign of each term being subtracted to its opposite, then use rules for adding like and unlike signs.

<u>Answers:</u> 1. a. binomial, 2 b. monomial, 2 c. monomial, 0 d. trinomial, 2 2. $3x^3 + 7x^2 - 13x + 2$
3. $-7x^3 + 4x^2 - 2x - 4$ 4. $4x^4 + 5x^3 - x^2 + 6x - 12$ 5. $5x^2 - 7x - 5$
6. $10x^4 + x^3 - 7x^2 - 4x + 5$
7.

x	$y = x^2 + 2$	y
-3	$y = (-3)^2 + 2$	
-2	$y = (-2)^2 + 2$	
-1	$y = (-1)^2 + 2$	
0	$y = (0)^2 + 2$	
1	$y = (1)^2 + 2$	
2	$y = (2)^2 + 2$	
3	$y = (3)^2 + 2$	

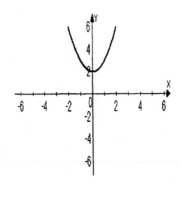

Mini Lecture 5.2
Multiplying Polynomials

Learning Objectives:
1. Use the product rule for exponents.
2. Use the power to power rule for exponents.
3. Use the products-to-powers rule for exponents.
4. Multiply monomials.
5. Multiply a monomial and a polynomial.
6. Multiply polynomials when neither is a monomial.

Examples:

Simplify each expression.

1. a. $x^5 \cdot x^2$ b. $a^2 \cdot a \cdot a^8$ c. $4^2 \cdot 4^4$ d. $y \cdot y \cdot y$

2. a. $(x^4)^2$ b. $(a^5)^5$ c. $(4^2)^4$ d. $(y^5)^2$

3. a. $(3a)^4$ b. $(6x^3)^2$ c. $(2a^2b^3c^5)^3$ d. $(-6x^3)^4$

4. $4y^2 \cdot 3y^4$ b. $(-3x)(-2x^3)$ c. $(8x^2y^2)(3x^2y^4)$ d. $(5x^3)(-3x^3y^7)$

5. a. $5a(a^2 + 2)$ b. $3x(2x - 4)$ c. $5y^2(y^2 - y + 2)$ d. $2x^2y(5x^3y - 2xy^3)$

6. a. $(a + 2)(a + 8)$ b. $(2x - 3)(3x - 2)$ c. $(y + 7)(2y - 3)$ d. $(2b - 5)(5b - 2)$

7. a. $(x + 2)(x^2 + 3x + 4)$ b. $(a + 4)(a^2 - 3a + 1)$
    c. $(y - 3)(2y^2 + 3y + 5)$ d. $(x - 2)(2x^3 - 4x^2 + 3x - 6)$

Teaching Notes:
- Have students write out exponent rules in words on one (1) page with examples for referral and study.
- Students find each rule easy as presented but the rules get jumbled when used together.
- Practice often and review.
- A very common mistake will be students multiplying bases if they are numbers -- warn against this! The base stays the same when multiplying like bases.

Answers: 1. a. x^7 b. a^{11} c. 4^6 d. y^3 2. a. x^8 b. a^{25} c. 4^8 d. y^{10} 3. a. $81a^4$ b. $36x^6$ c. $8a^6b^9c^{15}$ d. $1296x^{12}$ 4. a. $12y^6$ b. $6x^4$ c. $24x^4y^6$ d. $-15x^6y^7$ 5. a. $5a^3 + 10a$ b. $6x^2 - 12x$ c. $5y^4 - 5y^3 + 10y^2$ d. $10x^5y^2 - 4x^3y^4$ 6. a. $a^2 + 10a + 16$ b. $6x^2 - 13x + 6$ c. $2y^2 + 11y - 21$ d. $10b^2 - 29b + 10$ 7. a. $x^3 + 5x^2 + 10x + 8$ b. $a^3 + a^2 - 11a + 4$ c. $2y^3 - 3y^2 - 4y - 15$ d. $2x^4 - 8x^3 + 11x^2 - 12x + 12$

Mini Lecture 5.3
Special Products

Learning Objectives:
1. Use FOIL in polynomial multiplication.
2. Multiply the sum and difference of two terms.
3. Find the square of a binomial sum.
4. Find the square of a binomial difference.

Examples:
Use the FOIL method to find each product.

1. $(x+2)(x+4)$

2. $(3x-7)(2x+3)$

3. $(3-5x)(2+4x)$

4. Find each product using the rule for finding the product of the sum and difference of two terms.
   a. $(2y+4)(2y-4)$
   b. $(6x-1)(6x+1)$
   c. $(4x^3+8)(4x^3-8)$

5. Multiply using the rules for the square of a binomial.
   a. $(x+4)^2$
   b. $(3x+7)^2$
   c. $(5x-2)^2$
   d. $(4x+8)^2$

Teaching Notes:
- When multiplying two binomials, the FOIL method is often used.

F	**O**	**I**	**L**
product of **first** terms,	product of **outside** terms,	product of **inside** terms,	product of **last** terms

- When multiplying the sum and difference of two terms, $(A+B)(A-B)$, the outside product and inside product will eliminate one another resulting in an answer of A^2-B^2.
- When multiplying the square of a binomial sum $(A+B)^2$, the outside product and inside product will be identical resulting in $A^2+AB+AB+B^2 = A^2+2AB+B^2$.

Answers: 1. x^2+6x+8 2. $6x^2-5x-21$ 3. $6+2x-20x^2$ 4. a. $4y^2-16$ b. $36x^2-1$
c. $16x^6-64$ 5. a. $x^2+8x+16$ b. $9x^2+42x+49$ c. $25x^2-20x+4$ d. $16x^2+64x+64$

Mini Lecture 5.4
Polynomials in Several Variables

Learning Objectives:
1. Evaluate polynomials in several variables.
2. Know and understand polynomial vocabulary.
3. Add and subtract polynomials in several variables.
4. Multiply polynomials in several variables.

Examples:

Evaluate the following polynomial given values for the variables:

1. $2x^2 - xy + 3y^2$ a. $x = 2$ $y = -1$ b. $x = -2$ $y = -2$

2. $5x^3 + 2x^2y - 3xy - y^2$ a. $x = 1$ $y = 3$ b. $x = -2$ $y = -1$

Answer the following questions about the following polynomials:

3. $8x^4y^3 - 5xy^2 + 4x^3y - x^2y^6$ 4. $3x^5y - x^4y^3 + 2x^2y^2 + xy^3 + 4y^4$

     a. Name the coefficient of each term.
     b. Tell the degree of each term.
     c. What is the degree of the polynomial?

5.   Add or subtract the polynomials.
     a. $\left(6x^2y + 2xy - 3xy^2\right) + \left(4x^2y - xy + 5xy^2\right)$
     b. $\left(10x^3y^2 - 5x^2y + 2xy^2 - 3xy^3\right) - \left(4x^3y^2 - 5x^2y + 4xy^2 - 6xy\right)$
     c. $\left(3a^4b^2 + 2a^3b - 5a^2b^3\right) + \left(5a^4b^2 + 3ab^3 + 4a^2b^3\right)$
     d. $\left(5x^4y^3 + 3x^2y^2 + 2xy^4\right) - \left(3x^4y^4 - 3x^2y^2 - 4xy^4\right)$

6.   Multiply the polynomials.
     a. $\left(4x^2y^2\right)\left(7x^3y^3\right)$ b. $\left(-2xy^3\right)\left(5x^3y\right)$
     c. $5x^2y^2\left(3x^3y^2 - 4xy^3 + 6x^2y\right)$ d. $\left(2x + 3y\right)\left(x - 4y\right)$
     e. $\left(4a + 3b\right)\left(4a + b\right)$ f. $\left(3x + 5y\right)^2$
     g. $\left(2x - 8y\right)^2$ h. $\left(x - y\right)\left(2x^2 - 3xy + y^2\right)$

Teaching Notes:
- It is very important to use parentheses when substituting for a variable.
- Students need to be reminded that the sign in front of a term is the sign of the coefficient of the term.
- Students will have problems with the degree of the polynomial. Remind them it is the same as the one term with the highest degree. DO NOT add all the exponents in the polynomial.

Answers: 1. a. 13   b. 16   2. a. −7   b. −55   3. a. 8, −5, 4, −1   b. 7, 3, 4, 8   c. degree 8
4. a. 3, −1, 2, 1, 4   b. 6, 7, 4, 4, 4   c. degree 7   5. a. $10x^2y + xy + 2xy^2$ b. $6x^3y^2 - 2xy^2 + 3xy^3$
c. $8a^4b^2 + 2a^3b + 3ab^3 - a^2b^3$ d. $2x^4y^3 + 6x^2y^2 + 6xy^4$ 6. a. $28x^5y^5$ b. $-10x^4y^4$
c. $15x^5y^4 - 20x^3y^5 + 30x^4y^3$ d. $2x^2 - 5xy - 12y^2$ e. $16a^2 + 16ab + 3b^2$
f. $9x^2 + 30xy + 25y^2$ g. $4x^2 - 32xy + 64y^2$ h. $2x^3 - 5x^2 + 4xy^2 - y^3$

Learning Objectives:
1. Use the quotient rule for exponents.
2. Use the zero–exponent rule.
3. Use the quotients-to-powers rule.
4. Divide monomials.
5. Check polynomial division.
6. Divide a polynomial by a monomial.

Examples:
1.   Divide using the quotient rule:

    a. $\dfrac{7^5}{7^2}$ b. $\dfrac{x^{11}}{x^7}$ c. $\dfrac{y^8}{y}$

2.   Use the zero-exponent rule to simplify each expression.

    a. 8^0 b. $(-8)^0$ c. -8^0 d. $30x^0$ e. $(30x)^0$

3.   Simplify each expression using the quotient-to-powers rule.

    a. $\left(\dfrac{a}{6}\right)^2$ b. $\left(\dfrac{x^4}{3}\right)^3$ c. $\left(\dfrac{2y^3}{z^4}\right)^4$

4.   Divide the monomials.

    a. $\dfrac{-24x^8}{6x^4}$ b. $\dfrac{2x^6}{6x^6}$ c. $\dfrac{12x^6y^4}{2x^3y}$

5.   Find the quotient.

    a. $\dfrac{-16x^8+12x^5-2x^2}{2x}$ b. $\dfrac{30x^6-25x^5+10x^3}{5x^3}$ c. $\dfrac{24x^6y^3-6x^4y^2+12x^2y}{6xy}$

Teaching Notes:
- When dividing exponential expressions with the same nonzero base, subtract the denominator exponent from the numerator exponent. Ex: $\left(\dfrac{a^x}{a^y}\right)=a^{x-y}$.

- Any nonzero base raised to the 0 power equals 1.
- When raising quotients to a power, raise every factor in the parenthesis to the power. The base in the denominator $\neq$ zero $\left(\dfrac{a}{b}\right)^n=\dfrac{a^n}{b^n}$.

- When dividing monomials, divide the coefficients and divide the variables. When dividing the variables, keep the variable and subtract the exponents.
- To check a division problem, divisor · quotient = dividend.
- When dividing a polynomial a monomial by a monomial, divide each term by the monomial.

Answers: 1.a. 7^3 b. x^4 c. y^7 2.a. 1 b. 1 c. -1 d. 30 e. 1 3.a. $\dfrac{a^2}{36}$ b. $\dfrac{x^{12}}{27}$ c. $\dfrac{16y^{12}}{z^{16}}$

4.a. $-4x^4$ b. $\dfrac{1}{3}$ c. $6x^3y^3$ 5.a. $-8x^7+6x^4-x$ b. $6x^3-5x^2+2$ c. $4x^5y^2-x^3y+2x$

Mini Lecture 5.6
Long Division of Polynomials: Synthetic Division

Teaching Objectives:
- Use long division to divide by a polynomial containing more than one term.
- Divide polynomials using synthetic division.

Examples:

Divide and check: (no remainders)

1. a. $\dfrac{x^2 + 5x + 6}{x + 3}$

   b. $\dfrac{2a^2 - 9a - 5}{2a + 1}$

   c. $(a^2 + 9a + 20) \div (a + 4)$

Divide and check: (some will have remainders)

2. a. $\dfrac{x^2 + 5x + 6}{x + 3}$

   b. $\dfrac{x^2 + 5x - 6}{x + 1}$

   c. $(6a^2 + 5a + 1) \div (2a + 3)$

   d. $\dfrac{6a^3 - 13a^2 - 4a + 15}{3a - 5}$

   e. $(2x^4 - 13x^3 + 16x^2 - 9x + 20) \div (x - 5)$

   f. $\dfrac{7x^2 - 4x + 12 + 3x^3}{x + 1}$

   g. $(20x^3 - 8x^2 + 5x - 5) \div (5x - 2)$

Divide using synthetic division. Fill in any missing terms.

3. a. $(3x^4 - 25x^2 - 20) \div (x - 3)$

   b. $\dfrac{y^3 - 8}{y - 2}$

   c. $\dfrac{3x^2 - 4}{x - 1}$

Teaching Notes:
1. Dividing polynomials is like long division. Most students can divide using long division. Remind about writing remainders as fractions.
2. Teach this concept by comparing to long division.
3. Students often find it helpful to cover up the second term of a binomial before dividing.
4. Using parentheses before subtracting may help reduce sign errors.
5. It is often helpful to write these steps vertically on the page when doing examples with the students:
   Cover up; divide; uncover; multiply back; parentheses; subtract; bring down, cover up; divide, uncover; multiply back; parentheses; subtract; bring down... Students are able to follow the above pattern if they practice enough. Remind students that the divisor and the dividend must be in DESCENDING powers of the variable WITHOUT skipping any powers.
6. The sign errors when subtracting will be the biggest obstacle in getting the correct answer.
7. Students like to see how they can check their answers.
8. Synthetic division can be used to divide polynomials if the division is of the form $x - c$. This method provides a quotient more quickly than long division.

Answers: 1. a. $x + 2$ b. $a - 5$ c. $a + 5$ 2. a. $x + 2 + \dfrac{2}{x + 3}$ b. $x + 4 + \dfrac{-10}{x + 1}$ c. $3a - 2 + \dfrac{7}{a + 3}$

d. $2a^2 - a - 3$ e. $2x^3 - 3x^2 + x - 4$ f. $3x^2 + 4x - 8 + \dfrac{20}{x + 1}$ g. $4x^2 + 1 + \dfrac{-3}{5x - 2}$

3. a. $3x^3 + 9x^2 + 2x + 6 + \dfrac{-2}{x - 3}$ b. $y^2 + 2y + 4$ c. $3x + 3 + \dfrac{-1}{x - 1}$

Mini Lecture 5.7
Negative Exponents and Scientific Notation

Learning Objectives:
1. Use the negative exponent rule.
2. Simplify exponential expressions.
3. Convert from scientific notation to decimal notation.
4. Convert from decimal notation to scientific notation.
5. Compute with scientific notation.
6. Solve applied problems with scientific notation.

Examples:

1. Rewrite each expression with a positive exponent, then simplify if possible.

   a. 3^{-2} b. 4^{-3} c. $(-2)^{-4}$ d. -2^{-4} e. 5^{-1}

   f. $\dfrac{2^{-2}}{5^{-3}}$ g. $\left(\dfrac{5}{7}\right)^{-2}$ h. $\dfrac{1}{4y^{-3}}$ i. $\dfrac{x^{-3}}{y^{-5}}$

2. Simplify the following, make sure all answers are written with positive exponents.

   a. $x^{-10} \cdot x^{4}$ b. $\dfrac{x^{2}}{x^{9}}$ c. $\dfrac{24x^{3}}{8x^{7}}$

   d. $\dfrac{100y^{4}}{25y^{10}}$ e. $\dfrac{\left(3x^{3}\right)^{2}}{x^{10}}$ f. $\left(\dfrac{x^{6}}{x^{2}}\right)^{-3}$

3. Write each number in scientific notation.

   a. 3,840,000   b. 0.000158

4. Write each number in decimal notation.

   a. 9.2×10^{-3} b. 3.851×10^{5}

5. Perform the indicated computation writing final answers in scientific notation.

   a. $\left(4 \times 10^{4}\right)\left(2 \times 10^{8}\right)$ b. $\dfrac{4.2 \times 10^{8}}{2 \times 10^{-2}}$

6. If 3.29×10^{5} people live in your city, what is the population of your hometown in decimal notation?

Teaching Notes:

- To simplify exponential expressions remember: to remove all parentheses, no powers are raised to powers, each base occurs only once, no negative or zero exponents appear.

- If the base is any real number other than 0 and n is a negative number, then $x^{-n} = \dfrac{1}{x^n}$.

- A positive number is written in scientific notation when it is expressed in the form $a \times 10^n$ where $1 \le 10$ and n is an integer.

- When changing scientific notation to decimal notation, move the decimal to the right "n" places if n is negative.

Answers: 1. a. $\dfrac{1}{3^2} = \dfrac{1}{9}$ b. $\dfrac{1}{4^3} = \dfrac{1}{64}$ c. $\dfrac{1}{(-2)^4} = \dfrac{1}{16}$ d. $\dfrac{1}{-2^4} = -\dfrac{1}{16}$ e. $\dfrac{1}{5^1} = \dfrac{1}{5}$

f. $\dfrac{5^3}{2^2} = \dfrac{125}{4}$ g. $\left(\dfrac{7}{5}\right)^2 = \dfrac{49}{25}$ h. $\dfrac{y^3}{4}$ i. $\dfrac{y^5}{x^3}$ 2. a. $\dfrac{1}{x^6}$ b. $\dfrac{1}{x^7}$ c. $\dfrac{3}{x^4}$ d. $\dfrac{4}{y^6}$ e. $\dfrac{9}{x^4}$

f. $\dfrac{1}{x^{12}}$ 3. a. 3.84×10^6 b. 1.58×10^{-4} 4. a. 0.0092 b. $385,100$ 5. a. $\left(8 \times 10^{12}\right)$

b. $\left(2.1 \times 10^{10}\right)$ 6. $329,000$ people

Mini Lecture 6.1
The Greatest Common Factor and Factoring by Grouping

Learning Objectives:
1. Find the greatest common factor.
2. Factor out the greatest common factor of a polynomial.
3. Factor by grouping.

Examples:

1. Find the greatest common factor for each list of terms.
   a. $24x^3$ and $12x^2$
   b. $-18x^2, 30x^5,$ and $48x$
   c. $x^2y^4, x^3y,$ and x^5y^7

2. Factor the following:
   a. $9x^2 + 27$
   b. $45x^2 + 50x^5$
   c. $18x^6 - 6x^3 + 24x^2$
   d. $12x^2y^3 - 8x^3y^2 + 16xy^4$
   e. $10x^3y + 15x^2y^2 - 5xy$

3. Factor.
   a. $x^2(x-4) + 3(x-4)$
   b. $x(x^2+9) + (x^2+9)$

4. Factor by grouping.
   a. $6x^2 - 10x + 9x - 15$
   b. $2x^4 + 2x^2 - 5x^2 - 5$

Teaching Notes:
- To factor means to find an equivalent expression whose product gives the original polynomial.
- The greatest common factor (GCF) is an expression of the highest degree that will divide into each term of a polynomial.
- To factor by grouping: first group terms that have a common monomial factor. Next, factor out the common monomial from each group, and then factor out the remaining common binomial factor (if one exists).
- Factoring can be easily checked by multiplying the terms through distributing or FOIL (if two binomials.

Answers: 1. a. $12x^2$ b. $6x$ c. x^2y 2. a. $9(x^2+3)$ b. $5x^2(9+10x^3)$ c. $6x^2(3x^4 - x + 4)$
d. $4xy^2(3xy - 2x^2 + 4y^2)$ e. $5xy(2x^2 + 3xy - 1)$ 4. $4xy^2(3xy - 2x^2 + 4y^2)$ e. $5xy(2x^2 + 3xy - 1)$
3. a. $(x-4)(x^2+3)$ b. $(x^2+9)(x+1)$ 4. a. $(3x-5)(2x+3)$ b. $(x^2+1)(2x^2-5)$

Mini Lecture 6.2
Factoring Trinomials Whose Leading Coefficient is 1

Learning Objectives:

1. Factor trinomials of the form $ax^2 + bx + c$.

Examples:

Factor these similar problems. Make an observation of the signs.

1.   a. $x^2 + 9x + 18$ b. $x^2 - 9x + 18$ c. $x^2 - 3x - 18$ d. $x^2 + 3x - 18$

Factor each polynomial. Check using the FOIL method.

2. $x - 2x - 24$ 3. $a^2 - 14a - 72$ 4. $x^2 + 2xy + y^2$

5. $a - 15a + 24$ 6. $2y^2 + 14y + 24$ 7. $a^2 + 8a + 16$

8. $x^2 + 10x + 25$ 9. $a^2 - 13a - 30$ 10. $y^2 - 8y - 20$

11. $y^2 + y - 12$ 12. $3x^2 - 12x + 9$ 13. $a^2 + 10ab + 16b^2$

14. $x^2 - 6xy - 16y^2$ 15. $4y^2 - 20y + 16$ 16. $x^2 + 2x - 15$

Teaching Notes:

- Students need as much practice as possible to become comfortable factoring.
- Stress checking the answer! Especially the "oi" (outside + inside).

Answers: 1. a. $(x + 6)(x + 3)$ b. $(x - 6)(x - 3)$ c. $(x - 6)(x + 3)$ d. $(x + 6)(x - 3)$ 2. $(x - 6)(x + 4)$
3. $(a - 18)(a + 4)$ 4. $(x + y)(x + y)$ 5. $(a - 8)(a - 3)$ 6. $2(y + 3)(y + 4)$ 7. $(a + 4)(a + 4)$
8. $(x + 5)(x + 5)$ 9. $(a - 15)(a + 2)$ 10. $(y - 10)(y + 2)$ 11. $(y + 4)(y - 3)$ 12. $3(x - 3)(x - 1)$
13. $(a + 2b)(a + 8b)$ 14. $(x - 8y)(x + 2y)$ 15. $4(y - 4)(y - 1)$ 16. $(x + 5)(x - 3)$

Mini Lecture 6.3
Factoring Trinomials Whose Leading Coefficient is Not 1

Learning Objectives:
1. Factor trinomials by trial and error.
2. Factor trinomials by grouping.

Examples:
Factor each trinomial. Try both the trial and error method and grouping. If the trinomial is prime, so state. Show that the factorization is correct by multiplying the factors using the FOIL method.

1.	$6x^2 + 13x + 6$		2.	$3x^2 - 4x - 15$
3.	$5x^2 + x - 18$		4.	$6x^2 + 2x + 1$
5.	$7x^2 + 15 + 2$		6.	$3x^2 - 5x - 2$
7.	$3x^2 + 4x + 1$		8.	$4x^2 + 4x - 15$
9.	$18x^2 - 21x - 9$		10.	$6x^2 + 7x + 2$
11.	$8x^2 + 10x - 3$		12.	$15x^2 - 19x + 6$
13.	$6x^2 - 41x - 7$		14.	$9x^2 + 18x + 8$
15.	$3x^2 + 2x - 5$		16.	$4x^2 + 2xy - 6y^2$
17.	$6x^2 - 7xy - 3y^2$		18.	$4x^2 + 4xy - 3y^2$
19.	$6x^2 + 15x + 9$		20.	$2x^2 + 5x - 2$

Teaching Notes:
- When factoring $ax^2 + bx + c$, it is important to know the sign combinations. If the polynomial is in the form $ax^2 + bx + c$, then the factored form is (+)(+). If the polynomial is in the form $ax^2 + bx - c$, then the factored form is (+)(−) or (−) (+).
- When using the trial and error method in factoring $ax^2 + bx + c$, ALWAYS look for the greatest common factor first. If there is a GCF, factor it out first, then continue by finding 2 factors that equal ax^2 (__)(__). Then find two factors whose product equals c (__)(__). Check the sum of the outside and inside product because it must equal bx (___)(___). If no combination exists, the polynomial is prime.
- When using the grouping method to factor $ax^2 + bx + c$, if $a \neq 1$, first multiply the leading coefficient, a, and the constant, c. Then find two factors of ac whose sum is b. Rewrite the middle term, bx, as a sum or difference using the two factors found. Use the grouping method discussed in 7.1.

<u>Answers:</u> 1. $(3x + 2)(2x + 3)$ 2. $(3x + 5)(x - 3)$ 3. $(5x - 9)(x + 2)$ 4. prime 5. $(7x + 1)(x + 2)$
6. $(3x + 1)(x - 2)$ 7. $(3x + 1)(x + 1)$ 8. $(2x + 5)(2x - 3)$ 9. $3(3x + 1)(2x - 3)$ 10. $(3x + 2)(2x + 1)$
11. $(4x - 1)(2x + 3)$ 12. $(5x - 3)(3x - 2)$ 13. $(6x + 1)(x - 7)$ 14. $(3x + 4)(3x + 2)$
15. $(3x + 5)(x - 1)$ 16. $2(2x + 3y)(x - y)$ 17. $(3x + y)(2x - 3y)$ 18. $(2x + 3y)(2x - y)$
19. $3(x + 1)(2x + 3)$ 20. prime

Mini Lecture 6.4
Factoring Special Forms

Learning Objectives:
1. Factor the difference of two squares.
2. Factor perfect square trinomials.
3. Factor the sum or difference of two cubes.

Examples:
Factor each polynomial completely.

1.   a. $a^2 - 16$ b. $x^2 - 169$ c. $a^2 - b^2$ d. $4x^2 - 9y^2$

2.   a. $a^2 + 4a + 4$ b. $y^2 - 10y + 25$ c. $x^2 + 16x + 64$ d. $4a^2 - 20a + 25$

3.   a. $x^3 - 1$ b. $y^3 + 27$ c. $8a^3 + 27b^3$ d. $16x^3 - 2$

     e. $64 - y^3$ f. $a^6 + b^6$ g. $5x^3 - 5y^3$ h. $a^3 + 125$

Factor completely. (Some may be prime.)

4.   a. $16x^2 + 18y^2$ b. $x^4 - 81$ c. $a^2 + 12a + 36$ d. $25x^2 - 16y^2$

     e. $3x^2 + 18x + 27$ f. $125x^3 - 8$ g. $x^5 + 8x^2$ h. $27x^2 - 12$

Teaching Notes:
- Students must spend time learning to identify these special products.
- The difference of squares and perfect square trinomials seems to come fairly easily, but the cubes take more practice and simply must be memorized.
- A PST (Perfect Square Trinomial) always results in BS (Binomial Square or Binomials Same).

Answers: 1. a. $(a + 4)(a - 4)$ b. $(x + 13)(x - 13)$ c. $(a + b)(a - b)$ d. $(2x + 3y)(2x - 3y)$
2. a. $(a + 2)^2$ b. $(y - 5)^2$ c. $(x + 8)^2$ d. $(2a - 5)^2$ 3. a. $(x - 1)(x^2 + x + 1)$
b. $(y + 3)(y^2 - 3y + 9)$ c. $(2a + 3b)(4a^2 - 6ab + 9b^2)$ d. $2(2x - 1)(4x^2 + 2x + 1)$
e. $(4 - y)(16 + 4y + y^2)$ f. $(a^2 + b^2)(a^4 - a^2b^2 + b^4)$ g. $5(x - y)(x^2 + xy + y^2)$
h. $(a + 5)(a^2 - 5a + 25)$ 4. a. $2(8x^2 + 9y^2)$ b. $(x^2 + 9)(x + 3)(x - 3)$ c. $(a + 6)(a + 6)$
d. $(5x + 4y)(5x - 4y)$ e. $3(x + 3)(x + 3)$ f. $(5x - 2)(25x^2 + 10x + 4)$ g. $x^2(x + 2)(x^2 - 2x + 4)$
h. $3(3x + 2)(3x - 2)$

Learning Objectives:
1. Recognize the appropriate method for factoring a polynomial.
2. Use a general strategy for factoring polynomials.

Examples:
Factor the polynomials. Check your factorization by multiplying.

1. $9x^2 + 81$
2. $4x^2 - 64$
3. $27x^3 + 64y^3$
4. $x^3 - 1$
5. $81x^4 - 1$
6. $a^2 - 18a + 72$
7. $36a^2 + 66a + 24$
8. $12x^3 + 18x^2 - 30x^2 - 45x$
9. $2x^3 + 10x + x^2 + 5$
10. $2a^2 - 8ab + 12b^2$

Teaching Notes:
- Practice, practice, practice!
- When factoring, always look for a GCF first.
- Count the number of terms in the polynomial.
- If two terms – is it difference of squares, sum of two cubes, difference of two cubes?
- If three terms – is it a perfect square trinomial?
- With a trinomial, use trial and error or grouping method.
- If four or more terms, try factoring by grouping.
- Is the polynomial prime?

Answers: 1. $9(x^2 + 9)$ 2. $4(x + 4)(x - 4)$ 3. $(3x + 4y)(9x^2 - 12xy + 16y^2)$ 4. $(x - 1)(x^2 + x + 1)$
5. $(9x^2 + 1)(3x + 1)(3x - 1)$ 6. $(a - 12)(a - 6)$ 7. $6(3a + 4)(2a + 1)$ 8. $3x(2x - 5)(2x + 3)$
9. $(x^2 + 5)(2x + 1)$ 10. $2(a^2 - 4ab + 6b^2)$

Mini Lecture 6.6
Solving Quadratic Equations by Factoring

Learning Objectives:
1. Use the zero product principle.
2. Solve quadratic equations by factoring.
3. Solve problems using quadratic equations.

Examples:
1. Solve each equation.
   a. $(x-3)(x+2)=0$ b. $(2x-5)(x-10)=0$ c. $(x+4)(x+7)=0$

2. Put each equation in standard form. Make sure the leading coefficient is positive.
   a. $4x^2 + 3x = 10$ b. $5x = 20 - x^2$ c. $3x^2 - 6x = 2x^2 - 11$

3. Solve each quadratic equation by factoring.
   a. $2x^2 - 3x - 20 = 0$ b. $a^2 - 11a + 30 = 0$ c. $2x^2 - 5x = 12$

   d. $5x^2 = 2x$ e. $8x^3 - 2x^2 = 10x$ f. $x(14-x) = 48$

   g. $4x^2 - 49 = 0$ h. $3x^2 = 15x$ i. $3a^2 + 7a - 20 = 0$

Teaching Notes:
- Make sure students know what the standard form of a quadratic equation is and what the letters "*a*", "*b*", and "*c*" represent.
- Students need to be able to recognize a quadratic equation by the squared term.
- Students often want to shortcut the steps. Warn them not to take shortcuts when they should set each factor equal to zero and solve.

Answers: 1. a. $x=3$ $x=-2$ b. $x=\dfrac{5}{2}$ $x=10$ c. $x=-4$ $x=-7$ 2.a. $4x^2 + 3x - 10 = 0$

b. $x^2 + 5x - 20 = 0$ c. $x^2 - 6x + 11 = 0$ 3. a. $x=-\dfrac{5}{2}$ $x=4$ b. $a=6$ $a=5$ c. $x=-\dfrac{3}{2}$ $x=4$

d. $x=0$ $x=\dfrac{2}{5}$ e. $x=0$ $x=\dfrac{5}{4}$ $x=-1$ f. $x=6$ $x=8$ g. $x=-\dfrac{7}{2}$ $x=\dfrac{7}{2}$ h. $x=0$ $x=5$

i. $a=\dfrac{5}{3}$ $a=-4$

Mini Lecture 7.1
Rational Expressions and Their Simplification

Learning Objectives:
1. Find numbers for which a rational expression is undefined.
2. Simplify rational expressions.
3. Solve applied problems involving rational expressions.

Examples:
Find all the numbers for which the rational expression is undefined. If the rational expression is defined for all real numbers, so state.

1.   a. $\dfrac{3x-21}{4x+20}$ b. $\dfrac{7x-49}{x^2+5x+6}$ c. $\dfrac{x+3}{3}$

Simplify.

2.   a. $\dfrac{4x+24}{28x}$ b. $\dfrac{8x+56}{4x}$ c. $\dfrac{x^2+6x+5}{x+5}$

     d. $\dfrac{x^2+2x-15}{x^2+7x+10}$ e. $\dfrac{x+2}{4-x^2}$ f. $\dfrac{-c^2-3c}{c^2+2c-3}$

3. The rational expression $\dfrac{240}{r+20}$ describes the time, in hours, to travel 240 miles at a rate of $(r+20)$ miles per hour.
   a. Determine the value of r that would cause the expression to be undefined.
   b. Find the time in hours if $r = 40$.

Teaching Notes:
- Rational expressions are quotients of two polynomials. They indicate division and division by zero is undefined. We must always <u>exclude</u> any value(s) of the variable that make a denominator zero.
- When simplifying rational expressions, first, factor the numerator and denominator completely, then divide both the numerator and the denominator by any common factors. A rational expression is simplified if its numerator and denominator have no common factors other than 1 and -1.
- When reducing rational expressions, only <u>factors</u>, not common terms, that are common to the <u>entire</u> numerator and the <u>entire</u> denominator can be divided out.

Answers: 1. a. $x = -5$ b. $x = -3$ and $x = -2$ c. defined for all real numbers   2. a. $\dfrac{x+6}{7x}$

b. $\dfrac{2x+14}{x}$ c. $x+1$ d. $\dfrac{x-3}{x+2}$ e. $\dfrac{1}{-x+2}$ or $\dfrac{1}{2-x}$ f. $\dfrac{-c}{c-1}$ 3. a. $r = -20$ b. time = 4 hours

Mini Lecture 7.2
Multiplying and Dividing Rational Expressions

Learning Objectives:
1. Multiply rational expressions.
2. Divide rational expressions.

Examples:

Multiply as indicated.

1. a. $\dfrac{5}{x-3} \cdot \dfrac{x+2}{4}$
   b. $\dfrac{9}{2x-8} \cdot \dfrac{x-4}{3}$
   c. $\dfrac{4}{a-6} \cdot \dfrac{6}{a+4}$

2. a. $\dfrac{3x^3}{3x-6} \cdot \dfrac{x-2}{x^2}$
   b. $\dfrac{4a^2+4a}{a^2-25} \cdot \dfrac{a^2-5a}{4a}$
   c. $\dfrac{6x-12}{6x+12} \cdot \dfrac{3x+3}{12x-24}$

3. a. $\dfrac{x^2+5x+6}{x^2-x-6} \cdot \dfrac{2x^2-5x-3}{x^2+6x+9}$
   b. $\dfrac{x^2+8x+16}{x^2+4x} \cdot \dfrac{x^2-x-6}{x^2-16}$
   c. $\dfrac{x^2+5x-14}{x^2-8x+7} \cdot \dfrac{x-1}{x^2-49}$

Divide as indicated.

4. a. $\dfrac{3x+9}{x^2} \div \dfrac{6x+18}{x^3}$
   b. $a^2-4a-12 \div \dfrac{a+2}{a-6}$
   c. $\dfrac{x^2-3x-10}{x^2-8x+15} \div \dfrac{3x^2+2x-8}{x^2+x-12}$

   d. $\dfrac{x^2+5x+1}{8x-8} \div \dfrac{x^2+5x+1}{x-1}$
   e. $\left(a^2+5a-24\right) \div \dfrac{(a-3)}{(a+8)}$

Teaching Notes:
- "When in doubt, factor it out." Factor first – before multiplying.
- Remind students that in order to divide fractions, (in this section, rational expressions) you must multiply by the reciprocal of the divisor.

Answers: 1. a. $\dfrac{5x+10}{4x-12}$ b. $\dfrac{3}{2}$ c. $\dfrac{24}{a^2-2a-24}$ 2. a. x b. $\dfrac{a(a+1)}{a+5}$ c. $\dfrac{(x+1)}{4(x+2)}$

3. a. $\dfrac{2x+1}{x+3}$ b. $\dfrac{(x-3)(x+2)}{x(x-4)}$ c. $\dfrac{(x-2)}{(x-7)(x-7)}$ 4. a. $\dfrac{x}{2}$ b. $(a-6)^2$ c. $\dfrac{(x+4)}{(3x-4)}$

d. $\dfrac{1}{8}$ e. $(a+8)^2$

Mini Lecture 7.3
Adding and Subtracting Rational Expressions with the Same Denominator

Learning Objectives:
1. Add rational expressions with the same denominator.
2. Subtract rational expressions with the same denominator.
3. Add and subtract rational expressions with opposite denominators.

Examples:

Add. Simplify if possible.

1. a. $\dfrac{3x-4}{7}+\dfrac{4x+11}{7}$

    b. $\dfrac{x^2}{x^2-9}+\dfrac{9-6x}{x^2-9}$

Subtract, simplify if possible.

2. a. $\dfrac{6x+7}{x+2}-\dfrac{3x}{x+2}$

    b. $\dfrac{4x^2+3x}{x+1}-\dfrac{-2x-1}{x+1}$

    c. $\dfrac{2x^2+x-1}{x^2-2x-3}-\dfrac{x^2-x-2}{x^2-2x-3}$

    d. $\dfrac{x^2}{x-2}-\dfrac{4}{2-x}$

Add, making sure to find a common denominator first and simplify if possible.

3. $\dfrac{x}{x-1}+\dfrac{1}{1-x}$

Teaching Notes:
- To add rational expressions with the same denominator, add numerators and place and sum over the common denominator. Simplify the answer if possible.
- To subtract rational expressions with the same denominator, subtract numerators and place the difference over the common denominator. Simplify the answer if possible.
- When subtracting numerators with a common denominator, make sure to subtract every term in that expression.
- When one denominator is the additive inverse of the other, first multiply either rational expressions by $\dfrac{-1}{-1}$ to obtain a common denominator.

Answers: 1. a. $x+1$ b. $\dfrac{x-3}{x+3}$ 2. a. $\dfrac{3x+7}{x+2}$ b. $4x+1$ c. $\dfrac{x+1}{x-3}$ d. $\dfrac{x^2+4}{x-2}$ 3. 1

Mini Lecture 7.4
Adding and Subtracting Rational Expressions with Different Denominators

Learning Objectives:
1. Find the least common denominator (LCD).
2. Add and subtract rational expressions with different denominators.

Examples:

Find the least common denominator for the rational numbers or rational expressions. Factor the denominators first, then build the least common denominator from those factors.

1.   a. $\dfrac{1}{15}$ and $\dfrac{7}{24}$ b. $\dfrac{5}{4x^2}$ and $\dfrac{2x+3}{14x}$ c. $\dfrac{x+1}{x^2-16}$ and $\dfrac{2x-1}{x^2+6x+8}$

Rewrite each of the following as an equivalent expression with the given denominator.

2.   a. $\dfrac{3}{8}=\dfrac{}{40x}$ b. $\dfrac{x^2}{7xy}=\dfrac{}{21x^3y^2}$ c. $\dfrac{5}{x+3}=\dfrac{}{(x+3)(x-2)}$

Add or subtract.

3.   a. $\dfrac{2}{9}+\dfrac{5}{12}$ b. $\dfrac{3}{5x^2}+\dfrac{7}{10x}$ c. $\dfrac{3}{2a+4}+\dfrac{3}{a^2+2a}$

   d. $\dfrac{x-3}{6}-\dfrac{x-1}{10}$ e. $\dfrac{y+3}{y-2}-\dfrac{4y-13}{y^2-5y+6}$ f. $\dfrac{2}{x^2-1}-\dfrac{5}{x^2+3x-4}$

   g. $\dfrac{a-4}{a-3}+\dfrac{5}{a^2-a-6}$ h. $\dfrac{6}{y^2-9}-\dfrac{5}{y^2-y-6}$ i. $\dfrac{4x}{x^2+6x+5}-\dfrac{3x}{x^2+5x+4}$

Teaching Notes:
- Students may need to be reminded of factoring steps. It is very important to be able to factor quickly and completely.
- Students will find this concept easy if they can relate adding and subtracting rational expressions to adding and subtracting fractions.
- Watch the signs when subtracting!
- Students need to understand that the LCD is build with the factors of the denominators.

Answers: 1. a. 120 b. $28x^2$ c. $(x+4)(x-4)(x+2)$ 2. a. $\dfrac{15x}{40x}$ b. $\dfrac{3x^4y}{21x^3y^2}$ c. $\dfrac{5x-1}{(x+3)(x-2)}$

3. a. $\dfrac{23}{36}$ b. $\dfrac{6+7x}{10x^2}$ c. $\dfrac{3}{2a}$ d. $\dfrac{x-6}{15}$ e. $\dfrac{y-2}{y-3}$ f. $\dfrac{-3}{(x+1)(x+4)}$ g. $\dfrac{a+1}{a+2}$

h. $\dfrac{1}{(y+3)(y+2)}$ i. $\dfrac{x}{(x+5)(x+4)}$

ML-49

Learning Objectives:
1. Simplify complex rational expressions by dividing.
2. Simplify complex rational expressions by multiplying by the LCD.

Examples:
Simplify by dividing; simplify, if possible.

1.   a. $\dfrac{\dfrac{1}{2}+\dfrac{2}{3}}{\dfrac{7}{12}+\dfrac{5}{6}}$ b. $\dfrac{\dfrac{1}{x}+\dfrac{1}{y}}{\dfrac{1}{xy}}$ c. $\dfrac{4+\dfrac{1}{x}}{4-\dfrac{1}{x}}$

Simplify by the LCD method; simplify, if possible.

1.   a. $\dfrac{\dfrac{1}{2}+\dfrac{2}{3}}{\dfrac{7}{12}+\dfrac{5}{6}}$ b. $\dfrac{4+\dfrac{1}{x}}{4-\dfrac{1}{x}}$ c. $\dfrac{\dfrac{1}{x}+\dfrac{1}{y}}{\dfrac{1}{xy}}$

Teaching Notes:
- Complex rational expressions are called complex fractions. They have numerators or denominators containing one or more rational expressions.
- One method for simplifying a complex rational expression is to combine its numerator into a single expression and combine its denominator into a single expression, then divide by multiplying by the reciprocal of the term in the denominator.
- A second method for simplifying a complex rational expression is to multiply each term in the numerator and denominator by the least common denominator (LCD). This will produce an equivalent expression that does not contain fractions in the numerator or denominator.
- Both methods for simplifying complex rational expressions produce the same answer. See which method you prefer.

Answers: 1. a. $\dfrac{14}{17}$ b. $y+x$ c. $\dfrac{4x+1}{4x-1}$ 2. a. $\dfrac{14}{17}$ b. $y+x$ c. $\dfrac{4x+1}{4x-1}$

Mini Lecture 7.6
Solving Rational Equations

Learning Objectives:
1. Solve rational equations.
2. Solve problems involving formulas with rational expressions.
3. Solve a formula with a rational expression for a variable.

Examples:

What is the LCD in each problem?

1. a. $\dfrac{3}{2x} + \dfrac{1}{4} = \dfrac{5}{x}$ b. $\dfrac{5}{y} + 3 = \dfrac{2}{3y}$ c. $\dfrac{2x}{x-1} + \dfrac{3}{x} = 5$

Solve. Clear each equation of fractions first.

2. a. $\dfrac{x}{2} - \dfrac{x}{3} = 8$ b. $\dfrac{3}{x} - \dfrac{2}{3x} = \dfrac{14}{3}$ c. $\dfrac{y}{6} + \dfrac{y}{4} = 5$

3. a. $\dfrac{a-2}{a-5} = \dfrac{a-3}{a+5}$ b. $\dfrac{x+3}{x+2} = \dfrac{x+2}{x+3}$ c. $\dfrac{5}{x+5} = \dfrac{3}{x+7}$

    d. $\dfrac{1-y}{1+y} = \dfrac{2}{3}$ e. $\dfrac{x-2}{x+2} = \dfrac{x-4}{x+4}$ f. $\dfrac{a+4}{a-2} = \dfrac{a+5}{a-3}$

4. a. $\dfrac{8}{x-3} - 3 = \dfrac{2-3x}{x+3}$ b. $\dfrac{4}{x-2} - \dfrac{2x-3}{x^2-4} = \dfrac{5}{x+2}$ c. $\dfrac{3x^2-10}{2x^2-5x} - 1 = \dfrac{x}{2x-5}$

    d. $\dfrac{3x-5}{x^2+4x+3} + \dfrac{2x+2}{x+3} = \dfrac{x-3}{x+1}$ e. $4a - 3 = \dfrac{a+13}{a+1}$ f. $\dfrac{x-10}{5} - \dfrac{x-10}{3x} = 0$

Solve each formula for the specified variable.

4. a. $P = \dfrac{A}{1+r}$ for r b. $A = \dfrac{1}{2}bh$ for h c. $\dfrac{V_1}{V_2} = \dfrac{P_2}{P_1}$ for V_1

Teaching Notes:
- Students may need extra practice finding the LCD and may need to be reminded to <u>Factor First</u>.
- When all denominators are in factored form – list the restricted values. Restricted values is any numbers that would make any denominator zero.
- Some rational equations can be solved using cross products, but students need to be aware that the method can only be used when there is only one rational expression on each side of the equation.
- Students need to constantly be reminded to multiply <u>each</u> term or expression on <u>both</u> sides of the equation by the LCD to get ride of the fractions.
- Students <u>must</u> check solutions for restricted values.
- Stress to students when solving a formula for a variable we use the same procedure as when solving rational equation.

<u>Answers:</u> 1. a. $4x$ b. $3y$ c. $x(x+1)$ 2. a. 48 b. $\dfrac{1}{2}$ c. 12 3. a. $\dfrac{25}{11}$ b. $-\dfrac{5}{2}$ c. -10 d. $\dfrac{1}{5}$ e. 0

f. -1 4. a. 19 b. 7 c. 2 d. -6 e. $2, -2$ f. $\dfrac{5}{3}$, 10 5. a. $A = P(1+r)$ b. $h = \dfrac{2A}{b}$ c. $V_1 = \dfrac{P_2 V_2}{P_1}$

Mini Lecture 7.7
Applications Using Rational Equations and Proportions

Learning Objectives:
1. Solve problems involving motion.
2. Solve problems involving work.
3. Solve problems involving proportions.
4. Solve problems involving similar triangles.

Examples:
1.   A boat travels 5 km upstream in the same amount of time that the boat covers 15 km downstream. The current in the stream moves at a speed of 2 km/h. What is the speed of the boat in still water?

2.   John working alone can paint a room in 4 hours. His helper, Luke, would need 6 hours to do the job by himself. If they work together, how long will the paint job take to complete?

3.   A tree casts a shadow of 7.5 ft. At the same time, Elizabeth measures the length of her shadow which is 3 ft. If Elizabeth is 5.5 feet tall, how tall is the tree?

4.

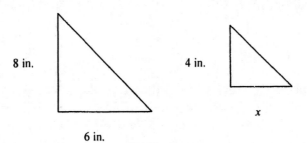

8 in.

6 in.

4 in.

x

Teaching Notes:
- Time in motion equation: $t = \dfrac{d}{r}$ time traveled = $\dfrac{\text{distance traveled}}{\text{rate of travel}}$

- Work problem equation:
  fractional part of job done + fractional part of job   =   1 job completed
  by one person   done by the second person

- Proportions: Set up proportions by listing the given ratio on one side and the ratio with the unknown quantity on the other side. Each respective quantity should occupy the same corresponding position on each side of the proportion.

- Similar Figures: Corresponding angles have the same measure and the ratios of the lengths of the corresponding sides are equal. In corresponding figures, the lengths of the corresponding sides are proportional. When triangles ABC and DEF are all similar then:

  $M\angle A = M\angle D,\ M\angle B = M\angle E,\ M\angle C = M\angle F$ $\dfrac{a}{d} = \dfrac{b}{e} = \dfrac{c}{f}$

Answers: 1. $\dfrac{5}{x-2} = \dfrac{15}{x+2}$, 4 km/h   2. $\dfrac{x}{4} + \dfrac{x}{6} = 1$, $2\dfrac{2}{5}$ hours   3. $\dfrac{x}{5.5} = \dfrac{7.5}{3}$, 13.75 feet   4. $x = 3$ in.

Mini Lecture 7.8
Modeling Using Variation

Learning Objectives:
1. Solve direct variation problems.
2. Solve inverse variation problems.
3. Solve combined variation problems.
4. Solve problems involving joint variation.

Examples:

Which equations show direct variation?

1.   a. $y = 4x$ b. $y = \dfrac{5}{x}$ c. $xy = 10$ d. $y = -7x$

Which equations show inverse variation?

2.   a. $y = \dfrac{4}{\sqrt{x}}$ b. $y = \dfrac{10}{x}$ c. $y = \dfrac{x+2}{5}$ d. $y = 4$

Which equations show joint variation?

3.   a. $p = x^2 y$ b. $m = \dfrac{4x^2}{y}$ c. $y = 5x$ d. $y = 6x^2 t$

Write a direction variation equation for each of the following and solve.
4.   a. If y varies directly to x and y is 10 when x is 2, find y when x is 7.
       b. If p varies directly to m, and p is –32 when $m = 4$, find p when m is –3.
       c. If d varies directly with t, and d is 120 when t is 2, find d if t is 3.5.

Write an inverse variation equation for each of the following and solve.
5.   a. If y varies inversely with x, and y is 8 when x is 5, find y when x is 2.
       b. If b varies inversely with a, and b is –2 when a is –3, find b when a is 12.

Write a joint variation equation for each of the following and solve.
6.   a. If m varies jointly with x and the square of y and m is 54 when x is 3 and y is 3, find m when $x = 2$ and $y = 4$.
       b. If a varies jointly with b and the square root of c, and a is 24 when b is 4 and c is 4, find a when b is 5 and c is 9.

Teaching Notes:
- Quantities can vary directly, inversely, or jointly.
- Direct Variation $y = kx$

  Inverse Variation $y = \dfrac{k}{x}$
- "k" is the constant of variation.

Answers: 1. a, d 2. a, b 3. a, d 4. a. $y = 35$ b. $p = 24$ c. $d = 210$ 5. a. $y = 20$ b. $b = \dfrac{1}{2}$

6. a. $m = 64$ b. $a = 45$

Mini Lecture 8.1
Introduction to Functions

Learning Objectives:
1. Find the domain and range of a relation.
2. Determine whether a relation is a function.
3. Evaluate a function.

Examples:
1. Find the domain and range of the relation.

   a. $\{(1, 5), (2, 10), (3, 15), (4, 20), (5, 25)\}$ b. $\{(1, -1), (0, 0), (-5, 5)\}$

2. Determine whether each relation is a function.

   a. $\{(5, 6), (5, 7), (5, 8), (5, 9), (5, 10)\}$ b. $\{(5, 6), (6, 7), (7, 8), (8, 9), (9, 10)\}$

3. Find the indicated function value.

   a. $f(3)$ for $f(x) = 3x - 2$ b. $g(-2)$ for $g(x) = 2x^2 - x + 4$

   c. $h(-1)$ for $h(t) = t^2 - 3t + 2$ d. $f(a+h)$ for $f(x) = 2x + 3$

4. Function g is defined by the table

x	$g\,(x)$
0	2
1	4
2	6
3	8
4	10

   Find the indicated function value.

   a. $g(2)$ b. $g(4)$

Teaching Notes:
- A <u>relation</u> is any set of ordered pairs.
- The set of all first terms "x-values" of the ordered pairs is called the <u>domain</u>.
- The set of all second terms "y-values" of the ordered pairs is called the <u>range</u>.
- A <u>function</u> is a relation in which each member of the domain corresponds to exactly one member of the range.
- A function is a relation in which no two ordered pairs have the same first component and different second components.
- The variable "x" is called the <u>independent variable</u> because it can be assigned any value from the domain.
- The variable "y" is called the <u>dependent variable</u> because its value depends on "x".
- The notation $f(x)$, read "f of x" represents the value of the function at the number "x".

<u>Answers:</u> 1. domain $\{1, 0, -5\}$ range $\{-1, 0, 5\}$ 2. a. not a function   b. function
3. a. 7   b. 14   c. 6   d. $2a + 2h + 3$ n   4. a. 6   b. 10

Mini Lecture 8.2
Graph of Functions

Learning Objectives:
1. Use the vertical line test to identify functions.
2. Obtain information about a function from its graph.
3. Review interval notation.
4. Identify the domain and range of a function from its graph.

Examples:
State the domain of each function.
1. Use the vertical line test to identify graphs in which y is a function of x.

   a. 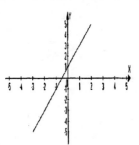   b. 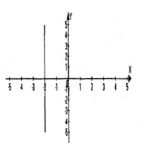   c.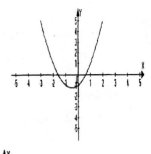

2. Use the graph of f to find the indicated function value.

   a. $f(2)$ b. $f(0)$ c. $f(1)$

   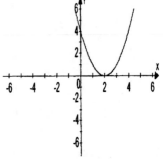

3. Express each interval in set-builder notation and graph the interval on a number line.

   a. $\{-2, 5]$ b. $(-\infty, 6)$ c. $[4, \infty)$

4. Use the graph each function to identify its domain and range.

   a. 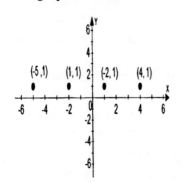   b.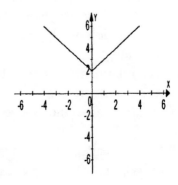

Teaching Notes:

- If a vertical line intersects a graph in more than one point, the graph does not define y as a function of x.
- Parentheses, ( ), indicate endpoints that are not included in a interval. Square brackets, [ ], indicate endpoints that are included in an interval. Parentheses are always used with ∞ or $-\infty$.

Answers:

1.a. yes b. no c. yes 2.a. 0 b. 4 c. 1

3.a. $\{x \mid -2 < x \le 5\}$

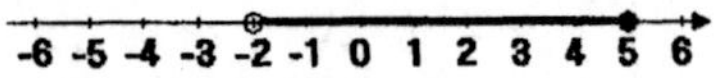

b. $\{x \mid x < 6\}$

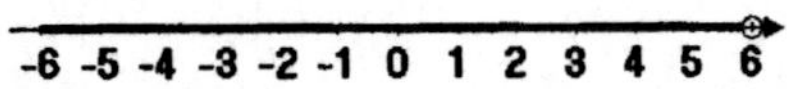

c. $\{x \mid x \ge 4\}$

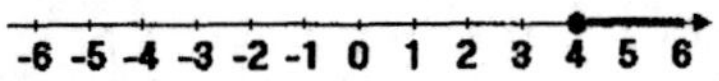

4. a. Domain: $\{x \mid x = -5,\ -2,\ 1,\ 4\}$ Range: $\{y \mid y = 1\}$

b. Domain: $\{x \mid x \ge 2\}$ Range: $\{x \mid x \text{ is a real number}\}$

Mini Lecture 8.3
The Algebra of Functions

Learning Objectives:
1. Find the domain of a function.
2. Use the algebra of functions to combine functions and determine domains.

Examples:
State the domain of each function.

1. a. $f(x) = \dfrac{2}{x-5}$ b. $g(x) = \dfrac{x+2}{x+6}$ c. $h(x) = x^2 + 2$ d. $p(x) = \dfrac{x-4}{x}$

2. a. $g(x) = \sqrt{x}$ b. $h(x) = \sqrt{x-7}$ c. $b(x) = \sqrt{x+3}$ d. $m(x) = x - 8$

3. Let $f(x) = x^2 - 2x$ and $g(x) = x + 3$. Find the following;
    a. $(f+g)(x)$ b. the domain of $f + g$ c. $(f+g)(-2)$

4. Let $f(x) = \dfrac{5}{x+2}$ and $g(x) = \dfrac{6}{x}$. Find the following;
    a. $(f+g)(x)$ b. The domain of $f + g$

5. Let $f(x) = x^2 + 1$ and $g(x) + x = 3$. Find the following;
    a. $(f+g)(x)$ b. $(f+g)(-2)$ c. $(f-g)(x)$

    d. $(f-g)(0)$ e. $\left(\dfrac{f}{g}\right)(-2)$

Teaching Notes:
- Students need to be reminded that division by zero is undefined. The value of "x" cannot be anything that would make the denominator of a fraction zero.
- Students often exclude values from the domain that would make the numerator zero, warn against this.
- Show students why the radicand of a square root function must be greater than or equal to zero. This is a good place to use the graphing calculator so students can "see" what happens.

Answers: 1. a. $\{x \mid x$ is a real number and $x \neq 5\}$ b. $\{x \mid x$ is a real number and $x \neq -6\}$
c. $\{x \mid x$ is a real number$\}$ d. $\{x \mid x$ is a real number and $x \neq 0\}$ 2. a. $\{x \mid x \geq 0\}$ b. $\{x \mid x \geq 7\}$
c. $\{x \mid x \geq -3\}$ d. $\{x \mid x$ is a real number$\}$

3. a. $x^w - x + 3$ b. $\{x \mid x$ is a real number$\}$ c. 9   4. a. $\dfrac{5}{x+2} + \dfrac{6}{x}$

b. $\{x \mid x$ is a real number and $x \neq -2\}$ and $x \neq 0\}$ 5. a. $x^2 + x - 2$ b. 0 c. $x^2 - x + 4$ d. 4 e. -1

Mini Lecture 8.4
Composite and Inverse Functions

Learning Objectives:
1. Form composite functions.
2. Verify inverse functions.
3. Find the inverse of a function.
4. Use the horizontal line test to determine if a function has an inverse function.
5. Use the graph of a one-to-one function to graph its inverse function.

Examples:
1. Given $f(x) = x - 1$ and $g(x) = x^2 - 2$, find each of the following composite functions.
   a. $(f \circ g)(x)$ b. $(g \circ f)(x)$

2. Given $f(x) = \dfrac{x-1}{2}$ and $g(x) = 2x + 1$, show that each function is the inverse of the other.
   a. $f(g(x))$ b. $g(f(x))$

3. Find the inverse of each given function:
   a. $f(x) = 2x - 1$ b. $g(x) = 4y$

4. If the points (4, 2), (6, 3) and (8, 4) are on the graph of f, give three points on the graph of f^{-1}.

Teaching Notes:
- $f \circ g$ and $g \circ f$ are not the same.
- In the notation, f^{-1}, -1 is not an exponent. f^{-1} represents the inverse function of x.
- $f(f^{-1}(x)) = x$ and $f^{-1}(f(x)) = x$.
- If f and g are inverses, then $f(g(x)) = x$ and $g(f(x)) = x$.
- Use the horizontal line test for inverse function.
- Only one-to-one functions have inverse functions.

Answers: 1. a. $x^2 - 3$ b. $x^2 - 2x - 1$ 2. a. $f(g(x)) = f(2x + 1) = \dfrac{2x+1-1}{2} = \dfrac{2x}{2} = x$

b. $g(f(x)) = g\left(\dfrac{x-1}{2}\right) = 2\left(\dfrac{x-1}{2}\right) + 1 = x - 1 + 1 = x$ 3. a. $f^{-1} = \dfrac{x+1}{2}$ b. $g^{-1} = \dfrac{x}{4}$ or $\dfrac{1}{4}x$

4. (2, 4), (3, 6), (4, 8)

Mini Lecture 9.1
Reviewing Linear Inequalities and Using Inequalities in Business Applications

Learning Objectives:
1. Review how to solve linear inequalities.
2. Use linear inequalities to solve problems involving revenue, cost, and profit.

Examples:

1.   a. $2x - 5 \geq 3$ b. $3x - 5 \leq 6x + 4$ c. $\dfrac{x+1}{4} > \dfrac{2x-1}{4} + \dfrac{3}{8}$

     d. $4(x+1) > 4x + 2$ e. $2x + 2 \leq 2x - 2$

2.   Use the revenue and cost functions
$$R(x) = 100x$$
$$C(x) = 160,000 + 75x$$
to write the profit function for producing and selling x units.
With the profit function, determine how many units must be produced and sold for the business to make money.

Teaching Notes:
- When multiplying or dividing both sides of an inequality by a negative quantity, remember to reverse the direction of the inequality symbol.
- When an inequality has been solved and the variable has been eliminated and the result is a false statement, the inequality has no solution, Ø.
- When an inequality has been solved and the variable has been eliminated and the result is a true statement, the solution for the inequality is all real numbers.
- Revenue and cost function: A company produces and sells x units of a product. The Revenue Function is: $R(x) = (\text{price per unit sold})x$ and the Cost Function is: $C(x) = $ fixed cost $+ (\text{cost per unit produced})x$.
- The Profit, $P(x)$, generated after producing and selling x units of a product is given by the profit function $P(x) = R(x) = C(x)$ where R and C are the revenue and cost functions, respectively.

Answers: 1.a. $\{x \mid x \geq 4\}$ or $[4, \infty)$

b. $\{x \mid x \geq -3\}$ or $[-3, \infty)$

c. $\{x \mid x < \frac{1}{2}\}$ or $(-\infty, \frac{1}{2})$

d. $\{x \mid x \text{ is a real number}\}$ or $(-\infty, \infty)$

-6 -5 -4 -3 -2 -1 0 1 2 3 4 5 6

e. $\varnothing$

-6 -5 -4 -3 -2 -1 0 1 2 3 4 5 6

2. $P(x) = 25x - 160,000$; more than 6400 units

Mini Lecture 9.2
Compound Inequalities

Learning Objectives:
1. Find the intersection of two sets.
2. Solve compound inequalities involving *and*.
3. Find the union of two sets
4. Solve compound inequalities involving *of*.

Examples:
1. Find the intersection of the sets.
   a. $\{-3, -1, 3, 5\} \cap \{-5, -3, 1, 3\}$ b. $\{0, 1, 2, 3, 4\} \cap \{2, 3, 5, 6\}$
   c. $\{2, 4, 6, 8\} \cap \{1, 3, 5, 7\}$

2. Solve. Give solutions in interval notation.
   a. $x + 1 < 6$ and $x + 5 > 8$ b. $-4x - 5 < 3$ and $x + 1 < 5$

   c. $-3 \leq 2x - 5 < 3$ d. $3 < \dfrac{x}{2} + 5 \leq 6$

3. Find the union of the sets.
   a. $\{-8, -7, -6\} \cup \{-5, -4, -3\}$ b. $\{2, 4, 6, 8\} \cup \{1, 3, 5, 7\}$
   c. $\{dogs) \cup \{cats\}$

4. Solve. Give solutions in interval notation.
   a. $x + 5 \leq -2$ or $x + 5 \geq 2$ b. $4x + 2 < -10$ or $5 - 2x < 9$
   c. $2x + 5 > 3x - 1$ or $x - 4 < 2x + 6$

5. Solve. Graph. Give solution in set builder notation and interval notation.
   a. $-6 < 2x + 2 \leq 14$ b. $5x - 3 \leq x + 1$ or $-8x \leq -16$
   c. $3(x + 1) < 2(x + 2)$ or $2(x - 1) \geq x + 2$ d. $2x + 4 < -8$ and $3x + 5 > 8$

Teaching Notes:
- It can be helpful when graphing compound inequalities involving *and* to graph each inequality on the same number line with different colored highlighters. This will enable the students to "see" the intersection of the two graphs.
- Students will again need to be reminded that when multiplying both sides of an equality by a negative number, the inequality sign must be reversed.
- Compound inequalities involving *or* indicate intersection.
- Compound inequalities involving *and* indicate union.

Answers: 1. a. $\{-3, 3\}$ b. $\{2, 3\}$ c. $\emptyset$ 2. a. $x < 5$ and $x > 3$; $(3, 5)$ b. $x > -2$ and $x < 4$; $(-2, 4)$
c. $1 \leq x < 4$; $[1, 4)$ d. $-4 < x \leq 12$; $(14, 12]$ 3. a. $\{-8, -7, -6, -5, -4, -3\}$ b. $\{1, 2, 3, 4, 5, 6, 7, 8\}$
c. $\{dogs, cats\}$ 4. a. $x \leq -7$ or $x \geq -3$; $(-\infty, -7] \cup [-3, \infty)$ b. $x < -3$ or $x > -2$; $(-\infty, -3) \cup (-2, \infty)$

c. $x < 6$ or $x > -10$; $(-\infty, \infty)$ 5. a. $-4 < x \le 6$; ![number line from -6 to 6]; $\{x \mid -4 < x \le 6\}$; $(-4, 6]$

b. $x \le 1$ or $x \ge 2$; ![number line from -6 to 6]; $\{x \mid x \le 1 \text{ or } x \ge 2\}$; $(-\infty, 1] \cup [2, \infty)$

c. $x < 1$ or $x \ge 4$; ![number line from -6 to 6]; $\{x \mid x < 1 \text{ or } x \ge 4\}$; $(-\infty, 1) \cup [4, \infty)$

d. $x < -6$ and $x > 1$; ![number line from -6 to 6] $\varnothing$

Mini Lecture 9.3
Equations and Inequalities Involving Absolute Values

Learning Objectives:
1. Solve equations involving absolute value.
2. Solve inequalities involving absolute value.
3. Recognize absolute value inequalities with no solution or all real numbers as solutions.

Examples:
1. Solve.

   a. $|3x - 2| = 5$ b. $2|y + 4| = 8$

   c. $|x - 2| + 4 = 2$ d. $|2x + 1| = |3x + 4|$

2. Solve and graph the solution set on a number line.

   a. $|x + 4.5| < 1.5$ b. $|2x - 3| \geq 6$

   c. $|3x + 4| < -2$ d.. $|2x - 2| > -4$

Teaching Notes:
- The absolute value of a, denoted $|a|$ is the distance from 0 to a on a number line.
- If c is a positive real number and x is an algebraic expression then rewrite an absolute value equation without absolute value bars. $|x| = c$ is equivalent to $x = \pm c$
- If c is a positive number and x is an algebraic expression then $|x| > c$ are the numbers $-c < x < c$. $|x| > c$ are the numbers $x < -c$ or $x > c$. These rules are true for $\leq$ or $\geq$ respectively.
- If c is a negative number and x is an algebraic expression then $|x| < c$ has no solution and $|x| > c$ is true for all real numbers for which x is defined.

Answers: 1.   a. -1 and $\dfrac{7}{3}$ or $\left\{-1, \dfrac{7}{3}\right\}$ b. 0 and -8 or $\{0, -8\}$ c. $\varnothing$ d. -3 and -1 or $\{-3, -1\}$

2. a. $\{x \mid -6 < x < -3\}$ or $(-6, -3)$ ‑6 ‑5 ‑4 ‑3 ‑2 ‑1 0 1 2 3 4 5 6

b. $\left\{x \mid x \leq \dfrac{-3}{2} \text{ or } x \geq \dfrac{9}{2}\right\}$ or $\left(-\infty, \dfrac{-3}{2}\right] \cup \left[\dfrac{9}{2}, \infty\right)$ ‑6 ‑5 ‑4 ‑3 ‑2 ‑1 0 1 2 3 4 5 6

c. $\varnothing$ ‑6 ‑5 ‑4 ‑3 ‑2 ‑1 0 1 2 3 4 5 6   d. $\{x \mid x \text{ is a real number}\}$ or $(-\infty, \infty)$ ‑6 ‑5 ‑4 ‑3 ‑2 ‑1 0 1 2 3 4 5 6

Mini Lecture 9.4
Linear Inequalities in Two Variables

Learning Objectives:
1. Graph linear inequalities in two variables.
2. Graph systems of linear inequalities.

Examples:
1. Graph each linear equality.
   a. $3y > x - 3$ b. $3x + y \leq 4$ c. $4x - 2y > 6$
   d. $6y > 4x$ e. $y \leq 5$ f. $x > -3$

2. Graph each system of inequalities.

   a. $y > x - 3$ b. $x + y \leq 4$ c. $y > \dfrac{1}{2}x - 4$

   $\quad y < -3x + 1$ $\quad x + 2y \geq 2$ $\quad x - 2y \geq -6$

   d. $x - y < -4$ e. $y \leq 3$ f. $3x + 4y > -12$
   $\quad 2x + y \geq 0$ $\quad y \geq 2x + 2$ $\quad -3x + y \geq 4$

Teaching Notes:
- When graphing an inequality involving $\geq$ or $\leq$, the boundary line should be solid.
- When graphing an inequality involving $>$ or $<$, the boundary line should be broken or dashed.
- Remind students to always use a check point when deciding which side of the line to shade just to be on the safe side. Some will quickly notice a shortcut (above the line or below the line) but should still check to be sure.

Answers: 1. a.
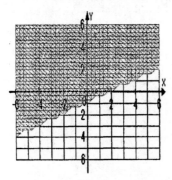
b.
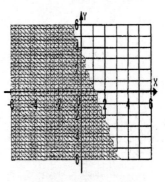

c.
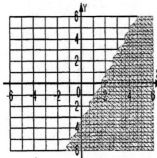
d..
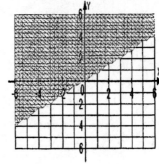

e.
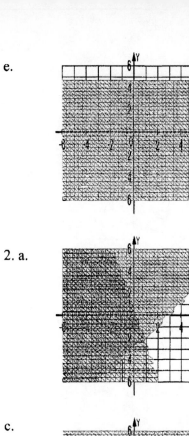

f.
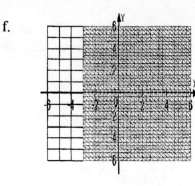

2. a.
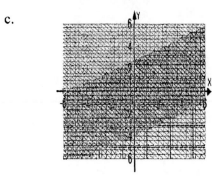

b.
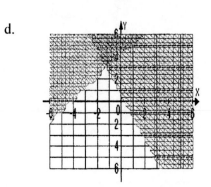

c.

d.
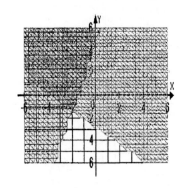

e.
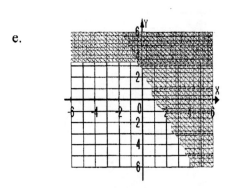

f.

Mini Lecture 10.1
Radical Expressions and Functions

<u>Learning Objectives:</u>
1. Evaluate square roots.
2. Evaluate square root functions.
3. Find the domain of square root functions.
4. Simplify expressions of the form $\sqrt{a^2}$.
5. Evaluate cube root functions.
6. Simplify expressions of the form $\sqrt[3]{a^3}$.
7. Find even and odd roots.
8. Simplify expressions of the form $\sqrt[n]{a^n}$.

<u>Examples:</u>

1. Evaluate the following:

   a. $\sqrt{49}$

   b. $-\sqrt{25}$

   c. $\sqrt{\dfrac{4}{9}}$

   d. $\sqrt{0.0064}$

   e. $\sqrt{64+36}$

   f. $\sqrt{64}+\sqrt{36}$

2. For each function, find the indicated function value.

   a. $f(x)=\sqrt{4x+5}$; $f(5)$

   b. $g(x)=\sqrt{4-2x}$; $g(-3)$

   c. $h(x)=\sqrt{2x-3}$; $h(9)$

3. Find the domain for each of the following:

   a. $f(x)=\sqrt{5x-20}$

   b. $g(x)=\sqrt{9-3x}$

4. Simplify each expression.

   a. $\sqrt{(-6)^2}$

   b. $\sqrt{(x-4)^2}$

   c. $\sqrt{81x^8}$

   d. $\sqrt{x^2+4x+4}$

5. For each function, find the indicated function value.

   a. $f(x)=\sqrt{2x-1}$; $f(5)$

   b. $g(x)=\sqrt[3]{x-9}$; $g(10)$

6. Simplify.

   a. $\sqrt[3]{-y^3}$

   b. $\sqrt[3]{8a^3}$

   c. $\sqrt[4]{1}$

   d. $-\sqrt[4]{81}$

   e. $\sqrt[4]{-256}$

   f. $\sqrt[5]{1}$

   g. $\sqrt[4]{(x-2)^4}$

   h. $\sqrt[5]{(2x+1)^5}$

   i. $\sqrt[6]{(-2)^6}$

Teaching Notes:

- If $b^2 = a$, then b is the square root of a.
- A square root of a negative number is not a real number.
- The symbol "$\sqrt{}$" is called a **radical sign**.
- The number under the radical sign is called the **radicand**.
- Together, the radical sign and the radicand are called the **radical expression**.
- A **square root function** is defined by $f(x) = \sqrt{x}$.
- For any real number a, $\sqrt{a^2} = |a|$.
- The **cube root** of a real number a is written $\sqrt[3]{a}$, the $\sqrt[3]{a} = b$ means $b^3 = a$.
- There is a **cube root function** defined by $f(x) = \sqrt[3]{x}$.
- In the radical expression $\sqrt[n]{a}$, the number n is the **index**. If n is an odd number, then the root is called an **odd root**. If n is even, then the root is called an **even root**.
- An even root of a negative number is **not** a real number.

Answers: 1. a. 7 b. –5 c. $\dfrac{2}{3}$ d. 0.08 e. 10 f. 14 2. a. $f(5) = 5$ b. $g(-3) = \sqrt{10} \approx 3.16$

c. $h(9) = \sqrt{15} \approx 3.87$ 3. a. domain of f is $\{x \mid x \geq 4\}$ or $[4, \infty)$ b. domain of g is $\{x \mid x \leq 3\}$ or $(-\infty, 3]$
4. a. –6 b. $|x - 4|$ c. $9|x^4|$ d. $|x + 2|$ 5. a. $f(5) = 3$ b. $g(10) = 1$ 6. a. $-y$ b. $2a$ c. 1 d. –3
3. not a real number f. 1 g. $|x - 2|$ h. $2x + 1$ i. 2

ML-68

Learning Objectives:

1. Use the definition of $a^{\frac{1}{n}}$.

2. Use the definition of $a^{\frac{m}{n}}$.

3. Use the definition of $a^{\frac{-m}{n}}$.

4. Simplify expressions with rational exponents.

5. Simplify radical expressions using rational exponents.

6. Apply the properties of exponents to rational exponents.

Examples:

Use the radical notation to rewrite each expression, then simplify if possible. Assume variables are positive.

1. a. $64^{\frac{1}{2}}$ b. $81^{\frac{1}{4}}$ c. $(-64)^{\frac{1}{3}}$ d. $(16x^4y^2)^{\frac{1}{2}}$

2. a. $16^{\frac{3}{4}}$ b. $(-27)^{\frac{2}{3}}$ c. $-25^{\frac{3}{2}}$ d. $(-9)^{\frac{1}{2}}$

3. a. $8^{\frac{-1}{3}}$ b. $16^{\frac{-3}{4}}$ c. $27^{\frac{-2}{3}}$ d. $(81x^8)^{\frac{-3}{4}}$

Rewrite each radical expression with rational exponents.

4. a. $\sqrt{5}$ b. $\sqrt[3]{30x}$ c. $\sqrt[3]{\dfrac{2}{3}}$ d. $\sqrt[6]{3xy^5}$

5. a. $4^{\frac{1}{4}} \cdot 4^{\frac{1}{4}}$ b. $(8^{\frac{1}{3}})^3$ c. $(27a^6b^3)^{\frac{2}{3}}$ d. $x^4y^3 \cdot x^{\frac{3}{4}}y^{\frac{2}{3}}$

Teaching Notes:

- The denominator of a rational exponent is the index of the equivalent radical.
- The numerator of a radical exponent is the power of which the radical is raised.
- Remind students that each base occurs only once in a simplified expression.
- A simplified expression should not contain any negative exponents.
- Remember, any base other than zero raised to the zero power is the number 1. A simplified expression should not have any zero exponents.

Answers:

1. a. $\sqrt{64} = 8$ b. $\sqrt[4]{81} = 3$ c. $\sqrt[3]{-64} = -4$ d. $\sqrt{16x^4y^2} = 4x^2y$ 2. a. $(\sqrt[4]{16})^3 = 8$

b. $(\sqrt[3]{-27})^2 = 9$ c. $-(\sqrt{25})^3 = -125$ d. $\sqrt{-9} = $ Not A Real Number 3. a. $\dfrac{1}{\sqrt[3]{8}} = \dfrac{1}{2}$

b. $(\dfrac{1}{\sqrt[4]{16}})^3 = \dfrac{1}{8}$ c. $\dfrac{1}{(\sqrt[3]{27})^2} = \dfrac{1}{9}$ d. $\dfrac{1}{(\sqrt[4]{81x^8})^3} = \dfrac{1}{27x^6}$ 4. a. $5^{\frac{1}{2}}$ b. $(30x)^{\frac{1}{3}}$ c. $\left(\dfrac{2}{3}\right)^{\frac{1}{3}}$

d. $(3xy^5)^{\frac{1}{6}}$ 5. a. 2 b. 8 c. $9a^4b^2$ d. $x^{\frac{19}{4}}y^{\frac{11}{3}}$

Mini Lecture 10.3
Multiplying and Simplifying Radical Expressions

Learning Objectives:
1. Use the product rule to multiply radicals.
2. Use factoring and the product rule to simplify radicals.
3. Multiply radicals and then simplify.

Examples:
1. Use the product rule to multiply.

     a. $\sqrt{3} \cdot \sqrt{7}$ b. $\sqrt{x-3} \cdot \sqrt{x+3}$

     c. $\sqrt[3]{5} \cdot \sqrt[3]{6}$ d. $\sqrt[5]{3x} \cdot \sqrt[5]{4x^2}$

2. If $f(x) = \sqrt{2x^2 + 8x + 8}$, express the function, f, in simplified form.

3. Simplify. Assume all variables in a radicand represent positive real numbers and no radicands involve negative quantities raised to even powers.

     a. $\sqrt{90}$ b. $\sqrt[3]{24}$

     c. $\sqrt[4]{243}$ d. $\sqrt{128x^3}$

     e. $\sqrt{x^8 y^7 z^6}$ f. $\sqrt[3]{16x^{10} y^{15}}$

     g. $\sqrt[5]{32x^9 y^7 z^{10}}$ h. $\sqrt{24x^2 y^5}$

4. Multiply and simplify. Assume all variables in a radicand represent positive real numbers and no radicands involve negative quantities raised to even powers.

     a. $\sqrt{3} \cdot \sqrt{4}$ b. $5\sqrt[3]{2} \cdot 10\sqrt[3]{16}$

     c. $\sqrt[4]{8x^2 y^4} \cdot \sqrt[4]{4x^5 y^2}$ d. $\sqrt{3x^7} \cdot \sqrt{20x^5}$

Teaching Notes:
- The **product rule for radicals** states: if $\sqrt[n]{a}$ and $\sqrt[n]{b}$ are real numbers then $\sqrt[n]{a} \cdot \sqrt[n]{b} = \sqrt[n]{ab}$.
- A number that is the square of an integer is a **perfect square**.
- A number is a **perfect cube** if it is the cube of an integer.
- A radical of index n is **simplified** when its radicand has no factors other than 1 that are perfect nth powers.
- For any non-negative real number, a, $\sqrt[n]{a^n} = a$.
- Perfect nth powers have exponents that are divisible by n.

Answers: 1. a. $\sqrt{21}$ b. $\sqrt{x^2 - 9}$ c. $\sqrt[3]{30}$ d. $\sqrt[5]{12x^3}$ 2. $f(x) = \sqrt{2}|x+2|$ 3. a. $3\sqrt{10}$
b. $2\sqrt[3]{3}$ c. $3\sqrt[4]{3}$ d. $8x\sqrt{2x}$ e. $x^4 y^3 z^3 \sqrt{y}$ f. $2x^3 y^5 \sqrt[3]{2x}$ g. $2xyz^2 \sqrt[5]{x^4 y^2}$ h. $2xy^2 \sqrt{6y}$
4. a. $2\sqrt{3}$ b. $100\sqrt[3]{4}$ c. $2xy\sqrt[4]{2x^3 y^2}$ d. $2x^6 \sqrt{15}$

Mini Lecture 10.4
Adding, Subtracting and Dividing Radical Expressions

Learning Objectives:

1. Add and subtract radical expressions.
2. Use the quotient rule to simplify radical expressions.
3. Use the quotient rule to divide radical expressions.

Examples:

Add or subtract. Be sure answers are in simplified form.

1. a. $6\sqrt{10} + 3\sqrt{10}$ b. $7\sqrt{18} - 3\sqrt{18}$ c. $4\sqrt{6} + 3\sqrt{6} - \sqrt{6}$

2. a. $4\sqrt{20} + 3\sqrt{5}$ b. $3\sqrt{32x} - 2\sqrt{18x}$ c. $3\sqrt{48} + 2\sqrt{27}$

3. a. $5\sqrt[3]{7} + 4\sqrt[3]{7}$ b. $12\sqrt[4]{32} - 3\sqrt[5]{32}$ c. $6\sqrt[3]{54x^3} + 2x\sqrt[3]{16}$

Simplify.

4. a. $\dfrac{\sqrt{8x^3}}{\sqrt{2x}}$ b. $\dfrac{\sqrt[3]{40x^5}}{\sqrt[3]{8x^2}}$ c. $\dfrac{\sqrt{25x^6}}{\sqrt{y^{12}}}$

Divide and simplify if possible.

5. a. $\dfrac{\sqrt{100x^5}}{\sqrt{4x^3}}$ b. $\dfrac{\sqrt[3]{40x^6y^5}}{\sqrt[3]{5x^3y^2}}$ c. $\dfrac{5\sqrt{20x^7}}{\sqrt{5x}}$

Teaching Notes:

- The radicand <u>and</u> the index must be the same in order to add or subtract radicals.
- Sometimes it is necessary to simplify radicals first to find out if they can be added or subtracted.
- The quotient rule can be used in two ways: $\dfrac{\sqrt[n]{a}}{\sqrt[n]{b}} = \sqrt[n]{\dfrac{a}{b}}$ or $\sqrt[n]{\dfrac{a}{b}} = \dfrac{\sqrt[n]{a}}{\sqrt[n]{b}}$.

<u>Answers:</u> 1. a. $9\sqrt{10}$ b. $12\sqrt{2}$ c. $6\sqrt{6}$ 2. a. $11\sqrt{5}$ b. $6\sqrt{2x}$ c. $18\sqrt{3}$

3. a. $9\sqrt[3]{7}$ b. cannot be subtracted c. $22x\sqrt[3]{2}$ 4. a. $2x$ b. $x\sqrt[3]{5}$ c. $\dfrac{5x^3}{y^6}$

5. a. $5x$ b. $2xy$ c. $10x^3$

Mini Lecture 10.5
Multiplying With More Than One Term and Rationalizing Denominators

Learning Objectives:
1. Multiply radicals with more than one term.
2. Use polynomial special products to multiply radicals.
3. Rationalize denominators containing one term.
4. Rationalize denominators containing two terms.

Examples:
1. Multiply.

a. $\sqrt{3}(x + \sqrt{6})$

b. $\sqrt[3]{x^2}(\sqrt[3]{x} - \sqrt[3]{4})$

c. $(2\sqrt{3} + 3\sqrt{5})(3\sqrt{3} - 2\sqrt{5})$

d. $(\sqrt{7} + \sqrt{5})^2$

e. $(\sqrt{6} + \sqrt{3})(\sqrt{6} - \sqrt{3})$

f. $(\sqrt{x} - \sqrt{5})(\sqrt{x} + \sqrt{5})$

2. Rationalize each denominator.

a. $\dfrac{\sqrt{2}}{\sqrt{5}}$

b. $\sqrt[3]{\dfrac{3}{4}}$

c. $\sqrt{\dfrac{3x}{5y}}$

d. $\dfrac{\sqrt[3]{2x}}{\sqrt[3]{y^2}}$

e. $\dfrac{3x}{\sqrt[5]{16x^3 y^4}}$

f. $\dfrac{6}{2\sqrt{5} + 4}$

g. $\dfrac{3 + \sqrt{6}}{\sqrt{6} - \sqrt{2}}$

Teaching Notes:
- To multiply radical expressions with more than one term use the distributive property and the FOIL method.
- To rationalize the denominator, multiply the numerator and the denominator by a radical of index n that produces a perfect nth power in the denominator's radicand.
- Radical expressions that involve the sum and difference of the same two terms are called **conjugates**.
- To rationalize a denominator with two terms and one or more square roots, multiply the numerator and denominator by the conjugate of the denominator.

Answers: 1. a. $x\sqrt{3} + 3\sqrt{2}$ b. $x - \sqrt[3]{4x^2}$ c. $-12 + 5\sqrt{15}$ d. $12 + 2\sqrt{35}$ e. 3 f. $x - 5$

2. a. $\dfrac{\sqrt{10}}{5}$ b. $\dfrac{\sqrt[3]{6}}{2}$ c. $\dfrac{\sqrt{15xy}}{5y}$ d. $\dfrac{\sqrt[3]{2xy}}{y}$ e. $\dfrac{3x\sqrt[5]{2x^2 y}}{2xy}$ f. $3\sqrt{5} - 6$ g. $\dfrac{3\sqrt{6} + 3\sqrt{2} + 6 + 2\sqrt{3}}{4}$

Learning Objectives:

1. Solve radical equations.
2. Use models that are radical functions to solve problems.

Examples:

Solve.

1. a. $\sqrt{4y+1} = 1$

   b. $\sqrt{6x-4} = -2$

   c. $\sqrt{3a+1} - 3 = 1$

   d. $\sqrt{4x-3} - 5 = 0$

   e. $\sqrt{x+4} = \sqrt{2x-5}$

   f. $\sqrt[3]{3x} + 4 = 7$

2. a. $\sqrt{3y+1} = y - 3$

   b. $\sqrt[3]{2a+7} = -1$

   c. $\sqrt{x+10} = x - 2$

   d. $\sqrt[4]{6a+7} = \sqrt[4]{a+2}$

   e. $y - 1 = \sqrt{6y+1}$

   f. $\sqrt[3]{3x+5} = \sqrt[3]{5-2x}$

Solve. Each of the following examples will require squaring both sides twice.

3. a. $\sqrt{x-8} = \sqrt{x} - 2$

   b. $\sqrt{a+5} = \sqrt{a-3} + 2$

   c. $\sqrt{y+8} = \sqrt{y-4} + 2$

Solve.

4. a. $(5x+7)^{\frac{1}{3}} = 2$

   b. $x + 1 = (5x+1)^{\frac{1}{2}}$

   c. $(5x-1)^{\frac{1}{2}} - 6 = 1$

Teaching Notes:

- When solving equations with radicals, isolate the radical on one side first.
- Raise both sides of the equation to the power that is the index of the radical in order to eliminate the radical. Sometimes this step must be done a second time to clear the equation of all radicals.
- Always check all solutions for extraneous solutions.

Answers: 1. a. 0 b. no solution c. 5 d. 7 e. 9 f. 9 2. a. 8 b. −4 c. 6 d. −1 e. 8
f. 0 3. a. 9 b. 4 c. 8 4. a. $\dfrac{1}{5}$ b. 0, 3 c. 10

Mini Lecture 10.7
Complex Numbers

Learning Objectives:
1. Express square roots of negative numbers in terms of i.
2. Add and subtract complex numbers.
3. Multiply complex numbers.
4. Divide complex numbers.
5. Simplify powers of i.

Examples:
1. Write as a multiple of i.

   a. $\sqrt{-81}$ b. $\sqrt{-13}$ c. $\sqrt{-60}$

2. Perform the indicated operation.

   a. $(3+4i)+(4-7i)$

   b. $(1+i)-(3+4i)$

   c. $4i(4-6i)$

   d. $(3+2i)(5-3i)$

   e. $\sqrt{-3}\cdot\sqrt{-4}$

3. Divide and simplify the form $a+bi$.

   a. $\dfrac{4+3i}{2i}$ b. $\dfrac{1+i}{2-3i}$

4. Simplify.

   a. i^{21} b. i^{30} c. i^{40} d. i^{7}

Teaching Notes:
- The **imaginary unit** i is defined as $i=\sqrt{-1}$ where $i^2=-1$.
- If b is a positive real number, then $\sqrt{-b}=\sqrt{b(-1)}=\sqrt{b}\cdot\sqrt{-1}=i\sqrt{b}$.
- The set of all numbers in the form $a+bi$, a is the **real part**, b is called the **imaginary part** of the **complex number** $a+bi$.
- When adding or subtracting complex numbers, add or subtract their real parts. Then add or subtract their imaginary parts and express the answer as a complex number. .

Answers: 1. a. $9i$ b. $i\sqrt{13}$ c. $2i\sqrt{15}$ 2. a. $7-3i$ b. $-2-3i$ c. $24+16i$ d. $21+i$
e. $-2\sqrt{3}$ 3. a. $\dfrac{3-4i}{2}$ or $\dfrac{3}{2}-2i$ b. $\dfrac{-1+5i}{13}$ or $-\dfrac{1}{13}+\dfrac{5}{13}i$ 4. a. i b. -1 c. 1 d. $-i$

Mini Lecture 11.1
The Square Root Property and Completing the Square; Distance and Midpoint Formulas

Learning Objectives:
1. Solve quadratic equations using the square root property.
2. Complete the square of a binomial.
3. Solve quadratic equations by completing the square.
4. Solve problems using the square root property.
5. Find the distance between two points.
6. Find the midpoint of a line segment.

Examples:

1. Solve using the square root property.

   a. $3x^2 = 18$

   b. $5x^2 - 7 = 0$

   c. $16x^2 + 25 = 0$

   d. $(x-2)^2 = 3$

2. What term should be added to each binomial so that it becomes a perfect square trinomial? Write and factor the trinomial.

   a. $x^2 + 8x$

   b. $x^2 - 5x$

   c. $x^2 + \frac{1}{2}x$

3. Solve by completing the square.

   a. $x^2 + 10x + 12 = 0$

   b. $2x^2 - 6x - 5 = 0$

4. Use the compound interest formula to find the annual interest rate, r.
   a. In 2 years, an investment of $3000 grows to $3307.50.
   b. In 4 years, an investment of $6000 grows to $8784.60.

5. Find the distance between each pair of points. If necessary, round answers to two decimals places.

   a. (6, 4) and (–2, 2)

   b. (1, 4) and (–3, 5)

6. Find the midpoint of the line segment with the given endpoints.

   a. (3, 7) and (9, 5)

   b. (3, –7) and (–4, –2)

Teaching Notes:
- The **square root property** states if u is an algebraic express and d is a non-zero real number, then $u^2 = d$ has two solutions. If $u^2 = d$, then $u = \sqrt{d}$ or $u = -\sqrt{d}$.
- When **completing the square**, if $x^2 + bx$ is a binomial, then by adding the square of half the coefficient of x, $\left(\frac{b}{2}\right)^2$, a perfect square trinomial will result

$$x^2 + bx + \left(\frac{b}{2}\right)^2 = (x + \frac{b}{x})^2.$$

- If solving quadratic equations by completing the square, be sure when you add a constant term to one side of the equation to complete the square, be certain to add the same constant to the other side of the equation.
- The formula for compound interest is $A = P(1+r)^t$ where A is the account balance, t is the years, P is the principal originally invested, and r is the interest rate.
- The distance, d, between the points (x, y) and (x_2, y_2), the coordinates of the segment's midpoints are: $\left(\dfrac{x_1 + x_2}{2}, \dfrac{y_1 + y_2}{2} \right)$

Answers: 1. a. $\pm\sqrt{6}$ b. $\pm\dfrac{\sqrt{35}}{5}$ c. $\pm\dfrac{5}{4}i$ d. $2\pm\sqrt{3}$ 2. a. $x^2 + 8x + 16 = (x+4)^2$

b. $x^2 - 5x + \dfrac{25}{4} = (x - \dfrac{5}{2})^2$ c. $x^2 + \dfrac{1}{2}x + \dfrac{1}{16} = (x + \dfrac{1}{4})^2$ 3. a. $-5\pm\sqrt{13}$ b. $\dfrac{3\pm\sqrt{19}}{2}$

4. a. 5% b. 10% 5. a. 10 units b. $\sqrt{17}$ or 4.12 units 6. a. (6, 6) b. $\left(-\dfrac{1}{2}, -\dfrac{9}{2} \right)$

Learning Objectives:
1. Solve quadratic equations using the quadratic formula.
2. Use the discriminant to determine the number and type of solutions.
3. Determine the most efficient method to use when solving different types of quadratic equations.
4. Write quadratic equations from solutions.
5. Use the quadratic formula to solve problems.

Examples:
1. Solve using the quadratic equation.

    a. $2x^2 - 5x = 3$ b. $3x^2 - 2x + 3 = 0$ c. $x^2 - 6x + 3 = 0$

    d. $3x^2 + 16x = -5$ e. $12x^2 - 4x + 5 = 0$ f. $x^2 + 6x = -13$

- Which problems in #1 could have been solved by factoring?

2. Find the value of the discriminant. Tell what kind and how many solutions each equation would have if solved.

    a. $9x^2 - 6x + 1 = 0$ b. $5x^2 = 4x - 6$ c. $x^2 + 4x = 1$

    d. $3x^2 - 4x = 2 = 0$ e. $2x^2 - 2x = 24$ f.. $4x^2 - 1 = 0$

3. Write an equation with the given solution set.

    a. $\{4, -2\}$ b. $\left\{\dfrac{-2}{3}, \dfrac{1}{5}\right\}$ c. $\left\{-\sqrt{5}, \sqrt{5}\right\}$ d. $\{3i, -3i\}$

Teaching Notes:
- Students <u>must</u> memorize the quadratic formula.
- The quadratic formula can always be used to solve a quadratic equation.
- Students need to be reminded of the standard form of a quadratic equation, $ax^2 + bx + c = 0$. When using the quadratic formula the equation should be in standard form.
- Have students write the quadratic formula each time they work a problem.
- Students need to have a firm grasp on how to choose a method for solving equations.

<u>Answers:</u> 1. a. $\left\{\dfrac{-1}{2}, 3\right\}$ b. $\left\{\dfrac{1 \pm 2i\sqrt{2}}{3}\right\}$ c. $\left\{3 \pm \sqrt{6}\right\}$ d. $\left\{\dfrac{-1}{3}, 5\right\}$ e. $\{-3 \pm 2i\}$

f. $\left\{\dfrac{2 \pm \sqrt{10}}{2}\right\}$ 2. a. $D = 0$; one rational solution b. $D = -104$; two imaginary solutions

c. $D = 20$: two irrational solutions d. $D = -8$; two imaginary solutions e. $D = 196$; two rational solutions f. $D = 16$; two rational solutions

Mini Lecture 11.3
Quadratic Functions and Their Graphs

Learning Objectives:
1. Recognize characteristics of parabolas.
2. Graph parabolas in the form $f(x) = a(x-h)^2 + k$.
3. Graph parabolas in the form $f(x) = ax^2 + bx + c$.
4. Determine a quadratic function's minimum or maximum value.

Examples:
1.   Graph the quadratic function. Identify the vertex, x and y intercepts. Use the graph to identify the function's domain and its range. State whether the function has a minimum value or a maximum value.

    a. $f(x) = -(x+2)^2 - 3$

    b. $f(x) = x^2 - 2x + 2$

    c. $f(x) = (x+1)^2 + 4$

    d. $f(x) = x^2 - 4$

Teaching Notes:

- The graph of a quadratic function $f(x) = ax^2 + bx + c$, $a \neq 0$ is called a parabola.
- Parabolas are symmetric with respect to an imaginary line which is called the **axis of symmetry**.
- To graph quadratic functions with equations in the form $f(x) = a(x-h)^2 + k$
    * Determine if the parabola opens up ($a > 0$) or opens down ($a < 0$).
    * Determine the vertex of the parabola (h, k).
    * Determine the x-intercept by replacing $f(x)$ with 0 and solving.
    * Determine the y-intercept by replacing x with 0 and solving.

- The vertex of a parabola whose equation is $f(x) = ax^2 + bx + c$ is $\left(\dfrac{-b}{2a}, f\left(\dfrac{-b}{2a}\right)\right)$.

- With a quadratic function, a maximum or minimum value will occur at the vertex point
    * if $a > 0$, then the minimum occurs at $x = \dfrac{-b}{2a}$ and the minimum value is $f\left(\dfrac{-b}{2a}\right)$.

    * if $a < 0$, then the maximum occurs at $x = \dfrac{-b}{2a}$ and the maximum value is $f\left(\dfrac{-b}{2a}\right)$.

Answers:
1. a.   vertex $(-2, -3)$
   x-intercept – none
   y-intercept – $(0, -7)$
   domain $\{x \mid x \text{ is a real number}\}$
   range $\{y \mid y \leq -3\}$
   maximum

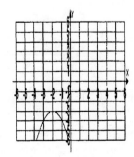

1. b. vertex (1, 1)
   x-intercept – none
   y-intercept – (0, 2)
   domain $\{x \mid x \text{ is a real number}\}$
   range $\{y \mid y \geq 1\}$
   minimum

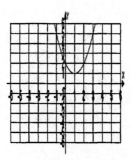

1. c. vertex (–1, 4)
   x-intercept – (–3, 0)(1
   y-intercept – (0, 3)
   domain $\{x \mid x \text{ is a real number}\}$
   range $\{y \mid y \leq 4\}$
   minimum

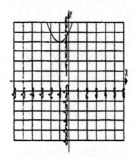

1. d. vertex (0, 4)
   x-intercept – (–2, 0)(2, 0)
   y-intercept – (0, –4)
   domain $\{x \mid x \text{ is a real number}\}$
   range $\{y \mid y \geq -4\}$
   minimum

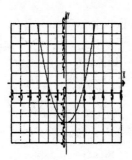

Mini Lecture 11.4
Equations Quadratic in Form

Learning Objectives:
1. Solve equations that are quadratic in form.

Examples:
Solve.

1. a. $x^4 - x^2 = 12$ b. $y^4 + 15 = 8y^2$ c. $4x^4 - 7x^2 - 2 = 0$

2. a. $(y+3)^2 - 3(y+3) = 70$ b. $(x-2)^2 - 4(x-2) - 60 = 0$ c. $3(4a-1)^2 + (4a-1) = 10$

3. a. $x - \sqrt{x} - 2 = 0$ b. $3y + \sqrt{y} = 2$ c. $x - 6\sqrt{x} + 8 = 0$

4. a. $y^{\frac{2}{3}} - 2y^{\frac{1}{3}} - 8 = 0$ b. $x^{-2} - 8x^{-1} + 7 = 0$ c. $y^{\frac{2}{3}} - 5y^{\frac{1}{3}} + 6 = 0$

Teaching Notes:
- An equation that is "quadratic in form" can be rewritten as a quadratic equation using an appropriate substitution.
- Remind students that if both sides of an equation are raised to an even power, they must check the solutions for extraneous solutions.
- A fourth degree equation will have four solutions.

Answers: 1. a. $\pm 2, \pm 3i$ b. $\pm\sqrt{5}, \pm\sqrt{3}$ c. $\pm\frac{1}{2}i, \pm\sqrt{2}$ 2. a. $7, -10$ b. $12, -4$ c. $\frac{2}{3}, -\frac{1}{4}$

3. a. 4 b. $\frac{4}{9}$ c. $16, 4$ 4. a. $64, -8$ b. $1, \frac{1}{7}$ c. $8, 27$

Mini Lecture 11.5
Polynomial and Rational Inequalities

Learning Objectives:
1. Solve polynomial inequalities.
2. Solve rational inequalities.
3. Solve problems modeled by polynomial or rational inequalities.

Examples:

1. Solve and write the answers in interval notation.

   a. $x^2 + x > 2$

   b. $x^3 + x^2 \leq 16x + 16$

   c. $2x^2 - 4x \leq 0$

2. Solve each rational inequality, and write the answers in interval notation.

   a. $\dfrac{x+5}{x-1} > 0$

   b. $\dfrac{x+3}{x} > 0$

   c. $\dfrac{x}{x-1} \geq 2$

3. A small rocket is shot up into the air with an initial speed of 128 ft/second. The function $f(x) = -16t + 128$ ft models the rocket's height above the ground. During which time period will the rocket be above the ground?

Teaching Notes:
- A polynomial inequality can be written in one of these forms, $f(x) < 0, f(x) > 0,$ $f(x) \leq 0, f(x) \geq 0$ where f is a polynomial function.
- When solving polynomial inequalities, solve the equation $f(x) = 0$. The real solutions are the **boundary points**.
- Never include the value that causes a rational function's denominator to equal zero in the solution set of a rational inequality. Remember division by zero is undefined.

Answers: 1. a. $\{x \mid x < -2 \text{ or } x > 1\}$ b. $\{x \mid x \leq -4 \text{ or } -1 \leq x \leq 4\}$ c. $\{x \mid 0 \leq x \leq 2\}$
2. a. $(-\infty, -5) \cup (1, \infty)$ b. $(-\infty, -3) \cup (0, \infty)$ c. $[1, 2]$ 3. 0 and 4 seconds, excluding $t = 0$ and $t = 4$.

Mini Lecture 12.1
Exponential Functions

Learning Objectives:
1. Evaluate exponential functions.
2. Graph exponential functions.
3. Evaluate functions with base e.
4. Use compound interest formulas.

Examples:

1. Approximate each number using a calculator, round your answer to two decimal places.

   a. $2^{1.2}$ b. $4^{\sqrt{2}}$ c. $e^{1.1}$ d. $e^{-0.25}$

2. Graph each function by making a table of coordinates.

   a. $f(x) = 3^x$ b. $g(x) = \left(\dfrac{2}{3}\right)^x$

3. Graph f and g in the same rectangular coordinate system. Select integers from -2 to 2 for x. Then describe how the graph of g is related to the graph of f.

   a. $f(x) = 4^x$ and $g(x) = 4^{x+1}$

   b. $f(x) = 3^x$ and $g(x) = 3^x + 2$

4. Find an accumulated value of an investment of $7000 for 5 years at an interest rate of 4% if the money is:
   a. compounded monthly.
   b. compounded semi-annually.
   c. compounded continuously.
   Use the compound interest formulas to solve. Round answers to the nearest cent.

Teaching Notes:
- The **exponential function** f with base b is $f(x) = b^x$ or $y = b^x$, $b > 0$ and $b \neq 1$ and x is any real number.
- The **domain** of an exponential function consists of all real numbers.
- The **range** of an exponential function consists of all positive real numbers.
- If $b > 1$, the graph of the exponential function will go up to the right and is an increasing function. The larger the value of b, the steeper the increase.
- If $0 < b < 1$, the graph of the exponential function goes down to the right and is a decreasing function. The small the value of b, the steeper the decrease.
- An irrational number, e, often appears as a base in applied exponential functions.
- The number e is called the **natural base**. "e" $\approx 2.71828...$

- The function $f(x) = e$ is called the **natural exponential function**.
- Formulas for **compound interest**:
  * for n compoundings per year $A = P(1 + \dfrac{r}{n})^{nt}$
  * for continuous compounding $A = Pe^{rt}$

After t years, the balance A in an account with principal P and as annual interest rate r.

Answers: 1. a. 2.30 b. 7.10 c. 3.00 d. 0.78 2. a.

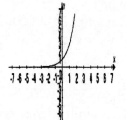   b.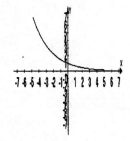

3. a. The graph of g is the graph of f shifted 1 unit to the left b. The graph of g is the graph of f shifted up 2 units 4. a. $8546.98 b. $8532.96 c. $8549.82

Mini Lecture 12.2
Logarithm Functions

Learning Objectives:
1. Change from logarithmic to exponential form.
2. Change from exponential to logarithmic form.
3. Evaluate logarithms.
4. Use basic logarithmic properties.
5. Graph logarithmic functions.
6. Find the domain of a logarithmic function.
7. Use common logarithms.
8. Use natural logarithms.

Examples:

1. Write each equation in its equivalent exponential form.
   a. $5 = \log_2 x$
   b. $2 = \log_b 16$
   c. $\log_5 18 = y$

2. Write each equation in its equivalent logarithmic form.
   a. $3^4 = 81$
   b. $b^3 = 8$
   c. $e^y = 11$

3. Evaluate.
   a. $\log_{10} 10000$
   b. $\log_5 5$
   c. $\log_{125} 5$
   d. $\log_4 4$
   e. $\log_7 1$
   f. $\log_3 3^4$
   g. $5^{\log_5 12}$
   h. $\ln 1$
   i. $\ln e$

4. Graph $f(x) = 4^x$ and $g(x) = \log_4 x$ in the same rectangular coordinate system.

5. Find the domain of each function:
   a. $f(x) = \log_2(x - 3)$
   b. $g(x) = \ln(5 - x)$

Teaching Notes:
- The function $f(x) = \log_b x$ is the **logarithmic function with base b**.
- The logarithmic form $y = \log_b x$ is equivalent to the exponential form $b^y = x$.
- The **domain** of a logarithmic function of the form $f(x) = \log_b x$ is the set of all positive real numbers.
- The **domain** of $f(x) = \log_b[g(x)]$ consists of all x for which $g(x) > 0$.
- The logarithmic function with base 10 is called the **common logarithmic function**.

- Properties of Common Logarithms

General Properties	Common Logarithms	Natural Logarithms
$\log_b 1 = 0$	$\log 1 = 0$	$\ln 1 = 0$
$\log_b b = 1$	$\log 10 = 1$	$\ln e = 1$
$\log_b b^x = x$	$\log 10^x = x$	$\ln e^x = x$
$b^{\log_b x} = x$	$10^{\log x} = x$	$e^{\ln x} = x$

Answers: 1. a. $2^5 = x$ b. $b^2 = 16$ c. $5^y = 18$ 2. a. $4 = \log_3 81$ b. $3 = \log_b 8$ c. $y = \log_e 11$

3. a. 4 b. 1 c. $\dfrac{1}{3}$ d. 1 e. 0 f. 4 g. 12 h. 0 i. 1 4.

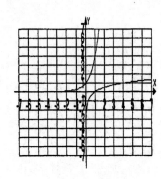

5. a. $\{x \mid x > 3\}$ or $(3, \infty)$ b. $\{x \mid x < 5\}$ or $(-\infty, 5)$

Mini Lecture 12.3
Properties of Logarithms

Learning Objectives:
1. Use the product, quotient and power rules for logarithms.
2. Expand logarithmic expressions.
3. Condense logarithmic expressions.
4. Use the change-of-base property.

Examples:

Expand.

1.   a. $\log_3(4 \cdot 18)$ b. $\log_8(12 \cdot 8)$ c. $\log_5(5x)$

2.   a. $\log_3\left(\dfrac{3}{x}\right)$ b. $\ln\left(\dfrac{e^3}{5}\right)$ c. $\log\left(\dfrac{10}{x}\right)$

3.   a. $\log_4 7^3$ b. $\log_2 y^3 z$ c. $\log_5 3^{\frac{1}{2}}$

4.   a. $\log\left(\dfrac{x^2}{\sqrt[3]{y}}\right)$ b. $\log_5 \dfrac{x}{y^4}$ c. $\log_7\left(\dfrac{6y^2}{\sqrt[4]{x}}\right)$

Condense. Write as a single logarithm.

5.   a. $\log_8 5 + \log_8 x$ b. $\log_6 18 + \log_6 2 - \log_6 9$

      c. $2\log_3 5 + \log_3 2$ d. $\log_2 x + \log_2 (x-3) - \log_2 3$

Use the change-of-base property and your calculator to find the decimal approximation.

6.   a. $\log_6 14$ b. $\log_9 27$ c. $\log_7 15$

Teaching Notes:
- Students must <u>know</u> properties and rules of logarithms and since this will be new to most students, a lot of practice is recommended.
- As rules are introduced, show several examples with numbers instead of letters.
- Make sure students know how to use their calculators to find decimal approximations.

Answers: 1. a. $\log_4 + \log_3 18$ b. $\log_8 12 + 1$ c. $1 + \log_5 x$ 2. a. $1 - \log_3 x$ b. $3 - \ln 5$

c. $1 - \log x$ 3. a. $3\log_4 7$ b. $3\log_2 y + \log_2 z$ c. $\dfrac{1}{2}\log_5 3$ 4. a. $2\log x - \dfrac{1}{3}\log y$

b. $\log_5 x - 4\log_5 y$ c. $\log_7 6 + 2\log_7 y - \dfrac{1}{4}\log_7 x$ 5. a. $\log_8 5x$ b. $\log_6 4$ c. $\log_3 50$

d. $\log_2\left(\dfrac{x^2 - 3x}{3}\right)$ 6. a. 1.4729   b. 1.5   c. 1.3917

Mini Lecture 12.4
Exponential and Logarithmic Functions

Learning Objectives:
1. Solve exponential equations.
2. Solve logarithmic equations.

Examples:
1. Solve

   a. $3^x = \dfrac{1}{81}$

   b. $8^x = 16$

   c. $27^x = 9$

2. Find the solution set and then use a calculator to obtain a decimal approximation to two decimal places for the solution.

   a. $3^x = 120$

   b. $5^{3x} = 30$

3. Solve.

   a. $\log_4(x-3) = 2$

   b. $\log_2 x + \log_2(x-2) = 3$

   c. $\log_4(x+1) - \log_4(x-2) = 1$

   d. $5\ln 2x = 15$

Teaching Notes:
- An **exponential equation** is an equation containing a variable with an exponent.
- To solve exponential equations, express each side of the equal as a power of the same base and then set the exponents equal to each other. If $b^m = b^n$, then $m = n$.
- When using rational logarithms to solve exponential equations, first, isolate the exponential expressions. Next, take the natural logarithm on both sides of the equation, simplify and solve for the variable.
- A **logarithmic equation** is an equation containing a variable in a logarithmic expression.
- ALWAYS check proposed solutions of a logarithmic equation in the original equation. Exclude from the solution set any proposed solution that produces the logarithm of a negative number of the logarithm of 0.

Answers: 1. a. -4 b. $\dfrac{4}{3}$ c. $\dfrac{2}{3}$ 2. a. $\dfrac{\ln 120}{\ln 3} \approx 4.36$ b. $\dfrac{\ln 6}{3} = \ln 2 \approx 0.69$ 3. a. 19 b. 4 c. 3

d. $\dfrac{e^3}{2}$

Exponential Growth and Decay; Modeling Data

Learning Objectives:
 1. Model exponential growth and decay.
 2. Model data with exponential and logarithmic functions.
 3. Express an exponential model in base e.

Examples:
Solve.

1. The population of a country is growing at a rate of 1.3% per year. Use the formula $t = \dfrac{\ln 2}{k}$, which models the time, t, for a population with a growth rate, k, to double, to find out how long it will take for the country's population to double. (Round to the nearest year).

2. Use the formula $A = A_0 e^{kt}$ to find the population of a small city five years from now if the population is now 57,000 people and it is growing at a rate of 2.6% annually.

3. Use the formula $A = A_0 e^{kt}$ to find out how long it will take to double an investment of $2300 if it earns 7.5% interest annually. (Round to the nearest year).

4. The half-life of a certain isotope is 80 days. How long will it take for 7 mg of the isotope to decay to 1 mg? (Round your answer).

5. Find the age of a bone (to the nearest 100), that originally had 150 mg of carbon-14 but now has 85 mg of carbon-14, if the half-life of carbon-14 is 5570 years.

6. Fifty grams of radium decays to 5 grams in about 5615 years. What is the half-life of the radium?

Teaching Notes:
 - The mathematical model for **exponential growth** or **decay** is given by: $f(t) - A_0 e^{kt}$ or $A = A_0 e^{kt}$.
 - If $K > 0$, the function models the amount, or size, of a <u>growing</u> entity.
 - If $K < 0$, the function models the amount, or size, of a <u>decaying</u> entity.
 - An exponential model in base e is given by: $y = ab^x$ is equivalent to $y = ae^{(\ln b) \cdot x}$.

<u>Answers</u>: 1. 43 years 2. 64,913 people 3. Approximately 9 years 4. 225 days 5. 4600 years
6. 1690 years

Mini Lecture 13.1
The Circle

Learning Objectives:
1. Write the standard form of a circle's equation.
2. Give the center and radius of a circle whose equation is in standard form.
3. Convert the general form of a circle's equation to standard form.

Examples:
1. Write the standard form of the equation of the circle with center (0, 0) and radius 5.

2. Write the standard form of the equation of the circle with center (3, -4) and radius 7.

3. Find the center and radius of the circle whose equation is $(x+1)^2 + (y-2)^2 = 9$ and graph.

4. Write in standard form and graph $x^2 + y^2 + 2x - 6y + 6 = 0$.

Teaching Notes:
- **Standard form of the equation of a circle:** $(x-h)^2 + (y-k)^2 = r^2$

  center: (h, k)

  radius: r

Answers: 1. $x^2 + y^2 = 25$ 2. $(x-3)^2 + (y+4)^2 = 49$

3. center: $(-1, 2)$, radius: 3 units   4. $(x+1)^2 + (y-3)^2 = 4$

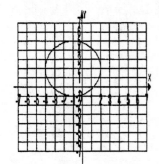

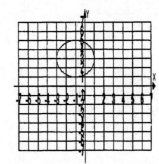

Mini Lecture 13.2
The Ellipse

Learning Objectives:
1. Graph ellipses centered at the origin.
2. Graph ellipses not centered at the origin.

Examples:
1. Graph each ellipse. Name the vertices.

   a. $\dfrac{x^2}{25} + \dfrac{y^2}{9} = 1$

   b. $\dfrac{x^2}{1} + \dfrac{y^2}{16} = 1$

   c. $25x^2 + 4y^2 = 100$

2. Find the standard form of the equation of each ellipse.

   a.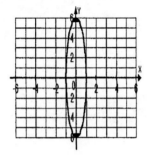

   b.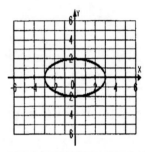

   c.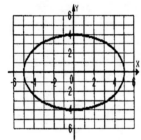

   d.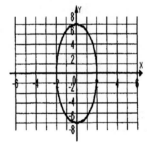

3. Graph each ellipse.

   a. $\dfrac{(x-1)^2}{16} + \dfrac{(y+2)^2}{1} = 1$

   b. $4(x+2)^2 + (y-3)^2 = 16$

Teaching Notes:
- An **ellipse** is the set of all points, P, in a plane, the sum of whose distances from two fixed points, F_1, and F_2, is constant. These two fixed points are called **foci**. The midpoint of the segment connecting the foci is the **center** of the ellipse.
- The line through the foci intersects the ellipse at two points, called the **vertices**. The line segment that joins the vertices is the **major axis**. The line segment whose end points are on the ellipse and that is perpendicular to the major axis at the center is called the **minor axis** of the ellipse.

- The **standard form of the equation of an ellipse** is: $\dfrac{x^2}{a^2} + \dfrac{y^2}{b^2} = 1$ or $\dfrac{x^2}{b^2} + \dfrac{y^2}{a^2} = 1$ with the center at the origin and major and minor axis of lengths $2a$ and $2b$.

- The **equation for ellipses centered at (h, k)** is: $\dfrac{(x-h)^2}{a^2} + \dfrac{(y-k)^2}{b^2} = 1$

<u>Answers</u>: 1. a. (5, 0)(–5,0)

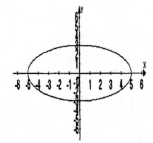

b. (0, 4)(0, –4)

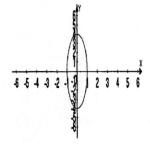

c. (0, 5)(0, –5)

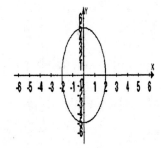

2. a. $\dfrac{x^2}{1} + \dfrac{y^2}{36} = 1$ b. $\dfrac{x^2}{9} + \dfrac{y^2}{4} = 1$ c. $\dfrac{x^2}{25} + \dfrac{y^2}{16} = 1$ d. $\dfrac{x^2}{4} + \dfrac{y^2}{49} = 1$

3. a.

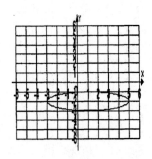

b.

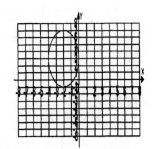

Mini Lecture 13.3
The Hyperbola

Learning Objectives:
1. Locate the hyperbola's vertices.
2. Graph hyperbolas centered at the origin.

Examples:

1. Find the vertices for each of the following hyperbolas with the given equation.

   a. $\dfrac{x^2}{36} - \dfrac{y^2}{9} = 1$ b. $\dfrac{y^2}{49} - \dfrac{x^2}{16} = 1$

2. Graph each hyperbola.

   a. $\dfrac{x^2}{16} - \dfrac{y^2}{4} = 1$ b. $\dfrac{y^2}{9} - \dfrac{x^2}{1} = 1$ c. $x^2 - 4y^2 = 4$

Teaching Notes:
- A **hyperbola** is the set of points in a plane the difference of whose distances from two fixed points, called foci, is constant.
- The standard form of the equation of a **hyperbola** with center at the origin is:

   $\dfrac{x^2}{a^2} - \dfrac{y^2}{b^2} = 1$ where the traverse axis lies on the *x*-axis **or**

   $\dfrac{y^2}{a^2} - \dfrac{x^2}{b^2} = 1$ where the traverse axis lies on the *y*-axis.

Answers: 1. a. (–6, 0) and (6, 0)   b. (0, –7) and (0, 7)

2. a.

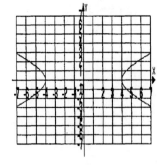

b.

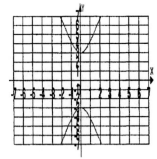

c.

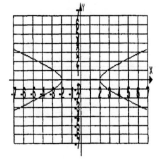

Mini Lecture 13.4
The Parabola: Identifying Conic Sections

Learning Objectives:
1. Graph horizontal parabolas.
2. Identify conic sections by their equations.

Examples:
1. Graph the following parabolas, name the vertex, give the equation for the parabola's axis of symmetry.

   a. $x = (y+4)^2 - 3$ b. $x = -(y-1)^2 + 2$

   c. $x = (y-3)^2$ d. $x = -2(y+2)^2 - 1$

   e. $x = y^2 + 4y + 4$ f. $x = -3y^2 - 6y - 3$

2. Indicate whether the graph of each equation is a circle, and ellipse, a hyperbola, or a parabola.

   a. $x = y^2 + 12y + 36$ b. $x^2 + y^2 = 100$

   c. $\dfrac{x^2}{9} - \dfrac{y^2}{25} = 1$ d. $(x-3)^2 + (y+1)^2 = 16$

   e. $\dfrac{x^2}{100} - \dfrac{y^2}{25} = 1$ f. $x = (y-1)^2 + 4$

   g. $\dfrac{x^2}{4} + \dfrac{y^2}{25} = 1$ h. $36x^2 + y^2 = 36$

Teaching Notes:
- A **parabola** is the set of all points in a plane that are equidistant from a fixed line known as the **directrix** and a fixed point known as the focus that is not on the line.
- The line passing through the focus and perpendicular to the directrix is the **axis of symmetry**. The point of intersection of the parabola with its axis of symmetry is the parabola's **vertex**.
- Parabolas that open up or down will have an equation in the form:
  $y = a(x-h)^2 + k$ or $y = ax^2 + bx + c$. If $a > 0$, the graph will open upward. If $a < 0$, the graph will open downward.
- Parabolas that open left or right will have an equation in the form:
  $x = a(y-k)^2 + h$ or $x = ay^2 + by + c$. If $a > 0$, the graph will open right. If $a < 0$, the graph will open left.

- **Recognize Conic Sections from Equations**

Conic Section	How to identify the equation	Example
Circle	When x^2 and y^2 terms are on the same side, they have the same coefficient.	$x^2 + y^2 = 16$
Ellipse	When x^2 and y^2 terms are on the same side, they have different coefficients of the same sign.	$4x^2 + 16y^2 = 64$ or $\dfrac{x^2}{16} + \dfrac{y^2}{4} = 1$
Hyperbola	When x^2 and y^2 terms are on the same side, they have coefficients with opposite signs.	$9y^2 - 4x^2 = 36$ or $\dfrac{y^2}{4} - \dfrac{x^2}{9} = 1$
Parabola	Only one of the variables is squared.	$x = y^2 + 4y - 5$

Answers:

1. a. 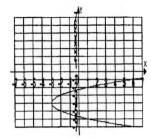 vertex $(-3, -4)$; axis of symmetry $y = -4$

1. b. 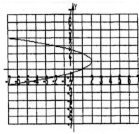 vertex $(2, 1)$; axis of symmetry $y = 1$

1. c. 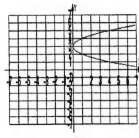 vertex $(0, 3)$; axis of symmetry $y = 3$

1. d. 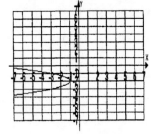 vertex $(-1, -2)$; axis of symmetry $y = -2$

1. e. 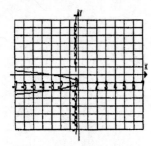 vertex (0. –2); axis of symmetry $y = -2$

1. f. 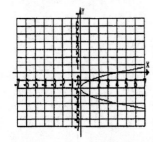 vertex (0, –1); axis of symmetry $y = -1$

2. a. parabola b. circle c. hyperbola d. circle e. hyperbola f. parabola g. ellipse h. ellipse

Mini Lecture 13.5
Systems of Nonlinear Equations in Two Variables

Learning Objectives:
1. Recognize systems of nonlinear equations in two variables.
2. Solve systems of nonlinear equations by substitution.
3. Solve systems of nonlinear equations by addition.

Examples:
1. Solve by the substitution method.

$$x^2 = -12y$$
$$2x - y = 15$$

2. Solve by the substitution method.

$$x + y = 14$$
$$x^2 + y^2 = 100$$

3. Solve the system by addition.

$$x^2 + y^2 = 25$$
$$x^2 - y^2 = 25$$

4. Solve the system by the method of your choice.

$$y = -3x^2$$
$$y = -9x + 6$$

Teaching Notes:
- A **nonlinear system** contains at least one equation that cannot be expressed in the form $Ax + By = C$.
- A **solution** of a nonlinear system in two variables is an ordered pair of real numbers that satisfies all equations in the system. The **solution set** of the system is the set of all such ordered pairs.
- Each solution corresponds to a point of intersection of the system's graphs.
- Systems can be solved by the substitution method or the addition method.

Answers: 1. $(-30, -75)$, $(6, -3)$ 2. $(6, 8)$, $(8, 6)$ 3. $(5, 0)$, $(-5, 0)$ 4. $(2, -12)$, $(1, -3)$

Mini Lecture 14.1
Sequences and Summation Notation

Learning Objectives:
1. Find particular terms of a sequence from the general term.
2. Use factorial notation.
3. Use summation notation.

Examples:
1. Write the first four terms of each sequence whose general term is given.

   a. $a_n = 3n + 2$ b. $a_n = (-2)^n + 1$ c. $a_n = \dfrac{5}{(n-1)!}$

2. Expand and evaluate the sum:

   a. $\displaystyle\sum_{i=1}^{4} i^2$ b. $\displaystyle\sum_{i=1}^{5} (-3)^i + 1$ c. $\displaystyle\sum_{i=1}^{6} 6$

3. Express each sum using summation notation.

   a. $3^1 + 3^2 + 3^3 + \ldots + 3^7$ b. $1 + \dfrac{1}{4} + \dfrac{1}{16} + \ldots + \dfrac{1}{4^{n-1}}$

Teaching Notes:
- The **Fibonacci Sequence** consists of the first terms being 1 then every term thereafter is the sum of the two preceding terms. 1, 1, 2, 3, 5, 8, 13, 21, 34, 55, 89, 144,...
- The notation a_n represents the nth term, or **general term** of a sequence. The entire sequence is represented by $\{a_n\}$.
- An **infinite series** $\{a_n\}$ is a function whose domain is the set of positive integers. The function values, or **terms**, of the sequence are represented by: $a_1, a_2, a_3, a_4, \ldots a_n \ldots$
- Sequences whose domain consists only of the first n positive integers are called **finite sequences**.
- **Factorial Notation**, by definition, is $n! = n(n-1)(n-2) \ldots (3)(2)(1)$. Zero factorial $(0!) = 1$.
- **Summation Notation** is the sum of the first n terms of a sequence.

  $\displaystyle\sum_{i=1}^{n} a_i = a_1 + a_2 + a_3 + a_4 \ldots + a_n$, where i is the **index of summation**, 1 is the **lower limit of summation**, and n is the **upper limit of summation**.

Answers: 1. a. 5, 8, 11, 14 b. $-1, 5, -7, 17$ c. $5, 5, \dfrac{5}{2}, \dfrac{5}{6}$ 2. a. $(1)^2 + (2)^2 + (3)^2 + (4)^2 = 30$

b. $((-3)^1 + 1) + ((-3)^2 + 1) + ((-3)^3 + 1) + ((-3)^4 + 1) + ((-3)^5 + 1) = -178$ c. $6 + 6 + 6 + 6 + 6 + 6 + = 36$

3. a. $\displaystyle\sum_{i=1}^{7} 3^n$ b. $\displaystyle\sum_{i=1}^{n} \dfrac{1}{4^{i-1}}$

Arithmetic Sequences

Learning Objectives:
1. Find the common difference for an arithmetic sequence.
2. Write terms of an arithmetic sequence.
3. Use the formula for the general term of an arithmetic sequence.
4. Use the formula for the sum of the first n terms of an arithmetic sequence.

Examples:
1. Find the common difference for each arithmetic sequence.
   a. $10, 5, 0, -5, -10, \ldots$
   b. $1, 2, 3, 4, 5, \ldots$
   c. $0, \dfrac{1}{8}, \dfrac{1}{4}, \dfrac{3}{8}, \dfrac{1}{2}, \ldots$

2. Write the first six terms of each arithmetic sequence with the given first term a_1, and common difference, d.
   a. $a_1 = 3 \quad d = 4$
   b. $a_1 = -8 \quad d = -3$
   c. $a_1 = -0.1 \quad d = 1.5$

3. Use the formula for the general terms of an arithmetic sequence to find the indicated terms of each sequence with the given first term, a_1, and common difference, d.
   a. Find a_{11} when $a_1 = 1$, $d = -3$.
   b. Find a_{24} when $a_1 = 2$, $d = 2$.
   c. Find a_{50} when $a_1 = 4$, $d = 4$.

4. Write a formula for the general term of each arithmetic sequence.
   a. $1, 5, 9, 13, \ldots$
   b. $6, 1, -4, -9, \ldots$

5. Find the sum of the first 10 terms of the arithmetic sequence : $2, 4, 6, 8, \ldots$

6. Use the formula for sum of the first n terms to find the indicated sum.
   a. $\displaystyle\sum_{i=1}^{10} (8i - 5)$
   b. $\displaystyle\sum_{i=1}^{250} i$

Teaching Notes:
- An **arithmetic sequence** is a sequence in which each term after the first differs from the preceding term by a constant amount.
- The difference between consecutive terms is called the **common difference** of the sequence.
- An arithmetic sequence is a linear function whose domain is the set of positive integers.

- The **general term** (nth term) of an arithmetic sequence with first term a and common difference d is: $a_n = a_1 + (n-1)d$.

- The sum of the first n terms of an arithmetic sequence is given by: $S_n = \dfrac{n}{2}(a_1 + a_n)$ where S_n is the sum of first n terms. a_1 is the first terms and a_l is the nth term.

Answers: 1. a. –5 b. 1 c. $\dfrac{1}{2}$ 2. a. 3, 7, 11, 15, 19, 23 b. –8, –11, –14, –17, –20, –23

c. –0.1, 1.4, 2.9, 4.4, 5.9, 7.4 3. a. –29 b. 48 c. 200 4. a. $a_n = 4n - 3$ b. $a_n = -5n + 11$

5. 110 6. a. 390 b. 31.375

Mini Lecture 14.3
Geometric Sequences and Series

Learning Objectives:
1. Find the common ratio of a geometric sequence.
2. Write terms of a geometric sequence.
3. Use the formula for the general term of a geometric sequence.
4. Use the formula for the sum of the first n terms of a geometric sequence.
5. Use the formula for the sum of an infinite geometric sequence.

Examples:
1. Find the common ratio for each geometric sequence:

   a. $3, 9, 27, 81\ldots$ b. $6, -24, 96, -384\ldots$ c. $4, -2, 1, -\dfrac{1}{2}\ldots$

2. Write the first five terms of each geometric sequence with the given first term a_1 and common ratio, r.

   a. $a_1 = 2, r = -3$ b. $a_1 = 1, r = -\dfrac{1}{5}$ c. $a_1 = 4, r = 3$

3. Use the formula for the general term of a geometric sequence to find the indicated term of each sequence with the given first term a, and common ratio r.

   a. Find a_6 when $a_1 = -2$ and $r = -\dfrac{1}{2}$ b. Find a_{20} when $a_1 = 3$ and $r = -1$

4. Write a formula for the general term of the geometric sequence. Then use the formula to find a_7.

   $1, \dfrac{3}{2}, \dfrac{9}{4}, \dfrac{27}{8}$

5. Find the indicated sum.

   $$\sum_{i=1}^{5} 2^i + 1$$

6. Find the sum of the infinite geometric series.

   $4 + 2 + 1 + \dfrac{1}{2} + \ldots$

Teaching Notes:
- A **geometric sequence** is a sequence in which each term after the first is obtained by multiplying the preceding term by a fixed non-zero constant.
- The amount by which we multiply each time in a geometric sequence is called the **common ratio** of the sequence.

- **General Term of a Geometric Sequence** $a_n = a_1 r^{n-1}$ where the n is the general term, and a_1 is the first term, and r is the common ratio.

- The **sum of the first n terms of a geometric sequence** $S_n = \dfrac{a_1(1-r^n)}{1-r}$ where S_n is the sum of the first n terms with a_1 as the first term and r the common ratio $(r \neq 1)$.

- The **sum of an infinite geometric series** is given by $s = \dfrac{a^1}{1-r}$ where s is the sum, a_1 is the first term and r is the ratio. If $|r| < 1$, then a sum exists, if $|r| \geq 1$, then the series does not have a sum.

<u>Answers</u>: 1. a. $r = 3$ b. $r = -4$ c. $r = -\dfrac{1}{2}$ 2. a. $2, -6, 18, -54, 162$ b. $1, -\dfrac{1}{5}, \dfrac{1}{25}, -\dfrac{1}{125}, \dfrac{1}{625}$

c. $4, 12, 36, 108, 324$ 3. a. $a_6 = \dfrac{1}{16}$ b. $a_{20} = -3$ 4. $a_n = \left(\dfrac{3}{2}\right)^{n-1}$, $a_7 = \dfrac{729}{64}$ 5. 67 6. 8

Mini Lecture 14.4
The Binomial Theorem

Learning Objectives:
1. Recognize patterns in binomial expansions.
2. Evaluate a binomial coefficient.
3. Expand a binomial raised to a power.
4. Find a particular term in a binomial expansion.

Examples:
1. Evaluate.

    a. $\binom{5}{2}$ b. $\binom{7}{7}$ c. $\binom{12}{5}$ d. $\binom{12}{7}$

2. Expand.

    a. $(x+3)^4$ b. $(2x+1)^6$ c. $(x+y)^5$

3. Find the term indicated in each expansion.

    a. $(a+2)^3$; third term

    b. $(x+2)^4$; second term

    c. $(4x-y)^3$; first term

    d. $(2x+y)^6$; fourth term

Teaching Notes:

- **Definition of a binomial coefficient** $\binom{n}{r}$ for non-negative integers n and r, with $n \geq r$, the expression $\binom{n}{r}$ is called a binomial coefficient. $\binom{n}{r} = \dfrac{n!}{r!(n-r)!}$

- To find a particular term in a binomial expansion, the $(r+1)$st term of the expansion of $(a+b)^n$ is: $\binom{n}{r} a^{n-r} b^r$.

- Formula for expanding binomials is known as the **Binomial Theorem**:
$$(a+b)^n$$
$$= \binom{n}{0} a^n + \binom{n}{1} a^{n-1}b + \binom{n}{2} a^{n-2}b^2 + \binom{n}{3} a^{n-3}b^3 + \ldots + \binom{n}{n} b^n$$
$$= \sum_{r=0}^{n} \binom{n}{r} a^{n-r} b^r$$

Answers: 1. a. 10 b. 1 c. 792 d. 792   2. a. $x^4 + 12x^3 + 54x^2 + 108x + 81$
b. $64x^6 + 192x^5 + 240x^4 + 160x^3 + 60x^2 + 12x + 1$ c. $x^5 + 5x^4y + 10x^3y^2 + 5xy^4 + y^5$
3. a. $12a$ b. $8x^3$ c. $64x^3$ d. $160x^3y^3$

Name _____   Date _____

Additional Exercises 1.1
Form I
Introduction to Algebra: Variables and Mathematical Models

Evaluate each expression for $x = 3$.

1. $4 + 3x$ 1. _____

2. $5(2 - x)$ 2. _____

Evaluate each expression for $x = 4$ and $y = 6$.

3. $5x - y$ 3. _____

4. $2x + 4y$ 4. _____

5. $6(y - x)$ 5. _____

In exercises 6 – 10, translate each English phrase to an algebraic expression. Let the variable x represent the number.

6. Twelve more than a number. 6. _____

7. The difference of a number and nine. 7. _____

8. Six times a number increased by fifteen. 8. _____

9. The quotient of twice a number and seven. 9. _____

10. The sum of three times a number and five. 10. _____

11.   Is 15 a solution to the equation $y + 16 = 21$?   11. _____

12.   Is 4 a solution to the equation $3x - 12 = 0$?   12. _____

13.   Is 10 a solution to the equation $25 - 2y = 13$?   13. _____

14.   Is 8 a solution to the equation $5x = 40$?   14. _____

15.   Is 30 a solution to $2x + 5 = 3x - 25$?   15. _____

Translate each sentence as an equation. Let the variable x represent the number.

16.   Six times a number is forty-two.   16. _____

17.   The product of a number and three is twenty-four.   17. _____

18.   The difference of a number and eight is equal to three times   18. _____
       the number.

19.   Fourteen less than a number is 15.   19. _____

20.   The quotient of a number and ten is equal to four.   20. _____

Name _____   Date _____

Additional Exercises 1.1
Form II
Introduction to Algebra: Variables and Mathematical Models

Evaluate each expression for $x = 5$.

1. $5x - 14$ 1. _____

2. $3(x - 2)$ 2. _____

Evaluate each expression for $x = 7$ and $y = 8$.

3. $3x - 2y$ 3. _____

4. $5(x + 2y)$ 4. _____

5. $\dfrac{6x + 6y}{x + y}$ 5. _____

In exercises 6 – 10, translate each English phrase to an algebraic expression. Let the variable x represent the number.

6.   A number less ten.   6. _____

7.   The quotient of a number and sixteen.   7. _____

8.   Four more than five times a number.   8. _____

9.   Seven times a number increased by eight.   9. _____

10.   Twice the sum of a number and seventeen.   10. _____

11.   Is 5 a solution to the equation $2x - 7 = 3$?   11. _____

12.   Is 14 a solution to the equation $4(x - 3) = 44$?   12. _____

13.   Is 8 a solution to the equation $5(x + 3) - 2x = 31$?   13. _____

14.   Is 20 a solution to the equation $3x - 14 = 2x + 28$?   14. _____

15.   Is 3 a solution to $2x + \dfrac{9}{x} = 9$?   15. _____

Translate each sentence as an equation. Let the variable x represent the number.

16.   A number increased by seventeen is forty.   16. _____

17.   Twice a number increased by thirteen is equal to fifty-nine.   17. _____

18.   The quotient of a number and sixteen is the same as   18. _____
        forty-eight.

19.   Eight less than a number equals twelve.   19. _____

20.   Four times the sum of a number and nine is fifty-four.   20. _____

Additional Exercises 1.1
Form III
Introduction to Algebra: Variables and Mathematical Models

Evaluate each expression for $x = 6$.

1. $3(2x + 4)$ 1. _____

2. $\dfrac{5x + 18}{2x}$ 2. _____

Evaluate each expression for $x = 8$ and $y = 12$.

3. $5x - 3y$ 3. _____

4. $2(x + y) + 4x - 3y$ 4. _____

5. $\dfrac{6x + 3y}{2x + y}$ 5. _____

In exercises 6 – 10, translate each English phrase to an algebraic expression. Let the variable x represent the number.

6.   The difference of three times a number and nine.   6. _____

7.   Twice the sum of a number and thirty-two.   7. _____

8.   The quotient of a number and eight increased by twice the number.   8. _____

9.   Twice a number decreased by sixty-three.   9. _____

10.   Fourteen less than a number.   10. _____

11.   Is 9 a solution to the equation $6(x - 4) = 30$?   11. _____

12.   Is 15 a solution to the equation $3x - (x - 6) = 24$?   12. _____

13.   Is 6 a solution to the equation $\dfrac{18}{x} - (14 - 2x) = 1$?   13. _____

Translate each sentence as an equation. Let the variable x represent the number.

14.   Twice the difference of a number and eighteen is four.   14. _____

15.   The quotient of three times a number and fifteen is equal to
       twice the number less seven.   15. _____

16.   Twenty-one less than a number equals twelve.   16. _____

17.   Three times the sum of ten and a number is forty-five.   17. _____

18.   A number increased by twenty-five is the same as twice the
       number less nineteen.   18. _____

The formula $n = T - h$ can be used to find a golfer's net score, n, where T, represents the total number of strokes and h, represents the golfer's handicap. Use this formula to answer 19 and 20.

19.   Find a golfer's net score if he shoots a 104 and has a
       handicap of 19.   19. _____

20.   Find a golfer's handicap if he shoots an 86 but has a
       net score of 79.   20. _____

Name _____   Date _____

Additional Exercises 1.2
Form I
Fractions in Algebra

Convert each mixed number to an improper fraction.

1. $3\dfrac{1}{3}$ 1. _____

2. $5\dfrac{7}{8}$ 2. _____

3. $10\dfrac{3}{4}$ 3. _____

Convert each improper fraction to a mixed number.

4. $\dfrac{8}{3}$ 4. _____

5. $\dfrac{22}{5}$ 5. _____

6. $\dfrac{86}{4}$ 6. _____

Reduce each fraction to its lowest terms.

7. $\dfrac{10}{18}$ 7. _____

8. $\dfrac{24}{36}$ 8. _____

9. $\dfrac{45}{105}$ 9. _____

Perform the indicated operation in each exercise. Reduce answers to lowest terms if possible.

10. $\dfrac{1}{7} \cdot \dfrac{2}{5}$ 10. _____

11. $\dfrac{1}{3} \cdot \dfrac{6}{7}$ 11. _____

12. $10 \cdot \dfrac{12}{15}$ 12. _____

13. $\dfrac{3}{4} \div \dfrac{4}{5}$ 13. _____

14. $\dfrac{5}{8} \div \dfrac{10}{12}$ 14. _____

15. $\left(3\dfrac{3}{8}\right)\left(2\dfrac{1}{3}\right)$ 15. _____

16. $\left(10\dfrac{4}{5}\right) \div \left(2\dfrac{5}{6}\right)$ 16. _____

17. $\dfrac{5}{7} + \dfrac{1}{7}$ 17. _____

18. $\dfrac{1}{4} + \dfrac{2}{3}$ 18. _____

19. $\dfrac{3}{5} + \dfrac{1}{6}$ 19. _____

20. $\dfrac{10}{11} - \dfrac{8}{11}$ 20. _____

21. $\dfrac{8}{15} - \dfrac{2}{5}$ 21. _____

22. $\dfrac{9}{10} - \dfrac{1}{6}$ 22. _____

23. $15\dfrac{3}{4} - 10\dfrac{1}{4}$ 23. _____

24. $18\dfrac{7}{8} - 14\dfrac{5}{16}$ 24. _____

25.   Is $\dfrac{2}{3}$ a solution to the equation $\dfrac{9}{10}x + \dfrac{2}{5} = 1$?   25. _____

Additional Exercises 1.2
Form II
Fractions in Algebra

Convert each mixed number to an improper fraction.

1. $4\dfrac{5}{12}$

1. _____

2. $12\dfrac{3}{10}$

2. _____

3. $15\dfrac{10}{16}$

3. _____

Convert each improper fraction to a mixed number.

4. $\dfrac{43}{3}$

4. _____

5. $\dfrac{96}{7}$

5. _____

6. $\dfrac{105}{9}$

6. _____

Reduce each fraction to its lowest terms.

7. $\dfrac{25}{40}$

7. _____

8. $\dfrac{16}{60}$

8. _____

9. $\dfrac{115}{120}$

9. _____

Perform the indicated operation in each exercise. Reduce answers to lowest terms if possible.

10. $\dfrac{3}{5} \cdot \dfrac{1}{2}$

10. _____

11. $\dfrac{5}{18} \cdot \dfrac{20}{25}$

11. _____

12. $200 \cdot \dfrac{4}{5}$ 12. _____

13. $\dfrac{9}{10} \div \dfrac{2}{5}$ 13. _____

14. $24 \div \dfrac{3}{4}$ 14. _____

15. $\left(12\dfrac{5}{8}\right) \div \left(4\dfrac{1}{4}\right)$ 15. _____

16. $\left(7\dfrac{3}{5}\right)\left(3\dfrac{2}{19}\right)$ 16. _____

17. $\dfrac{7}{10} + \dfrac{1}{10}$ 17. _____

18. $\dfrac{5}{12} + \dfrac{1}{4}$ 18. _____

19. $\dfrac{5}{9} + \dfrac{5}{6}$ 19. _____

20. $\dfrac{5}{21} - \dfrac{2}{21}$ 20. _____

21. $\dfrac{5}{9} - \dfrac{3}{8}$ 21. _____

22. $\dfrac{5}{7} - \dfrac{1}{4}$ 22. _____

23. $10\dfrac{9}{10} - 5\dfrac{1}{10}$ 23. _____

24. $12\dfrac{7}{8} - 6\dfrac{1}{3}$ 24. _____

25.   Is $\dfrac{3}{5}$ a solution to the equation $8 + 15x = 23 - 10x$?   25. _____

Additional Exercises 1.2
Form III
Fractions in Algebra

Convert each mixed number to an improper fraction.

1. $10\dfrac{3}{8}$ 1. _____

2. $16\dfrac{12}{17}$ 2. _____

3. $47\dfrac{13}{108}$ 3. _____

Convert each improper fraction to a mixed number.

4. $\dfrac{86}{9}$ 4. _____

5. $\dfrac{120}{14}$ 5. _____

6. $\dfrac{310}{65}$ 6. _____

Reduce each fraction to its lowest terms.

7. $\dfrac{80}{142}$ 7. _____

8. $\dfrac{108}{144}$ 8. _____

9. $\dfrac{285}{1125}$ 9. _____

Perform the indicated operation in each exercise. Reduce answers to lowest terms if possible.

10. $\dfrac{5}{8}\cdot\dfrac{5}{8}$ 10. _____

11. $350\cdot\dfrac{4}{5}$ 11. _____

Name _____   Date _____

12. $\left(4\frac{4}{5}\right)\left(5\frac{3}{8}\right)$

12. _____

13. $\frac{6}{8} \div \frac{2}{11}$

13. _____

14. $\frac{9}{16} \div \frac{5}{8}$

14. _____

15. $\left(16\frac{3}{7}\right) \div \left(8\frac{2}{6}\right)$

15. _____

16. $\frac{5}{12} + \frac{3}{8}$

16. _____

17. $\frac{3}{20} + \frac{5}{25}$

17. _____

18. $6\frac{1}{8} + 4\frac{3}{8}$

18. _____

19. $\frac{14}{15} - \frac{4}{15}$

19. _____

20. $\frac{7}{9} - \frac{1}{12}$

20. _____

21. $\frac{17}{18} - \frac{3}{4}$

21. _____

22. $23\frac{9}{10} - 15\frac{2}{5}$

22. _____

23. $42\frac{4}{5} - 13\frac{2}{3}$

23. _____

24. Is 20 a solution to the equation $\frac{1}{4}(x-3) = \frac{1}{3}(3x-18)$?

24. _____

25. Is $4\frac{4}{5}$ a solution to the equation $\left(x \div \frac{3}{5}\right) = x + 3\frac{1}{5}$?

25. _____

Name _____   Date _____

Use integers to represent the value in each expression.

1.   371 feet below sea level.   1. _____

2. $420 in debt.   2. _____

Graph the numbers on the number line.

3.   −6, −1, 0, 3   3.

4. $-3\frac{1}{2}$, −2.5, $4\frac{3}{4}$ 4.

Express each rational number as a decimal.

5. $\frac{1}{5}$ 5. _____

6. $\frac{4}{5}$ 6. _____

7. $7\frac{1}{4}$ 7. _____

8. $10\frac{1}{8}$ 8. _____

9.   For the set $\left\{-16,\ -7,\ 0,\ 2,\ \sqrt{10},\ 14\frac{1}{2}\right\}$ name the a) whole   9a. _____

       numbers, b) the rational numbers and c) the irrational numbers.   b. _____

                                                          c. _____

10. For the set $\left\{-14, -\sqrt{25}, 0, 3\pi, \sqrt{5}, \dfrac{7}{8}, 10, 16.5\right\}$ name the

    a) integers, b) irrational numbers and c) the natural numbers.

10a._____

   b. _____

   c. _____

Use either > or < to compare each pair of numbers.

11. -7 ☐ -3

11._____

12. $\dfrac{3}{4}$ ☐ $-\dfrac{1}{3}$

12._____

13. -5.5 ☐ 5.2

13._____

14. $\dfrac{5}{3}$ ☐ 2.7

14._____

Find each absolute value.

15. $|-11|$

15._____

16. $|11|$

16._____

Determine whether each inequality or statement is true or false.

17. $-12 > -11$

17._____

18. $4.5 \le -5.4$

18._____

19.   Every integer is a whole number.

19._____

20.   Rational numbers cannot be irrational.

20._____

Name _____   Date _____

Additional Exercises
1.3 Form II
The Real Numbers

Use integers to represent the value in each expression.

1. 7042 feet above sea level.

1. _____

2. Bank account overdrawn $62.53.

2. _____

Graph the numbers on the number line.

3. $-5.5,\ -3,\ -\dfrac{1}{4},\ 0,\ 0.75,\ 4\dfrac{7}{8}$

3.

Express each rational number as a decimal.

4. $\dfrac{3}{5}$

4. _____

5. $\dfrac{5}{6}$

5. _____

6. $1\dfrac{3}{8}$

6. _____

7. $19\dfrac{9}{20}$

7. _____

8. For the set $\left\{-11,\ -\sqrt{5},\ -\dfrac{5}{9},\ 0,\ 3,\ \pi,\ 12.6\right\}$ name the

    a) natural numbers, b) integers, and c) the rational numbers.

8a. _____

b. _____

c. _____

9. For the set $\left\{-6.8,\ -4,\ -\dfrac{1}{2},\ 1,\ 4\pi,\ \sqrt{6},\ 9\right\}$ name the a) whole numbers, b) irrational numbers and c) the real numbers.

9a. _____

b. _____

c. _____

Find each absolute value.

10. $|-4.5|$ 10. _____

11. $|4.5|$ 11. _____

Use either > or < to compare each pair of numbers.

12. $-18\ \square\ -11$ 12. _____

13. $\dfrac{5}{8}\ \square\ -\dfrac{3}{4}$ 13. _____

14. $-\dfrac{9}{10}\ \square\ -\dfrac{5}{6}$ 14. _____

15. $\left|-6\dfrac{3}{4}\right|\ \square\ \left|-5\dfrac{7}{8}\right|$ 15. _____

Determine whether each inequality or statement is true or false.

16. $-18 > -14$ 16. _____

17. $6.2 < |5.7|$ 17. _____

18. Every natural number is positive.   18. _____

19. Some numbers are rational and irrational.   19. _____

20. Whole numbers can be positive or negative.   20. _____

Name _____   Date _____

Additional Exercises
1.3 Form III
The Real Numbers

Use integers to represent the value in each expression.

1.   An overdrawn bank account of $12.82.   1. _____

2.   3050 feet above sea level.   2. _____

3.   A wind chill of 6° below zero.   3. _____

Express each rational number as a decimal.

4. $\dfrac{3}{8}$ 4. _____

5. $\dfrac{9}{20}$ 5. _____

6. $16\dfrac{3}{4}$ 6. _____

7. $25\dfrac{5}{6}$ 7. _____

8.   For the set $\left\{-9,\ -3.7,\ 0,\ 2\dfrac{7}{9},\ \sqrt{16},\ 15\right\}$ name the a) whole   8a. _____

      numbers, b) the rational numbers, and c) the integers.   b. _____

                                                                  c. _____

9.   For the set $\left\{-8.1,\ -\sqrt{15},\ -\dfrac{3}{11},\ -2,\ 6,\ \dfrac{\pi}{2},\ 7\dfrac{5}{9}\right\}$ name the   9a. _____

      a) irrational numbers, b) the rational numbers, and c) the real   b. _____

      numbers.   c. _____

Find each absolute value.

10. $\left| -8\frac{3}{5} \right|$

10. _____

11. $|6.47|$

11. _____

Use either > or < to compare each pair of numbers.

12. $-6\frac{4}{5}$ ☐ $-6\frac{11}{12}$

12. _____

13. -1.2 ☐ 1.1

13. _____

14. $|-8.3|$ ☐ 8

14. _____

15. $|3.25|$ ☐ $|-3.5|$

15. _____

Determine whether each in equality or statement is true or false.

16. $-25.6 > -25.4$

16. _____

17. $-8\frac{1}{7} < -7\frac{3}{7}$

17. _____

18.   All rational numbers are real numbers.

18. _____

19.   Absolute value is always positive.

19. _____

20.   Some integers are irrational.

20. _____

Name _____   Date _____

Additional Exercises 1.4
Form I
Basic Rules of Algebra

For each algebraic expression in exercises 1 – 3, (a) determine the number of terms, (b) identify the coefficient of each term, (c) identify the constant term if there is one and (d) name any like terms or state there are none.

1. $4x + 5$ 1a. _____

                                                                b. _____

                                                                c. _____

                                                                d. _____

2. $6x + 3y + 10$ 2a. _____

                                                                b. _____

                                                                c. _____

                                                                d. _____

3. $3x + y + 5x + 7z$ 3a. _____

                                                                b. _____

                                                                c. _____

                                                                d. _____

Use the indicated property to write an equivalent algebraic expression to the given expression.

4. $6x + 8$ (Commutative Property of Addition)   4. _____

5. $y \cdot 7$ (Commutative Property of Multiplication)   5. _____

6. $(x + 12) + 18$ (Associative Property of Addition)   6. _____

7. $6(3a)$ (Associative Property of Multiplication)   7. _____

Use the distributive property to rewrite each algebraic expression without parentheses.

8. $5(x + 7)$ 8. _____

AE-19

9. $9(2x - 3)$ 9. _____

10. $4(x + 2y + 3)$ 10. _____

11. $\dfrac{1}{2}(4a + 10)$ 11. _____

Simplify each algebraic expression.

12. $14x + 3x$ 12. _____

13. $16y + 6x - x$ 13. _____

14. $12a + 3a + a + 6$ 14. _____

15. $8x - 2x + 4y - 2y$ 15. _____

16. $10y + 18 + 7y$ 16. _____

17. $25m + 12 - 15m - 10$ 17. _____

18. $5(x + 2) + 3x$ 18. _____

19. $6(x + 1) + 2(x + 5)$ 19. _____

Write each English phrase as an algebraic expression. Then simplify the expression. Let x represent the number.

20.   The sum of three times a number and the number.   20. _____

21.   The difference of four times a number and the number.   21. _____

22.   Five times the product of a number and eight.   22. _____

23.   Six times the sum of a number and twelve.   23. _____

24.   Nine times the difference of seven and a number.   24. _____

Additional Exercises 1.4
Form II
Basic Rules of Algebra

For each algebraic expression in exercises 1 – 3, (a) determine the number of terms, (b) identify the coefficient of each term, (c) identify the constant term if there is one and (d) name any like terms or state there are none.

1. $12x + 3x + 8$

               1a. _____

               b. _____

               c. _____

               d. _____

2. $7x + \dfrac{1}{4}y + 2x + 5$

               2a. _____

               b. _____

               c. _____

               d. _____

3. $\dfrac{1}{5}x + \dfrac{1}{3}y + \dfrac{3}{5}x + \dfrac{1}{6}z$

               3a. _____

               b. _____

               c. _____

               d. _____

Use the indicated property to write an equivalent algebraic expression to the given expression.

4. $9 + 4x$ (Commutative Property of Addition)   4. _____

5. $a \cdot 12$ (Commutative Property of Multiplication) 5. _____

6. $(y + 25) + 15$ (Associative Property of Addition)   6. _____

7. $7(15a)$ (Associative Property of Multiplication) 7. _____

Name _____   Date _____

Use the distributive property to rewrite each algebraic expression without parentheses.

8. $3(4x + 3)$ 8. _____

9. $6(6x - 7)$ 9. _____

10. $9(x + y + 5)$ 10. _____

11. $\dfrac{1}{4}(4x - 8y - 12)$ 11. _____

Simplify each algebraic expression.

12. $18x - x$ 12. _____

13. $12y + 4 + 6y + 5$ 13. _____

14. $8a + 3 - 2a - 2$ 14. _____

15. $6.3x - 2.9x + 10y - 5.3y + 13$ 15. _____

16. $12(x + 4) + \dfrac{1}{2}(6x + 10)$ 16. _____

Write each English phrase as an algebraic expression. Then simplify the expression. Let x represent the number.

17.   Twice the sum of a number and ten.   17. _____

18.   Eight times the product of six and a number.   18. _____

19.   Fourteen increased by the product of twice a number and ten.   19. _____

20.   Five times the sum of a number and eight increased by   20. _____
      three times the difference of a number and three.

Additional Exercises 1.4
Form III
Basic Rules of Algebra

For each algebraic expression in exercises 1 – 3, (a) determine the number of terms, (b) identify the coefficient of each term, (c) identify the constant term if there is one and (d) name any like terms or state there are none.

1. $8x + 3y - 15$

1a. _____

b. _____

c. _____

d. _____

2. $12x + 10y - 3y + 12$

2a. _____

b. _____

c. _____

d. _____

3. $\dfrac{1}{4}a + \dfrac{3}{4}b + 8 + \dfrac{1}{8}a + \dfrac{1}{2}b$

3a. _____

b. _____

c. _____

d. _____

Use the indicated property to write an equivalent algebraic expression to the given expression.

4. $12y + 5x$ (Commutative Property of Addition)   4. _____

5. $a \cdot 21$ (Commutative Property of Multiplication)   5. _____

6. $3x + (4x + 19)$ (Associative Property of Addition)   6. _____

7. $32(5y)$ (Associative Property of Multiplication)   7. _____

Name _____   Date _____

Use the distributive property to rewrite each algebraic expression without parentheses.

8. $7(5 + 6y)$ 8. _____

9. $12(3 - 2x)$ 9. _____

10. $15(a - b - c)$ 10. _____

11. $\dfrac{3}{4}(12x + 16y + 4)$ 11. _____

Simplify each algebraic expression.

12. $12x + 5 - 3x - 3$ 12. _____

13. $0.08a + 0.14b + 0.16b + 0.12a$ 13. _____

14. $3(x + 7) + 4(x - 1)$ 14. _____

15. $\dfrac{1}{2}(8 + 2x) + \dfrac{1}{6}(6x + 12)$ 15. _____

16. $3(x + 5) + 2(x - 4) + 5(2x + 1)$ 16. _____

Write each English phrase as an algebraic expression. Then simplify the expression. Let x represent the number.

17.   Seven times the sum of a number and three increased   17. _____
      by four times the difference of a number and one.

18.   Five times a number increased by one-half the product   18. _____
      of a number and eight.

The cost C for a company to produce x number of jelly jars can be modeled by the formula $C = 0.4(x + 90{,}000) + 0.5x$.

19.   Simplify the formula.   19. _____

20.   Find the cost of producing 60,000 jelly jars.   20. _____

Additional Exercises 1.5
Form I
Addition of Real Numbers

Find the sum.

1. $10 + (-4)$

1. _____

2. $8 + (-3)$

2. _____

3. $-12 + 8$

3. _____

4. $-9 + 29$

4. _____

5. $-32 + 45$

5. _____

6. $-19 + (-11)$

6. _____

7. $-41 + (-18)$

7. _____

8. $-58 + 17$

8. _____

9. $-\dfrac{4}{11} + \dfrac{3}{11}$

9. _____

10. $-14.6 + (-3.3)$

10. _____

11. $\dfrac{5}{12} + \left(-\dfrac{11}{12}\right)$ 11. _____

12. $-\dfrac{9}{20} + \left(-\dfrac{3}{20}\right)$ 12. _____

13. $-8 + (-12) + (-17)$ 13. _____

14. $-13 + 25 + (-10) + 5$ 14. _____

15. $48 + (-52) + (-26) + 13$ 15. _____

Simplify each algebraic expression.

16. $8x + (-15x)$ 16. _____

17. $-12a + (-a)$ 17. _____

18. $-15y + 31y$ 18. _____

19. $-20x + 5y + 15x + (-5y)$ 19. _____

20. $16m + 18 + (-12m) + (-7) + (-3m)$ 20. _____

Additional Exercises 1.5
Form II
Addition of Real Numbers

Find the sum.

1. $-15+12$ 1. _____

2. $-23+87$ 2. _____

3. $52+(-13)$ 3. _____

4. $46+(-60)$ 4. _____

5. $-31+(-31)$ 5. _____

6. $-120+(-93)$ 6. _____

7. $-\dfrac{5}{13}+\dfrac{9}{13}$ 7. _____

8. $\dfrac{3}{2}+(-2)$ 8. _____

9. $0.26+(-3.057)$ 9. _____

10. $-15.8+(-4.2)$ 10. _____

11. $25 + 7 + (-11)$ 11. _____

12. $5.4 + (-5.6) + (-2.9)$ 12. _____

13. $-26 + \left(-\dfrac{8}{9}\right) + \left(\dfrac{5}{9}\right)$ 13. _____

14. $-19 + (-20) + (-15) + (-8)$ 14. _____

Simplify each algebraic expression.

15. $-4x + (-5x) + x$ 15. _____

16. $15b + (-2) + (-10b) + 7 + 5b$ 16. _____

17. $5(y + 10) + (-10) + (-9y)$ 17. _____

18. $6(2y + 3) + (-2y) + (-12)$ 18. _____

Solve.

19.   The temperature at 5p.m. on January 18 was $-11°$ Fahrenheit.   19. _____
        By 7 p.m. the temperature had risen 24 degrees. Find the
        temperature at 7 p.m.

20.   The deep-sea diver dives from the surface to 41 feet below   20. _____
        the surface. She then dives down 11 more feet. Find the
        diver's depth.

Additional Exercises 1.5
Form III
Addition of Real Numbers

Find the sum.

1. $45 + (-13)$ 1. _____

2. $114 + (-86)$ 2. _____

3. $-75 + 32$ 3. _____

4. $-28 + 56$ 4. _____

5. $-51 + (-37)$ 5. _____

6. $-106 + (-388)$ 6. _____

7. $-\dfrac{7}{15} + -\dfrac{2}{5}$ 7. _____

8. $-15.8 + 42.2$ 8. _____

9. $-\dfrac{3}{4} + \dfrac{7}{8}$ 9. _____

10. $-\dfrac{1}{3} + -\dfrac{1}{6} + -\dfrac{1}{4}$ 10. _____

11. $-14.7 + 21.32 + (-5.1)$ 11._____

12. $-55 + 63 + (-38) + 17$ 12._____

13. $-24 + \left(-\dfrac{5}{8}\right) + 35 + \left(-\dfrac{3}{8}\right)$ 13._____

Simplify each algebraic expression.

14. $6a + (-3a) + a$ 14._____

15. $-15y + 3(y + 5)$ 15._____

16. $6(x + 2) + (-2x) + (-18)$ 16._____

17. $-10m + (-3m) + (-12) + m + (-18)$ 17._____

Solve.

18.   The difference between a country's exports and imports is   18._____
        called the country's trade balance. If one country had a
        trade balance of –$102 billion in 1988, $142 billion in 1987,
        and –$42 billion in 1994 what was the total trade balance for
        these years?

19.   Scores in golf can be positive or negative integers. For example   19._____
        a score of 8 over par can be represented by +8 and a score
        of 3 under par can be represented by –3. If Donna had a score
        of 2 over par, 4 under par, and 6 under par for three games
        of golf. What was her total score.

20.   Brian played poker with the guys Saturday night. He had $50   20._____
        to begin play with. He played six hands of Texas Hold'em. On
        the first hand he lost $10,the next hand he lost $14, and on the
        third hand he won $16. Brian lost $32 on the fourth hand, won
        $18 on the fifth and won $26 on the last hand of the night. How
        much money did Brian take home, or how much did he lose?

Name _____   Date _____

Additional Exercises 1.6
Form I
Subtraction of Real Numbers

Perform the indicated subtraction.

1. $15 - 18$

1. _____

2. $-12 - 17$

2. _____

3. $16 - (-13)$

3. _____

4. $-25 - 25$

4. _____

5. $-10 - (-15)$

5. _____

6. $-\dfrac{1}{8} - \dfrac{3}{8}$

6. _____

7. $-6.7 - 3.4$

7. _____

8. $56 - (-18)$

8. _____

9. $\dfrac{3}{8} - \left(-\dfrac{5}{8}\right)$

9. _____

10. $(-0.85) - (-0.20)$

10. _____

11. $7.196 - (-0.125)$ 11. _____

12. $-76 - 37$ 12. _____

Simplify each series of additions and subtractions.

13. $-14 - 6 + 12 - (-3)$ 13. _____

14. $26 - (-3) - 42 + 7$ 14. _____

15. $3 - \dfrac{3}{4} - \dfrac{1}{4} + 2$ 15. _____

Simplify each algebraic expression.

16. $5x - 11x$ 16. _____

17. $16 - 3x - 4x$ 17. _____

18. $3a - 15 - 15 - 6a$ 18. _____

Solve.

19.   Beth is 62 inches tall. Bria is 67 inches tall. How much   19. _____
       taller is Bria than Beth?

20.   At 4:00 p.m. the temperature was 37° F. At 11:00 p.m.   20. _____
       the temperature was −1° F. What was the change in the
       temperature?

Name _____   Date _____

Perform the indicated subtraction.

1. $65 - (-12)$ 1. _____

2. $-17 - (-25)$ 2. _____

3. $11 - (-15)$ 3. _____

4. $-18 - 18$ 4. _____

5. $-57 - 32$ 5. _____

6. $-45 - (-28)$ 6. _____

7. $-\dfrac{4}{5} - \dfrac{1}{5}$ 7. _____

8. $-\dfrac{8}{7} - \dfrac{13}{7}$ 8. _____

9. $6.124 - (-0.37)$ 9. _____

10. $-4.2 - 6.3$ 10. _____

11. $68.7 - 93.1$ 11. _____

12. $-54 - (-32.7)$ 12. _____

Simplify each series of additions and subtractions.

13. $-5 + (-7) - 5 + 12$ 13. _____

14. $-4 - 14 - (-12) + (-16)$ 14. _____

15. $8 - 15 - (-3) - 21 - (-6)$ 15. _____

Simplify each algebraic expression.

16. $-15y - 9x - 6x$ 16. _____

17. $-8 - 5a - 12 + 3a$ 17. _____

18. $-7y + 6 - 7 + 2 + y - 1$ 18. _____

Solve.

19.   Trader Tower stands at 2855 feet high. Exchange Emporium is   19. _____
      889 feet tall. How much taller is Trader Tower than Exchange
      Emporium?

20.   The temperature at 5:00 a.m. was $-7°$ F. Four hours later, it was   20. _____
      $-12°$ F. What was the change in the temperature?

Additional Exercises 1.6
Form III
Subtraction of Real Numbers

Perform the indicated subtraction.

1. $-42 - 42$ 1. _____

2. $-63 - (-15)$ 2. _____

3. $27 - 43$ 3. _____

4. $-93 - (-93)$ 4. _____

5. $-\dfrac{3}{4} - \dfrac{1}{6}$ 5. _____

6. $5.8 - (-5.8)$ 6. _____

7. $-3.72 - 6.817$ 7. _____

8. $-\dfrac{7}{9} - \dfrac{11}{9}$ 8. _____

9. $0.53 - 4.62$ 9. _____

10. $66 - 143$ 10. _____

11. $-10\pi - 3\pi$ 11. _____

12. $\dfrac{1}{8} - \left(-\dfrac{1}{24}\right)$ 12. _____

Simplify each series of additions and subtractions.

13. $-19 - 16 + 26 - (-15)$ 13. _____

14. $37 - (-17) - 82 + 47$ 14. _____

15. $-\dfrac{5}{8} + \dfrac{3}{4} - \left(-\dfrac{5}{6}\right) - \dfrac{1}{12}$ 15. _____

16. $-18.03 - (-6.15) + 0.85 - 11.2$ 16. _____

Simplify each algebraic expression.

17. $-12a - 18 - 5a + 27$ 17. _____

18. $25 - (-4x) + 13 - 6x$ 18. _____

19. $-6x - 8y - (-5) - (-3y) + 9x$ 19. _____

Solve.

20.   City A has an elevation of 13,438 feet above sea level while   20. _____
      City B has an elevation of 17,028 feet below sea level. Find
      the difference in elevation between those two cities.

Name _____   Date _____

Additional Exercises 1.7
Form I
Multiplication and Division of Real Numbers

Multiply.

1.　　−8(3)

1. _____

2.　　7(−6)

2. _____

3.　　(−5)(−4)

3. _____

4.　　$\left(\dfrac{1}{8}\right)\left(-\dfrac{4}{5}\right)$

4. _____

5.　　$\left(-\dfrac{1}{4}\right)(-12)$

5. _____

6.　　0.13(−0.4)

6. _____

7.　　(−3)(−2)(−1)(−4)

7. _____

8.　　(−5)(2)(−6)(4)(−3)

8. _____

Divide.

9.　　$-\dfrac{15}{3}$

9. _____

10. $\dfrac{10}{0}$ 10. _____

11. $-72 \div -8$ 11. _____

12. $0 \div 14$ 12. _____

13. $\left(-\dfrac{5}{9}\right) \div \left(-\dfrac{10}{3}\right)$ 13. _____

14. $-42 \div \dfrac{1}{3}$ 14. _____

15. $-73.8 \div -9$ 15. _____

16. $-8 \div \dfrac{1}{8}$ 16. _____

Simplify each algebraic expression.

17. $-6(3x)$ 17. _____

18. $-4\left(-\dfrac{1}{4}y\right)$ 18. _____

19. $-5(3x - 2)$ 19. _____

20.   Is -3 a solution to $5x = 2x + 9$?   20. _____

Name _____   Date _____

Additional Exercises 1.7
Form II
Multiplication and Division of Real Numbers

Multiply.

1. $-7(-5)$ 1. _____

2. $-12(6)$ 2. _____

3. $9(-7)$ 3. _____

4. $(-0.23)(-15)$ 4. _____

5. $\left(-\dfrac{3}{8}\right)\left(\dfrac{10}{11}\right)$ 5. _____

6. $(-4)(-12)(-2)(-3)$ 6. _____

7. $(-5)(4)(-1)(5)(-2)$ 7. _____

Divide.

8. $-\dfrac{28}{7}$ 8. _____

9. $-48 \div -4$ 9. _____

10. $\dfrac{12}{0}$ 10. _____

Name _____ Date _____

11. $-12 \div \left(-\dfrac{1}{3}\right)$ 　　　　　　　　　11. _____

12. $-50 \div \dfrac{5}{8}$ 　　　　　　　　　12. _____

13. $15 \div -\dfrac{1}{15}$ 　　　　　　　　　13. _____

14. $-43.8 \div -6$ 　　　　　　　　　14. _____

Simplify each algebraic expression.

15. $-12\left(-\dfrac{1}{12}x\right)$ 　　　　　　　　　15. _____

16. $-6(3x-4)$ 　　　　　　　　　16. _____

17. $-5x-(2x-7)$ 　　　　　　　　　17. _____

18. $-4(6-x)-2(x-6)$ 　　　　　　　　　18. _____

Determine whether the given number is a solution to the equation.

19. $-3y-10=-7y+14 \, ; \, 6$ 　　　　　　　　　19. _____

20. $5(x-4)=-4(2-2x) \; ; \, 4$ 　　　　　　　　　20. _____

Name _____   Date _____

Multiply or divide as indicated.

1. $-18(-4)$ 1. _____

2. $25(-8)$ 2. _____

3. $(-63) \div (-3)$ 3. _____

4. $126 \div (-9)$ 4. _____

5. $(-6.82)(-3.1)$ 5. _____

6. $-\dfrac{18}{25} \cdot \dfrac{5}{8}$ 6. _____

7. $-20 \div \dfrac{4}{5}$ 7. _____

8. $-40 \div -\dfrac{8}{9}$ 8. _____

9. $-15 \div 0$ 9. _____

10. $(-8)(-5)(-2)(-4)(-1)$ 10. _____

11. $-\dfrac{5}{6}\cdot 12\cdot -\dfrac{3}{4}$ 11. _____

12. $(6)(-3)(15)(0)(-4)$ 12. _____

13. $-\dfrac{15}{16}\div -\dfrac{10}{18}$ 13. _____

Simplify each algebraic expression.

14. $-\dfrac{1}{18}(-18x)$ 14. _____

15. $-8(7-4x)$ 15. _____

16. $6(5-x)-(12-8x)$ 16. _____

17. $-(x-6)-(5-2x)$ 17. _____

18. $\dfrac{1}{4}(4x-8)-\dfrac{1}{3}(6-9x)$ 18. _____

Determine whether the given number is a solution to the equation.

19. $5x-18=14-3x\,;\,4$ 19. _____

20. $6(x+2)-3x=5(4-x)\,;\,-1$ 20. _____

Additional Exercises 1.8
Form I
Exponents and Order of Operations

Evaluate each exponential expression.

1. 8^2 1. _____

2. $(-8)^2$ 2. _____

3. -8^2 3. _____

Simplify each algebraic expression, if possible.

4. $5x^2 + 11x^2$ 4. _____

5. $8x^4 + 2x^4$ 5. _____

6. $14x^3 - x^3$ 6. _____

Evaluate each algebraic expression for the given value of the variable.

7. $x^2 - x$ for $x = 3$ 7. _____

8. $2x^3 + x^2$ for $x = -1$ 8. _____

9. $5x^3 - x$ for $x = -2$ 9. _____

10. $x^4 - 2x^2 + x$ for $x = 2$ 10. _____

Use the order of operations to simplify each expression.

11. $4 + 2 \cdot 6$ 11. _____

12. $3 \cdot 5 + 2 \cdot 6$ 12. _____

13. $-6(12 \div 2 \cdot 3) - 6^2$ 13. _____

14. $4(-3)^2 - 3(-4)^2$ 14. _____

15. $(6 - 10)^2 - (3^2 - 5)^2$ 15. _____

16. $5(4 - 8)^2 - 2(1 - 4)^2$ 16. _____

17. $3[4(5 - 7)^2] \div (-2)^3$ 17. _____

18. $\dfrac{10 + 8 \div 2}{2^3 - 1}$ 18. _____

19. $\dfrac{5^2 + 20 \div 2(2)}{3^2}$ 19. _____

Simplify by removing parentheses and brackets.

20. $7[3(x - 4) - 1]$ 20. _____

Additional Exercises 1.8
Form II
Exponents and Order of Operations

Evaluate each exponential expression.

1. -9^2 1. _____

2. $(-9)^2$ 2. _____

3. -7^3 3. _____

Simplify each algebraic expression, if possible.

4. $24x^3 - 12x^3$ 4. _____

5. $15x^2 + x^2$ 5. _____

6. $10x^4 - 9x^3$ 6. _____

Evaluate each algebraic expression for the given value of the variable.

7. $3x^3 - 4$ for $x = -2$ 7. _____

8. $-5x^2 + 9x$ for $x = 4$ 8. _____

9. $-x^3 - x^2 - x$ for $x = -1$ 9. _____

10. $2x^4 - x^3 + x^2$ for $x = -3$ 10. _____

Name _____   Date _____

Use the order of operations to simplify each expression.

11. $5 \cdot 8 + 6 \cdot 4$ 11. _____

12. $-7(24 \div 6 \cdot 2) - 5^2$ 12. _____

13. $5(3)^2 - 4(-2)^3$ 13. _____

14. $(5-12)^2 - (10 \div -2)^2$ 14. _____

15. $6(9-5)^2 + 4(12 \cdot 6 \div 3)$ 15. _____

16. $-6\,[3(8-12)^2 - (4-18 \div 3)]$ 16. _____

17. $\dfrac{-18 \div 2 \cdot 3}{5^2 - 4^2}$ 17. _____

18. $\left[-\dfrac{3}{5} - \dfrac{3}{10}\right] \cdot \left[\dfrac{4}{5} \div \dfrac{2}{15}\right] + \dfrac{2}{5}$ 18. _____

Simplify by removing parentheses and brackets.

19. $-3(2x - 10) - 4x + 6$ 19. _____

20. $4\,[4(x+4) + 5]$ 20. _____

Additional Exercises 1.8
Form III
Exponents and Order of Operations

Evaluate each exponential expression.

1. $(-11)^2$ 1. _____

2. -14^2 2. _____

3. -8^3 3. _____

Simplify each algebraic expression, if possible.

4. $5x^3 - 2x^2$ 4. _____

5. $x^3 + 4x^3$ 5. _____

6. $9x^2 - x^2 - 3x^2$ 6. _____

Evaluate each algebraic expression for the given value of the variable.

7. $-x^2 - 5x$ for $x = -3$ 7. _____

8. $3x^3 + x^2 - x$ for $x = -2$ 8. _____

9. $\dfrac{x^2 + 5x}{-x + x^2}$ for $x = 4$ 9. _____

10. $-5(x+3) + 2x^2 - (x+4)$ for $x = -1$ 10. _____

Name _____   Date _____

Use the order of operations to simplify each expression.

11. $(-2)(4)^3 - (-20)(-5)$ 11. _____

12. $-4[16 - (4-6)^2] \div [24 \div 4 \cdot 2]$ 12. _____

13. $(-4-8)(-5+4) - 4^4$ 13. _____

14. $10 - 6[4^3 - 48 \div 4] + 4^4$ 14. _____

15. $\dfrac{6(8-4) + 6(3)}{7(1-4)}$ 15. _____

16. $\dfrac{14 + 18 \div 6(2)}{-3^2 - 1}$ 16. _____

Simplify by removing parentheses and brackets.

17. $4 - 5[3(3x - 4)]$ 17. _____

18. $15 \div 3[4(3x - 4) - 5x]$ 18. _____

19. As the relative humidity increases, the temperature seems   19. _____
     higher than it really is. The model $T = 0.114x + 59.63$
     approximates the apparent temperature of 65° F, where x is the
     relative humidity. What is the apparent temperature (to the nearest
     degree) for a humidity of 70%?

20. The winning times (in seconds) in a speed skating event for men   20. _____
     can be represented by the model $T = 46.39 - 0.093x$, where x
     represents the year, with $x = 0$ corresponding to 1920. (For example,
     1992 – 1920 = 72.) What would the winning time be in 1997
     according to the model? Round your answer to the nearest
     hundredth.

Additional Exercises 2.1
Form I
The Addition Property of Equality

Identify the following equations in one variable as linear or not linear.

1. $x + 7 = 5$

2. $x^2 + 4 = 7$

3. $\dfrac{11}{x} = 5$

4. $|x + 4| = 8$

1. _____

2. _____

3. _____

4. _____

Solve the equation using the addition property of equality.

5. $a - 21 = -9$

6. $x + 17 = 28$

7. $4 = b - 9$

8. $t - 8 = 15$

9. $x + \dfrac{2}{6} = \dfrac{2}{6}$

10. $x + 0.7 = 1.5$

11. $8 = -14 + x$

12. $-31 = x - 14$

5. _____

6. _____

7. _____

8. _____

9. _____

10. _____

11. _____

12. _____

13. $-14.5 = 12.2 + x$ 13. _____

14. $13 + 6p = 7p$ 14. _____

15. $8y = 7y - 8.8$ 15. _____

Solve.

16.   The cost of having a car towed is given by the formula   16. _____
      $C = 3x + 65$, where C is in dollars and x is the number of
      miles the car is towed. Find the cost of having a car towed
      3 miles.

17.   The formula $C = 537x + 165$ models the cost to produce x units   17. _____
      of product, where C is given in dollars. Find the total cost if
      100 units are produced.

18.   The monthly cost of a certain long distance service is given by   18. _____
      the formula $C = 0.07t + 4.95$ where C is in dollars and t is the
      amount of time in minutes called in a month. Find the cost of
      calling long distance for 100 minutes a month.

19.   The amount of water in a leaky bucket is given by the formula   19. _____
      $f = 115 - 7t$, where f is in ounces and t is in minutes. Find the
      amount of water in the bucket after 5 minutes.

20.   The altitude above sea level of an airplane just after taking off   20. _____
      from an airport on a high plateau is given by the formula
      $h = 700t + 2882$, where h is in feet and t is the time in minutes
      since takeoff. Find the altitude of the airplane after 3 minutes.

Additional Exercises 2.1
Form II
The Addition Property of Equality

Identify the following equations in one variable as linear or not linear.

1. $x + 1 = 11$

1. _____

2. $x^2 - 8 = 12$

2. _____

3. $\dfrac{9}{x} = 4$

3. _____

4. $3x = 15$

4. _____

Solve the equation using the addition property of equality.

5. $21 + x = 7$

5. _____

6. $-8 + y = 11$

6. _____

7. $\dfrac{1}{3} + y = \dfrac{2}{3}$

7. _____

8. $\dfrac{1}{5} + x = 3$

8. _____

9. $2.4 + y = 3.6$

9. _____

10. $\dfrac{2}{5} + b = \dfrac{1}{4}$

10. _____

11. $1.3 + x = 19.2$

11. _____

12. $x + \dfrac{1}{4} = -\dfrac{7}{2}$ 12. _____

13. $510 + y = 820$ 13. _____

14. $-7.1 + y = 7.1$ 14. _____

15. $y + \dfrac{5}{7} = \dfrac{5}{7}$ 15. _____

Solve.

16.   The cost of having a car towed is given by the formula   16. _____
        $C = 3x + 65$, where C is in dollars and x is the number of
        miles the car is towed. Find the cost of having a car towed
        12 miles.

17.   The formula $C = 537x + 165$ models the cost to produce x units   17. _____
        of product, where C is given in dollars. Find the total cost if 125
        units are produced.

18.   The monthly cost of a certain long distance service is given by   18. _____
        the formula $C = 0.07t + 4.95$ where C is in dollars and t is the
        amount of time in minutes called in a month. Find the cost of
        calling long distance for 120 minutes a month.

19.   The amount of water in a leaky bucket is given by the formula   19. _____
        $f = 115 - 7t$, where f is in ounces and t is in minutes. Find the
        amount of water in the bucket after 10 minutes.

20.   The altitude above sea level of an airplane just after taking off   20. _____
        from an airport on a high plateau is given by the formula
        $h = 700t + 2882$, where h is in feet and t is the time in minutes
        since takeoff. Find the altitude of the airplane after 5 minutes.

Additional Exercises 2.1
Form III
The Addition Property of Equality

Identify the following equations in one variable as linear or not linear.

1. $x + 51 = 80$ 1. _____

2. $x^2 + 13 = 20$ 2. _____

3. $\dfrac{5}{x} = 7$ 3. _____

4. $|9 + x| = 10$ 4. _____

Solve the equation using the addition property of equality.

5. $x - \dfrac{1}{2} = \dfrac{9}{10}$ 5. _____

6. $x + \dfrac{1}{6} = -\dfrac{5}{12}$ 6. _____

7. $510 + x = -805$ 7. _____

8. $x + 1.3 = 7$ 8. _____

9. $x + 9.5 = -4$ 9. _____

10. $-4y + 9 = -5y - 11$ 10. _____

11. $6x + 4 = 5(x + 2)$ 11. _____

12. $9x + 11 + 2 = 8(x - 6)$ 12. _____

13. $14 - 3s = 12 - 4s$ 13. _____

14. $-4x + 5 + 3x = 12 - 4$ 14. _____

15. $-4.1 + 5x = 4x - 4.1$ 15. _____

Solve.

16. The cost of having a car towed is given by the formula   16. _____
     $C = 3x + 65$, where C is in dollars and x is the number of
     miles the car is towed. Find the cost of having a car towed
     52 miles.

17. The formula $C = 537x + 165$ models the cost to produce x units   17. _____
     of product, where C is given in dollars. Find the total cost if 210
     units are produced.

18. The monthly cost of a certain long distance service is given by   18. _____
     the formula $C = 0.07t + 4.95$ where C is in dollars and t is the
     amount of time in minutes called in a month. Find the cost of
     calling long distance for 200 minutes a month.

19. The amount of water in a leaky bucket is given by the formula   19. _____
     $f = 115 - 7t$, where f is in ounces and t is in minutes. Find the
     amount of water in the bucket after 12 minutes.

20. The altitude above sea level of an airplane just after taking off   20. _____
     from an airport on a high plateau is given by the formula
     $h = 700t + 2882$, where h is in feet and t is the time in minutes
     since takeoff. Find the altitude of the airplane after 10 minutes.

Additional Exercises 2.2
Form I
The Multiplication Property of Equality

Solve the equation using the multiplication property of equality.

1. $\dfrac{1}{5}x = 4$

1. _____

2. $-\dfrac{1}{3}x = 7$

2. _____

3. $9x = 27$

3. _____

4. $-5x = -40$

4. _____

5. $-8x = 2$

5. _____

6. $-x = 11$

6. _____

7. $3x - x = 20$

7. _____

8. $2x + 4 = 16$

8. _____

9. $3x - 4 = 8$

9. _____

10. $-15 = 3x + 3$

10. _____

11. $4x = -2x + 42$

11. _____

12. $6x + 9 = 4x - 5$

12. _____

13. $8x + 1 = 6x + 1$

13. _____

14. $-2x + 5 = -4x + 7$ 14. _____

15. $5x + 8 = x + 4$ 15. _____

Solve the problem.

16. The time it takes to travel a given distance at constant speed is   16. _____
     given by the formula $t = \dfrac{d}{r}$, where t is the time, d is the
     distance, and r is the rate of travel. At 30 miles per hour, what
     distance can be traveled in 5 hours?

17. The time it takes to travel a given distance at constant speed is   17. _____
     given by the formula $t = \dfrac{d}{r}$, where t is the time, d is the
     distance, and r is the rate of travel. At 0.7 mile per minute, what
     distance can be traveled in 20 minutes?

18. To convert meters to feet, you can use the formula $f = \dfrac{m}{0.3038}$,   18. _____
     where f is the distance in feet and m is the distance in meters.
     How many meters (to the nearest tenth) is 23 feet?

19. Power is the time rate of doing work and is commonly measured   19. _____
     in watts. Power is given by the formula $P = \dfrac{W}{t}$, where P is power,
     W is work (in joules), and t is time in seconds. If 500 watts of
     power are used in 12 seconds, how much work (in joules) was done?

20. The speed of a ball dropped from a tower is given by the formula   20. _____
     $f = 32t$ where f is in feet per second and t is the number of
     seconds since the ball was dropped. Find the speed of the ball after
     9 seconds.

Additional Exercises 2.2
Form II
The Multiplication Property of Equality

Solve the equation using the multiplication property of equality.

1. $\dfrac{1}{8}x = -3$

1. _____

2. $-\dfrac{1}{11}x = 4$

2. _____

3. $\dfrac{x}{2} = 11$

3. _____

4. $-3a = 1$

4. _____

5. $-6x = -30$

5. _____

6. $\dfrac{2}{5}x = \dfrac{4}{25}$

6. _____

7. $\dfrac{n}{4} = 9$

7. _____

8. $\dfrac{3}{8}x = -\dfrac{6}{5}$

8. _____

9. $-x = -15$

9. _____

10. $5x - 1 = 7$

10. _____

11. $7n - 4 = 66$

11. _____

12. $-12 = 5x - 8$ 12. _____

13. $5y + 7 = -4 + 3y$ 13. _____

14. $5x + 1 = -2x - 8$ 14. _____

15. $8x + 1 = 4x + 3$ 15. _____

Solve the problem.

16.   The time it takes to travel a given distance at constant speed is   16. _____
       given by the formula $t = \dfrac{d}{r}$, where t is the time, d is the
       distance, and r is the rate of travel. At 55 miles per hour, what
       distance can be traveled in 4.5 hours?

17.   The time it takes to travel a given distance at constant speed is   17. _____
       given by the formula $t = \dfrac{d}{r}$, where t is the time, d is the
       distance, and r is the rate of travel. At 0.6 mile per minute, what
       distance can be traveled in 25 minutes?

18.   To convert meters to feet, you can use the formula $f = \dfrac{m}{0.3038}$,   18. _____
       where f is the distance in feet and m is the distance in meters.
       How many meters (to the nearest tenth) is 26 feet?

19.   Power is the time rate of doing work and is commonly measured   19. _____
       in watts. Power is given by the formula $P = \dfrac{W}{t}$, where P is power,
       W is work (in joules), and t is time in seconds. If 600 watts of
       power are used in 11 seconds, how much work (in joules) was done?

20.   The speed of a ball dropped from a tower is given by the formula   20. _____
       $f = 32t$ where f is in feet per second and t is the number of
       seconds since the ball was dropped. Find the speed of the ball after
       8 seconds.

Name _____   Date _____

Additional Exercises 2.2
Form III
The Multiplication Property of Equality

Solve the equation using the multiplication property of equality.

1. $\dfrac{1}{13}x = 7$ 1. _____

2. $-\dfrac{1}{23}a = 0$ 2. _____

3. $\dfrac{x}{4} = -8$ 3. _____

4. $-5a = 45$ 4. _____

5. $-8x = -50$ 5. _____

6. $\dfrac{2}{3}m = \dfrac{2}{5}$ 6. _____

7. $\dfrac{x}{7} = -5$ 7. _____

8. $-\dfrac{2}{9}k = -\dfrac{2}{3}$ 8. _____

9. $-12 = -x$ 9. _____

10. $4r + 2 = 22$ 10. _____

11. $8x - 5 = 61$ 11. _____

12. $-21 = 5x - 6$ 12. _____

13. $2x + 9 = -3 + 5x$ 13. _____

14. $7x + 3 = -3x - 7$ 14. _____

15. $9x - 7 = 4x + 9$ 15. _____

Solve the problem.

16.   The time it takes to travel a given distance at constant speed is   16. _____
       given by the formula $t = \dfrac{d}{r}$, where t is the time, d is the
       distance, and r is the rate of travel. At 70 miles per hour, what
       distance can be traveled in 6 ¼ hours?

17.   The time it takes to travel a given distance at constant speed is   17. _____
       given by the formula $t = \dfrac{d}{r}$, where t is the time, d is the
       distance, and r is the rate of travel. At 0.7 mile per minute, what
       distance can be traveled in 32 minutes?

18.   To convert meters to feet, you can use the formula $f = \dfrac{m}{0.3038}$,   18. _____
       where f is the distance in feet and m is the distance in meters.
       How many meters (to the nearest tenth) is 27 feet?

19.   Power is the time rate of doing work and is commonly measured   19. _____
       in watts. Power is given by the formula $P = \dfrac{W}{t}$, where P is power,
       W is work (in joules), and t is time in seconds. If 550 watts of
       power are used in 15 seconds, how much work (in joules) was done?

20.   The speed of a ball dropped from a tower is given by the formula   20. _____
       $f = 32t$ where f is in feet per second and t is the number of
       seconds since the ball was dropped. Find the speed of the ball after
       12 seconds.

Name _____   Date _____

Additional Exercises 2.3
Form I
Solving Linear Equations

Solve the equation.

1. $7x - (3x - 1) = 2$ 1. _____

2. $6(4x - 1) = 24$ 2. _____

3. $(y - 2) - (y + 8) = 4y$ 3. _____

4. $3(5x - 2) = 9$ 4. _____

5. $2(2 + 4x) = 52$ 5. _____

6. $-2(2x - 1) = -4$ 6. _____

7. $3x - 10 = 5(x - 4)$ 7. _____

8. $4(2x - 3) = 20$ 8. _____

Solve each equation. Begin your work by rewriting each equation without fractions.

9. $\dfrac{f}{5} - 4 = 1$ 9. _____

10. $\dfrac{2x}{5} - \dfrac{x}{3} = 3$ 10. _____

11. $\dfrac{x}{7} = 10 - \dfrac{x}{3}$ 11. _____

12. $\dfrac{x}{3} - 1 = -\dfrac{x}{2}$ 12. _____

13. $\dfrac{3x}{10} - \dfrac{1}{2} = \dfrac{x}{5}$ 13. _____

14. $\dfrac{x}{2} = \dfrac{x + 5}{3}$ 14. _____

15. $\dfrac{2x}{3} + \dfrac{5}{6} = \dfrac{3x}{2}$ 15. _____

16. Forensic scientists use the length of certain bones to   16. _____
calculate the height of a person. When the femur (f),
the bone from the knee to the hip socket is used, the
following formula applies for men: $h = 69.09 + 2.24f$,
where h is the height and f is the length of the femur.
Find the height of a man with a femur measuring
59 centimeters.

17. There is a formula that gives a correspondence between   17. _____
women's shoe sizes in the United States and those in
Italy. The formula is $S = 2(x + 12)$, where S is the size
in Italy and x is the size in the United States. What
would be the US size for an Italian size of 32?

18. In one state, speeding fines are determined by the   18. _____
formula $F = 6(x - 60) + 75$, where F is the cost,
in dollars, of the fine if a person is caught driving x
miles per hour. If the fine comes to $249, how fast
was the person driving?

19. When you buy an item on which sales tax is charged,   19. _____
the total cost is calculated by the formula

$T = P + \dfrac{S}{100}P$, where T is the total cost, P is the item's

price, and S is the sales tax rate (as a percent). If you pay
$20.045 for an item priced at $19, what is the tax rate?

20. To convert a Fahrenheit temperature to Celsius, one   20. _____

formula to use is $F = \dfrac{9}{5}C + 32$ where F is the

Fahrenheit temperature (in degrees) and C is the
Celsius temperature. What is the Celsius temperature
(to the nearest degree) when Fahrenheit temperature
is 86°?

Additional Exercises 2.3
Form II
Solving Linear Equations

Solve the equation.

1. $9(x + 2) = 3(x - 2)$ 1. _____

2. $7(5x - 2) = 6(6x - 1)$ 2. _____

3. $2(x + 1) = 29 - x$ 3. _____

4. $13(6x - 7) = 8x - 2$ 4. _____

5. $4(x + 3) = 5(x - 7)$ 5. _____

6. $4(2x - 2) = 7(x + 2)$ 6. _____

7. $5(3 + x) - x = 4(x + 2) + 7$ 7. _____

8. $2(6x - 3) = 3(4x + 7)$ 8. _____

Solve each equation. Begin your work by rewriting each equation without fractions.

9. $\dfrac{x}{3} + \dfrac{x}{4} = \dfrac{7}{4}$ 9. _____

10. $\dfrac{3x}{5} = \dfrac{1}{20} + \dfrac{x}{2}$ 10. _____

11. $\dfrac{x}{5} - \dfrac{1}{5} = -3$ 11. _____

12. $\dfrac{x}{7} - 7 = -3$ 12. _____

13. $\dfrac{2x}{5} = \dfrac{x}{3} + 5$ 13. _____

14. $3x - 1 = \dfrac{x}{5} + \dfrac{4x}{5}$ 14. _____

15. $\dfrac{x + 3}{3} - \dfrac{x}{4} = \dfrac{x - 2}{5}$ 15. _____

16.   Forensic scientists use the length of certain bones to   16. _____
       calculate the height of a person. When the femur (*f*),
       the bone from the knee to the hip socket is used, the
       following formula applies for men: $h = 69.09 + 2.24f$,
       where *h* is the height and *f* is the length of the femur.
       Find the height of a man with a femur measuring
       57 centimeters.

17.   There is a formula that gives a correspondence between   17. _____
       women's shoe sizes in the United States and those in
       Italy. The formula is $S = 2(x + 12)$, where *S* is the size
       in Italy and *x* is the size in the United States. What
       would be the US size for an Italian size of 30?

18.   In one state, speeding fines are determined by the   18. _____
       formula $F = 6(x - 60) + 75$, where *F* is the cost,
       in dollars, of the fine if a person is caught driving *x*
       miles per hour. If the fine comes to $225, how fast
       was the person driving?

19.   When you buy an item on which sales tax is charged,   19. _____
       the total cost is calculated by the formula
       $T = P + \dfrac{S}{100}P$, where *T* is the total cost, *P* is the item's
       price, and *S* is the sales tax rate (as a percent). If you pay
       $20.235 for an item priced at $19, what is the tax rate?

20.   To convert a Fahrenheit temperature to Celsius, one   20. _____
       formula to use is $F = \dfrac{9}{5}C + 32$ where *F* is the
       Fahrenheit temperature (in degrees) and *C* is the
       Celsius temperature. What is the Celsius temperature
       (to the nearest degree) when Fahrenheit temperature
       is 95°?

Name _____   Date _____

Additional Exercises 2.3
Form III
Solving Linear Equations

Solve the equation.

1. $7(x-3) - 2x = 5(x-3)$ 1. _____

2. $3(x-4) = 6(x-3)$ 2. _____

3. $3(x+2) - 4x = x + 16$ 3. _____

4. $5x + 2(1-x) = 2(2x-1)$ 4. _____

5. $4(x+2) = 14 - 2(3 - 2x)$ 5. _____

6. $5(x+3) + 9 = 3(x-2) + 6$ 6. _____

7. $5(2z-2) = 9(z+3)$ 7. _____

8. $-3x + 7(-3x - 7) = -68 - 5x$ 8. _____

Solve each equation. Begin your work by rewriting each equation without fractions.

9. $\dfrac{1}{2}x + 2 - \dfrac{2}{3}x + \dfrac{2}{3} = 3$ 9. _____

10. $\dfrac{1}{4}x - 1 = \dfrac{1}{2}x + \dfrac{3}{2}$ 10. _____

11. $2x - \dfrac{10}{3} = 6 - \dfrac{1}{3}x$ 11. _____

12. $\dfrac{1}{4}x - \dfrac{1}{12} = \dfrac{1}{6}x + \dfrac{1}{6}$ 12. _____

13. $\dfrac{5}{2} = \dfrac{3}{2}x + \dfrac{7}{4}$ 13. _____

14. $\dfrac{r}{5} + \dfrac{6}{5} = \dfrac{r}{7} + \dfrac{8}{7}$ 14. _____

15. $\dfrac{y}{5} - \dfrac{2}{5} = \dfrac{1}{3} - y$ 15. _____

16.   Forensic scientists use the length of certain bones to   16. _____
       calculate the height of a person. When the femur (*f*),
       the bone from the knee to the hip socket is used, the
       following formula applies for men: $h = 69.09 + 2.24f$,
       where *h* is the height and *f* is the length of the femur.
       Find the height of a man with a femur measuring
       53 centimeters.

17.   There is a formula that gives a correspondence between   17. _____
       women's shoe sizes in the United States and those in
       Italy. The formula is $S = 2(x + 12)$, where *S* is the size
       in Italy and *x* is the size in the United States. What
       would be the US size for an Italian size of 34?

18.   In one state, speeding fines are determined by the   18. _____
       formula $F = 6(x - 60) + 75$, where *F* is the cost,
       in dollars, of the fine if a person is caught driving *x*
       miles per hour. If the fine comes to $261, how fast
       was the person driving?

19.   When you buy an item on which sales tax is charged,   19. _____
       the total cost is calculated by the formula

       $T = P + \dfrac{S}{100}P$, where *T* is the total cost, *P* is the item's

       price, and *S* is the sales tax rate (as a percent). If you pay
       $20.425 for an item priced at $19, what is the tax rate?

20.   To convert a Fahrenheit temperature to Celsius, one   20. _____

       formula to use is $F = \dfrac{9}{5}C + 32$ where *F* is the

       Fahrenheit temperature (in degrees) and *C* is the
       Celsius temperature. What is the Celsius temperature
       (to the nearest degree) when Fahrenheit temperature
       is 77°?

Additional Exercises 2.4
Form I
Formulas and Percents

Solve the formula for the specified variable.

1. $I = Prt$ for t 1. _____

2. $V = \dfrac{1}{3}Bh$ for h 2. _____

3. $P = s_1 + s_2 + s_3$ for s_3 3. _____

4. $y = mx + b$ for b 4. _____

Express the decimal as a percent.

5.   0.88   5. _____

6.   0.1   6. _____

7.   2.3   7. _____

8.   0.009   8. _____

Express the percent as a decimal.

9.   72%   9. _____

10. 3.2%   10. _____

11. 100%   11. _____

12. 0.04%   12. _____

Name _____   Date _____

Solve the problem.

13.   What number is 54% of 38?   13. _____

14.   What number is 11% of 67?   14. _____

15.   45% of what number is 112.5?   15. _____

16.   What percent of 8 is 2?   16. _____

17.   Jeans are on sale at the local department store for 20% off. 17. _____
       If the jeans originally cost $57, find the sale price.

18.   Due to a lack of funding, the number of students enrolled   18. _____
       at City College went from 10,000 to 7700 this year. Find the
       percent of decrease in enrollment. (Round answer to the
       nearest tenth if necessary.)

19.   Attendance this year at the homecoming football game is 165% 19. _____
       of what it was last year. If last year's homecoming football
       game attendance was 21,000, what is this year's attendance?

20.   Of the students at a university, 8% attended a lecture. If 7000 20. _____
       students are enrolled at the university, about how many
       students attended the lecture?

Additional Exercises 2.4
Form II
Formulas and Percents

Solve the formula for the specified variable.

1. $Ax + By = C$ for A 1. _____

2. $V = \dfrac{1}{3}Bh$ for B 2. _____

3. $F = \dfrac{9}{5}C + 32$ for C 3. _____

4. $P = 2l + 2w$ for w 4. _____

Express the decimal as a percent.

5.   0.21   5. _____

6.   0.7   6. _____

7.   0.0091   7. _____

8.   4   8. _____

Express the percent as a decimal.

9.   81%   9. _____

10.   4.6%   10. _____

11.   600%   11. _____

12.   0.09%   12. _____

Solve the problem.

13.   What number is 70% of 136?   13. _____

14.   What number is 40% of 180?   14. _____

15.   36% of what number is 21.6?   15. _____

16.   What percent of 2.5 is 3?   16. _____

17.   Jeans are on sale at the local department store for 15% off.   17. _____
        If the jeans originally cost $75, find the sale price.

18.   Due to a lack of funding, the number of students enrolled   18. _____
        at City College went from 9,000 to 2000 this year. Find the
        percent of decrease in enrollment. (Round answer to the
        nearest tenth if necessary.)

19.   Attendance this year at the homecoming football game is 115%   19. _____
        of what it was last year. If last year's homecoming football
        game attendance was 21,000, what is this year's attendance?

20.   Of the students at a university, 17.5% attended a lecture. If   20. _____
        7000 students are enrolled at the university, about how many
        students attended the lecture?

Additional Exercises 2.4
Form III
Formulas and Percents

Solve the formula for the specified variable.

1. $S = 2\pi rh + 2\pi r^2$ for h 1. _____

2. $Ax + By = C$ for B 2. _____

3. $S = \dfrac{1}{2}(a + b + c)$ for a 3. _____

4. $PV = nRT$ for R 4. _____

Express the decimal as a percent.

5.   0.152   5. _____

6.   0.5   6. _____

7.   9.8   7. _____

8.   2.05   8. _____

Express the percent as a decimal.

9.   92.5%   9. _____

10.   3.17%   10. _____

11.   150%   11. _____

12.   0.011%   12. _____

Solve the problem.

13.   What number is 85% of 112?   13. _____

14.   What number is 32% of 225?   14. _____

15.   21% of what number is 17.85?   15. _____

16.   What percent of 7.5 is 9?   16. _____

17.   Jeans are on sale at the local department store for 25% off.   17. _____
        If the jeans originally cost $99.50, find the sale price.

18.   Due to a lack of funding, the number of students enrolled   18. _____
        at City College went from 8500 to 6250 this year. Find the
        percent of decrease in enrollment. (Round answer to the
        nearest tenth if necessary.)

19.   Attendance this year at the homecoming football game is 127%   19. _____
        of what it was last year. If last year's homecoming football
        game attendance was 24,500, what is this year's attendance?

20.   Of the students at a university, 13% attended a lecture. If   20. _____
        8000 students are enrolled at the university, about how many
        students attended the lecture?

Additional Exercises 2.5
Form I
An Introduction to Problem Solving

Let x represent the number. Write the English phrase as an algebraic expression.

1. The product of eleven and a number, added to thirteen.   1. _____

2. Seven times a number, decreased by fifty-nine.   2. _____

3. The quotient of forty-two and the product of a number and   3. _____
    negative seven.

4. The product of negative twenty-seven and the sum of a number   4. _____
    and twenty-five.

5. Twice the sum of a number and negative forty-one.   5. _____

6. The quotient of twenty-five times a number and negative eight. 6. _____

Let x represent the number. (a)Use the given conditions to write an equation. (b) Solve the equation and find the number.

7. Four times a number added to 7 times the number equals 44.   7a. _____
    Find the number.   b. _____

8. Three-fourths of a number is $\frac{1}{2}$. Find the number in lowest   8a. _____

    terms.   b. _____

9. The quotient of a number and 42 increased by 7 is 13. Find   9a. _____
    the number.   b. _____

10. The president of a certain university makes three times as much 10a. _____
    money as one of the department heads. If the total of their   b. _____
    salaries is $180,000, find each person's salary.

11. 30 marbles are to be divided into three bags so that the second 11a. _____
    bag has three times as many marbles as the first bag and the   b. _____
    third bag has twice as many marbles as the first bag. If x is the
    number of marbles in the first bag, find the number of marbles
    in each bag.

12. A promotional deal for long distance phone service charges a   12a. _____
    $15 basic fee plus $0.05 per minute for all calls. If Joe's phone b. _____
    bill was $55 under this promotional deal, how many minutes of
    phone calls did he make? (Round to the nearest integer, if
    necessary.)

Name _____   Date _____

Additional Exercises 2.5
Form II
An Introduction to Problem Solving

Let x represent the number. Write the English phrase as an algebraic expression.

1. The sum of eleven and three times a number.   1. _____

2. The product of eight and a number decreased by nine.   2. _____

3. The quotient of seven and nine times a number.   3. _____

4. Fourteen times the difference of a number and five.   4. _____

5. Two subtracted from the quotient of a number and eight.   5. _____

6. Two-fifths of a number increased by three   .   6. _____

Let x represent the number. (a) Use the given conditions to write an equation. (b) Solve the equation and find the number.

7. When 3 times a number is subtracted from 7 times the number,   7a. _____
    the result is 44. Find the number.   b. _____

8. The sum of four times a number and 7 is equal to the difference   8a. _____
    of twice the number and 8. Find the number.   b. _____

9. Nine times a number decreased by six is the same as three times   9a. _____
    the number.   b. _____

10. Two angles are complementary if their sum is 90°. If the measure   10a. _____
    of the first angle is $x°$, and the measure of the second angle is b. _____
    $(3x - 2)°$, find the measure of each angle.

11. Rooms in Dormitory A each have 120 square feet of floor space.   11a. _____
    These rooms have twice as much floor space as each room in   b. _____
    Dormitory B. About how much floor space does a room in
    Dormitory B have?

12. A rectangle is twice as long as it is wide. The perimeter is   12a. _____
    120 meters. Find the dimensions.   b. _____

Name _____   Date _____

Additional Exercises 2.5
Form III
An Introduction to Problem Solving

Let x represent the number. Write the English phrase as an algebraic expression.

1.   The product of three-sevenths and a number increased by four.   1. _____

2.   Thirteen less four times a number.   2. _____

3.   The quotient of 19 and the product of a number and negative two.   3. _____

4.   The product of negative eleven and the difference of a number   4. _____
        and eight.

5.   Twice the sum of nine and a number.   5. _____

6.   Triple a number increased by forty.   .   6. _____

Let x represent the number. (a)Use the given conditions to write an equation. (b) Solve the equation and find the number.

7.   If 5 times a number is added to –6, the result is equal to 11 times   7a. _____
        the number.   b. _____

8.   Six times the sum of a number and 2 is equal to 48. Find the   8a. _____
        number.   b. _____

9.   Seven times a number increased by five is the same as twice the   9a. _____
        number increased by ten.   b. _____

10.   An isosceles triangle contains two angles of the same measure.   10a. _____
        If the measure of the third angle is 45° less than the measure of   b. _____
        the angles. (Hint: The sum of the angles of a triangle is 180°.)

11.   There are 18 more sophomores than juniors in an 8 A.M. algebra   11a. _____
        class. If there are 108 students in this class, find the number of   b. _____
        sophomores and the number of juniors in the class.

12.   The length of a rectangle is five times the width. The perimeter is 12a. _____
        144 inches. Find the lengths of each sides.   b. _____

Name _____   Date _____

Additional Exercises 2.6
Form I
Problem Solving in Geometry

Use the formulas for perimeter, area, circumference and volume to solve the problems.

1. Find the a) perimeter and b) area of a rectangle that is 7 inches long and 4 inches wide.

    1a. _____

    b. _____

2. Find the a) perimeter and b) area of the triangle.

    2a. _____

    b. _____

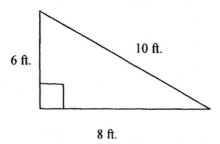

3. Find the a) perimeter and b) area of a trapezoid with bases measuring 20 inches, 16 inches, sides of 8 inches, and 10 inches and a height of 12 inches.

    3a. _____

    b. _____

For exercises 4 – 10, express answers in terms of π. Then give the answer rounded to the nearest whole number.

4. Find the area of a circle with a radius of 8 centimeters.

    4. _____

5. Find the area of a circle with a diameter of 12 inches.

    5. _____

6. Find the circumference of a circle with a radius of 4 feet.

    6. _____

7. Find the circumference of a circle with a diameter of 20 centimeters.

    7. _____

8.   Find the volume of a mini volleyball if the radius of the volleyball is 3 inches.

                                                      8. _____

9.   Find the volume of a cone that has a radius of 4 centimeters and a height of 12 centimeters.

                                                      9. _____

10.   Find the volume of a circular cylinder that has a radius of 2 inches and a height of 5 inches.

                                                      10. _____

Solve each problem.

11.   Find the volume of a box that measures 7 in. by 3 in. by 5 in.   11. _____

12.   Find the supplement of a 42° angle.   12. _____

13.   Find the complement of a 27° angle.   13. _____

14.   The perimeter of a rectangle is 36 feet. Find the dimensions of the rectangle if the length is 4 feet longer than the width.

                                                      14. _____

15.   The perimeter of a triangle is 31. The shortest side is 10 inches less than the longest side and the third side is 4 inches less than the longest side. Find the length of each side.

                                                      15. _____

16.   A triangle has angles of $4x$ degrees, $3x + 6$ degrees and $2x + 21$ degrees. Find the measure of each angle.

                                                      16. _____

Name _____   Date _____

Use the formulas for perimeter, area, circumference and volume to solve the problems.

1.   Find the a) perimeter and b) area of a rectangle that is 12 inches   1a. _____

long and $6\frac{1}{2}$ inches wide.   b. _____

2.   Find the a) perimeter and b) area of the triangle.   2a. _____

b. _____

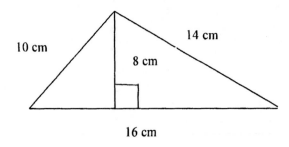

3.   Find the area of a trapezoid with bases measuring 20 inches   3. _____
and 17 inches, and a height of 16 inches.

For exercises 4 – 9, express answers in terms of π. Then give the answer rounded to the nearest whole number.

4.   Find the area of a circle with a diameter of 14 inches.   4. _____

5.   Find the area of a circle with a radius of 4.5 centimeters.   5. _____

6.   Find the circumference of a circle with a radius of 2.4 feet.   6. _____

7.   Find the volume of a cone with a radius of 2 centimeters and   7. _____
a height of 12 centimeters.

8.   Find the volume of a cylindrical trash can that has a diameter   8. _____
      of 24 inches and a height of 32 inches.

9.   Find the volume of a sphere with a diameter of 3 decimeters.   9. _____

Solve the problem.

10.   The circumference of a circle is 6π meters. Find the circle's   10. _____
      radius.

11.   Two angles are complementary. One angle is 22° larger than the   11. _____
      other angle. Find the measure of each angle.

12.   A rectangle has a perimeter of 33 feet. The length is twice the   12. _____
      width. Find the dimensions of the rectangle.

13.   Find the volume of a rectangular trash container that measures   13. _____
      8 feet by 5 feet by 6 feet.

14.   The angles of a triangle measure $2x$ degrees, $4x + 7$ degrees and   14. _____
      $3x + 2$ degrees. Find the measure of each angle.

15.   One angle of a triangle is 5 degrees larger than the smallest angle.   15. _____
      The third angle is 6 degrees less than 3 times the smallest angle.

16.   A rectangular piece of carpet has a perimeter of 218 inches. The   16. _____
      length of the carpet is 75 inches more than the width. Find the
      dimensions of the carpet.

Additional Exercises 2.6
Form III
Problem Solving in Geometry

Use the formulas for perimeter, area, circumference and volume to solve the problems.

1. Find the a) perimeter and b) area of a rectangle that is 12.24   1a. _____
    inches long and 4.8 inches wide.

                                                                            b. _____

2. Find the a) perimeter and b) area of a right triangle with leg   2a. _____
    lengths of 12.2 centimeters and 10.4 centimeters and a
    hypotenuse of 16.03 centimeters.   b. _____

3. Find the area of a trapezoid with bases measuring 14.5 inches   3. _____
    and 22.3 inches, sides measuring 9 inches and 7.6 inches, and a
    height of 18 inches.

For exercises 4 – 9, express answers in terms of π. Then give the answer rounded to the nearest whole number.

4. Find the area of a circle with a radius of 18.2 millimeters.   4. _____

5. Find the circumference of a circle with a diameter of 24.8 inches.   5. _____

6. Find the volume of a cone with a diameter of 4 inches and a   6. _____
    height of 6 inches.

7. Find the volume of a soft drink can that has a diameter of   7. _____
    5.3 centimeters and a height of 11.6 centimeters.

8. Find the volume of a stress ball with a diameter of 3.3 inches.   8. _____

9.   Find the area of a round trampoline mat if the diameter of the   9. _____
      whole trampoline including the frame is 8 feet and the mat is
      10 inches in from the frame. (Give your answer in inches.)

Solve the problem.

10.   The circumference of a circle is 28π meters. Find the circle's   10. _____
      radius.

11.   The volume of a circular cylinder is 128π cubic inches. Find the   11. _____
      height of the cylinder if the radius is 4 inches.

12.   Find the volume of a packing crate that measures 6.2 feet by   12. _____
      3.2 feet by 2 feet.

13.   Two angles are supplementary. One angle is 15° less than twice   13. _____
      the other angle. Find the measure of each angle.

14.   One of the base angles of an isosceles triangle is 39°. Find the   14. _____
      measures of the other two angles.

15.   One angle of a triangle is two times as large as another. The   15. _____
      measure of the third angle is 98° greater than that of the smallest
      angle. Find the measure of each angle.

16.   The rooms of a house have the following measurements: 16. _____
            kitchen   12.5' × 15.5'
            living area   20' × 18'
            bedroom   10' × 10.8'
            bedroom   9' × 12'
            bedroom   11' × 14'
            bathroom   8.5' × 6.5'

      Find the total area of the house.

Additional Exercises 2.7
Form I
Solving Linear Inequalities

Graph the solution of the inequality on a number line.

1. $x < 5$

1.

2. $x \geq -2$

2.

3. $x \leq -2$

3.

4. $2 < x < 5$

4.

5. $2 \leq x < 5$

5.

Describe the graph using set-builder notation.

6.

6. _____

7.

7. _____

8.

8. _____

9.

9. _____

Name _____   Date _____

Solve the inequality. Express the solution set in (a) set-builder notation and (b) graph the set on a number line.

10. $x - 2 > -4$ 10a. _____

       b.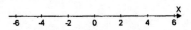

11. $7x + 6 > 6x + 8$ 11a. _____

       b.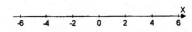

12. $-2 \leq \dfrac{x}{2}$ 12a. _____

       b.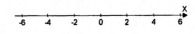

13. $7x > 21$ 13a. _____

       b.

14. $15x + 15 > 3(4x + 3)$ 14a. _____

       b.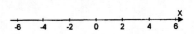

15. $3x - 2 < 3(x - 5)$ 15a. _____

                                                 b.

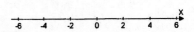

Additional Exercises 2.7
Form II
Solving Linear Inequalities

Graph the solution of the inequality on a number line.

1. $x > -4$

1.

2. $x \leq 0$

2.

3. $x \geq 4$

3.

4. $-1 \leq x < 1$

4.

5. $-3 < x \leq 4$

5.

Describe the graph using set-builder notation.

6.

6. _____

7.

7. _____

8.

8. _____

9.

9. _____

Name _____ Date _____

Solve the inequality. Express the solution set in (a) set-builder notation and (b) graph the set on a number line.

10. $x + 10 < 5$

10a. _____

b.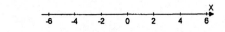

11. $-11x - 5 \le -12x - 1$

11a. _____

b.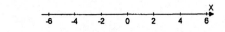

12. $-1 \ge \dfrac{x}{3}$

12a. _____

b.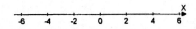

13. $8x < -16$

13a. _____

b.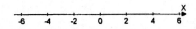

14. $-6(6x - 3) < -42x + 48$

14a. _____

b.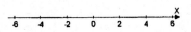

15. $3(x + 2) > 3x + 4$

15a. _____

b.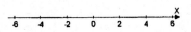

Additional Exercises 2.7
Form III
Solving Linear Inequalities

Graph the solution of the inequality on a number line.

1. $x < 1$

1.

2. $x \geq -3$

2.

3. $x < 2$

3.

4. $-3 < x \leq 3$

4.

5. $-1 < x < 3$

5.

Describe the graph using set-builder notation.

6.

6. _____

7.

7. _____

8.

8. _____

9.

9. _____

Name _____ Date _____

Solve the inequality. Express the solution set in (a) set-builder notation and (b) graph the set on a number line.

10. $x + 11 < 15$ 10a. _____

b.

```
    +----+----+----+----+----+----+---> X
    -6   -4   -2   0    2    4    6
```

11. $11 - 9x + 7 \geq -10x + 13$ 11a. _____

b.

```
    +----+----+----+----+----+----+---> X
    -6   -4   -2   0    2    4    6
```

12. $-2 \geq \dfrac{x}{-3}$ 12a. _____

b.

```
    +----+----+----+----+----+----+---> X
    -6   -4   -2   0    2    4    6
```

13. $4x \geq -8$ 13a. _____

b.

```
    +----+----+----+----+----+----+---> X
    -6   -4   -2   0    2    4    6
```

14. $-14x + 6 \leq -2(6x - 1)$ 14a. _____

b.

```
    +----+----+----+----+----+----+---> X
    -6   -4   -2   0    2    4    6
```

15. $5x + 4 \leq 5(x + 1)$ 15a. _____

b.

```
    +----+----+----+----+----+----+---> X
    -6   -4   -2   0    2    4    6
```

Name _____   Date _____

Additional Exercises 3.1
Form I
Graphing Linear Equations in Two Variables

Plot the given points in a rectangular coordinate system and then state the quadrant in which each point lies.

1.   (3, 5)   1. _____

2.   (–4, 1)   2. _____

3.   (–1, –2)   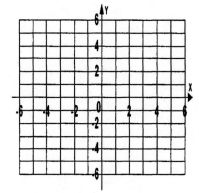   3. _____

4.   (2, 3)   4. _____

5.   (3, –4)   5. _____

Determine whether the ordered pair is a solution of the given equation.

6.   (2, –2)   6. _____
       $y = x - 4$

7.   (–1, –4)   7. _____
       $x - y = 3$

8.   (2, 0)   8. _____
       $2x - y = -4$

Find the solution to the equation using the value given for x.

9. $y = 7x$; $x = 6$ 9. _____

10. $y = 6x + 5$; $x = 2$ 10. _____

11. $y = -3x - 4$; $x = -1$ 11. _____

Name _____   Date _____

Graph the linear equation in two variables.

12. $y = 2x$ 12.

13. $y = -x - 1$ 13.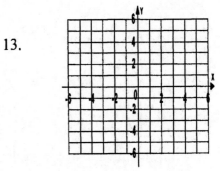

14. $y = 4x + 3$ 14.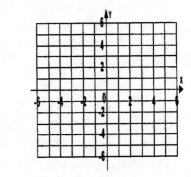

15. $y = \dfrac{1}{3}x - 5$ 15.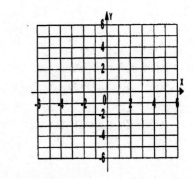

16. $y = 3$ 16.

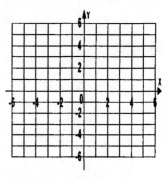

17. $x = 2$ 17.

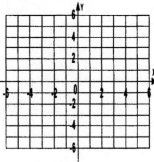

18.   The linear equation in two variables $y = 0.10x + 175$ 18. _____
        models the total weekly cost, y, in dollars, for renting
        and driving it x miles. the equation indicates that the
        rental company charges a fixed amount of $175 for
        the week plus a cost of $0.10 for each mile the car is
        driven. Find the solution of $y = 0.10x + 175$ using
        185 for x .

19.   The linear equation in two variables $y = 32x$ models the   19. _____
        speed, y, in feet per second, of a ball dropped from a tower
        x seconds after it is dropped. The equation indicates that
        the speed of the ball increases by 32 feet per second for
        every second that passes. Find a solution of $y = 32x$
        using 3 for x.

20.   The linear equation in two variables $y = 124 - 8x$ models   20. _____
        the amount of water, y, in ounces, remaining in a leaky
        bucket x minutes after the bucket is filled. The equation
        indicates that the bucket initially contains 124 ounces of
        water and loses 8 ounces each minute. Find a solution of
        $y = 124 - 8x$ using 3 for x.

Name _____ Date _____

Additional Exercises 3.1
Form II
Graphing Linear Equations in Two Variables

Plot the given points in a rectangular coordinate system and then state the quadrant in which each point lies.

1. $(1, -5)$

2. $(-2, 4)$

3. $(-3, -3)$

4. $(6, 1)$

5. $(-4, 2)$

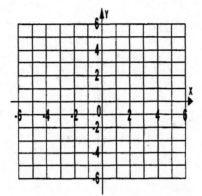

1. _____

2. _____

3. _____

4. _____

5. _____

Determine whether the ordered pair is a solution of the given equation.

6. $(3, 1)$
    $y = x - 4$

6. _____

7. $(3, -5)$
    $x - y = 2$

7. _____

8. $(1, 2)$
    $2x + 3y = 8$

8. _____

Find the solution to the equation using the value given for x.

9. $y = -7x - 6$; $x = 5$

9. _____

10. $y = -8x - 3$; $x = 4$

10. _____

11. $y = -2x + 5$; $x = -1$

11. _____

Name _____   Date _____

Graph the linear equation in two variables.

12. $y = -3x$ 12.

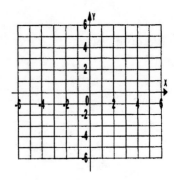

13. $y = 2x - 4$ 13.

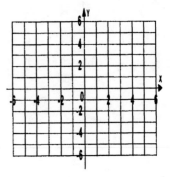

14. $y = \dfrac{4}{5}x + 1$ 14.

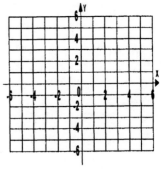

15. $y = -\dfrac{2}{3}x - 3$ 15.

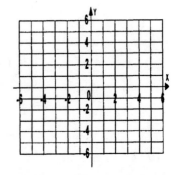

16. $y = 5x$ 16.

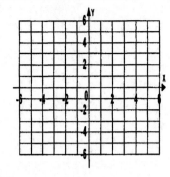

17. $y = -1$ 17.

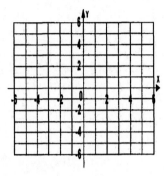

Solve the problem.

18.   The linear equation in two variables $y = 2x + 40$ 18. _____
        models the total cost, y, in dollars, for towing
        a car x miles. The equation indicates that the
        towing company charges a fixed amount of $40 to
        send a truck to pickup the car plus a cost $2 for each
        mile the car is towed. Find the solution of
        $y = 2x + 40$ using 3 for x .

19.   The linear equation in two variables $y = 0.05x + 12.95$ 19. _____
        models the total monthly charge, y, in dollars, for a
        long distance telephone customer who talked for x
        minutes long distance. The equation indicates that the
        customer is charged a fixed amount of $12.95 per month
        plus a charge of $0.05 for each minute of long distance.
        Find the solution of $y = 0.05x + 12.95$ using 205 for x.

20.   The linear equation in two variables $y = 500x + 2993$ 20. _____
        models the altitude above sea level, y, in feet, of an
        airplane x minutes after taking off from a high
        plateau. The equation indicates that the airplane's
        altitude is initially 2993 feet above sea level and
        increases 500 feet each minute. Find a solution
        of $y = 500x + 2993$ using 2 for x.

Name _____   Date _____

Additional Exercises 3.1
Form III
Graphing Linear Equations in Two Variables

Plot the given points in a rectangular coordinate system and then state the quadrant in which each point lies.

1.   (4, −1)

2.   (−2, −3)

3.   (3, 2)

4.   (2, −3)

5.   (−1, 4)

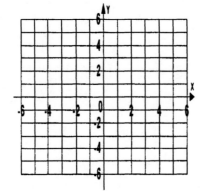

1. _____

2. _____

3. _____

4. _____

5. _____

Determine whether the ordered pair is a solution of the given equation.

6. $\left(-\dfrac{1}{2}, \dfrac{1}{4}\right)$
      $x + 2y = 0$

6. _____

7.   (−4, 0)
      $x − 4 = 0$

7. _____

8.   (6, −4)
      $2x − 3y = 12$

8. _____

Find the solution to the equation using the value given for x.

9. $y = \dfrac{2}{3}x$; $x = −4$

9. _____

10. $y = \dfrac{1}{5}x$; $x = 5$

10. _____

11.　　$y = -2x - 3$; $x = \dfrac{1}{2}$　　　　　　　　11. _____

Graph the linear equation in two variables.

12.　　$y = \dfrac{1}{3}x - 2$　　　　　　　　12.

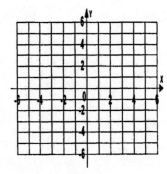

13.　　$y = -2$　　　　　　　　13.

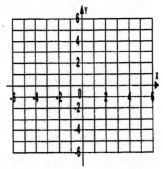

14.　　$y = -\dfrac{3}{2}x + 1$　　　　　　　　14.

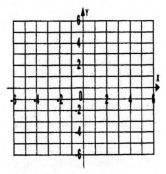

15.　　$y = \dfrac{1}{4}x$　　　　　　　　15.

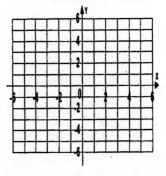

16. $y = -\dfrac{1}{2}x - 2$ 16.

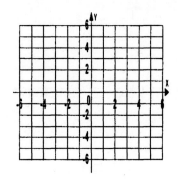

17. $y = \dfrac{5}{2}x + 1$ 17.

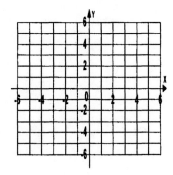

Solve the problem.

18. The linear equation in two variables $y = 0.25x + 150$
     models the total weekly cost, y, in dollars, for renting
     and driving it x miles. the equation indicates that the
     rental company charges a fixed amount of $150 for
     the week plus a cost of $0.25 for each mile the car is
     driven. Find the solution of $y = 0.25x + 150$ using
     215 for x.   18. _____

19. The linear equation in two variables $y = 3x + 45$
     models the total cost, y, in dollars, for towing
     a car x miles. The equation indicates that the
     towing company charges a fixed amount of $45 to
     send a truck to pickup the car plus a cost $3 for each
     mile the car is towed. Find the solution of
     $y = 3x + 45$ using 10 for x.   19. _____

20. The linear equation in two variables $y = 33.5x$ models the
     speed, y, in feet per second, of a ball dropped from a tower
     x seconds after it is dropped. The equation indicates that
     the speed of the ball increases by 33.5 feet per second for
     every second that passes. Find a solution of $y = 33.5x$
     using 4 for x.   20. _____

Name _____   Date _____

Additional Exercises 3.2
Form I
Graphing Linear Equations Using Intercepts

Use the graph to identify the *x*- and *y*-intercepts or state that there is no *x*- or *y*-intercept.

1.

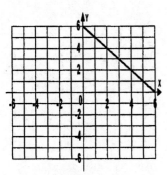

1. _____

2.

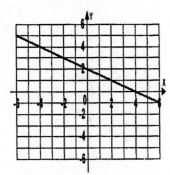

2. _____

3.

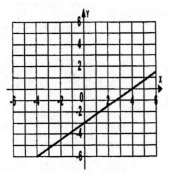

3. _____

4.

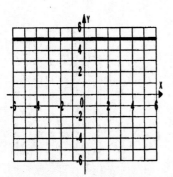

4. _____

Name _____   Date _____

Find the *x*-intercept and the *y*-intercept of each equation.

5. $x + y = 3$ 5. _____

6. $2x + y = -6$ 6. _____

7. $-2x + 5y = -10$ 7. _____

8. $-3x + 3y = -6$ 8. _____

For each problem, (a) find the *x*- and *y*-intercepts and (b) then graph the equation.

9. $x - 4y = -4$ 9a. _____
                             b.

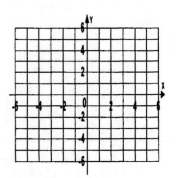

10. $x = -1$ 10a. _____
                             b.

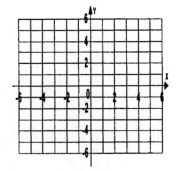

11. $3x + 9y = 9$ 11a. _____
                             b.

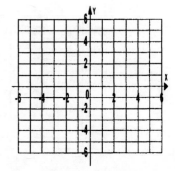

12. $6x - 24y = 0$

12a. _____

b.

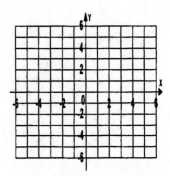

Write the equation for the graphs.

13.

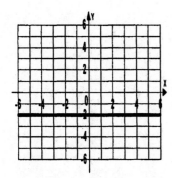

13. _____

14.

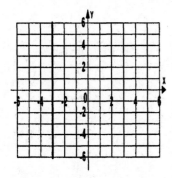

14. _____

Name _____   Date _____

Additional Exercises 3.2
Form II
Graphing Linear Equations Using Intercepts

Use the graph to identify the *x*- and *y*-intercepts or state that there is no *x*- or *y*-intercept.

1.

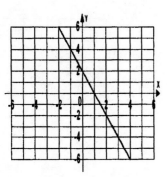

1. _____

2.

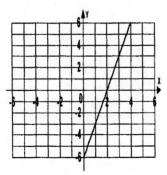

2. _____

3.

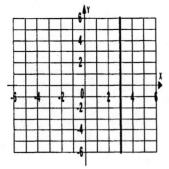

3. _____

4.

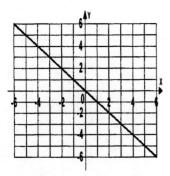

4. _____

Name _____   Date _____

Find the *x*-intercept and the *y*-intercept of each equation.

5. $x + y = 6$ 5. _____

6. $2x - y = 8$ 6. _____

7. $-3x - 5y = 30$ 7. _____

8. $4x - 3y = 18$ 8. _____

For each problem, (a) find the *x*- and *y*-intercepts and (b) then graph the equation.

9. $2x - 3y = 6$ 9a. _____

                                                                     b.

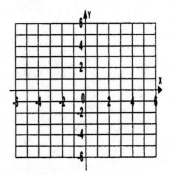

10. $y = -2$ 10a. _____

                                                                     b.

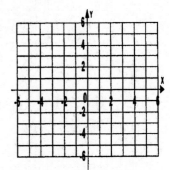

11. $2x - 5y = 5$ 11a. _____

                                                                     b.

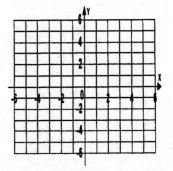

12. $2x + 6y = 0$

12a. _____

b.

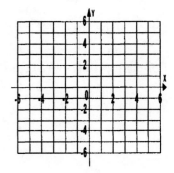

Write the equation for the graphs.

13.

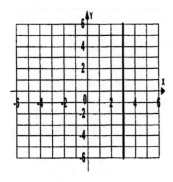

13. _____

14.

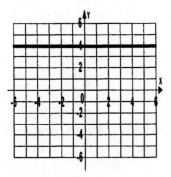

14. _____

Name _____   Date _____

Additional Exercises 3.2
Form III
Graphing Linear Equations Using Intercepts

Use the graph to identify the *x*- and *y*-intercepts or state that there is no *x*- or *y*-intercept.

1.

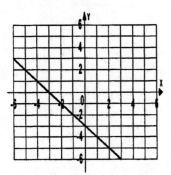

1. _____

2.

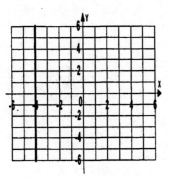

2. _____

3.

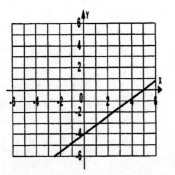

3. _____

4.

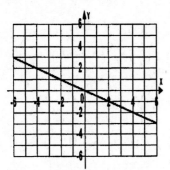

4. _____

Name _____   Date _____

Find the *x*-intercept and the *y*-intercept of each equation.

5. $2x - 3y = 15$ 5. _____

6. $3x + 4y = 9$ 6. _____

7. $5x + 3y = 12$ 7. _____

8. $6x - 5y = 24$ 8. _____

For each problem, (a) find the *x*- and *y*-intercepts and (b) then graph the equation.

9. $12y - 3x = -9$ 9a. _____

                                                  b.

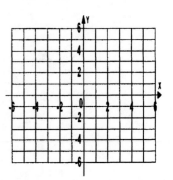

10. $y = 4$ 10a. _____

                                                  b.

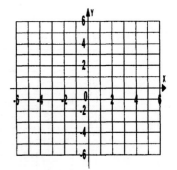

11. $5x - 4y = 8$ 11a. _____

                                                  b.

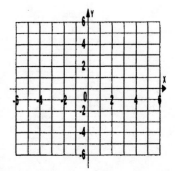

AE-104

12. $4x + 3y = 0$

12a. _____

b.

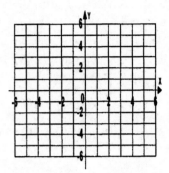

Write the equation for the graphs.

13.

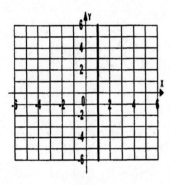

13. _____

14.

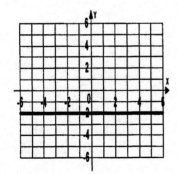

14. _____

Name _____ Date _____

(a) Find the slope of the line passing through the pair of points or state that the slope is undefined. (b) Then indicate whether the line through the points rises, falls, is horizontal or is vertical.

1.   (9, 8) and (–2, 6)   1a. _____

                                              b. _____

2.   (–11, –10) and (–6, 11)   2a. _____

                                              b. _____

3.   (–6, 7) and (8, 1)   3a. _____

                                              b. _____

4.   (–6, 7) and (–6, –2)   4a. _____

                                              b. _____

5.   (5, –1) and (–6, –1)   5a. _____

                                              b. _____

Fine the slope of the following lines .

6.   6. _____

7.   7. _____

8.

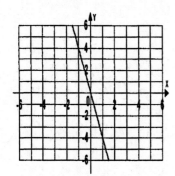

8. _____

9.

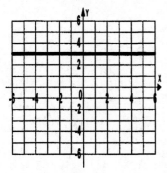

9. _____

10.

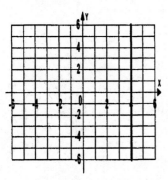

10. _____

Determine if the lines passing through the given pairs of points are parallel, perpendicular, or neither.

11.   Line 1: (–5, 2) and (7, 4)   11. _____
        Line 2: (3, 4) and (9, 5)

12.   Line 1: (4, 0) and (18, –14)   12. _____
        Line 2: (–9, –6) and (–2, 1)

13.   Line 1: (–7, 8) and (–27, 26)   13. _____
        Line 2: (–5, –10) and (5, –1)

Name _____   Date _____

Solve.

14.   A section of a roller coaster track has the dimensions shown   14. _____
        in the diagram. Find the grade of the track, which is the
        slope written as a percent. Round to the nearest whole
        percent.

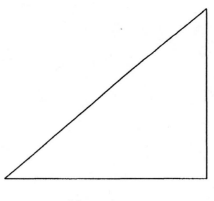

9.46 meters

22 meters

15.   A tent has the dimensions shown in feet. Find d so that the   15. _____
        pitch of the left side of the roof is $\frac{5}{3}$.

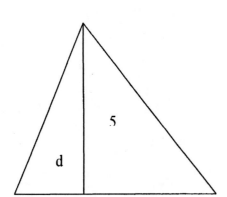

5

d

Name _____   Date _____

Additional Exercises 3.3
Form II
Slope

(a) Find the slope of the line passing through the pair of points or state that the slope is undefined. (b) Then indicate whether the line through the points rises, falls, is horizontal or is vertical.

1.   (6, 7) and (4, 6)   1a. _____

                                                 b. _____

2.   (3, 4) and (3, –8)   2a. _____

                                                 b. _____

3.   (2, 4) and (–3, 1)   3a. _____

                                                 b. _____

4.   (6, 2) and (–4, 8)   4a. _____

                                                 b. _____

5.   (1, 5) and (–7, 5)   5a. _____

                                                 b. _____

Fine the slope of the following lines .

6.   6. _____

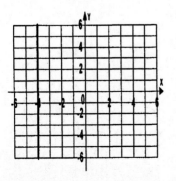

7.   7. _____

8.

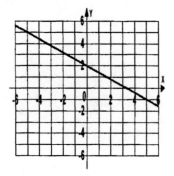

8. _____

9.

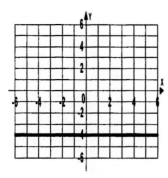

9. _____

10.

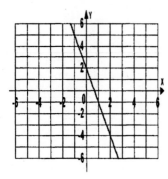

10. _____

Determine if the lines passing through the given pairs of points are parallel, perpendicular, or neither.

11.   Line 1: (1, –8) and (2, –3)   11. _____
       Line 2: (4, 5) and (6, –2)

12.   Line 1: (3, 2) and (–17, 2)   12. _____
       Line 2: (5, –8) and (–5, –8)

13.   Line 1: (2, 5) and (3, 1)   13. _____
       Line 2: (3, 2) and (7, 3)

Name _____   Date _____

Solve.

14.   A tent has the dimensions shown in feet. Find the   14. _____
       pitch (slope) of the left side of the roof.

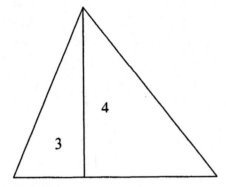

15.   The approach ramp used by a daredevil motorcyclist for   15. _____
       flying over a collection of flaming barrels of oil has a rise
       of 44 feet for every 80 feet in horizontal distance. Find
       the grade of the ramp. Round the nearest whole percent.

Name _____ Date _____

Additional Exercises 3.3
Form III
Slope

(a) Find the slope of the line passing through the pair of points or state that the slope is undefined. (b) Then indicate whether the line through the points rises, falls, is horizontal or is vertical.

1. $(1, 6)$ and $(1, -3)$ 1a. _____

                                                  b. _____

2. $(2, 4)$ and $(-3, 5)$ 2a. _____

                                                  b. _____

3. $(-3, 7)$ and $(2, -8)$ 3a. _____

                                                  b. _____

4. $(7, 2)$ and $(-7, 2)$ 4a. _____

                                                  b. _____

5. $(5, 1)$ and $(-8, -3)$ 5a. _____

                                                  b. _____

Fine the slope of the following lines .

6.

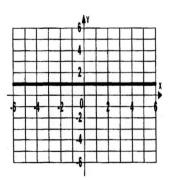   6. _____

7.

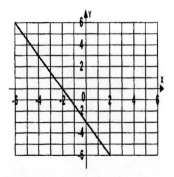   7. _____

8.

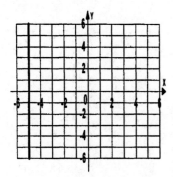

8. _____

9.

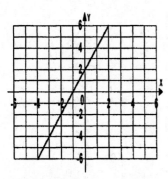

9. _____

10.

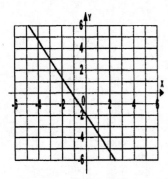

10. _____

Determine if the lines passing through the given pairs of points are parallel, perpendicular, or neither.

11.   Line 1: (1, 5) and (2, 7)
         Line 2: (4, 5) and (6, –2)

11. _____

12.   Line 1: (6, 4) and (6, 2)
         Line 2: (–1, 8) and (2, 8)

12. _____

13.   Line 1: (7, –9) and (4, –10)
         Line 2: (3, –3) and (6, –2)

13. _____

Name _____   Date _____

Solve.

14. A section of a roller coaster track has the dimensions shown
in the diagram. Find the grade of the track, which is the
slope written as a percent. Round to the nearest whole
percent.

14. _____

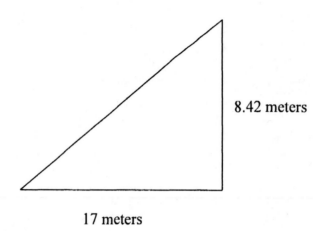

8.42 meters

17 meters

15. The approach ramp used by a daredevil motorcyclist for
flying over a collection of flaming barrels of oil has a rise
of 52 feet for every 90 feet in horizontal distance. Find
the grade of the ramp. Round the nearest whole percent.

15. _____

Additional Exercises 3.4
Form I
The Slope-Intercept Form of the Equation of a Line

Find the slope of the line.

1. $y = -8x$ 1. _____

2. $y = 6x - 7$ 2. _____

3. $y = 10$ 3. _____

4. $y = 6 - x$ 4. _____

5. $-7x + y = 38$ 5. _____

6. $3x + y = 8$ 6. _____

Find the y-intercept.

7. $y = -2x$ 7. _____

8. $y = 4x - 7$ 8. _____

9. $y = 2$ 9. _____

10. $2x + y = 4$ 10. _____

Name _____   Date _____

Graph the linear equation using the slope and y-intercept.

11. $y = 2x - 4$ 11.

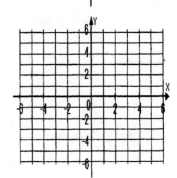

12. $y = -3x + 2$ 12.

13. $y = -\dfrac{1}{3}x$ 13.

(a) Graph both linear equations on the rectangular coordinate system and (b) decide whether or not the lines are parallel.

14. $y = 2x + 3$ 14.
        $y = 2x - 1$

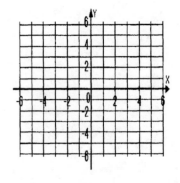

15.   When a tow truck is called, the cost of service is given by the   15. _____
        linear function $y = 3x + 65$, where y is in dollars and x is the
        number of miles the car is towed. Find and interpret the slope
        and the y-intercept of the linear equation.

Additional Exercises 3.4
Form II
The Slope-Intercept Form of the Equation of a Line

Find the slope of the line.

1. $y = -\dfrac{2}{3}x + 4$

    1. _____

2. $y = \dfrac{3}{5}x - 1$

    2. _____

3. $y = -5$

    3. _____

4. $2y = 7x - 4$

    4. _____

5. $3x + 5y = 11$

    5. _____

6. $3x + 4y = 13$

    6. _____

Find the y-intercept.

7. $2x - 4y = 6$

    7. _____

8. $x - 6y = 15$

    8. _____

9. $3y = -9$

    9. _____

10. $2x + 4y = -2$

    10. _____

Name _____   Date _____

Graph the linear equation using the slope and *y*-intercept.

11. $2x + 4y = -16$ 11.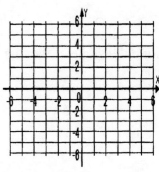

12. $3x - y = 2$ 12.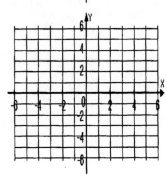

13. $5y = -2x + 10$ 13.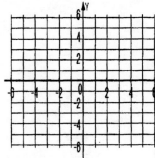

(a) Graph both linear equations on the rectangular coordinate system and (b) decide whether or not the lines are parallel.

14. $y = x - 4$ 14.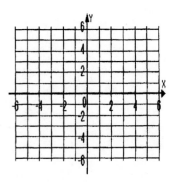
        $y = -x + 4$

15.   The amount of water in a leaky bucket is given by the linear function $y = 110 - 3x$, where y is in ounces and x is in minutes. Find and interpret the slope and *y*-intercept of the linear equation.   15. _____

Additional Exercises 3.4
Form III
The Slope-Intercept Form of the Equation of a Line

Find the slope of the line.

1. $3y = 4x - 5$ 1. _____

2. $-8y = 4$ 2. _____

3. $2x - 5y = 9$ 3. _____

4. $2y = 7x - 4$ 4. _____

5. $x - 5y = 2$ 5. _____

6. $2x - y = 11$ 6. _____

Find the y-intercept.

7. $-3y = 2x + 5$ 7. _____

8. $x - 4y = 7$ 8. _____

9. $-3y = -1$ 9. _____

10. $-2x + 8y = 8$ 10. _____

Name _____ Date _____

Graph the linear equation using the slope and y-intercept.

11. $3x + y = -2$ 11.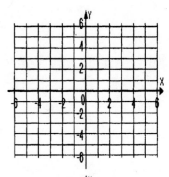

12. $5x - 2y = 4$ 12.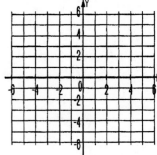

13. $3x = 2y$ 13.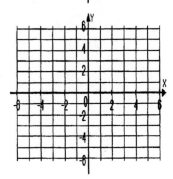

(a) Graph both linear equations on the rectangular coordinate system and (b) decide whether or not the lines are parallel.

14. $3x - y = -2$ 14.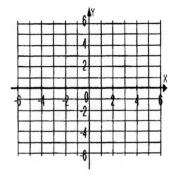
     $x + 3y = 6$

15. The speed of a ball dropped from a tower is given by the linear   15. _____
     function $y = 32x$, where y is in feet per second and x is the
     number of seconds since the ball was dropped. Find and
     interpret the slope and y-intercept of the linear equation.

AE-120

Additional Exercises 3.5
Form I
The Point-Slope Form of the Equation of a Line

(a) Find the point-slope form of the line satisfying the given conditions and use this to write the (b) slope-intercept form of the equation.

1.   Slope = 1, passing through (2, 1)   1a. _____

                                                                      b. _____

2.   Slope = –2, passing through (4, 4)   2a. _____

                                                                      b. _____

3.   Slope = 4, passing through (0, 2)   3a. _____

                                                                      b. _____

4.   Slope = 8, passing through (4, 2)   4a. _____

                                                                      b. _____

5.   Slope = –9, passing through (4, 3)   5a. _____

                                                                      b. _____

6.   Slope = 5, passing through (–3, –4)   6a. _____

                                                                      b. _____

7.   Passing through (0, 1) and (4, 5)   7a. _____

                                                                      b. _____

8.   Passing through (0, 8) and (2, 6)   8a. _____

                                                                      b. _____

Name _____   Date _____

9.   Passing through (2, 0) and (4, 2)   9a. _____

                                                           b. _____

10.   Passing through (–4, 1) and (–1, 4)   10a. _____

                                                           b. _____

Use the given conditions to write an equation for each line in (a) point-slope form and (b) slope intercept form.

11.   Passing through (–3, 1) and parallel to the line whose equation   11a. _____
       is $y = -2x + 4$.

                                                           b. _____

12.   Passing through (–4, –6) and parallel to the line whose equation   12a. _____
       is $y = x + 6$.

                                                           b. _____

13.   Passing through (2, –2) and perpendicular to the line whose   13a. _____
       equation is $y = \dfrac{1}{3}x + 5$.   b. _____

14.   A faucet is used to add water to a large bottle that already   14. _____
       contained some water. After it has been filling for 5 seconds, the
       gauge on the bottle indicates that it contains 22 ounces of water.
       After it has been filling for 11 seconds, the gauge indicates the
       bottle contains 46 ounces of water. Let y be the amount of water
       in the bottle x seconds after the faucet was turned on. Write a
       linear equation that models the amount of water in the bottle in
       terms of x.

15.   A vendor has learned that, by pricing hot dogs at $1.00, sales   15. _____
       reach 135 hot dogs per day. Raising the price to $1.75 will cause
       the sales to fall to 105 hot dogs per day. Let y be the number of
       hot dogs the vendor sells at x dollars each. Write a linear equation
       that models the number of hot dogs per day when the price is x
       dollars each.

Name _____   Date _____

Additional Exercises 3.5
Form II
The Point-Slope Form of the Equation of a Line

(a) Find the point-slope form of the line satisfying the given conditions and use this to write the (b) slope-intercept form of the equation.

1. Slope $= \dfrac{5}{3}$, passing through $(0, 5)$

1a. _____

b. _____

2. Slope $= -\dfrac{2}{3}$, passing through $(0, 2)$

2a. _____

b. _____

3. Slope $= -\dfrac{3}{5}$, passing through $(10, 3)$

3a. _____

b. _____

4. Slope $= \dfrac{5}{3}$, passing through $(0, 5)$

4a. _____

b. _____

5. Slope $= -\dfrac{4}{5}$, passing through $(-5, 10)$

5a. _____

b. _____

6. Slope $= \dfrac{3}{4}$, passing through $(8, -8)$

6a. _____

b. _____

7. Passing through $(1, -5)$ and $(-5, 1)$

7a. _____

b. _____

Name _____   Date _____

8.   Passing through (0, –3) and (3, 6)   8a. _____

                                                           b. _____

9.   Passing through (–1, –9) and (–3, –15)   9a. _____

                                                           b. _____

10.   Passing through (2, 3) and (–6, 1)   10a. _____

                                                           b. _____

Use the given conditions to write an equation for each line in (a) point-slope form and (b) slope intercept form.

11.   Passing through (4, 6) and parallel to the line whose equation   11a. _____
      is $y = \dfrac{1}{2}x - 3$.   b. _____

12.   Passing through (–3, 5) and perpendicular to the line whose   12a. _____
      equation is $y = -3x + 2$.
                                                                          b. _____

13.   Passing through (4, 4) and parallel to the line whose equation   13a. _____
      is $3x + 4y = 6$.
                                                                          b. _____

14.   When making a telephone call using a calling card, a call lasting   14. _____
      3 minutes cost $1.05. A call lasting 11 minutes cost $2.65. Let y
      be the cost of making a call lasting x minutes using a calling card.
      Write a linear equation that models the cost of making a call
      lasting x minutes.

15.   A vendor has learned that, by pricing caramel apples at $1.25,   15. _____
      sales will reach 133 caramel apples per day. Raising the price to
      $2.25 will cause the sales to fall to 81 caramel apples per day.
      Let y be the number of caramel apples the vendor sells at x dollars
      each. Write a linear equation that models the number of caramel
      apples sold per day when the price is x dollars each.

Additional Exercises 3.5
Form III
The Point-Slope Form of the Equation of a Line

(a) Find the point-slope form of the line satisfying the given conditions and use this to write the
(b) slope-intercept form of the equation.

1. Slope $= -\dfrac{1}{3}$, passing through $(1, -5)$

1a. _____

b. _____

2. Slope $= -\dfrac{2}{7}$, passing through $(2, 4)$

2a. _____

b. _____

3. Slope $= -\dfrac{4}{5}$, passing through $(-1, 2)$

3a. _____

b. _____

4. Slope $= \dfrac{3}{4}$, passing through $(1, 0)$

4a. _____

b. _____

5. Slope $= \dfrac{1}{2}$, passing through $(2, -5)$

5a. _____

b. _____

6. Slope $= \dfrac{3}{5}$, passing through $(-1, 4)$

6a. _____

b. _____

7. Passing through $(1, 2)$ and $(-3, 5)$

7a. _____

b. _____

8.   Passing through (4, 7) and (–1, 6)   8a. _____

                                                                  b. _____

9.   Passing through (–2, 5) and (4, 6)   9a. _____

                                                                  b. _____

10.   Passing through (3, 3) and (–5, 7)   10a. _____

                                                                  b. _____

Use the given conditions to write an equation for each line in (a) point-slope form and (b) slope intercept form

11.   Passing through (3, –2) and parallel to the line whose equation   11a. _____
      is $2x - 3y = 6$.

                                                                  b. _____

12.   Passing through (–1, 0) and perpendicular to the line whose   12a. _____
      equation is $y = -\dfrac{4}{5}x - 7$.   b. _____

13.   Passing through (–8, –4) and perpendicular to the line whose   13a. _____
      equation is $2x - 5y = 9$.

                                                                  b. _____

14.   The average value of a certain type of automobile was $13,440   14. _____
      in 1993 and depreciated to $4860 in 1996. Let y be the average
      value of the automobile in the year x, where $x = 0$ represent 1993.
      Write a linear equation that models the value of the automobile
      in terms of the year x.

15.   An investment is worth $2342 in 1995. By 1999 it has grown to   15. _____
      $3930. Let y be the value of the investment in the year x, where
      $x = 0$ represents 1995. Write a linear equation that models the
      value of the investment in the year x.

Additional Exercises 4.1
Form I
Solving Systems of Linear Equations by Graphing

Determine whether the given ordered pair is a solution of the system.

1. $(5, 2)$
    $x + y = 7$
    $x - y = 3$

    1. _____

2. $(-1, -4)$
    $x + y = -5$
    $x - y = -3$

    2. _____

3. $(0, 5)$
    $x = 5$
    $2x + y = 5$

    3. _____

Solve each system by graphing. If there is no solution or an infinite number of solutions, so state. Use set notation to express solution sets.

4. $y = x + 2$
    $y = 2x - 1$

    4.

    _____

5. $y = \dfrac{1}{2}x - 5$
    $y = x - 6$

    5.

    _____

6. $y = 3x - 2$
     $y = -2x + 3$

6.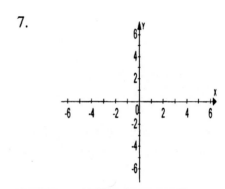

_____

7. $y = -\dfrac{2}{3}x - 3$
     $x + y = -2$

7.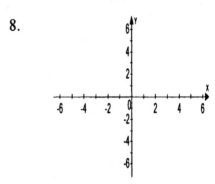

_____

8. $2x + y = -4$
     $y = 4$

8.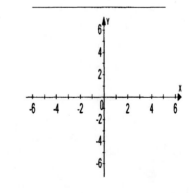

_____

9. $x - 3y = -15$
     $2x + y = 5$

9.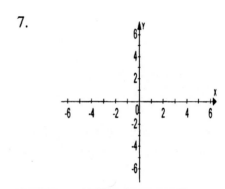

_____

10. $3x + y = -2$
     $-x - 2y = -6$

10.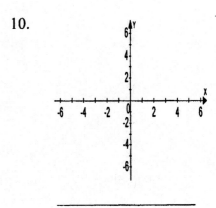

11. $y - 6x = 2$

     $2y = 12x + 4$

11.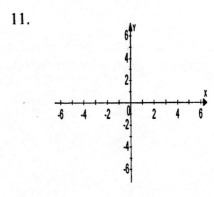

12. $x + 3y = 12$
     $-3x - 9y = 18$

12.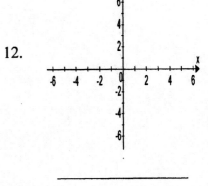

Name _____   Date _____

Additional Exercises 4.1
Form II
Solving Systems of Linear Equations by Graphing

Determine whether the given ordered pair is a solution of the system.

1. $(7, -2)$
    $x + y = 5$
    $2x - 3y = 8$

1. _____

2. $(-3, -4)$
    $x - y = 1$
    $3x - 2y = -1$

2. _____

3. $(2, 0)$
    $x = 2$
    $y = 0$

3. _____

Solve each system by graphing. If there is no solution or an infinite number of solutions, so state. Use set notation to express solution sets.

4. $y = -\dfrac{2}{3}x + 4$

    $y = x - 6$

4.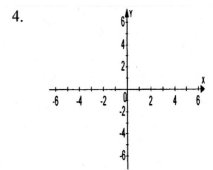

_____

5. $x + 2y = 2$

    $y = -\dfrac{1}{2}x - 4$

5.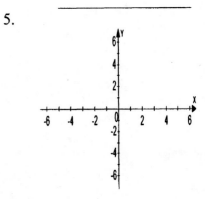

_____

6. $5x - 5y = 5$
    $2x + y = 8$

6.

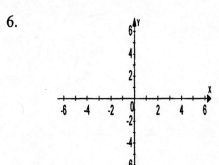

_____

7. $3x - 2y = 10$
    $-2x + 2y = -6$

7.

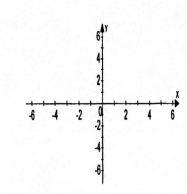

_____

8. $3x - 3y = 6$
    $y = x - 2$

8.

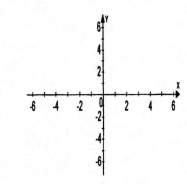

_____

9. $x - y = 1$
    $2x + 3y = 27$

9.

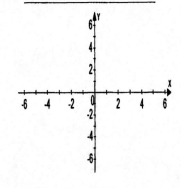

_____

Name _____   Date _____

10. $-x + 4y = 20$
        $x + 2y = -2$

10.

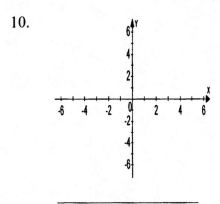

_____

11. $x - y = 3$
        $5x + 2y = -6$

11.

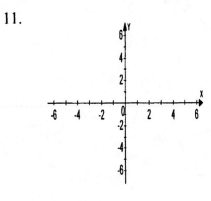

_____

12. $x = 5$
        $y = -3$

12.

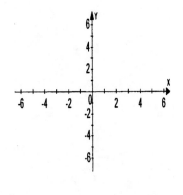

_____

Name _____   Date _____

Additional Exercises 4.1
Form III
Solving Systems of Linear Equations by Graphing

Determine whether the given ordered pair is a solution of the system.

1.   (5, 2)   1. _____
       $4x + y = 18$
       $3x + 4y = 7$

2.   (–2, –5)   2. _____
       $4x + y = -13$
       $2x + 4y = -24$

3.   (4, 1)   3. _____
       $x = 1$
       $y = 4$

Solve each system by graphing. If there is no solution or an infinite number of solutions, so state. Use set notation to express solution sets.

4. $y = -\dfrac{1}{4}x + 6$ 4.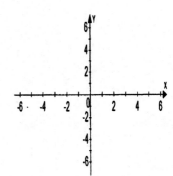

       $y = x + 1$

5. $2x + y = 7$ 5.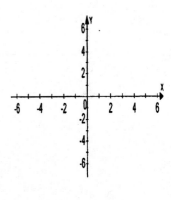
       $6x + 3y = 21$

AE-133

Name _____   Date _____

6. $2x + y = 1$
        $2x + y = -4$

6.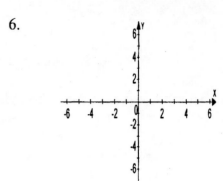

_____

7. $2x - y = 1$
        $3x - 2y = 0$

7.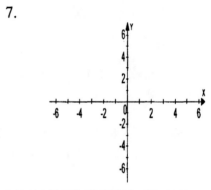

_____

8. $6x + 12y = 12$
        $x + y = -2$

8.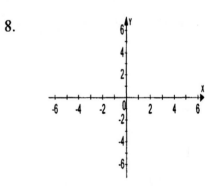

_____

9. $2x + y = 5$
        $2x - 8y = 32$

9.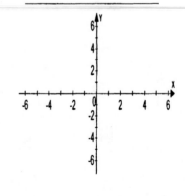

_____

10. $x = -y$
       $x - y = 6$

10.

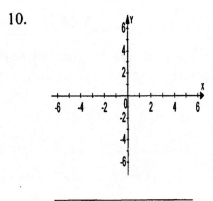

_____

11. $3x = 2y + 12$
       $2x + 3y = 21$

11.

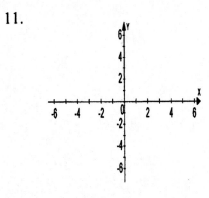

_____

12. $x - 5y = 5$
       $x + 5y = -15$

12.

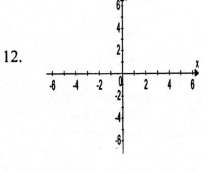

_____

Additional Exercises 4.2
Form I
Solving Systems of Linear Equations by the Substitution Method

Solve each system by the substitution method. If there is no solution or infinitely many solutions, so state. Use set notation to express solution sets.

1. $y = x + 3$
   $x + 2y = 18$

   1. _____

2. $2x - 2y = 2$
   $x = 3y + 5$

   2. _____

3. $3x - 2y = 9$
   $y = 2x - 5$

   3. _____

4. $2x - y = 15$
   $y = x - 5$

   4. _____

5. $3x + 3y = 12$
   $x = 4 - y$

   5. _____

6. $3x + y = 10$
   $5x - 2y = 2$

   6. _____

7. $x - 5y = 35$
   $4x + 2y = 8$

   7. _____

8. $12x - 4y = 16$
   $3x - y = -4$

8. _____

9. $5x + y = -10$
   $2x - 6y = -4$

9. _____

10. $x + 8y = -56$
    $-2x + 9y = -63$

10. _____

11. $6x + 4y = 12$
    $2x - 2y = -14$

11. _____

12. $3x - 2y = 25$
    $4x + 8y = -20$

12. _____

13. $2x + 3y = 9$
    $3x + 2y = 1$

13. _____

14. $2x + y = 14$
    $4x + 2y = -28$

14. _____

15. $x = 8 - 5y$
    $x = 3y - 8$

15. _____

16. $y = 2x + 3$
    $y = 4x + 7$

16. _____

Additional Exercises 4.2
Form II
Solving Systems of Linear Equations by the Substitution Method

Solve each system by the substitution method. If there is no solution or infinitely many solutions, so state. Use set notation to express solution sets.

1. $x = 1 - 6y$
   $2x + 8y = 6$

   1. _____

2. $y = 3x + 4$
   $5x - y = 4$

   2. _____

3. $6x - 2y = 14$
   $3x - y = 7$

   3. _____

4. $x + 5y = 18$
   $2x + 2y = 20$

   4. _____

5. $6x + y = -12$
   $5x + 2y = 4$

   5. _____

6. $9x - 3y = 3$
   $3x - y = 12$

   6. _____

7. $x + 7y = 1$
   $2x + 8y = 2$

   7. _____

8. $2x + y = 14$
   $6x - 3y = 18$

   8. _____

9. $2x + y = 8$
     $-3x + 2y = -19$

9. _____

10. $6x - y = -1$
     $6x - 5y = -17$

10. _____

11. $5x - 10y = 6$
     $x - y = 1$

11. _____

12. $7x + 15y = 12$
     $x + 9y = 4$

12. _____

13. $x - \dfrac{3}{4}y = 3$

     $-2x + \dfrac{3}{2}y = -5$

13. _____

14. $\dfrac{1}{4}x + \dfrac{1}{2}y = 5$

     $4x - y = 26$

14. _____

15. $3x - 2y = 3$

     $-\dfrac{4}{3}x + y = \dfrac{1}{3}$

15. _____

16. $3x + 6y = 3$
     $2x + 8y = 22$

16. _____

Additional Exercises 4.2
Form III
Solving Systems of Linear Equations by the Substitution Method

Solve each system by the substitution method. If there is no solution or infinitely many solutions, so state. Use set notation to express solution sets.

1. $4x + 3y = 11$
      $y = 2x - 13$ 1. _____

2. $5x - 3y = 11$
      $x = 12 + 2y$ 2. _____

3. $y = 2x + 3$
      $y = 4x + 7$ 3. _____

4. $x = 5y - 35$
      $5x - 6y = -61$ 4. _____

5. $2x + y = 14$
      $4x + 2y = 28$ 5. _____

6. $5x + 5y = 0$
      $x - y = -4$ 6. _____

7. $x + 2y = 32$
      $3x - 5y = -14$ 7. _____

8. $4x - 12y = 15$
      $x - 3y = 4$ 8. _____

9. $6x + 4y = 12$
      $2x - 4y = -44$ 9. _____

10. $x + 3y = -1$
    $8x - 8y = 4$

    10. _____

11. $15x - y = 14$
    $3x - 4y = 18$

    11. _____

12. $\dfrac{4}{5}x + \dfrac{1}{2}y = 6$
    $3x + y = 19$

    12. _____

13. $\dfrac{1}{3}x + \dfrac{1}{3}y = 0$
    $x - y = 14$

    13. _____

14. $\dfrac{1}{2}x - \dfrac{2}{3}y = -1$
    $\dfrac{3}{7}x + y = 18$

    14. _____

15. An electronic company kept comparative statistics on two products, A and B. For the years 1980 to 1988, the total number of Product A sold (in thousands) is given by the equation $y = 72x + 689$ where x is the number of years since 1980. For the same time period, the total number of Product B sold (in thousands) is given by the equation $y = -30x + 434$, where x is the number is years since 1980. Use the substitution method to solve the system and describe what the solution means.

    15. _____

16. One number is 1 less than a second number. Twice the second number is 19 less than 5 times the first. Find the two numbers.

    16. _____

Additional Exercises 4.3
Form I
Solving Systems of Linear Equations by the Addition Method

Solve each system by the addition method. If there is no solution, or an infinite number of solutions, so state. Use set notation to express solution sets.

1. $x + y = -1$
    $x - y = -7$

    1. _____

2. $x + 4y = 12$
    $-x - 6y = -16$

    2. _____

3. $x + 3y = -7$
    $2x - 3y = 22$

    3. _____

4. $4x + 5y = 18$
    $-4x - 5y = 9$

    4. _____

5. $6x - y = -24$
    $-6x + 7y = -12$

    5. _____

6. $x + 9y = 19$
    $-6x + 9y = 12$

    6. _____

7. $x + 8y = 16$
    $-6x + 9y = 18$

    7. _____

8. $x - 5y = -7$
    $4x - 6y = 14$

    8. _____

9. $11x - 14y = 6$ 9. _____

          $3x - 7y = 8$

10. $2x + 5y = 17$ 10. _____

          $3x - 6y = 12$

11. $9x + 4y = 13$ 11. _____

          $6x + 5y = 32$

12. $4x - 6y = 10$ 12. _____

          $6x - 9y = 15$

13. $6x - 7y = 16$ 13. _____

          $3x + 4y = -7$

14. $5x - 2y = 12$ 14. _____

          $3x + 3y = 66$

15. $10x + 5y = 1$ 15. _____

          $15x - 20y = 18$

16. $-7x - 17 = 8y$ 16. _____

          $-2x + 2y = -8$

Additional Exercises 4.3
Form II
Solving Systems of Linear Equations by the Addition Method

Solve each system by the addition method. If there is no solution, or an infinite number of solutions, so state. Use set notation to express solution sets.

1. $3x + y = 16$
     $5x - y = 16$

1. _____

2. $7x - 4y = -13$
     $5x + 4y = -23$

2. _____

3. $8x + 3y = -10$
     $-8x - 11y = 58$

3. _____

4. $x + 6y = 24$
     $3x - 2y = -8$

4. _____

5. $10x - 4y = 0$
     $3x + y = -11$

5. _____

6. $6x + 3y = 27$
     $2x + y = 9$

6. _____

7. $9x + 2y = 21$
     $3x - 4y = 63$

7. _____

8. $10x - 4y = -6$
     $5x + 2y = 5$

8. _____

9. $8x - 12y = 23$ 9. _____

          $4x + 4y = -6$

10. $7x - 2y = 5$ 10. _____

          $-14x + 4y = -20$

11. $12x + 8y = -14$ 11. _____

          $9x - 12y = 12$

12. $5x - 7y = -46$ 12. _____

          $-3x - 4y = 3$

Solve each system by the method of your choice. If there is no solution, or an infinite number of solutions, so state.

13. $6x - 4y = 4$ 13. _____

          $8y = 8 + 16x$

14. $4x + y = 10$ 14. _____

          $12x + 3y = 48$

15. $x + 7y = 15$ 15. _____

          $8x = 20 - 6y$

16. $\dfrac{x}{4} + \dfrac{y}{8} = 3$ 16. _____

          $\dfrac{x}{5} - \dfrac{y}{4} = 8$

Additional Exercises 4.3
Form III
Solving Systems of Linear Equations by the Addition Method

Solve each system by the addition method. If there is no solution, or an infinite number of solutions, so state. Use set notation to express solution sets.

1.　　$x + 4y = 0$
　　　$x - 4y = 72$

1. _____

2.　　$-6x + 3y = 12$
　　　$6x - 5y = 8$

2. _____

3.　　$2x + 8y = 6$
　　　$x + 4y = 8$

3. _____

4.　　$6x - 4y = -4$
　　　$12x - 8y = -8$

4. _____

5.　　$5x + 7y = 16$
　　　$3x + 2y = 3$

5. _____

6.　　$9x + 8y = 117$
　　　$-7x + 5y = -91$

6. _____

7.　　$3x - 2y = 4$
　　　$6x - 4y = 7$

7. _____

8.　　$9x - 6y = 30$
　　　$7x + 4y = 58$

8. _____

9. $8x - 4y = -8$ 9. _____

         $3x + 3y = 4$

10. $10x + 8y = -5$ 10. _____

         $-15x + 16y = 18$

11. $\dfrac{x}{2} + \dfrac{y}{3} = \dfrac{13}{6}$ 11. _____

         $\dfrac{x}{4} - \dfrac{x}{6} = \dfrac{17}{12}$

12. $5x + \dfrac{y}{8} = -22$ 12. _____

         $\dfrac{x}{4} - 3y = 47$

Solve each system by the method of your choice. If there is no solution, or an infinite number of solutions, so state.

13. $4x = 12y - 8$ 13. _____

         $9x - 11y = 46$

14. $y = \dfrac{2}{3}x + 8$ 14. _____

         $y = \dfrac{3}{4}x + \dfrac{37}{4}$

15. $5(2x + 3y) = 45$ 15. _____

         $6x = 18y$

16. $6x = 7y - 17$ 16. _____

         $2x + 2y = -10$

Additional Exercises 4.4
Form I
Problem Solving Using Systems of Equations

Use the given conditions to write a system of equations. Then solve.

1. The sum of two numbers is 12. Four times the first number equals   1. _____
    two times the second number. Find the two numbers.

2. One number is four less than twice another number. Their sum   2. _____
    is 20. Find the two numbers.

3. The cost of two bath towels and three washcloths is $26. The   3. _____
    cost of three bath towels and two washcloths is $29. Find the
    price of a single bath towel and the price of a single washcloth.

4. Jayden bought four shirts and three pairs of pants for $200. His   4. _____
    brother bought two shirts and two pair of pants for $116. How
    much did a pair of pants cost? How much did a shirt cost?

5. On a buying trip in Los Angeles, Rosa Perez ordered 120 pieces   5. _____
    of jewelry for her store. She bought bracelets costing $4 each and
    necklaces costing $11 each. Rosa wrote a check for $830 to pay
    for the order. How many bracelets and necklaces did Rosa purchase?

6. The youth group at the church decided to plant geraniums and   6. _____
    daisies around the church grounds as a group project. Geraniums
    in 6" pots cost $4 each and daisy plants cost $6 each. The youth
    group spent $410 on 80 plants. How many geraniums and how many
    daisy plants did the group buy?

7.   The perimeter of a rectangle is 36 inches. If the length is 4 inches   7. _____
     longer than the width, find the dimensions of the rectangle.

8.   The perimeter of a rectangle is 968 cm. The width is one-third   8. _____
     as long as the length. Find the dimensions of the rectangle.

9.   In a triangle, the sum of the measures of the angles is always   9. _____
     180°. One angle of a triangle measures 40°. Find the measures
     of the other two angles if the larger angle is five less than four
     times the smaller.

10. You invested $8000 in two accounts pay 5% and 7% annual   10. _____
     interest. If the total interest earned for the year was $500, how
     much was invested at each rate?

11. A coin purse contains a mixture of 15 coins in nickels and dimes.   11. _____
     The coins have a total value of $1.25. Determine the number of
     each kind of coin in the purse.

12. Julie and Eric row their boat (at a constant speed) 40 miles down-   12. _____
     stream for 4 hours, helped by the current. Rowing at the same rate,
     the trip back against the current takes 10 hours. Find the rate of the
     current.

Name _____   Date _____

Additional Exercises 4.4
Form II
Problem Solving Using Systems of Equations

Use the given conditions to write a system of equations. Then solve.

1. The sum of two numbers is −12. Their difference is 4. Find the   1. _____
    two numbers.

2. One number is 7 more than another. The sum of the two   2. _____
    numbers is 41. Find the two numbers.

3. The difference of two numbers is 20. The sum of three times   3. _____
    the first and four times the second is 18. Find the two numbers.

4. Devon purchased tickets to an air show for 9 adults and 2   4. _____
    children. The total cost was $192. The cost of a child's ticket was
    $3 less than the cost of an adult's ticket. Find the price of an
    adult's ticket and a child's ticket.

5. Jackson always throws loose change into a pencil holder on   5. _____
    his desk and takes it out every two weeks. This time it was all
    nickels and dimes. There are seven times as many dimes as
    nickels and he has $10.50. Find the number of dimes and nickels.

6. The library had a used book sale to raise money to redecorate   6. _____
    the children's area. Hardback books cost $3 each and paperback
    books cost $1.50 each. A total of 833 books were sold and the
    library raised $1822.50. How many hardback books and paperback
    books were sold?

7.   The three angles in a triangle always add up to 180°. In a   7. _____
triangle, one angle measures 32° and the second angle is 5 times
larger than the third angle. Find the measures of the angles.

8.   Jarod is having a problem with rabbits getting into his garden,   8. _____
so he will fence it in. The length of the garden is 12 feet more
than four times the width. He needs 94 feet of fencing to do the
job. Find the length and width of the garden.

9.   The morning and afternoon pre-school classes at Children's   9. _____
Fun Station went on a field trip to the zoo. While at the zoo, the
children enjoyed snacks and drinks. For the morning classes, the
teacher purchased 15 bags of popcorn and 16 juice boxes for a
total cost of $42.50. In the afternoon, she spent $42 on 12 bags
of popcorn and 18 juice boxes. Find the cost of a bag of popcorn
and the cost of a juice box.

10.   You invested $6000 in two accounts pay 6% and 9% annual   10. _____
interest. If the total interest earned for the year was $480, how
much was invested at each rate?

11.   A barge takes 3 hours to go (at a constant rate) downstream 27   11. _____
miles with a current of 3 miles per hour. If the barge's engines
are set at the same pace, find the time of the return trip against
the current.

12.   Ellen and Kent are able to canoe down the river 18 miles in 3   12. _____
hours, but on the return trip, they can only get 12 miles up-
stream in 3 hours. Find the speed of the river's current.

Name _____   Date _____

Additional Exercises 4.4
Form III
Problem Solving Using Systems of Equations

Use the given conditions to write a system of equations. Then solve.

1.   The sum of two numbers is 92. The first number is four more than   1. _____
     three times the second number. Find the two numbers.

2.   The sum of nine times the first number and five times a second   2. _____
     number is 24. The second number is seventeen less than twice the
     first. Find the two numbers.

3.   The sum of twice one number and four times a second number is   3. _____
     78. If $\frac{1}{2}$ the second number is subtracted from the first number,
     the result is 9. Find the two numbers.

4.   The Johnson family spent the afternoon at the baseball game.   4. _____
     Mr. Johnson purchased three hot dogs and three sodas on his first
     trip to the concession stand and spent $22.50. On his second trip
     to the concession stand, he spent $24.00 on five sodas and two hot
     dogs. How much does a hot dog cost? How much does a soda cost?

5.   Paul throws his loose change into a pencil holder on his desk and   5. _____
     takes it out every two weeks. This time it was all quarters and
     nickels. There are four times as many quarters as nickels. He had a
     total of $13.65. Find the number of quarters and nickels.

6.   The Lone Star Volleyball tournament is held annually and teams   6. _____
     from all over the United States participate in the tournament.
     Tickets for spectators are $5 for adults and $2 for children under 12.
     A total of 1800 tickets were sold and the revenue from the ticket
     sales was $7412. Find the number of adult tickets and children's
     tickets sold.

7.   The sum of the measures of the angles of any triangle is 180°. In a 7. _____
triangle, if one angle has a measure of 43°, find the measures of
the other two angles if one of the angles is four less than twice the
other angle.

8.   You invested $12,000 in two accounts pay 7% and 10% annual 8. _____
interest. If the total interest earned for the year was $1050, how
much was invested at each rate?

9.   The perimeter of a rectangular swimming pool is 80 feet. The 9. _____
width is half the length increased by 3.7 feet. Find the dimensions
of the pool.

10.   Ken and Hector live 25.2 miles apart in southeastern Missouri. 10. _____
They decide to bicycle toward each other and meet somewhere
in between. Hector's rate of speed is 80% of Ken's. They start at
the same time and meet two hours later. Find Hector's rate of
speed and Ken's rate of speed.

11.   The Indian Guides are canoeing down the Lazy River. It takes 11. _____
them 2 hours to go 15 miles down the river with the current and
3 hours to get back up the river to their starting point. Find the
speed of the canoe in still water and the speed of the current.

12.   Jane is going to rent a car while in Charlotte. The Crazy Car 12. _____
Company rents midsize cars for $17.50 per day plus $0.31 per
mile driven. The Rent A Heap Company rents midsize cars for
$21.00 per day plus $0.24 per mile. How many miles would Jane
have to drive before the two plans were equal? What would be the
cost?

Additional Exercises 4.5
Form I
Systems of Linear Equations in Three Variables

Determine if the given ordered triple is a solution of the system.

1.　　(1, –2, 3)   1. _____
　　　$x + y + z = 2$
　　　$x - y + 2z = 9$
　　　$3x + 2y + z = 2$

2.　　(–3, –1, 2)   2. _____
　　　$x + y + z = -2$
　　　$x - y + 5z = -12$
　　　$3x + y + z = 2$

3.　　(0, 3, –1)   3. _____
　　　$x - y + 2z = -5$
　　　$4x + z = -1$
　　　$x + 5y + z = 14$

4.　　(5, –3, –2)   4. _____
　　　$x + y - z = 4$
　　　$x - 2y - 2z = 15$
　　　$2x + 3y + 2y = -3$

5.　　(4, –4, –5)   5. _____
　　　$x + 4y + 2z = -22$
　　　$3y + 5z = -37$
　　　$z = -5$

Solve each system. If there is not solution or if there are infinitely many solutions and the system's equations are dependent, so state.

6.　　$x + y + z = 6$ 6. _____
　　　$2x - y - 3z = -5$
　　　$4x + y - 3z = 5$

7. $x + y + z = 4$
    $x - y + 2z = 1$
    $x + y - 3z = 0$

7. _____

8. $3x - 2y + z = 2$
    $x + 3y - z = 14$
    $2x - y + 2z = 4$

8. _____

9. $3x - y + 2z = 6$
    $3x + y - z = 5$
    $x + 2y + z = 3$

9. _____

10. $x - y + 3z = -1$
    $2x - 2y + z = 3$
    $3x - 3y - 2z = 8$

10. _____

11. $x + 5y + 4z = 33$
    $3y + 3z = 24$
    $z = 5$

11. _____

12. $2x + y - 3z = -3$
    $4x + 2y - 6z = -6$
    $3x - 2y + 4z = 1$

12. _____

13. $x - 2y + z = 9$
    $3x - y + 2z = 4$
    $-x + 2y - z = 6$

13. _____

14. $x - y + 3z = 1$
    $3x + z = 0$
    $-x + y - 3z = -5$

14. _____

Additional Exercises 4.5
Form II
Systems of Linear Equations in Three Variables

Determine if the given ordered triple is a solution of the system.

1. $(4, -2, -4)$ 1. _____
$$x - y + z = 2$$
$$x + y + z = -2$$
$$x + y - z = 6$$

2. $(2, -4, 3)$ 2. _____
$$x - y + z = -5$$
$$x + y + z = 1$$
$$x + y - z = -5$$

3. $(3, 0, -5)$ 3. _____
$$2x + 3y - 2z = 16$$
$$5x - 3y = 0$$
$$x + y - z = 8$$

4. $(1, -2, -1)$ 4. _____
$$x + 2y + 2z = -5$$
$$5y - 4z = 1$$
$$y = -1$$

Solve each system. If there is not solution or if there are infinitely many solutions and the system's equations are dependent, so state.

5. $x + y + z = 4$ 5. _____
$$x - 3y - 2z = -1$$
$$2x + 3y + 3z = 7$$

6. $x - y + z = -9$ 6. _____
$$x + y - z = 5$$
$$x + y + z = -1$$

7. $x - 5y + z = 3$
    $3x + 4y + 6z = 0$
    $x + 3y - 3z = 15$

8. $3x + 6y - 3z = 15$
    $3x + 2y + 6z = 11$
    $-x - 2y + z = -5$

9. $5x - 2y + 4z = 9$
    $x + y - 8z = -6$
    $-2x - 2y - 4z = 7$

10. $x + 2y - 3z = 12$
    $3x - y + 2z = 8$
    $-2x - 4y + 6z = 16$

11. $3x - 7y + 6z = 71$
    $-15x + 35y - 30z = -355$
    $12x - 28y + 24z = 284$

12. $\dfrac{1}{2}x + \dfrac{1}{3}y - \dfrac{1}{4}z = 4$

    $x - \dfrac{2}{3}y + z = -2$

    $2x + \dfrac{1}{3}y + \dfrac{1}{2}z = 7$

13. $5x + 10y + 5z = 8$
    $3x + y + 5z = 4$
    $x + y = z$

14. $2x - 3y - 2z = 11$
    $x + 2y + 4z = 5$
    $3x - y + 14z = -2$

Use the given conditions to write a system of equations. Solve the system of three equations to solve the problem.

15.   The sum of three numbers is 15. The sum of twice the first   15. _____
       number and half the second number is 12. If the second number
       is decreased by twice the third number, the result is 2. Find the
       numbers.

16.   A basketball player scored 20 points in a game. The number   16. _____
       of three-point field goals the player made was 10 less than
       three times the number of free throws (each worth 1 point).
       Twice the number of two-point field goals the player made
       was 8 more than the number of three-point field goals made.
       Find the number of free-throws, two-point field goals, and
       three-point field goals that the player made in the game.

Additional Exercises 4.5
Form III
Systems of Linear Equations in Three Variables

Determine if the given ordered triple is a solution of the system.

1. $(-5, -3, -1)$ 1. _____
    $x + y - z = -7$
    $2x - 3y - 4z = 3$
    $x - 2y - 3z = 4$

2. $\left(\dfrac{1}{2}, 4, \dfrac{-1}{3}\right)$ 2. _____
    $2x + 2y + 3z = 7$
    $4x - 2y - 6z = -4$
    $2x + y - 9z = 8$

3. $(6, -1.5, -3.2)$ 3. _____
    $x + 2y - 5z = 19$
    $2x - 4y + 2z = 11.6$
    $x + 2y + 5z = -7$

Solve each system. If there is not solution or if there are infinitely many solutions and the system's equations are dependent, so state.

4. $2x - y + 2z = 6$ 4. _____
    $x + 2y + z = 3$
    $3x + 4y - z = 5$

5. $5x + 3y + 3z = 16$ 5. _____
    $2x - y + z = -1$
    $3x + 2y + 2z = 11$

6. $2x - 8y + 6z = 1$ 6. _____
    $3x - y + z = 0$
    $-x + 4y - 3z = 2$

7. $x + y + z = 1$
    $6x + 12y + 4z = 6$
    $-3x + 6y + 8z = 4$

    7. _____

8. $5x + 4y + 3z = 8$
    $2x - 2y - 7z = 14$
    $3x + y + 4z = 9$

    8. _____

9. $x - 5y - z = 6$
    $2x - 10y - 2z = 12$
    $3x - 15y - 3z = 18$

    9. _____

10. $\dfrac{1}{2}x + \dfrac{3}{4}y + \dfrac{1}{8}z = 0$

    $4x - 2y + \dfrac{1}{2}z = 9$

    $x - y + 3z = -3$

    10. _____

11. $0.2x + 0.1y - 0.3z = -1.4$
    $0.5x - 1.5y + 2z = 11$
    $0.75x + 0.5y + 0.25z = 0$

    11. _____

12. $\dfrac{x}{5} + \dfrac{y}{3} - \dfrac{z}{2} = -2$

    $3x - 2y + \dfrac{3}{4}z = 24$

    $x - \dfrac{2}{3}y + z = 11$

    12. _____

Name _____   Date _____

Use the given information to write a system of equations. Then solve the system of equations to solve the problem.

13. The circus is putting on a show for the residents of a small   13. _____
     Arkansas town, population 256. The price of tickets is as
     follows: Senior citizens, $2.00, ages 16-60, $5.00 and under
     16 is $1.00. Everyone in town attended the circus and the total
     receipts for the tickets totaled $660. If 64 more children went to
     the circus than Senior citizens, how many of each price ticket were
     sold?

14. A vendor sells hot dogs, bags of potato chips, and soft drinks.   13. _____
     A customer buys 4 hot dogs, 2 bags of potato chips, and 5 soft
     drinks for $15.50. The price of a hot dog is $1.25 more than the
     price of potato chips. The cost of a soft drink is $2.00 less than
     the price of two hot dogs. Find the cost of each item.

Name _____   Date _____

Identify the polynomial as a monomial, binomial, or trinomial. Give the degree of the polynomial.

1. $18x$ 1. _____

2. $-6y^4 - 3y^3 - 1$ 2. _____

3. $9x^5 + 8x^4 + 6x^3$ 3. _____

4. -15 4. _____

Add the polynomials.

5. $(2y^5 - 7y^3) + (3y^5 - 8y^3)$ 5. _____

6. $(8y^7 + 6y^6 + 9y) + (4y^7 + 2y^6 + 4y)$ 6. _____

7. $5y^6 - 3y^3 - 5$ 7. _____
        $\underline{9y^6 + 9y^3 - 2}$

8. $6y^5 + 9y^3$ 8. _____
        $\underline{6y^5 - 7y^3}$

9. $12y^4 - 8y^3 + 3y^2 + y$ 9. _____
        $\underline{9y^4 + 6y^3 - 2y^2 - 2y}$

Name _____   Date _____

Subtract the polynomials.

10. $(-8x+12)-(4x+6)$ 10. _____

11. $(2y^3+6y^2)-(-5y^3+19y^2)$ 11. _____

12. $(4x^5-16x^4+17)-(8x^5-5x^4+20)$ 12. _____

13. $\begin{aligned}3x^4&-4x^2\\-(15x^4&-7x^2)\end{aligned}$ 13. _____

14. $\begin{aligned}5y^5-18y^3&+20\\-(9y^5-13y^3&-15)\end{aligned}$ 14. _____

15.   If the cost, y, for manufacturing x units of a certain product is given by $y=x^2-60x+4000$, find the cost of manufacturing 90 units.   15. _____

Additional Exercises 5.1
Form II
Adding and Subtracting Polynomials

Identify the polynomial as a monomial, binomial, or trinomial. Give the degree of the polynomial.

1. $8x^3 - 6$ 1. _____

2. 2 2. _____

3. $5x^6 - 3x^4 + 9$ 3. _____

4. $4x^2 + 5x$ 4. _____

Add the polynomials.

5. $(3x^3 + 2x^2) + (-4x^2 - 5)$ 5. _____

6. $(7x^5 - 4x^3 + 2) + (-3x^5 + 2x - 1)$ 6. _____

7. $\begin{aligned} 8x^4 - 3x^3\ - 4 \\ -4x^4 + 2x^3 - 5x \end{aligned}$ 7. _____

8. $(-3x^5 + 4x^4 + 7x^3) + (2x^4 - 6x^3 + 1)$ 8. _____

9. $\begin{aligned} 10x^3 - 5x^2 + 7x - 3 \\ 2x^3 + 4x^2 - 6x + 5 \end{aligned}$ 9. _____

Subtract the polynomials.

10. $(-4x^2 + 5x - 3) - (3x + 1)$ 10. _____

11. $(5x^5 + 3x^2 - 2x + 1) - (4x^2 + 7x - 4)$ 11. _____

12. $(6x^4 - 3x - 7) - (2x^3 + 5x^2 - x)$ 12. _____

13. $7x^3 - 2x^2$ 13. _____
       $\underline{-(21x^3 - x^2)}$

14. $8x^4 + 6x^3 - 2x^2$ 14. _____
       $\underline{-(3x^4 - x^3 + 7x^2)}$

15.   The force in newtons needed to stretch a certain spring x   15. _____
       centimeters from its resting position is given by the
       polynomial function $y = 10x^2$ where 10 is the spring constant.
       Find the force needed to stretch the spring 6 centimeters.

Additional Exercises 5.1
Form III
Adding and Subtracting Polynomials

Identify the polynomial as a monomial, binomial, or trinomial. Give the degree of the polynomial.

1. $-12x^9 - 18x^7$ 1. _____

2. $4x^3 - 2x^2 + 5x$ 2. _____

3. 11 3. _____

4. $12x^5 - 18x + 11$ 4. _____

Add the polynomials.

5. $\left(\dfrac{1}{4}x^3 + \dfrac{2}{7}x^2 - \dfrac{1}{3}x\right) + \left(-\dfrac{3}{4}x^3 + \dfrac{1}{3}x + \dfrac{7}{9}\right)$ 5. _____

6. $\left(\dfrac{5}{7}x^3 - \dfrac{2}{3}x^2 + \dfrac{1}{5}\right) + \left(-\dfrac{4}{7}x^3 + x^2 - \dfrac{3}{4}x\right)$ 6. _____

7. $\left(-\dfrac{3}{5}x^2 + \dfrac{1}{2}x + \dfrac{4}{5}\right) + \left(\dfrac{4}{5}x^2 + \dfrac{1}{4}x + \dfrac{3}{4}\right)$ 7. _____

8. $\dfrac{3}{7}x^2 - \dfrac{1}{4}x + \dfrac{3}{5}$ 8. _____

       $\dfrac{2}{7}x^2 - \dfrac{3}{4}x + \dfrac{1}{5}$
       _____

9. $\dfrac{4}{5}x^2 - \dfrac{2}{5}x - \dfrac{2}{5}$

      $-\dfrac{1}{5}x^2 + \dfrac{2}{3}x - \dfrac{3}{5}$

      $\overline{\phantom{-\dfrac{1}{5}x^2 + \dfrac{2}{3}x - \dfrac{3}{5}}}$

9. _____

Subtract the polynomials.

10. $(4x^5 - 16x^4 + 17) - (-5x^4 + 2x^3 - 8)$

10. _____

11. $\left(\dfrac{3}{8}x^4 + \dfrac{2}{5}x^3 - \dfrac{3}{7}\right) - \left(\dfrac{1}{8}x^4 - \dfrac{1}{5}x^3 - \dfrac{2}{7}\right)$

11. _____

12. $\left(\dfrac{3}{4}x^3 + \dfrac{2}{3}x^2 - \dfrac{2}{5}x\right) - \left(\dfrac{1}{4}x^3 + \dfrac{1}{3}x^2 - \dfrac{1}{5}x + \dfrac{3}{8}\right)$

12. _____

13. $\dfrac{9}{8}x^3 + \dfrac{2}{5}x^2 \quad -8$

      $-\left(\dfrac{1}{8}x^3 - \dfrac{2}{5}x^2 - x\right)$

      $\overline{\phantom{-\left(\dfrac{1}{8}x^3 - \dfrac{2}{5}x^2 - x\right)}}$

13. _____

14. $7y^6 + 7y^4 + 17y$

      $-(5y^6 + 16y^4 + 19y)$

      $\overline{}$

14. _____

15.   The number of fires in a county for the years 1994-1998, where 1 represents 1994, 2 represents 1995, and so on can be approximated using the third-degree polynomial $y = -0.53x^3 + 0.55x^2 + 56.34x + 3126.4$. Use this function to predict the number of fires in 2003.

15. _____

Additional Exercises 5.2
Form I
Multiplying Polynomials

Perform the indicated operations.

1. $y \cdot y^7$

1. _____

2. $3^6 \cdot 3^8$

2. _____

3. $x^4 \cdot x^7 \cdot x^5$

3. _____

4. $(5^6)^4$

4. _____

5. $(y^8)^6$

5. _____

6. $(-3x)^2$

6. _____

7. $(-4x^6)^3$

7. _____

8. $(2x^8)(-7x^5)$

8. _____

9. $\left(\dfrac{1}{8}x^3\right)\left(-\dfrac{1}{7}x^9\right)$

9. _____

10. $x(x+11)$

10. _____

11. $4x^2(-3x-12)$

11. _____

12. $-7x^4(-8x^6-7x^4)$

12. _____

13. $8x^2(4x^7 + 10x^6 + 11)$ 13. _____

14. $(3x + 10)(x - 11)$ 14. _____

15. $(x - 8)(x + 4)$ 15. _____

16. $(x - 2)(x^2 + 2x + 10)$ 16. _____

17. $(x^2 + x - 10)(x^2 + x - 7)$ 17. _____

18.   Multiply: $(x^2 + 8x + 2)(7x + 6)$ 18. _____

19.   Write an expression for the area of the larger rectangle below   19. _____
      in two different ways.

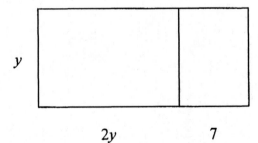

20.   Find the area of a triangle with a base of $6x$ inches and a height   20. _____
      of $(8x + 4)$ inches.

Name _____   Date _____

Perform the indicated operations.

1. $x \cdot x^9$

1. _____

2. $4^4 \cdot 4^6$

2. _____

3. $y^5 \cdot y^8 \cdot y^3$

3. _____

4. $(6^2)^6$

4. _____

5. $(y^4)^9$

5. _____

6. $(-2x)^3$

6. _____

7. $(-5x^4)^2$

7. _____

8. $(3x^9)(-6x^5)$

8. _____

9. $\left(\frac{3}{4}x^4\right)\left(-\frac{6}{7}x^5\right)$

9. _____

10. $x(2x-5)$

10. _____

11. $3x^3(-2x-5)$

11. _____

12. $-5x^6(-3x^4-2x^3)$

12. _____

13. $7x^3(2x^5 + 4x^4 + 14)$ 13. _____

14. $(4x - 3)(x + 7)$ 14. _____

15. $(x - 3)(x + 9)$ 15. _____

16. $(2x - 3)(x^2 - 4x + 6)$ 16. _____

17. $(x^2 - x + 9)(x^2 + 2x - 3)$ 17. _____

18.   Multiply: $(3x^2 - 2x + 4)(5x - 1)$ 18. _____

19.   Write an expression for the area of the larger rectangle below   19. _____
        in two different ways.

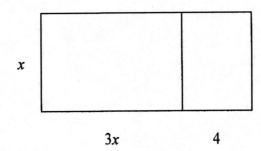

20.   Find the area of a triangle with a base of $4x$ inches and a height   20. _____
        of $(9x + 3)$ inches.

Additional Exercises 5.2
Form III
Multiplying Polynomials

Perform the indicated operations.

1. $x^5 \cdot x^9$

1. _____

2. $4^5 \cdot 4^8$

2. _____

3. $x^6 \cdot x \cdot x^9$

3. _____

4. $(6^5)^8$

4. _____

5. $(y^8)^6$

5. _____

6. $(-4x)^3$

6. _____

7. $(-5x^5)^2$

7. _____

8. $(3x^6)(-8x^5)$

8. _____

9. $\left(\dfrac{2}{7}x^5\right)\left(-\dfrac{3}{5}x^4\right)$

9. _____

10. $x^2(x-8)$

10. _____

11. $9x^3(-2x-12)$

11. _____

12. $-5x^5(-4x^8 - 6x^2)$

12. _____

13. $9x^4(3x^5 + 7x^4 - 10)$ 13. _____

14. $(2x - 8)(3x - 4)$ 14. _____

15. $(x - 5)(x + 8)$ 15. _____

16. $(3x - 4)(x^2 - 2x - 8)$ 16. _____

17. $(x^2 + x - 11)(x^2 - x + 5)$ 17. _____

18.   Multiply: $x^2 - 3x + 5$ 18. _____

                              $\underline{4x + 7}$

19.   Write an expression for the area of the larger rectangle below   19. _____
          in two different ways.

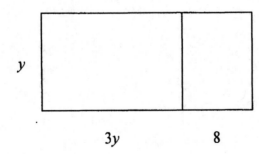

20.   Find the area of a triangle with a base of $8x$ inches and a height   20. _____
          of $(3x + 7)$ inches.

Name _____   Date _____

Perform the indicated operations.

1. $(x+4)(x-3)$ 1. _____

2. $(2x-1)(x+4)$ 2. _____

3. $(3x-5)(4x+7)$ 3. _____

4. $(5-x)(7-2x)$ 4. _____

5. $(x+5)(x^2-25)$ 5. _____

6. $(a+2)(a-2)$ 6. _____

7. $(3+m)(3-m)$ 7. _____

8. $(5-7r)(5+7r)$ 8. _____

9. $\left(3x+\dfrac{1}{3}\right)\left(3x-\dfrac{1}{3}\right)$ 9. _____

10. $(x^2+1)(x^2-1)$ 10. _____

11. $(n+11)^2$ 11. _____

12. $(w-8)^2$ 12. _____

13. $(3a-7)^2$ 13. _____

14. $\left(2x+\dfrac{1}{2}\right)^2$ 14. _____

15. $\left(7x-\dfrac{1}{7}\right)^2$ 15. _____

16. $(8-4m)^2$ 16. _____

17. $\left(n^3+9\right)^2$ 17. _____

18. Find the area of the shaded region. Write the answer as   18. _____
     a polynomial in descending powers of x.

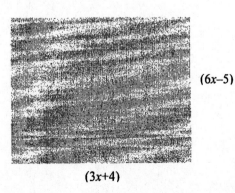

$(6x-5)$

$(3x+4)$

Name _____   Date _____

19.   Find the area of the shaded region. Write the answer as   19. _____
      a polynomial in descending powers of x.

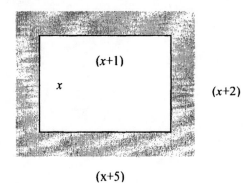

20.   Express the volume of the box as a polynomial in standard   20. _____
      form.

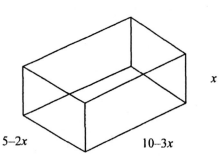

Name _____   Date _____

Perform the indicated operations.

1. $(x+2)(x+8)$ 1. _____

2. $(4x+9)(x-6)$ 2. _____

3. $(2x-8)(6x+11)$ 3. _____

4. $(7-2x)(6-4x)$ 4. _____

5. $(x+3)(x^2-9)$ 5. _____

6. $(a-1)(a+1)$ 6. _____

7. $(4+m)(4-m)$ 7. _____

8. $(3-10r)(3+10r)$ 8. _____

9. $\left(5x+\dfrac{1}{5}\right)\left(5x-\dfrac{1}{5}\right)$ 9. _____

10. $(x^2+5)(x^2-5)$ 10. _____

11. $(n+16)^2$ 11. _____

12. $(w-10)^2$ 12. _____

13. $(8a-9)^2$ 13. _____

14. $\left(3x+\dfrac{1}{3}\right)^2$ 14. _____

15. $\left(5x-\dfrac{1}{5}\right)^2$ 15. _____

16. $(11-10m)^2$ 16. _____

17. $(n^3+12)^2$ 17. _____

18.   Find the area of the area of the shaded region Write the answer as a polynomial in descending powers of x.   18. _____

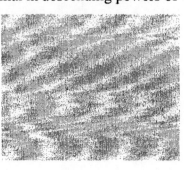

$(8x-10)$

$(4x-10)$

Name _____   Date _____

19.   Find the area of the shaded region. Write the answer as   19. _____
      a polynomial in descending powers of x.

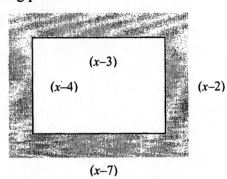

20.   Express the volume of the box as a polynomial in standard   20. _____
      form.

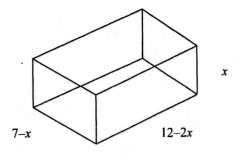

Name _____   Date _____

Additional Exercises 5.3
Form III
Special Products

Perform the indicated operations.

1. $(x+9)(x+4)$

    1. _____

2. $(5x+8)(x-7)$

    2. _____

3. $(3x-7)(4x+12)$

    3. _____

4. $(9-3x)(8-5x)$

    4. _____

5. $(x+5)(x^2-7)$

    5. _____

6. $(a-13)(a+13)$

    6. _____

7. $(7+m)(7-m)$

    7. _____

8. $(5-11r)(5+11r)$

    8. _____

9. $\left(8x+\dfrac{1}{8}\right)\left(8x-\dfrac{1}{8}\right)$

    9. _____

10. $(x^2+7)(x^2-7)$

    10. _____

Name _____   Date _____

11. $(n+21)^2$ 11._____

12. $(w-14)^2$ 12._____

13. $(9a-11)^2$ 13._____

14. $\left(7x+\dfrac{1}{7}\right)^2$ 14._____

15. $\left(9x-\dfrac{1}{9}\right)^2$ 15._____

16. $(12-8m)^2$ 16._____

17. $\left(n^3+15\right)^2$ 17._____

18.   Find the area of the area of the rectangle Write the   18._____
      answer as a polynomial in descending powers of x.

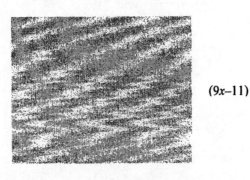

$(9x-11)$

$(5x-2)$

AE-181

Name _____   Date _____

19.   Find the area of the shaded region. Write the answer as   19. _____
       a polynomial in descending powers of x.

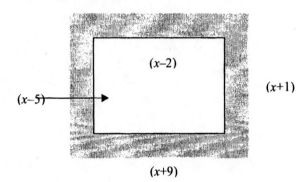

$(x-2)$

$(x+1)$

$(x-5)$

$(x+9)$

20.   Express the volume of the box as a polynomial in standard   20. _____
       form.

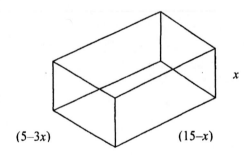

x

$(5-3x)$ $(15-x)$

Name _____ Date _____

Additional Exercises 5.4
Form I
Polynomials in Several Variables

Evaluate the polynomial for the given values of x and y.

1. $2x + 5y - 4$; $x = -2$ and $y = -5$ 1. _____

2. $x^2 + 3y^2$; $x = -1$ and $y = 3$ 2. _____

3. $2y^2 - xy$; $x = 2$ and $y = 3$ 3. _____

4. $4x^2 - 2y^3$; $x = 2$ and $y = -1$ 4. _____

5. $x^3 + 2x^2 y + 2xy^2 + y^3$; $x = -2$ and $y = -3$ 5. _____

Add or subtract as indicated.

6. $\left(-2x^2 y^2 - 4y^4\right) + \left(6x^2 y^2 + 8y^4\right)$ 6. _____

7. $\left(18x^2 y^2 + 7y^4\right) - \left(-5x^4 - 7x^2 y^2 + 5y^4\right)$ 7. _____

8. $\left(3x^2 - xy - y^2\right) + \left(x^2 + 2xy + 4y^2\right)$ 8. _____

9. Add: 9. _____
$6x^2 - xy - y^2$
$\underline{2x^2 + 4xy + 8y^2}$

10. Subtract: 10. _____
$\left(3x^5 + 5x^4 y + 2y^2\right)$
$\underline{-\left(2x^5 - 3x^4 y - 10y^2\right)}$

Find the product.

11. $\left(-3x^3y\right)\left(-2x^4y^7\right)$ 11. _____

12. $\left(6xy^4\right)\left(-2x^3y^5\right)$ 12. _____

13. $4ab^5\left(-3ab^3 + 8b^2\right)$ 13. _____

14. $(x + 7y)(3x + 5y)$ 14. _____

15. $(5x + 2y)(4x - 8y)$ 15. _____

16. $(2x + 7y)^2$ 16. _____

17. $(5x - 2y)^2$ 17. _____

18. $(5x - 4y)(3x - 6y + 2)$ 18. _____

19. $(2a + b)(2a - b)$ 19. _____

20. $(2x - y + 1)(2x - y - 1)$ 20. _____

Name _____   Date _____

Evaluate the polynomial for the given values of x and y.

1. $3x + 7y - 3$; $x = -2$ and $y = -5$ 1. _____

2. $-x^2 + 4y^2$; $x = -1$ and $y = 3$ 2. _____

3. $4y^2 - 3xy$; $x = 2$ and $y = 3$ 3. _____

4. $7x^2 - 4y^3$; $x = 2$ and $y = -1$ 4. _____

5. $x^3 + 3x^2y + 3xy^2 + y^3$; $x = -2$ and $y = -3$ 5. _____

Add or subtract as indicated.

6. $\left(-6x^2y^2 - 6y^4\right) + \left(11x^2y^2 + 16y^4\right)$ 6. _____

7. $\left(24x^2y^2 + 13y^4\right) - \left(8x^4 - 12x^2y^2 + 13y^4\right)$ 7. _____

8. $\left(4x^2 - xy - y^2\right) + \left(x^2 + 6xy + 11y^2\right)$ 8. _____

9. Add: 9. _____
    $9x^2 - xy - y^2$
    $\underline{x^2 + 7xy + 9y^2}$

10. Subtract: 10. _____
    $\left(2x^5 + 6x^4y + 5y^2\right)$
    $\underline{-\left(5x^5 - 4x^4y - 15y^2\right)}$

Name _____   Date _____

Find the product.

11. $\left(-8x^4y\right)\left(-8x^3y^6\right)$ 11. _____

12. $\left(8xy^5\right)\left(-4x^2y^3\right)$ 12. _____

13. $6ab^7\left(-6ab^4+11b^2\right)$ 13. _____

14. $\left(x+11y\right)\left(4x+6y\right)$ 14. _____

15. $\left(7x+4y\right)\left(5x-10y\right)$ 15. _____

16. $\left(3x+5y\right)^2$ 16. _____

17. $\left(7x-9y\right)^2$ 17. _____

18. $\left(7x-12y\right)\left(6x-12y+1\right)$ 18. _____

19. $\left(4a+b\right)\left(4a-b\right)$ 19. _____

20. $\left(3x-y+5\right)\left(3x-y-5\right)$ 20. _____

Additional Exercises 5.4
Form III
Polynomials in Several Variables

Evaluate the polynomial for the given values of x and y.

1. $-6x - 4y - 2$; $x = -2$ and $y = -5$ 1. _____

2. $-x^2 + 6y^2$; $x = -1$ and $y = 3$ 2. _____

3. $5y^2 - 6xy$; $x = 2$ and $y = 3$ 3. _____

4. $9x^2 - 5y^3$; $x = 2$ and $y = -1$ 4. _____

5. $2x^3 - 3x^2y - 4xy^2 + y^3$; $x = -2$ and $y = -3$ 5. _____

Add or subtract as indicated.

6. $\left(8x^2y^2 - 7y^4\right) + \left(15x^2y^2 + 20y^4\right)$ 6. _____

7. $\left(36x^2y^2 + 15y^4\right) - \left(-9x^4 - 15x^2y^2 - 17y^4\right)$ 7. _____

8. $\left(8x^2 - 2xy - 6y^2\right) + \left(3x^2 + 9xy + 15y^2\right)$ 8. _____

9. Add: 9. _____
    $11x^2 - 4xy - 7y^2$
    $\underline{-3x^2 + 8xy + 11y^2}$

10. Subtract: 10. _____
    $\left(7x^5 + 9x^4y + 6y^2\right)$
    $\underline{-\left(6x^5 - 3x^4y - 12y^2\right)}$

Name _____   Date _____

Find the product.

11. $\left(-9x^5y\right)\left(-9x^2y^7\right)$ 11. _____

12. $\left(6xy^6\right)\left(-8x^2y^3\right)$ 12. _____

13. $7ab^6\left(-6a^2b^4+12b^2\right)$ 13. _____

14. $(x+19y)(3x+2y)$ 14. _____

15. $(6x-7y)(5x-11y)$ 15. _____

16. $\left(4x+8y\right)^2$ 16. _____

17. $\left(8x-9y\right)^2$ 17. _____

18. $\left(4x-11y\right)\left(5x-13y+7\right)$ 18. _____

19. $\left(5a+2b\right)\left(5a-2b\right)$ 19. _____

20. $\left(4x-2y+6\right)\left(4x-2y-6\right)$ 20. _____

Name _____   Date _____

Additional Exercises 5.5
Form I
Dividing Polynomials

Perform the indicated operation.

1. $\dfrac{2^5}{2^3}$

2. $\dfrac{x^{11}}{x^9}$

3. $\dfrac{x^4 y^6}{x^2 y^2}$

4. 2^0

5. -3^0

6. (-5^0)

7. $7y^0$

8. $(8x)^0$

9. $\left(\dfrac{-2}{a}\right)^2$

10. $\left(\dfrac{3x^2}{y}\right)^3$

1. _____

2. _____

3. _____

4. _____

5. _____

6. _____

7. _____

8. _____

9. _____

10. _____

11. $\left(\dfrac{2pv^2}{s^3}\right)^2$ 11. _____

12. $\dfrac{-20x^6}{5x^2}$ 12. _____

13. $\dfrac{15x^5y^2z^3}{3x^2yz^2}$ 13. _____

14. $\dfrac{-36x^7y^5}{6x^2y^2}$ 14. _____

15. $\dfrac{-2x^5}{6x^4}$ 15. _____

16. $\dfrac{7x^5y^7}{15x^5y^7}$ 16. _____

17. $\dfrac{21r^6-14r^3}{7}$ 17. _____

18. $\dfrac{-5x^{10}+10x^7}{-5x^5}$ 18. _____

19. $\dfrac{30x^7+40x^6}{10x^3}$ 19. _____

20. $\dfrac{18x^5y^4-27x^7y^5+36x^3y^3}{9x^3y^3}$ 20. _____

Name _____   Date _____

Perform the indicated operation.

1. $\dfrac{4^6}{4^4}$

1. _____

2. $\dfrac{x^{15}}{x^{10}}$

2. _____

3. $\dfrac{x^{13}y^7}{x^2y^3}$

3. _____

4. 3^0

4. _____

5. -2^0

5. _____

6. $(-4)^0$

6. _____

7. $12y^0$

7. _____

8. $(9y)^0$

8. _____

9. $\left(\dfrac{-3}{a}\right)^2$

9. _____

10. $\left(\dfrac{4x^3}{y^2}\right)^4$

10. _____

11. $\left(\dfrac{2p^3v^4}{s^4}\right)^2$ 11. _____

12. $\dfrac{-40x^{13}}{5x^4}$ 12. _____

13. $\dfrac{20x^{12}y^{11}z^3}{4x^4y^2z^2}$ 13. _____

14. $\dfrac{-64x^{12}y^5}{8x^2y^2}$ 14. _____

15. $\dfrac{-3x^{11}}{12x^7}$ 15. _____

16. $\dfrac{8x^6y^{13}}{11x^6y^{13}}$ 16. _____

17. $\dfrac{15r^7-25r^4}{5}$ 17. _____

18. $\dfrac{-8x^{10}+4x^7}{-2x^4}$ 18. _____

19. $\dfrac{20x^{12}+50x^8}{5x^4}$ 19. _____

20. $\dfrac{16x^7y^8-32x^5y^6-36x^3y^4}{4x^3y^4}$ 20. _____

Name _____   Date _____

Additional Exercises 5.5
Form III
Dividing Polynomials

Perform the indicated operation.

1. $\dfrac{11^8}{11^2}$

1. _____

2. $\dfrac{x^{21}}{x^{17}}$

2. _____

3. $\dfrac{x^{11}y^5}{x^9 y^2}$

3. _____

4. 9^0

4. _____

5. -11^0

5. _____

6. $(-8)^0$

6. _____

7. $18y^0$

7. _____

8. $(15y)^0$

8. _____

9. $\left(\dfrac{-7}{a^5}\right)^2$

9. _____

10. $\left(\dfrac{5x^5}{y^3}\right)^4$

10. _____

Name _____   Date _____

11. $\left(\dfrac{5p^6v^8}{s^7}\right)^2$ 11. _____

12. $\dfrac{-80x^{17}}{-10x^5}$ 12. _____

13. $\dfrac{45x^{18}y^{13}z^{12}}{15x^7y^5z}$ 13. _____

14. $\dfrac{-98x^{15}y^4}{49x^{12}y}$ 14. _____

15. $\dfrac{-7x^{10}}{12x^5}$ 15. _____

16. $\dfrac{17x^7y^{12}}{23x^7y^{12}}$ 16. _____

17. $\dfrac{34x^8-51x^5}{17}$ 17. _____

18. $\dfrac{-49x^7+42x^5}{-7x^3}$ 18. _____

19. $\dfrac{55x^8+33x^5}{11x^2}$ 19. _____

20. $\dfrac{50x^7y^8-40x^5y^6-90x^3y^4}{10x^3y^4}$ 20. _____

Name _____   Date _____

Additional Exercises 5.6
Form I
Long Division of Polynomials; Synthetic Division

Divide using long division.

1. $\dfrac{x^2 + 11x + 30}{x + 6}$

1. _____

2. $\dfrac{x^2 - 4x - 5}{x + 1}$

2. _____

3. $\dfrac{x^2 + 4x + 4}{x + 2}$

3. _____

4. $\dfrac{x^2 - 9}{x - 3}$

4. _____

5. $\dfrac{x^2 + x - 6}{x + 3}$

5. _____

6. $\dfrac{x^2 - x - 20}{x - 5}$

6. _____

7. $\dfrac{x^2 - 6x - 27}{x + 3}$

7. _____

8. $\dfrac{x^2 + 15x + 56}{x + 7}$

8. _____

Divide using synthetic division.

9. $\dfrac{x^2 - x - 30}{x - 6}$

9. _____

10. $\dfrac{x^2 + 8x - 9}{x + 9}$

10. _____

11. $\dfrac{6x^2 - x - 2}{2x + 1}$

11. _____

12. $\dfrac{7m^2 + 42m - 49}{m + 7}$

12. _____

13. $\dfrac{7m^3 + 11m^2 + 2m + 16}{m + 2}$

13. _____

14. $\dfrac{6r^3 - 43r^2 - 36r - 32}{r - 8}$

14. _____

15. $\dfrac{-20x^3 + 27x^2 + 7x - 12}{-4x + 3}$

15. _____

Name _____   Date _____

Divide using long division.

1. $\dfrac{x^2 - 4x - 5}{x - 1}$

1. _____

2. $\dfrac{x^2 - 10x - 25}{x - 5}$

2. _____

3. $\dfrac{x^2 + 4x - 14}{x + 6}$

3. _____

4. $\dfrac{x^3 + 6x - 9}{x - 3}$

4. _____

5. $\dfrac{x^3 + 8}{x + 2}$

5. _____

6. $\dfrac{27x^3 + 64}{3x + 4}$

6. _____

7. $\dfrac{p^2 + 4p - 27}{p + 8}$

7. _____

8. $\dfrac{x^2 + 11x + 21}{x + 3}$

8. _____

Name _____   Date _____

Divide using long division.

9. $\dfrac{6x^2 + 7x - 20}{3x - 4}$

9. _____

10. $\dfrac{6y^3 - 8y + 5}{2y - 4}$

10. _____

11. $\dfrac{x^4 - 2x + 5}{x - 2}$

11. _____

12. $\dfrac{3x^3 - 5x^2 + 2x - 1}{x - 2}$

12. _____

13. $\dfrac{y^3 - 1}{y + 1}$

13. _____

14. $\dfrac{r^4 - 16}{r + 2}$

14. _____

15. $\dfrac{x^3 + 3x^2 + 5x + 3}{x + 1}$

15. _____

Name _____   Date _____

Additional Exercises 5.6
Form III
Long Division of Polynomials: Synthetic Division

Divide using long division.

1. $\dfrac{5x^2 - 12x + 16}{5x - 2}$

   1. _____

2. $\dfrac{8y^3 - 22y^2 - 5y + 12}{4y + 3}$

   2. _____

3. $\dfrac{y^6 - 13y^3 + 42}{y^3 - 7}$

   3. _____

4. $\dfrac{a^4 + 9a^2 + 20}{a^2 + 4}$

   4. _____

5. $\dfrac{y^4 - 6y^2 + 9}{y - 3}$

   5. _____

6. $\dfrac{2y^3 - 9y^2 + 11y - 3}{2y - 3}$

   6. _____

7. $\dfrac{3x^4 - 4x^3 - x^2 - 16x - 12}{3x + 2}$

   7. _____

8. $\dfrac{x^3 - 7x + 10}{x + 3}$

   8. _____

Divide using synthetic division.

9. $\dfrac{x^3 - x^2 + x - 1}{x - 1}$

9. _____

10. $\dfrac{y^4 + 2y^3 - y - 2}{y + 2}$

10. _____

11. $\dfrac{x^4 - x^3 + 3x^2 - 2x + 2}{x^2 + 2}$

11. _____

12. $\dfrac{6x^3 - 8x^2 - 2x + 21}{3x + 2}$

12. _____

13. $\dfrac{x^3 - 64}{x - 4}$

13. _____

14. $\dfrac{a^4 - a^3 + 3a^2 - 2a + 2}{a^2 + 2}$

14. _____

15. $\dfrac{15x^3 - 25x^2 - 2x + 26}{-3x + 2}$

15. _____

Additional Exercises 5.7
Form I
Negative Exponents and Scientific Notation

Write the expression with positive exponents only. Then simplify, if possible.

1. -3^{-2} 1. _____

2. $3^{-1} + 2^{-1}$ 2. _____

3. $\dfrac{3^{-3}}{4^{-2}}$ 3. _____

4. $\dfrac{1}{2x^{-2}}$ 4. _____

Simplify the expression.

5. $x^{-8} \cdot x^3$ 5. _____

6. $2x^{-1}$ 6. _____

7. $\dfrac{6p^{-6}}{5}$ 7. _____

8. $x^4 y^{-10}$ 8. _____

9. $\dfrac{8}{x^{-2}}$ 9. _____

Write the number in decimal notation with the use of exponents.

10. 1.25×10^3 10. _____

11. 3.957×10^{-2} 11. _____

12. 2.0351×10^{-4} 12. _____

13. 4.7×10^0 13. _____

Write the number in scientific notation.

14.   34.18   14. _____

15.   19,000   15. _____

16.   0.0014   16. _____

17. $\dfrac{6 \times 10^5}{2 \times 10^3}$ 17. _____

18. $(1 \times 10^2)(2 \times 10^{-3})$ 18. _____

19. $(3 \times 10^2)^2$ 19. _____

20.   A bacterium measures 0.000000251 centimeters. Rewrite   20. _____
       the number in scientific notation.

Additional Exercises 5.7
Form II
Negative Exponents and Scientific Notation

Write the expression with positive exponents only. Then simplify, if possible.

1. $-(4)^{-2}$ 1. _____

2. $\dfrac{1}{23} \cdot \dfrac{1}{(4)^{-2}}$ 2. _____

3. $\dfrac{(4)^{-2}}{(5)^{-2}}$ 3. _____

4. $\dfrac{1}{3x^{-3}}$ 4. _____

Simplify the expression.

5. $x^{-7} \cdot x^{5}$ 5. _____

6. $\dfrac{12x^{2}}{6x^{6}}$ 6. _____

7. $\dfrac{5p^{-7}}{2p^{3}}$ 7. _____

8. $(x^{-1}y^{6})^{-2}$ 8. _____

9. $\dfrac{(3x^{4})^{3}}{x^{15}}$ 9. _____

Write the number in decimal notation with the use of exponents.

10. 1.18×10^{7} 10. _____

11. 7.36×10^{-4} 11. _____

12. 1.0483×10^{-7} 12. _____

13. 4.48×10^{0} 13. _____

Write the number in scientific notation.

14.   697.35   14. _____

15.   65,000,000   15. _____

16.   0.00007948   16. _____

17. $\dfrac{8 \times 10^{-9}}{2 \times 10^{-6}}$ 17. _____

18. $(4 \times 10^{3})(2 \times 10^{-6})$ 18. _____

19. $(2 \times 10^{3})^{2}$ 19. _____

20.   A bacterium measures 0.0000000896 centimeters. Rewrite   20. _____
       the number in scientific notation.

Name _____   Date _____

Additional Exercises 5.7
Form III
Negative Exponents and Scientific Notation

Write the expression with positive exponents only. Then simplify, if possible.

1. -6^{-3}

         1. _____

2. $8^{-1} + 11^{-1}$

         2. _____

3. $\dfrac{5^{-3}}{7^{-3}}$

         3. _____

4. $\dfrac{1}{8x^{-6}}$

         4. _____

Simplify the expression.

5. $x^{-11} \cdot x^{9}$

         5. _____

6. $\dfrac{18x^{5}}{3x^{9}}$

         6. _____

7. $\dfrac{7p^{-9}}{3p^{2}}$

         7. _____

8. $(x^{-3}y^{4})^{-2}$

         8. _____

9. $\dfrac{(5x^{6})^{3}}{x^{12}}$

         9. _____

Name _____   Date _____

Write the number in decimal notation with the use of exponents.

10. 3.05×10^{4} 10. _____

11. 9.18×10^{-3} 11. _____

12. 1.1936×10^{-8} 12. _____

13. 5.7×10^{0} 13. _____

Write the number in scientific notation.

14.   1045.7   14. _____

15.   29,000,000,000   15. _____

16.   0.0000057   16. _____

17. $\dfrac{16 \times 10^{-8}}{4 \times 10^{-6}}$ 17. _____

18. $(6 \times 10^{4})(3 \times 10^{-2})$ 18. _____

19. $(5 \times 10^{-3})^{4}$ 19. _____

20.   A bacterium measures 0.00000077 centimeters. Rewrite   20. _____
      the number in scientific notation.

Name _____   Date _____

Additional Exercises 6.1
Form I
The Greatest Common Factor and Factoring by Grouping

Find the greatest common factor of each list of monomials.

1. $10x^2$ and $15x$ 1. _____

2. $12y^3$ and $8y^2$ 2. _____

3. $16a^2$, $24a^3$ and $32a^4$ 3. _____

4. $6x^3y^2$, $15x^2y$ and $21x^4$ 4. _____

Factor the greatest common factor from the polynomial. If there is no factor other then 1 and the polynomial cannot be factored, so state.

5. $5x^2 + 20$ 5. _____

6. $6a^3 + 18a^2$ 6. _____

7. $3y^3 + 5y^2 + 6y$ 7. _____

8. $24x^4 + 18x^2 - 12x$ 8. _____

9. $16x^4y^3 - 20x^3y^2 + 12xy$ 9. _____

10. $4x^5y^2 + 10x^4y^4 - 14x^3y^3$ 10. _____

Factor out the common binomial factor from each polynomial.

11. $x(y+14)+6(y+14)$ 11. _____

12. $a(b-7)-3(b-7)$ 12. _____

13. $11(x+10)-y(x+10)$ 13. _____

Factor by grouping.

14. $xy+4y+2x+8$ 14. _____

15. $ab+3b-6a-18$ 15. _____

16. $xy-5y+x-5$ 16. _____

17. x^3-2x^2+2x-4 17. _____

18. $6ab+2b+9a+3$ 18. _____

19. $5xy+2y-10x-4$ 19. _____

20. x^4-x^3+2x-2 20. _____

Name _____   Date _____

Additional Exercises 6.1
Form II
The Greatest Common Factor and Factoring by Grouping

Find the greatest common factor of each list of monomials.

1. $12x^2$ and $20x$ 1. _____

2. $45x^2y^2$ and $36xy$ 2. _____

3. $64a^9b^2$ and $88a^5b^9$ 3. _____

4. $24m^5n^3$, $18m^4n^4$ and $30m^3n^2$ 4. _____

Factor the greatest common factor from the polynomial. If there is no factor other then 1 and the polynomial cannot be factored, so state.

5. $14x^3 + 21x^2$ 5. _____

6. $6x^5 - 5x^7$ 6. _____

7. $24a^9 - 30a^5 + 15a^3$ 7. _____

8. $20x^6y^3 - 44x^5y^4 + 36x^3y^6$ 8. _____

9. $40x^8y^8 - 16x^3y^6 - 20x^6y^4$ 9. _____

10. $15x^6y^5 - 25x^4y^3 + 55x^3y^4 - 60x^2y^4$ 10. _____

AE-209

Factor out the common binomial factor from each polynomial.

11. $x(y-7) - 2(y-7)$

11. _____

12. $a^2(b+3) + 4(b+3)$

12. _____

13. $4a(8+b) - (8+b)$

13. _____

Factor by grouping.

14. $x^3 - 2x^2 - 3x + 6$

14. _____

15. $xy + 5y + 4x + 20$

15. _____

16. $b^3 + 2ab^2 + 4b + 8a$

16. _____

17. $6xy + 4y + 15x + 10$

17. _____

18. $14xy - 2x - 21y + 3$

18. _____

19. $4x^4 - 8x^3 - 3x + 6$

19. _____

20. $20a^3 + 15a^2b - 16ab^2 - 12b^3$

20. _____

Additional Exercises 6.1
Form III
The Greatest Common Factor and Factoring by Grouping

Find the greatest common factor of each list of monomials.

1. $28x^4$ and $24x^2$

1. _____

2. $18x^8$, $45x^6$ and $21x^4$

2. _____

3. $12x^6y^4$, $30x^9y^2$ and $84x^5y^5$

3. _____

Factor the greatest common factor from the polynomial. If there is no factor other then 1 and the polynomial cannot be factored, so state.

4. $21y^3 - 9y^2 + 12y$

4. _____

5. $32x^5 + 24x^3y - 96xy^3$

5. _____

6. $20a^3 - 15a^2 + 5a$

6. _____

7. $48x^8y^9 + 40x^6y^6 + 64x^4y^3$

7. _____

8. $16m^3n^3 - 48n^2n - 64mn^2$

8. _____

Factor out the common binomial factor from each polynomial.

9. $x^2(x-3) + 6(x-3)$

9. _____

10. $y(x+7) - (x+7)$

10. _____

11. $6x^2(2x-7)+(2x-7)$ 11. _____

Factor by grouping.

12. $x^4-3x^3-4x^2+12x$ 12. _____

13. $ab-4b^2+6a-24b$ 13. _____

14. $10xy+16y-5x-8$ 14. _____

15. $6mn+2n-27m-9$ 15. _____

16. $9x^3-6x^2+15x-10$ 16. _____

17. $20x^4-25x^3+12x^2-15x$ 17. _____

18. $12a^3-16a^2-9a+12$ 18. _____

Solve.

19.   The area of a rectangle is $2x^2+6xy+4xy+12y^2$. The width   19. _____
        of the rectangle is $x+3y$. Write a polynomial for the length
        of the rectangle.

20.   The width of a rectangle is $2x+y$. The length of the rectangle   20. _____
        is $2x^2-5$. Write a polynomial for the area of the rectangle.

Name _____   Date _____

Factor each trinomial, or state that the trinomial is prime.

1. $x^2 + 5x + 4$

1. _____

2. $x^2 + 7x + 12$

2. _____

3. $y^2 + 8y + 12$

3. _____

4. $a^2 - 6a + 8$

4. _____

5. $x^2 - 8x + 15$

5. _____

6. $y^2 - 8y + 7$

6. _____

7. $a^2 + a - 6$

7. _____

8. $x^2 - 3x - 40$

8. _____

9. $m^2 - 3m - 4$

9. _____

10. $a^2 + 4ab - 21b^2$

10. _____

11. $a^2 - 6xy - 27y^2$ 11. _____

12. $x^2 - 6xy - 27y^2$ 12. _____

13. $a^2 - 11a + 30$ 13. _____

14. $x^2 + 11x + 28$ 14. _____

Factor each trinomial completely.

15. $2x^2 - 4x - 6$ 15. _____

16. $3a^2 - 15a + 18$ 16. _____

17. $x^3 + 7x^2 + 6x$ 17. _____

18. $x^3y + 2x^2y - 35xy$ 18. _____

19. $4x^2 - 32x + 48$ 19. _____

20. $8a^3 + 56a^2 + 96a$ 20. _____

Name _____   Date _____

Factor each trinomial, or state that the trinomial is prime.

1. $x^2 + 10x + 16$ 1. _____

2. $x^2 - 10x + 24$ 2. _____

3. $x^2 - x - 30$ 3. _____

4. $a^2 + 10a + 21$ 4. _____

5. $y^2 + 9y - 36$ 5. _____

6. $x^2 - 15x + 54$ 6. _____

7. $x^2 + 5x - 36$ 7. _____

8. $a^2 + 14a + 33$ 8. _____

9. $m^2 + 6m + 10$ 9. _____

10. $x^2 - 11x + 10$ 10. _____

11. $y^2 + y - 42$ 11. _____

12. $a^2 + 9a + 20$ 12. _____

13. $x^2 - 9x - 8$ 13. _____

14. $y^2 - 12y + 32$ 14. _____

Factor each trinomial completely.

15. $5x^2 + 10x - 15$ 15. _____

16. $4x^2 + 28x + 48$ 16. _____

17. $x^4 + 2x^3 - 48x^2$ 17. _____

18. $2a^3 + 18a^2 + 40a$ 18. _____

19. $x^3y^2 + 3x^2y^2 - 40xy^2$ 19. _____

20. $6y^3 + 66y^2 + 148y$ 20. _____

Name _____   Date _____

Factor each trinomial, or state that the trinomial is prime.

1. $x^2 + 14x + 45$ 1. _____

2. $a^2 - 5a - 24$ 2. _____

3. $y^2 + 9y + 14$ 3. _____

4. $x^2 - 18x + 32$ 4. _____

5. $x^2 - 13x + 12$ 5. _____

6. $y^2 - 3y - 88$ 6. _____

7. $a^2 + 15ab - 16b^2$ 7. _____

8. $x^2 + 3x + 12$ 8. _____

9. $y^2 - 16y + 39$ 9. _____

10. $a^2 - 25a + 136$ 10. _____

11. $x^2 + 21xy + 54y^2$ 11. _____

12. $y^2 - 8y + 12$ 12. _____

13. $a^2 - 11a + 28$ 13. _____

14. $x^2 - 11xy - 60y^2$ 14. _____

Factor each trinomial completely.

15. $4x^3 - 8x^2 + 16x$ 15. _____

16. $5x^2 - 30x - 80$ 16. _____

17. $3a^3 + 27a^2 + 60a$ 17. _____

18. $x^4y + 2x^3y - 24x^2y$ 18. _____

19. $6y^3 - 30y^2 - 216$ 19. _____

20. $8x^3 + 56x^2y + 96xy^2$ 20. _____

Additional Exercises 6.3
Form I
Factoring Trinomials Whose Leading Coefficient is Not 1

Use the method of your choice to factor each trinomial, or state that the trinomial is prime.

1. $2x^2 + 9x + 4$ 1. _____

2. $3x^2 + 16x + 5$ 2. _____

3. $4a^2 + 11a + 6$ 3. _____

4. $3x^2 + 22x - 16$ 4. _____

5. $2y^2 - y - 15$ 5. _____

6. $3x^2 - 14x - 5$ 6. _____

7. $4a^2 - 13a + 10$ 7. _____

8. $6x^2 - 19x + 3$ 8. _____

9. $6y^2 - 13y + 6$ 9. _____

10. $8x^2 + 6x + 1$ 10. _____

11. $10x^2 - 17x + 3$ 11. _____

12. $12y^2 + 4y - 5$ 12. _____

13. $16a^2 - 34a - 15$ 13. _____

Factor completely.

14. $6x^2 + 26x + 8$ 14. _____

15. $24x^2 - 66x + 15$ 15. _____

16. $10a^4 + a^3 - 2a^2$ 16. _____

17. $8y^3 + 28y^2 + 24y$ 17. _____

18. $3x^4 - 4x^3 - 4x^2$ 18. _____

19. $8a^3 - 18a^2 - 18a$ 19. _____

20. $10x^2 + 45x + 50$ 20. _____

Name _____   Date _____

Additional Exercises 6.3
Form II
Factoring Trinomials Whose Leading Coefficient is Not 1

Use the method of your choice to factor each trinomial, or state that the trinomial is prime.

1. $6x^2 + 11x + 3$ 1. _____

2. $4x^2 + 11x + 6$ 2. _____

3. $10x^2 + 27x + 5$ 3. _____

4. $8x^2 - 14x + 5$ 4. _____

5. $12x^2 - 25x + 5$ 5. _____

6. $10x^2 + x - 24$ 6. _____

7. $8x^2 + 33x + 4$ 7. _____

8. $14x^2 + 17x - 6$ 8. _____

9. $6x^2 - 7x - 10$ 9. _____

10. $16x^2 - 8x - 15$ 10. _____

11. $12x^2 + 52xy - 9y^2$ 11. _____

12. $16x^2 + 34x - 15$ 12. _____

13. $3x^2 - 5xy - 28y^2$ 13. _____

Factor completely.

14. $8a^2 + 12a + 4$ 14. _____

15. $18a^2 + 66a - 24$ 15. _____

16. $20y^2 - 35y - 10$ 16. _____

17. $12x^3 + 18x^2 + 24x$ 17. _____

18. $12a^3 - 12a^2 - 45a$ 18. _____

19. $32y^3 + 68y^2 - 30y$ 19. _____

20. $48x^2 - 40x - 32$ 20. _____

Additional Exercises 6.3
Form III
Factoring Trinomials Whose Leading Coefficient is Not 1

Use the method of your choice to factor each polynomial, or state that the polynomial is prime.

1. $7x^2 + 18x + 11$ 1. _____

2. $2a^2 - a - 28$ 2. _____

3. $2x^2 + 7x + 1$ 3. _____

4. $15x^2 + 28x + 12$ 4. _____

5. $9x^2 + 14x - 8$ 5. _____

6. $10a^2 + 7a - 12$ 6. _____

7. $24y^2 + 29y - 4$ 7. _____

8. $15x^2 + xy - 2y^2$ 8. _____

9. $x^4 + 7x^3 + 6x^2$ 9. _____

10. $15b^2 + 14b - 8$ 10. _____

11. $20x^2 + 21x - 27$ 11. _____

12. $4x^2 - 14xy - 8y^2$ 12. _____

13. $10a^2 - 11a + 18$ 13. _____

14. $42x^2 + 35x - 42$ 14. _____

15. $12a^2 + 19a + 4$ 15. _____

16. $18y^2 - 78y - 60$ 16. _____

17. $60x^2 + 35xy + 5y^2$ 17. _____

18. $8x^2 - 30x + 25$ 18. _____

19. $16x^3y^4 + 40x^2y^5 + 25xy^6$ 19. _____

20.   The area of a rectangle is $36x^2 + 66x + 30$. If the length is   20. _____
        $6x + 6$, express the width as a binomial.

Additional Exercises 6.4
Form I
Factoring Special Forms

Factor each difference of two squares.

1. $x^2 - 64$ 1. _____

2. $a^2 - 1$ 2. _____

3. $y^2 - 100$ 3. _____

4. $4x^2 - 25$ 4. _____

Factor any perfect square trinomials, or state that the polynomial is prime.

5. $x^2 + 10x + 25$ 5. _____

6. $y^2 + 6y + 9$ 6. _____

7. $a^2 - 8a + 16$ 7. _____

8. $a^2 - 20a + 100$ 8. _____

Factor each sum or difference of two cubes.

9. $x^3 - 1$ 9. _____

10. $y^3 + 64$

10. _____

11. $x^3 - 8y^3$

11. _____

12. $a^3 + 27b^3$

12. _____

Factor each polynomial completely, or state that the polynomial is prime.

13. $2x^2 - 2$

13. _____

14. $3x^2 - 24x + 48$

14. _____

15. $x^3 - 16x$

15. _____

16. $5y^2 + 20y + 20$

16. _____

17. $7x^2 - 28$

17. _____

18. $100x^2 - 400y^2$

18. _____

19. $4a^2 - 40a + 100$

19. _____

20. $8x^2 + 48x + 72$

20. _____

Name _____   Date _____

Factor each difference of two squares.

1. $x^2 - 121$ 1. _____

2. $4a^2 - 81$ 2. _____

3. $16y^2 - 169$ 3. _____

4. $x^2 - 225$ 4. _____

Factor any perfect square trinomials, or state that the polynomial is prime.

5. $x^2 - 4x + 4$ 5. _____

6. $y^2 + 3y + 9$ 6. _____

7. $x^2 - 10xy + 25y^2$ 7. _____

8. $4x^2 + 6xy + 9$ 8. _____

Factor each sum or difference of two cubes.

9. $x^3 - 1000$ 9. _____

10. $a^3 + 8b^3$ 10. _____

11. $y^3 - 27$ 11. _____

12. $25x^2 + 30xy + 9y^2$ 12. _____

Factor each polynomial completely, or state that the polynomial is prime.

13. $5x^2 - 20$ 13. _____

14. $12x^2 + 60x + 75$ 14. _____

15. $x^2 + 25$ 15. _____

16. $ab^4 - 64a^3b^2$ 16. _____

17. $9y^3 - 9y$ 17. _____

18. $12x^3 + 84x^2 + 147x$ 18. _____

19. $x^4 - 16$ 19. _____

20. $20x^2 - 125$ 20. _____

Additional Exercises 6.4
Form III
Factoring Special Forms

Factor each difference of two squares.

1. $49x^2 - 64$ 1. _____

2. $y^2 + 16$ 2. _____

3. $x^2 - 12x + 36$ 3. _____

4. $18a^2 - 72$ 4. _____

5. $9x^2 - 30x + 25$ 5. _____

6. $32x^2 + 48x + 18$ 6. _____

7. $a^3 + 125b^3$ 7. _____

8. $49x^2 + 14x + 1$ 8. _____

9. $4x^3 - 36xy + 81y^2$ 9. _____

10. $8 - m^3$ 10. _____

11. $32x^2 - 98$ 11. _____

12. $16x^2 + 64y^2$ 12. _____

13. $20x^2 + 100xy + 125y^2$ 13. _____

14. $54x^4 + 128y^3$ 14. _____

15. $25x^2 + 121$ 15. _____

16. $16a^3 - 54b^3$ 16. _____

17. $81m^2 + 234mn + 169n^2$ 17. _____

18. $x^6 - 81y^4$ 18. _____

19. $(x + 8)^2 - 4$ 19. _____

20. $25a^2 + 150a + 225$ 20. _____

Name _____   Date _____

Factor each polynomial completely, or state that the polynomial is prime.

1. $x^2 - 64$

1. _____

2. $8x^2 + 10x - 3$

2. _____

3. $a^2 - 14a + 14$

3. _____

4. $3x^2 - 18$

4. _____

5. $10x^2 + 17x + 3$

5. _____

6. $x^2 + 9x + 14$

6. _____

7. $x^4 + 4x^3 - 12x^2$

7. _____

8. $xy + 5y - 4x - 20$

8. _____

9. $2a^2 + 4a + 2$

9. _____

10. $y^3 - 5y^2 - 24y$

10. _____

11. $6m^2 + 17m + 12$ 11. _____

12. $4x^2 - 64$ 12. _____

13. $x^3 - 8x^2 + 4x - 32$ 13. _____

14. $14x^2 - 7x - 105$ 14. _____

15. $2y^3 - 16$ 15. _____

16. $16a^2 + 9b^2$ 16. _____

17. $4x^5 - 8x^3$ 17. _____

18. $30x^3y - 9x^2y - 12xy$ 18. _____

19. $40x^3 - 5$ 19. _____

20. $4x^2y^2 + 16y^2 - 32x^2 - 128$ 20. _____

Name _____   Date _____

Additional Exercises 6.5
Form II
A General Factoring Strategy

Factor each polynomial completely, or state that the polynomial is prime.

1. $y^3 - 64$ 1. _____

2. $3x^2 - 75$ 2. _____

3. $16x^2 - 16x - 60$ 3. _____

4. $x^2y - 4x^2 + 6y - 24$ 4, _____

5. $21x^2 - 52x + 32$ 5. _____

6. $36x^2 - 25y^2$ 6. _____

7. $4a^3 + 256$ 7. _____

8. $5x^3y - 4xy^2$ 8. _____

9. $6x^2 + 84x + 294$ 9. _____

10. $12x^2 + 41x + 24$ 10. _____

11. $48y^3 - 6$

11. _____

12. $18xy - 12x + 45y - 10$

12. _____

13. $16a^2 + 81$

13. _____

14. $a^3b^2 + 2a^2b^3 + ab^4$

14. _____

15. $48x^2 - 64x - 35$

15. _____

16. $4x^2 + 8x + 25$

16. _____

17. $3a^3 - 375b^3$

17. _____

18. $16x^4 - 81$

18. _____

19. $18x^3 + 12x^2 + 2x$

19. _____

20. $x^3y^3 - 3xy^3 + 4x^3 - 12x$

20. _____

Additional Exercises 6.5
Form III
A General Factoring Strategy

Factor each polynomial completely, or state that the polynomial is prime.

1. $a^4 - 81$ 1. _____

2. $18x^2 + 9x - 35$ 2. _____

3. $8y^3 - 125$ 3. _____

4. $12x^2y^2 + 9x^2 - 8y^2 - 6$ 4. _____

5. $44a^2 + 44a - 33$ 5. _____

6. $64y^2 - 25$ 6. _____

7. $5x^2y + 14x^2y - 24xy$ 7. _____

8. $40a^2b + 32a^2 - 50ab^2 - 40ab$ 8. _____

9. $36y^2 - 84y + 49$ 9. _____

10. $81x^4 - 625$ 10. _____

11. $45a^2 - 120a + 80$ 11. _____

12. $16x^2 + 20xy + 25y^2$ 12. _____

13. $18x^3y^2 - 25x^2y^3 - 50xy^4$ 13. _____

14. $54a^3 + 16$ 14. _____

15. $25y^2 - 100$ 15. _____

16. $10x^2 - 21x - 108$ 16. _____

17. $x^6 - y^6$ 17. _____

18. $45x^2 + 162x - 72$ 18. _____

19. $a^6 - 8b^6$ 19. _____

20. $16a^{10} + 9b^{10}$ 20. _____

Name _____   Date _____

Solve each equation using the zero product principle.

1. $(x-9)(x+7)=0$ 1. _____

2. $(y+12)(y+8)=0$ 2. _____

3. $(3x+1)(2x-1)=0$ 3. _____

4. $x(x-5)=0$ 4. _____

5. $x(x+3)(5x-4)=0$ 5. _____

Use factoring to solve each quadratic equation.

6. $x^2-5x+4=0$ 6. _____

7. $3x^2-10x-8=0$ 7. _____

8. $x^2-x=20$ 8. _____

9. $x^2+4x=12$ 9. _____

10. $6x^2 = 2 - x$ 10. _____

11. $y^2 = 49$ 11. _____

12. $3x^2 - 27x + 60 = 0$ 12. _____

13. $8x^2 - 28x = 120$ 13. _____

14. $2x(x - 5) = 12$ 14. _____

15. $18y^2 - 30y = 0$ 15. _____

16. $9x^2 = 12x - 4$ 16. _____

Solve.

17.   The width of a rectangle is 6 meters less than the length.   17. _____
        The area of the rectangle is 40 square meters. Find the
        dimensions of the rectangle.

18.   An object is thrown upward from the top of a 160 foot   18. _____
        building with an initial velocity of 48 feet per second. The
        height h of the object after t seconds is given by the quadratic
        equation $h = -16t^2 + 48t + 160$. How long will it take for the
        object to hit the ground?

Additional Exercises 6.6
Form II
Solving Quadratic Equations by Factoring

Solve each equation using the zero product principle.

1. $(x - 7)(x - 10) = 0$ 1. _____

2. $(y + 4)(y + 12) = 0$ 2. _____

3. $(5x - 4)(x + 9) = 0$ 3. _____

4. $x(x + 6)(x - 7) = 0$ 4. _____

5. $4x(x + 3)(4x - 7) = 0$ 5. _____

Use factoring to solve each quadratic equation.

6. $y^2 - 9y + 8 = 0$ 6. _____

7. $4x^2 + 13x - 12 = 0$ 7. _____

8. $5x^2 - 23x = 10$ 8. _____

9. $4x^2 - 25 = 0$ 9. _____

10. $3x^2 - 20x = 7$ 10. _____

11. $2x(4x + 13) = 7$ 11. _____

12. $3x^2 = 14x + 80$ 12. _____

13. $25y^2 + 25y + 6 = 0$ 13. _____

14. $24x^2 + 42x = 0$ 14. _____

15. $x^3 + 15x = 8x^2$ 15. _____

16. $4x(x^2 + 2) = 9x^2$ 16. _____

Solve.

17.   The length of a rectangle is 8 inches less than twice the width.   17. _____
        If the area of the rectangle is 90 square inches, what are the
        dimensions of the rectangle?

18.   A window washer accidentally drops a bucket from the top of a   18. _____
        64 foot building. The height h of the bucket after t seconds is
        given by the quadratic equation $h = -16t^2 + 64$. When will the
        bucket hit the ground?

Name _____ Date _____

Solve each equation using the zero product principle.

1. $(7x+4)(x-2)=0$ 1. _____

2. $(x-8)(3x-10)=0$ 2. _____

3. $x(3x+15)=0$ 3. _____

4. $y(y+17)=0$ 4. _____

5. $x(5x-1)(x-8)=0$ 5. _____

Use factoring to solve each quadratic equation.

6. $5x^2-4x-9=0$ 6. _____

7. $x^2-24x=25$ 7. _____

8. $13y^2-6y=0$ 8. _____

9. $16x^2=25$ 9. _____

10. $4x^2 = 20x - 25$ 10. _____

11. $16x^3 + 28x^2 = 30x$ 11. _____

12. $x(3x - 5) = 28$ 12. _____

13. $x(5x + 8) = 4$ 13. _____

14. $3x^3 - 75x = 0$ 14. _____

15. $y(2y + 5) = 2(36 - y)$ 15. _____

16. $5x(x - 5) = 3(x + 4)$ 16. _____

Solve.

17.   The length of a rectangle is 6 feet less than twice the width.   17. _____
        If the area of the rectangle is 216 square feet, find the
        dimensions of the rectangle.

18.   If the sides of a square are increased by 2 meters, the area   18. _____
        becomes 64 square meters. Find the length of a side of the
        original square.

19.   A window washer accidentally drops a bucket from the top of   19. _____
        a 100 foot tall building. The height h of the bucket after t seconds
        is given by $h = -16t^2 + 100$. How long will it be before the bucket
        hits the ground?

20.   Each cycle of a screen saver program generates and then erases   20. _____
        numbers of little animated figures called *froobies*. The formula
        $P = -2x^2 + 106x - 674$ models the population, P, of froobies
        after x minutes within a cycle. How many minutes into a cycle
        will the *froobie* population first reach 118?

Name _____   Date _____

Find all values that make the expression undefined.

1. $\dfrac{7}{a+1}$

1. _____

2. $\dfrac{4}{a-3}$

2. _____

3. $\dfrac{x-2}{5}$

3. _____

4. $\dfrac{m+4}{3-m}$

4. _____

5. $\dfrac{3x-2}{y^2-16}$

5. _____

6. $\dfrac{x^2-64}{x^2-4x-5}$

6. _____

7. $\dfrac{6}{x^2+9}$

7. _____

8. $\dfrac{24x^4}{6x^3}$

8. _____

Name _____   Date _____

Simplify the expression.

9. $\dfrac{2x+4}{2}$

9. _____

10. $\dfrac{3x-9}{x-3}$

10. _____

11. $\dfrac{8-m}{m-8}$

11. _____

12. $\dfrac{x+5}{x^2-25}$

12. _____

13. $\dfrac{5x+1}{5x-1}$

13. _____

14. $\dfrac{x^2-25}{x^2-10x+25}$

14. _____

15. A tennis racket company has manufacturing costs given by the
equation $C = \dfrac{40x+40{,}000}{x}$ where x is the number of rackets
manufactured and C is the cost to manufacture each racket. Find
the cost per racket when manufacturing 1000 rackets.

15. _____

Additional Exercises 7.1
Form II
Rational Expressions and Their Simplification

Find all values that make the expression undefined.

1. $\dfrac{9}{a-8}$ 1. _____

2. $\dfrac{4}{a+6}$ 2. _____

3. $\dfrac{r-7}{4}$ 3. _____

4. $\dfrac{m-8}{6-m}$ 4. _____

5. $\dfrac{5y-4}{y^2-49}$ 5. _____

6. $\dfrac{x^2-100}{x^2+13x+40}$ 6. _____

7. $\dfrac{x^2-36}{x^2-10x+16}$ 7. _____

Simplify the expression.

8. $\dfrac{10k^3}{5k}$ 8. _____

9. $\dfrac{4x+4}{12x^2+20x+8}$ 9. _____

10. $\dfrac{y^2+14y+49}{y^2+15y+56}$ 10. _____

11. $\dfrac{4-m}{m-4}$ 11. _____

12. $\dfrac{2k-4}{14-7k}$ 12. _____

13. $\dfrac{4x^2-10x+6}{x-1}$ 13. _____

14. $\dfrac{7x^2+21x^3}{4x+12x^2}$ 14. _____

15.   A tennis racket company has manufacturing costs given by the   15. _____
equation $C = \dfrac{40x+40{,}000}{x}$ where x is the number of rackets
manufactured and C is the cost to manufacture each racket. Find
the cost per racket to manufacture 5000 rackets.

Name _____   Date _____

Additional Exercises 7.1
Form III
Rational Expressions and Their Simplification

Find all values that make the expression undefined.

1. $\dfrac{a+7}{a^2-25}$

1. _____

2. $\dfrac{x-8}{x^2-6x+9}$

2. _____

3. $\dfrac{7x}{3x^2-5x-2}$

3. _____

4. $\dfrac{2x+9}{4x^2-25x-21}$

4. _____

5. $\dfrac{a-7}{3a^2-a-4}$

5. _____

6. $\dfrac{17}{5a^2-19a-4}$

6. _____

7. $\dfrac{x^3+4x^2}{x^2+49}$

7. _____

Simplify the expression.

8. $\dfrac{x^2-7x+12}{x^2-9x+20}$

8. _____

9. $\dfrac{6x+24}{x^2-16}$

9. _____

10. $\dfrac{x^2-y^2}{x^3-y^3}$

10. _____

11. $\dfrac{x^2-4x-12}{x^2+8x+12}$

11. _____

12. $\dfrac{a^2-ab+10a-10b}{a+10}$

12. _____

13. $\dfrac{y^3-8}{y-2}$

13. _____

14. $\dfrac{x^2+4x+25}{x^2+5x+6}$

14. _____

15. A tennis racket company has manufacturing costs given by the equation $C=\dfrac{40x+40{,}000}{x}$ where x is the number of rackets manufactured and C is the cost to manufacture each racket. Find the cost per racket to manufacture 32,000 rackets.

15. _____

Name _____ Date _____

Additional Exercises 7.2
Form I
Multiplying and Dividing Rational Expressions

Perform the indicated operations. Simplify if possible.

1. $\dfrac{3x^2}{4} \cdot \dfrac{32}{x^3}$

1. _____

2. $\dfrac{3z^3}{5} \cdot \dfrac{30}{z^2}$

2. _____

3. $\dfrac{a}{b} \cdot \dfrac{b}{c} \cdot \dfrac{c}{d}$

3. _____

4. $\dfrac{5}{x} \cdot \dfrac{x^2}{15}$

4. _____

5. $\dfrac{8x}{3} \cdot \dfrac{9}{12x^2}$

5. _____

6. $8x^4 \cdot \dfrac{x^2 y}{16x^3 y^2}$

6. _____

7. $\dfrac{y+5}{y} \cdot \dfrac{y}{y^2-25}$

7. _____

8. $\dfrac{x+y}{x-y} \cdot \dfrac{x^2-y^2}{2x+2y}$

8. _____

9. $\dfrac{2x^2}{5} \div \dfrac{x^3}{35}$ 9. _____

10. $\dfrac{3p-3}{p} \div \dfrac{10p-10}{9p^2}$ 10. _____

11. $\dfrac{(y-2)^2}{3} \div \dfrac{3y-6}{9}$ 11. _____

12. $\dfrac{21x-21}{12} \div \dfrac{7x-7}{60}$ 12. _____

13. $\dfrac{x^2-y^2}{x^2+y^2} \div (x+y)$ 13. _____

14. $\dfrac{4x-12}{4} \div \dfrac{5x-15}{8}$ 14. _____

15. $\dfrac{4}{x^2-16} \div \dfrac{8x-4}{x+4}$ 15. _____

Name _____   Date _____

Additional Exercises 7.2
Form II
Multiplying and Dividing Rational Expressions

Perform the indicated operations. Simplify if possible.

1. $\dfrac{4p-4}{p} \cdot \dfrac{3p^2}{5p-5}$

    1. _____

2. $\dfrac{a^2-16}{a^2-25} \cdot \dfrac{a-5}{a-4}$

    2. _____

3. $\dfrac{x-3}{x-2} \cdot \dfrac{x^2-4}{x^2-9}$

    3. _____

4. $\dfrac{x^2-4}{3x-12} \cdot \dfrac{x-4}{x^2+6x+8}$

    4. _____

5. $x^2-49 \cdot \dfrac{5}{x+7}$

    5. _____

6. $\dfrac{3x-3}{3} \cdot \dfrac{1}{x^2-3x+2}$

    6. _____

7. $\dfrac{x^2-6x+9}{x+2} \cdot \dfrac{x^2-4}{x-3}$

    7. _____

8. $\dfrac{x^2+7x+12}{12} \cdot \dfrac{4}{x+4}$

    8. _____

9. $\dfrac{x+y}{x-y} \div \dfrac{y+x}{y-x}$

                                                      9. _____

10. $x^2 - 5x - 14 \div \dfrac{x^2 - 4x - 21}{x+3}$

                                                      10. _____

11. $\dfrac{x^2 - 4x + 4}{5x - 10} \div \dfrac{11x - 22}{55}$

                                                      11. _____

12. $\dfrac{x^2 + 13x + 40}{x - 5} \div x + 8$

                                                      12. _____

13. $\dfrac{x^2 - 81}{x^2 - 18x + 81} \div \dfrac{1}{x^2 - 9x}$

                                                      13. _____

14. $\dfrac{x^2 - 6x + 8}{x^2 - 5x + 6} \div \dfrac{x^2 - 7x + 12}{x^2 - 4x + 4}$

                                                      14. _____

15. $\dfrac{x^2 - 64}{x^2 - 16} \div \dfrac{x - 8}{x - 4}$

                                                      15. _____

Name _____   Date _____

Additional Exercises 7.2
Form III
Multiplying and Dividing Rational Expressions

Perform the indicated operations. Simplify if possible.

1. $\dfrac{k^2+11k+18}{k^2+18k+81} \cdot \dfrac{k^2+9k}{k^2-7k-18}$

1. _____

2. $\dfrac{k^2+12k+32}{k^2+15k+56} \cdot \dfrac{k^2+7k}{k^2+13k+36}$

2. _____

3. $\dfrac{k^2+12k+36}{k^2+11k+30} \cdot \dfrac{k^2+13k+40}{k^2+14k+48}$

3. _____

4. $\dfrac{x^2-15x+56}{x^2-17x+60} \cdot \dfrac{x^2-6x+5}{x^2-19x+88}$

4. _____

5. $\dfrac{x^3+1}{x^3-x^2+x} \cdot \dfrac{4x}{-48x-48}$

5. _____

6. $\dfrac{x^3-1}{x+1} \div \dfrac{x^2+x+1}{x^2+2x+1}$

6. _____

7. $\dfrac{x^3+8}{x-2} \div \dfrac{x^2-2x+4}{x^2-4x+4}$

7. _____

8. $\dfrac{x^3+y^3}{(x+y)^3} \cdot \dfrac{x^2-xy+y^2}{x^2+2xy+y^2}$

8. _____

9. $\dfrac{z^2 + 12z + 32}{z^2 + 15z + 56} \div \dfrac{z^2 + 4z}{z^2 + 15z + 56}$

9. _____

10. $\dfrac{z^2 + 11z + 28}{z^2 + 13z + 42} \div \dfrac{z^2 + 4z}{z^2 + 2z - 24}$

10. _____

11. $\dfrac{a^2 - 21a + 108}{9 - a} \div (a + 12)$

11. _____

12. $\dfrac{p^2 - 10p + pq - 10q}{2p^2 - 2q^2} \div \dfrac{p - 10}{7p - 7q}$

12. _____

13. $\dfrac{x^2 - 2x + 1}{3x^2 + 7x - 20} \div \dfrac{x^2 + 3x - 4}{3x^2 - 2x - 5}$

13. _____

14. $\dfrac{2x^2 - 5x - 12}{4x^2 + 8x + 3} \div \dfrac{x^2 - 16}{2x^2 + 7x + 3}$

14. _____

15. $\dfrac{x^3 + 2x^2 - 9x - 18}{x^4 + 3x^3 - 4x^2 - 12x} \div \dfrac{x^2 - x - 6}{x^3 + 5x^2 + 6x}$

15. _____

Name _____   Date _____

Additional Exercises 7.3
Form I
Adding and Subtracting Rational Expressions with the Same Denominator

Perform the indicated operations and simplify.

1. $\dfrac{8}{14x} + \dfrac{3}{14x}$

1. _____

2. $\dfrac{10}{13x} - \dfrac{5}{13x}$

2. _____

3. $\dfrac{x+7}{5} + \dfrac{3x-2}{5}$

3. _____

4. $\dfrac{8a+3b}{2} - \dfrac{8a-3b}{2}$

4. _____

5. $\dfrac{3}{x+2} + \dfrac{5}{x+2}$

5. _____

6. $\dfrac{9}{x-1} - \dfrac{8}{x-1}$

6. _____

7. $\dfrac{x}{x+2} + \dfrac{3x+1}{x+2}$

7. _____

8. $\dfrac{10}{8x^2} - \dfrac{3}{8x^2}$

8. _____

9. $\dfrac{9}{x-3} + \dfrac{7}{3-x}$ 9. _____

10. $\dfrac{10}{x-4} - \dfrac{7}{4-x}$ 10. _____

11. $\dfrac{9}{x-2} + \dfrac{8}{2-x}$ 11. _____

12. $\dfrac{5}{x-8} - \dfrac{4}{8-x}$ 12. _____

13. $\dfrac{5}{x-2} - \dfrac{8}{2-x}$ 13. _____

14. $\dfrac{6}{x-5} + \dfrac{3}{5-x}$ 14. _____

15. $\dfrac{7}{x-1} - \dfrac{9}{1-x}$ 15. _____

Additional Exercises 7.3
Form II
Adding and Subtracting Rational Expressions with the Same Denominator

Perform the indicated operations and simplify.

1. $\dfrac{x}{x+3}+\dfrac{3}{x+3}$ 1. _____

2. $\dfrac{5}{y-5}-\dfrac{y}{y-5}$ 2. _____

3. $\dfrac{6m}{m-3}+\dfrac{-18}{m-3}$ 3. _____

4. $\dfrac{3y^2}{y-1}+\dfrac{-3y}{y-1}$ 4. _____

5. $\dfrac{16}{q-7}-\dfrac{8}{q-7}$ 5. _____

6. $\dfrac{2x+1}{5x-7}-\dfrac{-3x-5}{5x-7}$ 6. _____

7. $\dfrac{2x-3}{x-2}-\dfrac{x-1}{x-2}$ 7. _____

8. $\dfrac{7x-1}{3x+5}-\dfrac{4x-3}{3x+5}$ 8. _____

9. $\dfrac{3x+1}{x-3} - \dfrac{x+2}{3-x}$

9. _____

10. $\dfrac{5-x}{x-3} - \dfrac{x-2}{3-x}$

10. _____

11. $\dfrac{2x+3}{x-6} - \dfrac{4x-2}{6-x}$

11. _____

12. $\dfrac{3x+7}{x-5} + \dfrac{2x+1}{5-x}$

12. _____

13. $\dfrac{m^2-11m}{m-5} + \dfrac{30}{m-5}$

13. _____

14. $\dfrac{8}{x+3} - \dfrac{6}{-x-3}$

14. _____

15. $\dfrac{2-x}{x-6} - \dfrac{2x-3}{6-x}$

15. _____

Additional Exercises 7.3
Form III
Adding and Subtracting Rational Expressions with the Same Denominator

Perform the indicated operations and simplify.

1. $\dfrac{y^2 + 2y}{y^2 + y - 12} - \dfrac{3y + 6}{y^2 + y - 12}$

1. _____

2. $\dfrac{4x^2}{3x^3} + \dfrac{6x - x^2}{3x^3}$

2. _____

3. $\dfrac{4x^2 + 10x}{2x + 3} + \dfrac{4x^2 - 3}{2x + 3}$

3. _____

4. $\dfrac{x^2}{x - 4} + \dfrac{16}{4 - x}$

4. _____

5. $\dfrac{2x^2 + 5x + 9}{x^2 + x - 30} + \dfrac{6x - 15}{x^2 + x - 30}$

5. _____

6. $\dfrac{3y}{x^2 - y^2} + \dfrac{3x}{y^2 - x^2}$

6. _____

7. $\dfrac{2y^2}{4y^2 - 9} - \dfrac{7y + 15}{4y^2 - 9}$

7. _____

8. $\dfrac{2x^2}{x^2 - 6x - 7} + \dfrac{11x + 21}{7 + 6x - x^2}$

8. _____

9. $\dfrac{2x}{2x-5} - \dfrac{5}{2x-5}$

9. _____

10. $\dfrac{x-5}{x^2-9} - \dfrac{x-5}{9-x^2}$

10. _____

11. $\dfrac{17}{x-8} - \dfrac{2}{8-x}$

11. _____

12. $\dfrac{10y^2+20y+26}{9y^2-64} - \dfrac{7y^2-6}{9y^2-64}$

12. _____

13. $\dfrac{11y^2+7}{2y^2+3y+1} - \dfrac{6-9y}{2y^2+3y+1} - \dfrac{6y^2+3y}{2y^2+3y+1}$

13. _____

14. $\dfrac{6y}{x^2-y^2} + \dfrac{6x}{y^2-x^2}$

14. _____

15. $\dfrac{x^2+16}{x^2-6x-16} + \dfrac{4-8x}{16+6x-x^2}$

15. _____

Additional Exercises 7.4
Form I
Adding and Subtracting Rational Expressions with Different Denominators

Find the least common denominator (LCD) of the rational expressions.

1.　$\dfrac{4}{12x}$ and $\dfrac{7}{15x^3}$

1. _____

2.　$\dfrac{3}{4x}$ and $\dfrac{5}{18x^5}$

2. _____

3.　$\dfrac{11}{2xy^2}$ and $\dfrac{14}{5x^2y}$

3. _____

4.　$\dfrac{4}{15xy}$ and $\dfrac{6}{10x^2}$

4. _____

5.　$\dfrac{5}{t}$ and $\dfrac{4}{t-2}$

5. _____

6.　$\dfrac{9}{x+2}$ and $\dfrac{4}{x-3}$

6. _____

7.　$\dfrac{2}{x(x+1)}$ and $\dfrac{5}{x^2}$

7. _____

Add or subtract as indicated. Simplify the result, if possible.

8.　$\dfrac{2}{y}+\dfrac{5}{y^2}$

8. _____

9. $4 + \dfrac{1}{x}$ 9. _____

10. $\dfrac{2}{5x} + \dfrac{1}{2x^2}$ 10. _____

11. $\dfrac{6}{z^2} - \dfrac{9}{z}$ 11. _____

12. $\dfrac{-2}{5} - \dfrac{7}{3x}$ 12. _____

13. $\dfrac{2x - y}{x^2 y} + \dfrac{x + y}{xy^2}$ 13. _____

14. $\dfrac{11}{z} - 5$ 14. _____

15.   The LCD of $\dfrac{1}{x-1}$ and $\dfrac{1}{1-x}$ is?   15. _____

Name _____   Date _____

Additional Exercises 7.4
Form II
Adding and Subtracting Rational Expressions with Different Denominators

Find the least common denominator (LCD) of the rational expressions.

1. $\dfrac{3}{x-5}$ and $\dfrac{5}{x+3}$

1. _____

2. $\dfrac{5}{x^2-9}$ and $\dfrac{7}{x-3}$

2. _____

3. $\dfrac{4}{3a-6}$ and $\dfrac{7}{a^2-2a}$

3. _____

4. $\dfrac{5}{x^2-4}$ and $\dfrac{4}{x(x-2)}$

4. _____

5. $\dfrac{11}{a+1}$ and $\dfrac{9}{(a+1)^2}$

5. _____

6. $\dfrac{2x+1}{4x-4}$ and $\dfrac{3x}{8x-8}$

6. _____

7. $\dfrac{x^2}{x+2}$ and $\dfrac{7x}{x^2+5x+6}$

7. _____

Add or subtract as indicated. Simplify the result, if possible.

8. $\dfrac{2}{r}+\dfrac{8}{r-3}$

8. _____

9. $\dfrac{-8x-4}{x} + \dfrac{-9x+1}{9x}$ 9. _____

10. $\dfrac{3}{w-12} - \dfrac{4}{12-w}$ 10. _____

11. $\dfrac{6}{x+5} - \dfrac{3}{x-5}$ 11. _____

12. $\dfrac{x}{x-3} + \dfrac{5}{4x-12}$ 12. _____

13. $\dfrac{x}{x-5} + \dfrac{x-5}{x}$ 13. _____

14. $\dfrac{3}{x-1} - \dfrac{2}{(x-1)^2}$ 14. _____

15.   The LCD of $\dfrac{1}{2x-3}$ and $\dfrac{1}{3-2x}$ is?   15. _____

Additional Exercises 7.4
Form III
Adding and Subtracting Rational Expressions with Different Denominators

Find the least common denominator (LCD) of the rational expressions.

1. $\dfrac{1}{r^2 + 2r + 1}$ and $\dfrac{1}{r^2 + r}$ 1. _____

2. $\dfrac{3}{m^2 + 6m}$ and $\dfrac{5}{m^2 + 9m + 18}$ 2. _____

3. $\dfrac{3}{x^2 + 7x + 12}$ and $\dfrac{4}{x^2 + 6x + 9}$ 3. _____

4. $\dfrac{3}{x^2 - 5x + 6}$ and $\dfrac{12x}{x^2 - 4x + 4}$ 4. _____

5. $\dfrac{14}{x^2 - 4}$ and $\dfrac{9x^2}{x^2 + 5y + 6}$ 5. _____

6. $\dfrac{4}{y^3 - y^2}$ and $\dfrac{9}{y^4 - y^2}$ 6. _____

7. $\dfrac{5}{x^2 + 3x + 2}$ and $\dfrac{3}{x^2 - 4}$ 7. _____

Add or subtract as indicated. Simplify the result, if possible.

8. $\dfrac{m + 1}{m^2 + 3m - 4} + \dfrac{5m + 3}{m^2 + 10m + 24}$ 8. _____

9. $\dfrac{3}{y^2 - 3y + 2} + \dfrac{7}{y^2 - 1}$ 9. _____

10. $\dfrac{x}{x^2 - 16} - \dfrac{6}{x^2 + 5x + 4}$ 10. _____

11. $\dfrac{2}{x^2 - x - 6} + \dfrac{3}{x^2 - 9}$ 11. _____

12. $\dfrac{8x}{x^2 - 16} - \dfrac{5}{x + 4}$ 12. _____

Two formulas that approximate the dosage of a drug prescribed for children are:

Young's Rule: $C = \dfrac{DA}{A + 12}$ and Cowling's Rule: $C = \dfrac{D(A + 1)}{24}$.

In each formula, A = the child's age in years, D = an adult dosage, and C= the proper child's dosage. The formulas apply for ages 2 through 13.

13. Use Young's Rule to find the difference in a child's dosage   13. _____
    for a 9-year-old and a 2-year-old child. Express the answer
    as a single rational (or fractional) expression in terms of D

14. Use Cowling's Rule to find the difference in a child's dosage   14. _____
    for a 12-year-old child and a 5-year-old child. Express the
    answer as a single rational (or fractional) expression in terms
    of D.

15. The LCD of $\dfrac{1}{3x - 5}$ and $\dfrac{1}{5 - 3x}$ is?   15. _____

Name _____   Date _____

Additional Exercises 7.5
Form I
Complex Rational Expressions

Simplify each complex expression.

1. $\dfrac{\dfrac{3}{4}}{\dfrac{2}{3}}$

1. _____

2. $\dfrac{\dfrac{x}{8}}{\dfrac{5x}{16}}$

2. _____

3. $\dfrac{\dfrac{x}{y^2}}{\dfrac{x}{y}}$

3. _____

4. $\dfrac{\dfrac{1}{7}+\dfrac{1}{5}}{\dfrac{1}{3}+\dfrac{1}{8}}$

4. _____

5. $\dfrac{\dfrac{1}{3}-\dfrac{1}{6}}{\dfrac{1}{8}-\dfrac{1}{7}}$

5. _____

6. $\dfrac{\dfrac{1}{6}+5}{3+\dfrac{1}{7}}$

6. _____

7. $\dfrac{\dfrac{5}{x}}{\dfrac{1}{x}-\dfrac{1}{2x}}$

7. _____

8. $\dfrac{\dfrac{8}{a}+1}{\dfrac{8}{a}-1}$

8. _____

9. $\dfrac{9+\dfrac{3}{x}}{\dfrac{x}{4}+\dfrac{1}{12}}$

9. _____

10. $\dfrac{\dfrac{1}{x}+\dfrac{1}{y}}{\dfrac{1}{x}-\dfrac{1}{y}}$

10. _____

11. $\dfrac{\dfrac{1}{x}+\dfrac{1}{2y}}{\dfrac{1}{x}-\dfrac{1}{y}}$

11. _____

12. $\dfrac{4+\dfrac{2}{x}}{\dfrac{x}{4}+\dfrac{1}{8}}$

12. _____

13. $\dfrac{\dfrac{9s^2-49t^2}{st}}{\dfrac{3}{t}-\dfrac{7}{s}}$

13. _____

14. $\dfrac{1-\dfrac{3}{x}}{1+\dfrac{2}{x}}$

14. _____

15. The express $\dfrac{y+5}{y-3}$ is defined for what values of y?

15. _____

Additional Exercises 7.5
Form II
Complex Rational Expressions

Simplify each complex expression.

1. $\dfrac{\dfrac{x}{7}}{\dfrac{4}{x+9}}$

1. _____

2. $\dfrac{\dfrac{y}{5}}{\dfrac{3}{y+9}}$

2. _____

3. $\dfrac{\dfrac{2}{y}}{\dfrac{9}{y+4}}$

3. _____

4. $\dfrac{\dfrac{4}{y}}{\dfrac{6}{y+7}}$

4. _____

5. $\dfrac{\dfrac{10}{5r-1}-10}{\dfrac{10}{5r-1}+10}$

5. _____

6. $\dfrac{\dfrac{5}{x^2y}+\dfrac{2}{xy^2}}{\dfrac{7}{xy}-\dfrac{9}{x^2y^2}}$

6. _____

7. $\dfrac{1-\dfrac{1}{x}-\dfrac{6}{x^2}}{1-\dfrac{4}{x^2}}$

7. _____

8. $\dfrac{3+\dfrac{11}{x}+\dfrac{10}{x^2}}{3+\dfrac{5}{x}-\dfrac{12}{x^2}-\dfrac{20}{x^3}}$ 8. _____

9. $\dfrac{\dfrac{1}{x}+\dfrac{1}{3}}{\dfrac{1}{x}-\dfrac{1}{3}}$ 9. _____

10. $\dfrac{1-\dfrac{9}{x^2}}{1-\dfrac{1}{x}-\dfrac{6}{x^2}}$ 10. _____

11. $\dfrac{1}{x+\dfrac{1}{x}}$ 11. _____

12. $\dfrac{3-\dfrac{1}{a+3}}{3+\dfrac{1}{a+3}}$ 12. _____

13. $\dfrac{5+\dfrac{1}{x}}{5-\dfrac{1}{x}}$ 13. _____

14. $\dfrac{\dfrac{2x}{3}+2}{\dfrac{5x}{3}-\dfrac{15}{x}}$ 14. _____

15. The express $\dfrac{y+1}{2y-3}$ is defined for what values of y?   15. _____

Additional Exercises 7.5
Form III
Complex Rational Expressions

Simplify each complex expression.

1. $\dfrac{1 - \dfrac{1}{x+1}}{1 + \dfrac{1}{x-1}}$

1. _____

2. $\dfrac{\dfrac{x-5}{x^2-4}}{\dfrac{x^2-25}{x+2}}$

2. _____

3. $\dfrac{4 - \dfrac{1}{y^2}}{\dfrac{1}{y^2} + \dfrac{4}{y} + 4}$

3. _____

4. $\dfrac{1 - \dfrac{1}{x} - \dfrac{6}{x^2}}{1 - \dfrac{9}{x^2}}$

4. _____

5. $\dfrac{\dfrac{4a}{2a^3+2}}{\dfrac{8a}{4a+4}}$

5. _____

6. $\dfrac{2 + \dfrac{5}{x} - \dfrac{3}{x^2}}{2 - \dfrac{5}{x} + \dfrac{2}{x^2}}$

6. _____

7. $\dfrac{x - \dfrac{5x}{x+5}}{x + \dfrac{5x}{x-5}}$

7. _____

8. $\dfrac{\dfrac{1}{x}-\dfrac{1}{3-3x}}{\dfrac{1}{1-x}-\dfrac{3}{x}}$

8. _____

9. $\dfrac{\dfrac{x-y}{x+y}+\dfrac{y}{x}}{\dfrac{x}{y}-\dfrac{x-y}{x+y}}$

9. _____

10. $\dfrac{\dfrac{1}{x-x^2}-\dfrac{1}{x^2+x}}{\dfrac{1}{x^2+1}-\dfrac{1}{x^2-1}}$

10. _____

11. $\dfrac{\dfrac{4}{x+2}-\dfrac{4}{x-2}}{\dfrac{8}{x^2-4}}$

11. _____

12. $\dfrac{x+5-\dfrac{14}{x}}{x+15+\dfrac{56}{x}}$

12. _____

13. $\dfrac{\dfrac{1}{k+6}}{\dfrac{3}{k^2-36}}$

13. _____

14. $\dfrac{\dfrac{4}{9r-1}-4}{\dfrac{4}{9r-1}+4}$

14. _____

15. The express $\dfrac{y-\dfrac{2}{3}}{y+\dfrac{7}{8}}$ is defined for what values of y?

15. _____

Additional Exercises 7.6
Form I
Solving Rational Equations

Solve each rational equation.

1. $\dfrac{x}{8} - \dfrac{x}{9} = 2$ 1. _____

2. $\dfrac{41}{x} = 7 - \dfrac{1}{x}$ 2. _____

3. $\dfrac{3x}{2} + 2 = \dfrac{1}{4}$ 3. _____

4. $\dfrac{x+7}{8} = \dfrac{x+8}{9}$ 4. _____

5. $\dfrac{x-7}{3} = \dfrac{x+3}{7}$ 5. _____

6. $\dfrac{2}{3} = \dfrac{1}{x} + \dfrac{5}{6}$ 6. _____

7. $x + \dfrac{4}{x} = -5$ 7. _____

8. $\dfrac{x+2}{x-7} = 4$ 8. _____

9. $\dfrac{x}{8} = \dfrac{1}{8} + \dfrac{x}{12}$ 9. _____

10. $\dfrac{1}{x} + 3 = \dfrac{4}{3}$ 10. _____

Solve the equation for the specified variable.

11. $P = \dfrac{A}{1+rt}$ for A 11. _____

12. $F = \dfrac{mv^2}{r}$ for m 12. _____

13. $\dfrac{1}{p} + \dfrac{1}{q} = \dfrac{1}{f}$ for p 13. _____

14. $\dfrac{V_1}{V_2} = \dfrac{P_2}{P_1}$ for P_2 14. _____

15. $\dfrac{1}{R} = \dfrac{1}{R_1} + \dfrac{1}{R_2}$ for R_1 15. _____

Name _____   Date _____

Solve each rational equation.

1. $\dfrac{6x-2}{2x-1} = \dfrac{9x}{3x+1}$

    1. _____

2. $\dfrac{x}{x-3} + 3 = \dfrac{3}{x-3}$

    2. _____

3. $\dfrac{y+3}{2y} + \dfrac{5}{y-1} = \dfrac{1}{2}$

    3. _____

4. $\dfrac{5}{2x} + \dfrac{1}{12} = \dfrac{2}{x}$

    4. _____

5. $\dfrac{5}{x} = \dfrac{3}{x^2} - 2$

    5. _____

6. $\dfrac{x}{10} - \dfrac{3}{5} = \dfrac{x-1}{5}$

    6. _____

7. $1 + \dfrac{1}{x} = \dfrac{90}{x^2}$

    7. _____

8. $6 = \dfrac{7}{x} + \dfrac{5}{x^2}$

    8. _____

9. $\dfrac{4y+1}{3} = \dfrac{3}{5} + \dfrac{2y+1}{5}$

9. _____

10. $\dfrac{8}{x} - \dfrac{1}{4} = \dfrac{4}{x}$

10. _____

Solve the equation for the specified variable.

11. $\dfrac{1}{a} + \dfrac{1}{b} = c$ for a

11. _____

12. $\dfrac{1}{a} + \dfrac{1}{b} = \dfrac{1}{c}$ for b

12. _____

13. $P = \dfrac{A}{1+rt}$ for t

13. _____

14. $A = \dfrac{1}{2}h(B+b)$ for b

14. _____

15. $P = \dfrac{Fd}{t}$ for d

15. _____

Additional Exercises 7.6
Form III
Solving Rational Equations

Solve each rational equation.

1. $\dfrac{x+3}{2} = \dfrac{x+4}{4}$

1. _____

2. $\dfrac{x-1}{x-5} = \dfrac{4}{x-5}$

2. _____

3. $\dfrac{5}{x-3} = 1 + \dfrac{30}{x^2-9}$

3. _____

4. $\dfrac{4}{x-2} = \dfrac{5}{x+2} + \dfrac{2x-3}{x^2-4}$

4. _____

5. $\dfrac{4}{2a-6} = \dfrac{12}{a^2-9} + \dfrac{12}{4a+12}$

5. _____

6. $\dfrac{y+2}{y^2-y} = \dfrac{6}{y^2-1}$

6. _____

7. $10 - \dfrac{1}{x} = \dfrac{3}{x^2}$

7. _____

8. $\dfrac{2}{a+1} = \dfrac{5}{a} + \dfrac{3}{a+1}$

8. _____

9. $\dfrac{2x}{x+1} = 2 - \dfrac{5}{2x}$ 9. _____

10. $\dfrac{7}{y+4} - \dfrac{2}{y-4} = \dfrac{14}{y^2 - 16}$ 10. _____

Solve the equation for the specified variable.

11. $V = \dfrac{4}{3}\pi r^2 h$ for h 11. _____

12. $P = \dfrac{R - C}{n}$ for n 12. _____

13. $\dfrac{1}{f} = \dfrac{1}{a} + \dfrac{1}{b}$ for b 13. _____

14. $V = \dfrac{mv}{m + M}$ for m 14. _____

15. $F = \dfrac{Gm_1 m_2}{r^2}$ for m_2 15. _____

Name _____   Date _____

Additional Exercises 7.7
Form I
Applications Using Rational Equations and Proportions

1. A cyclist bikes at a constant speed for 20 miles. He then returns   1. _____
    home at the same speed but takes a different route. His return
    trip takes one hour longer and is 25 miles. Find his speed

2. A boat travels 8 miles upstream and then back 8 miles in 3 hours.   2. _____
    The current of the river is 2 mph. What is the speed of the boat
    in still water?

3. Mark and Rachel both work for Smith Landscaping Company.   3. _____
    Mark can finish a planting job in 3 hours, while it takes Rachel
    5 hours to finish the same job. If Mark and Rachel will work
    together on the job, and the cost of labor is $45 per hour, what
    should the labor estimate be? (Round to the nearest cent, if
    necessary.)

4. One pump can drain a pool in 7 minutes. When a second pump   4. _____
    is also used, the pool only takes 2 minutes to drain. How long
    would it take the second pump to drain the pool if it were the only
    pump in use?

5. The tax on a property with an assessed value of $70,000 is $840.   5. _____
    Find the tax on a property with an assessed value of $162,500.

6. To estimate the number of rainbow trout in a lake, wildlife   6. _____
    biologists tagged 40 trout and released them in the lake. Later,
    they netted 120 and found 48 of them were tagged. Approximately
    how many trout are in the lake?

7. A person's hair is proportional to the number of years it has been 7. _____
    growing. After 2 years, a person's hair grows 8 inches. If Susie's
    hair has been growing for 7 years, how long is her hair?

8. A tree casts a shadow 10 feet long. At the same time, a vertical   8. _____
    rod 5 feet high casts a shadow 2 feet long. How tall is the tree?

Name _____   Date _____

9.   Find the missing length in the similar triangles.   9. _____

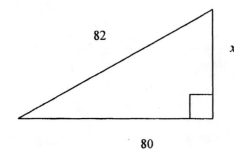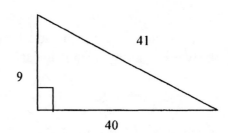

10.   Find the missing length in the similar triangles.   10. _____

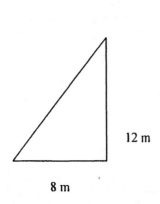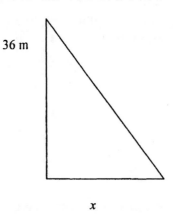

AE-280

Name _____   Date _____

Additional Exercises 7.7
Form II
Applications Using Rational Equations and Proportions

1. A car travels 400 miles on level terrain in the same amount of time it travels 160 miles on mountainous terrain. If the rate of the car is 30 miles per hour less in the mountains than on level ground, find its rate in the mountains.

    1. _____

2. A boat travels 9 kilometers upstream in the same amount of time. it moves 16 kilometers downstream. If the rate of the current is 6 kilometers per hour, find the rate of the boat in still water.

    2. _____

3. In a race, Car A starts 1 mile behind Car B. Car A is traveling at 65 miles per hour, while Car B is traveling at 55 miles per hour. How long will it take for Car A to overtake Car B?

    3. _____

4. One conveyor belt can move 1000 boxes in 11 minutes. Another can move 1000 boxes in 12 minutes. If another conveyor belt is added and all three are used, the boxes are moved in 3 minutes. How long would it take the third conveyor belt alone to do the same job?

    4. _____

5. The tax on a property with an assessed value of $125,000 is $2500. Find the tax on a property with an assessed value of $275,000.

    5. _____

6. To estimate the number of rainbow trout in a lake, wildlife biologists tagged 32 trout and released them in the lake. Later, they netted 150 and found 80 of them were tagged. Approximately how many trout are in the lake?

    6. _____

7. A person's hair is proportional to the number of years it has been growing. After 2 years, a person's hair grows 8 inches. If Susie's hair has been growing for 9 years, how long is her hair?

    7. _____

Name _____   Date _____

8.   A tree casts a shadow 4 feet long. At the same time, a vertical   8. _____
     rod 15 feet high casts a shadow 10 feet long. How tall is the tree?

9.   Find the missing length in the similar triangles.   9. _____

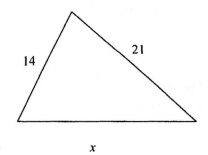
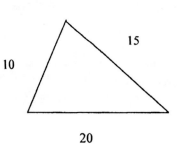

10. Find the missing length in the similar triangles.   10. _____

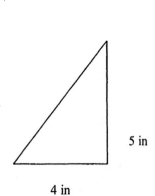
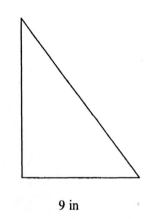

Additional Exercises 7.7
Form III
Applications Using Rational Equations and Proportions

1. The sports car travels 40 km/h faster than the loaded SUV and   1. _____
    trailer. While the SUV travels 150 km, the sports car goes 350 km.
    Find their speeds.

2. Jim can run 5 miles per hour on level ground on a still day. One   2. _____
    windy day, he runs 15 miles with the wind, and in the same
    amount of time runs 4 miles against the wind. What is the rate
    of the wind?

3. A painter can finish painting a house in 4 hours. Her assistant   3. _____
    takes 6 hours to finish the same job. How long would it take for
    them to complete the job if they were working together?

4. A baker can decorate the day's cookie supply four times as fast as   4. _____
    his new assistant. If they decorate all the cookies working
    together in 12 minutes, how long would it take for each of them
    to decorate the cookies working individually?

5. The tax on a property with an assessed value of $315,000 is   5. _____
    $4725. Find the tax on a property with an assessed value of
    $375,000.

6. To estimate the number of rainbow trout in a lake, wildlife   6. _____
    biologists tagged 21 trout and released them in the lake. Later,
    they netted 85 and found 15 of them were tagged. Approximately
    how many trout are in the lake?

7. A person's hair is proportional to the number of years it has been   7. _____
    growing. After 2 years, a person's hair grows 8 inches. If Susie's
    hair has been growing for 3 years, how long is her hair?

Name _____   Date _____

8.   A tree casts a shadow 5 feet long. At the same time, a vertical   8. _____
      rod 6 feet high casts a shadow 3 feet long. How tall is the tree?

Find the missing length in the similar triangles.

9.   9. _____

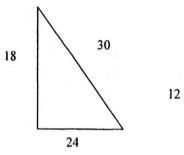

10.   10. _____

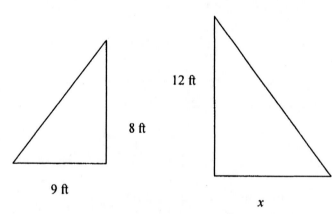

Name _____   Date _____

Solve the problem.

1. y varies directly as z and $y = 84$ when $z = 12$. Find y when   1. _____
     z is 9.

2. y varies directly as z^2 and $y = 15$ when $z = 3$. Find y when   2. _____
     z is 24.

3. s varies directly as t^2 and $s = 81$ when $t = 3$. Find s when t is 4.   3. _____

4. m varies directly as p and $m = 54$ when $p = 9$. Find m when   4. _____
     p is 7.

5. x varies inversely as v and $x = 42$ when $v = 2$. Find x when   5. _____
     $v = 14$.

6. x varies inversely as y^2 and $x = 4$ when $y = 12$. Find x when   6. _____
     $y = 4$.

7. f varies jointly as q^2 and h, and $f = 224$ when $q = 2$ and   7. _____
     $h = 7$. Find f when $q = 1$ and $h = 4$.

8. f varies jointly as q^2 and h, and $f = -96$ when $q = 4$ and   8. _____
     $h = 9$. Find f when $q = 3$ and $h = 4$.

9. f varies jointly as q^2 and h, and $f = 96$ when $q = 4$ and   9. _____
     $h = 2$. Find q when $f = 135$ and $h = 5$.

10. f varies jointly as q^2 and h, and $f = 36$ when $q = 3$ and   10. _____
     $h = 2$. Find h when $f = 192$ and $q = 4$.

11.   The amount of water used to take a shower is directly
      proportional to the amount of time that the shower is in use.
      A shower lasting 18 minutes requires 10.8 gallons of water.
      Find the amount of water used in a shower lasting 5 minutes.

11. _____

12.   If the resistance in an electrical circuit is held constant, the
      amount of current flowing through the circuit is directly
      proportional to the amount of voltage applied to the circuit.
      When 9 volts are applied to a circuit, 180 milliamperes or
      current flow through the circuit. Find the new current if the
      voltage is increased to 12 volts.

12. _____

13.   The amount of gas that a helicopter uses is directly proportional
      to the number of hours spent flying. The helicopter flies for
      3 hours and uses 36 gallons of fuel. Find the number of gallons
      of fuel that the helicopter uses to fly for 5 hours.

13. _____

14.   The distance that an object falls when it is dropped is directly
      proportional to the square of the amount of time since it was
      dropped. An object falls 39.2 meters in 2 seconds. Find the
      distance the object falls in 3 seconds.

14. _____

15.   When the temperature stays the same, the volume of a gas is
      inversely proportional to the pressure of the gas. If a balloon
      is filled with 228 cubic inches of a gas at a pressure of 14
      pounds per square inch, find the new pressure of the gas if the
      volume is decreased to 38 cubic inches.

15. _____

16.   The amount of time it takes a swimmer to swim a race is   16. _____
        inversely proportional to the average speed of the swimmer.
        A swimmer finishes a race in 200 seconds with an average speed
        of 3 feet per second. Find the average speed of the swimmer if
        it takes 120 seconds to finish the race.

17.   If the voltage V, in an electric circuit is held constant, the   17. _____
        current, I, is inversely proportional to the resistance, R. If the
        current is 420 milliamperes when the resistance is 5 ohms,
        find the current when the resistance is 35 ohms.

18.   The amount of paint needed to cover the walls of a room varies   18. _____
        jointly as the perimeter of the room and the height of the wall.
        If a room with a perimeter of 30 feet and 6-foot walls requires 1.8
        quarts of paint, find the amount of paint needed to cover the walls
        of a room with a perimeter of 35 feet and 8-foot walls.

19.   The amount of simple interest earned on an investment over a   19. _____
        fixed amount of time is jointly proportional to the principle
        invested and the interest rate. A principle investment of
        $1600.00 with an interest rate of 3% earned $96.00 in simple
        interest. Find the amount of simple interest earned if the
        principle is $4600.00 and the interest rate is 8%.

20.   The power that a resistor must dissipate is jointly proportional   20. _____
        to the square of the current flowing through the resistor and
        the resistance of the resistor. If a resistor needs to dissipate 300
        watts of power when 5 amperes of current is flowing through
        the resistor whose resistance is 6 ohms, find the power that a
        resistor needs to dissipate when 4 amperes of current are
        flowing through a resistor whose resistance is 3 ohms.

Name _____   Date _____

Solve the problem.

1. y varies directly as z and $y = 132$ when $z = 12$. Find y when z is 9.

1. _____

2. y varies directly as z^2 and $y = 108$ when $z = 3$. Find y when z is 4.

2. _____

3. s varies directly as t^2 and $s = 192$ when $t = 4$. Find s when t is 5.

3. _____

4. m varies directly as p and $m = 72$ when $p = 4$. Find m when p is 6.

4. _____

5. x varies inversely as v and $x = 40$ when $v = 3$. Find x when $v = 6$.

5. _____

6. x varies inversely as y^2 and $x = 5$ when $y = 15$. Find x when $y = 5$.

6. _____

7. f varies jointly as q^2 and h, and $f = 96$ when $q = 4$ and $h = 3$. Find f when $q = 2$ and $h = 3$.

7. _____

8. f varies jointly as q^2 and h, and $f = -3$ when $q = 3$ and $h = 6$. Find f when $q = 4$ and $h = 7$.

8. _____

9. f varies jointly as q^2 and h, and $f = 500$ when $q = 5$ and $h = 4$. Find q when $f = 1600$ and $h = 5$.

9. _____

10. f varies jointly as q^2 and h, and $f = 240$ when $q = 4$ and $h = 3$. Find h when $f = 1260$ and $q = 6$.

10. _____

11. The amount of water used to take a shower is directly proportional to the amount of time that the shower is in use. A shower lasting 15 minutes requires 10.5 gallons of water. Find the amount of water used in a shower lasting 11 minutes.

11. _____

12. If the resistance in an electrical circuit is held constant, the amount of current flowing through the circuit is directly proportional to the amount of voltage applied to the circuit. When 10 volts are applied to a circuit, 200 milliamperes or current flow through the circuit. Find the new current if the voltage is increased to 11 volts.

12. _____

13. The amount of gas that a helicopter uses is directly proportional to the number of hours spent flying. The helicopter flies for 4 hours and uses 52 gallons of fuel. Find the number of gallons of fuel that the helicopter uses to fly for 7 hours.

13. _____

14. The distance that an object falls when it is dropped is directly proportional to the square of the amount of time since it was dropped. An object falls 90.9 meters in 3 seconds. Find the distance the object falls in 4 seconds.

14. _____

15. When the temperature stays the same, the volume of a gas is inversely proportional to the pressure of the gas. If a balloon is filled with 320 cubic inches of a gas at a pressure of 15 pounds per square inch, find the new pressure of the gas if the volume is decreased to 40 cubic inches.

15. _____

16. The amount of time it takes a swimmer to swim a race is   16. _____
     inversely proportional to the average speed of the swimmer.
     A swimmer finishes a race in 240 seconds with an average speed
     of 3.5 feet per second. Find the average speed of the swimmer if
     it takes 120 seconds to finish the race.

17. If the voltage V, in an electric circuit is held constant, the   17. _____
     current, I, is inversely proportional to the resistance, R. If the
     current is 400 milliamperes when the resistance is 6 ohms,
     find the current when the resistance is 40 ohms.

18. The amount of paint needed to cover the walls of a room varies   18. _____
     jointly as the perimeter of the room and the height of the wall.
     If a room with a perimeter of 35 feet and 6-foot walls requires 2.1
     quarts of paint, find the amount of paint needed to cover the walls
     of a room with a perimeter of 40 feet and 8-foot walls.

19. The amount of simple interest earned on an investment over a   19. _____
     fixed amount of time is jointly proportional to the principle
     invested and the interest rate. A principle investment of
     $2100.00 with an interest rate of 5% earned $199.50 in simple
     interest. Find the amount of simple interest earned if the
     principle is $3200.00 and the interest rate is 6.5%.

20. The power that a resistor must dissipate is jointly proportional   20. _____
     to the square of the current flowing through the resistor and
     the resistance of the resistor. If a resistor needs to dissipate 320
     watts of power when 4 amperes of current is flowing through
     the resistor whose resistance is 8 ohms, find the power that a
     resistor needs to dissipate when 5 amperes of current are
     flowing through a resistor whose resistance is 2 ohms.

Name _____   Date _____

Solve the problem.

1. y varies directly as z and $y = 156$ when $z = 13$. Find y when   1. _____
      z is 16.

2. y varies directly as z^2 and $y = 64$ when $z = 4$. Find y when   2. _____
      z is 9.

3. s varies directly as t^2 and $s = 441$ when $t = 7$. Find s when t is 5.   3. _____

4. m varies directly as p and $m = 198$ when $p = 11$. Find m when   4. _____
      p is 15.

5. x varies inversely as v and $x = 75$ when $v = 3$. Find x when   5. _____
      $v = 15$.

6. x varies inversely as y^2 and $x = 6$ when $y = 24$. Find x when   6. _____
      $y = 6$.

7. f varies jointly as q^2 and h, and $f = 1350$ when $q = 5$ and   7. _____
      $h = 6$. Find f when $q = 7$ and $h = 3$.

8. f varies jointly as q^2 and h, and $f = -200$ when $q = 5$ and   8. _____
      $h = 2$. Find f when $q = 5$ and $h = 8$.

9. f varies jointly as q^2 and h, and $f = 2268$ when $q = 6$ and   9. _____
      $h = 9$. Find q when $f = 2016$ and $h = 8$.

10. f varies jointly as q^2 and h, and $f = 600$ when $q = 5$ and   10. _____
      $h = 4$. Find h when $f = 1176$ and $q = 7$.

11.   The amount of water used to take a shower is directly   11. _____
       proportional to the amount of time that the shower is in use.
       A shower lasting 12 minutes requires 9.6 gallons of water.
       Find the amount of water used in a shower lasting 7 minutes.

12.   If the resistance in an electrical circuit is held constant, the   12. _____
       amount of current flowing through the circuit is directly
       proportional to the amount of voltage applied to the circuit.
       When 11 volts are applied to a circuit, 275 milliamperes or
       current flow through the circuit. Find the new current if the
       voltage is increased to 14 volts.

13.   The amount of gas that a helicopter uses is directly proportional   13. _____
       to the number of hours spent flying. The helicopter flies for
       4.5 hours and uses 49.5 gallons of fuel. Find the number of
       gallons of fuel that the helicopter uses to fly for 7.25 hours.

14.   The distance that an object falls when it is dropped is directly   14. _____
       proportional to the square of the amount of time since it was
       dropped. An object falls 163.2 meters in 4 seconds. Find the
       distance the object falls in 5 seconds.

15.   When the temperature stays the same, the volume of a gas is   15. _____
       inversely proportional to the pressure of the gas. If a balloon
       is filled with 330 cubic inches of a gas at a pressure of 16
       pounds per square inch, find the new pressure of the gas if the
       volume is decreased to 40 cubic inches.

16. The amount of time it takes a swimmer to swim a race is
     inversely proportional to the average speed of the swimmer.
     A swimmer finishes a race in 315 seconds with an average speed
     of 4 feet per second. Find the average speed of the swimmer if
     it takes 150 seconds to finish the race.

16. _____

17. If the voltage V, in an electric circuit is held constant, the
     current, I, is inversely proportional to the resistance, R. If the
     current is 450 milliamperes when the resistance is 5 ohms,
     find the current when the resistance is 45 ohms.

17. _____

18. The amount of paint needed to cover the walls of a room varies
     jointly as the perimeter of the room and the height of the wall.
     If a room with a perimeter of 40 feet and 6-foot walls requires 2.4
     quarts of paint, find the amount of paint needed to cover the walls
     of a room with a perimeter of 45 feet and 8-foot walls.

18. _____

19. The amount of simple interest earned on an investment over a
     fixed amount of time is jointly proportional to the principle
     invested and the interest rate. A principle investment of
     $1200.00 with an interest rate of 4% earned $86.40 in simple
     interest. Find the amount of simple interest earned if the
     principle is $3500.00 and the interest rate is 7.5%.

19. _____

20. The power that a resistor must dissipate is jointly proportional
     to the square of the current flowing through the resistor and
     the resistance of the resistor. If a resistor needs to dissipate 256
     watts of power when 8 amperes of current is flowing through
     the resistor whose resistance is 4 ohms, find the power that a
     resistor needs to dissipate when 6 amperes of current are
     flowing through a resistor whose resistance is 3 ohms.

20. _____

Name _____   Date _____

Find the (a) domain and (b) range.

1. $\{(1,4),(2,5),(3,6)\}$

1a. _____

1b. _____

2. $\{(3,5),(3,7),(3,9)\}$

2a. _____

2b. _____

Determine whether the relation defines a function.

3. $\{(2,2),(3,3),(4,4)\}$

3. _____

4. $\{(5,6),(7,8),(9,10)\}$

4. _____

5. $\{(1,1),(1,2),(1,3)\}$

5. _____

Given the following functions, find the indicated value.

$$f(x) = x + 2 \qquad g(x) = x - 6 \qquad h(x) = 2x + 1$$

6. $f(0)$

6. _____

7. $f(2)$

7. _____

8. $f(-6)$

8. _____

9. $g(0)$

9. _____

10. $g(2)$

10. _____

11. $g(-6)$

11. _____

12.   h(0)   12. _____

13.   h(2)   13. _____

14.   h(−6)   14. _____

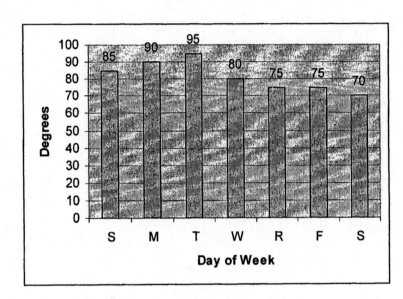

The bar graph shows the high temperature in Central City for the first week in June.

15.   Name the domain using the horizontal axis.   15. _____

16.   Name the range using the vertical axis.   16. _____

17.   Write the ordered pairs represented by the graph
        (day of week, temperature)   17. _____

18.   What makes a relation a function?   18. _____

19.   Is the relation illustrated a function?   19. _____

20.   Why or why not?   20. _____

Additional Exercises 8.1
Form II
Introduction to Functions

Find the (a) domain and (b) range.

1. $\{(-1,2),(-3,-6),(-8,4)\}$ 1a. _____

                                                              1b. _____

2. $\{(1,4),(-2,4),(-3,4)\}$ 2a. _____

                                                              2b. _____

Determine whether the relation defines a function.

3. $\{(-8,7),(-7,8),(-7,-8)\}$ 3. _____

4. $\{(-3,4),(4,-5),(-5,6)\}$ 4. _____

5. $\{(-2,3),(-1,5),(-1,-7)\}$ 5. _____

Given the following functions, find the indicated value.

   $f(x) = 3x + 4$ $g(x) = 4x - 2$ $h(x) = x^2 + x + 1$

6. $f(a)$ 6. _____

7. $f(-2)$ 7. _____

8. $f(3)$ 8. _____

9. $g(a)$ 9. _____

10. $g(-2)$ 10. _____

11. $g(3)$ 11. _____

12. $h(a)$ 12. _____

13. $h(-2)$ 13. _____

14. $h(3)$ 14. _____

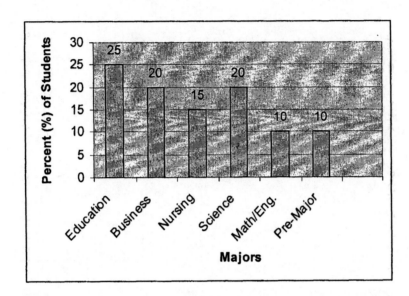

The bar graph shows the declared majors for incoming freshmen at the University of the Southwest.

15.   Name the domain using the horizontal axis.   15. _____

16.   Name the range using the vertical axis.   16. _____

17.   Write the ordered pairs represented by the graph
        (major, percent)   17. _____

18.   What makes a relation a function?   18. _____

19.   Is the relation illustrated a function?   19. _____

20.   Why or why not?   20. _____

Additional Exercises 8.1
Form III
Introduction to Functions

Find the (a) domain and (b) range.

1. $\{(-8,-2),(-5,-7),(2,-1)\}$

1a. _____

1b. _____

2. $\{(3,6),(2,-4),(-6,9)\}$

2a. _____

2b. _____

Determine whether the relation defines a function.

3. $\{(1,-8),(-2,4),(-3,0)\}$

3. _____

4. $\{(0,1),(0,-4),(0,6)\}$

4. _____

5. $\{(-1,1),(-2,2),(-3,3)\}$

5. _____

Given the following functions, find the indicated value.

$$f(x) = 2x^2 - 4 \qquad g(x) = 3x^2 - x + 2 \qquad h(x) = \frac{2x-1}{x+4}$$

6. $f(-4)$

6. _____

7. $f(2)$

7. _____

8. $f(a+h)$

8. _____

9. $g(-4)$

9. _____

10. $g(2)$

10. _____

11. $g(a+h)$

11. _____

12. $h(-4)$ 12. _____

13. $h(2)$ 13. _____

14. $h(a+h)$ 14. _____

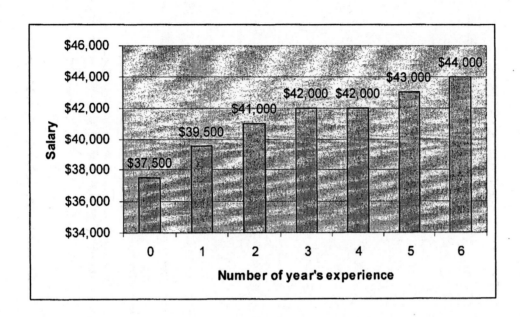

The bar graph shows the salary scale of teachers at Fort Bend in relationship to the number of year's experience.

15. Name the domain using the horizontal axis.   15. _____

16. Name the range using the vertical axis.   16. _____

17. Write the ordered pairs represented by the graph
     (years of experience, salary).   17. _____

18. What makes a relation a function?   18. _____

19. Is the relation illustrated a function?   19. _____

20. Why or why not?   20. _____

Name _____ Date _____

Use the vertical line test to determine whether or not the graph
is a graph of a function.

1.

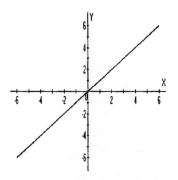

2.

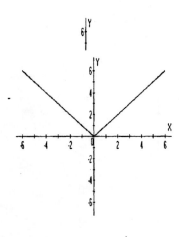

1. _____

2. _____

3.

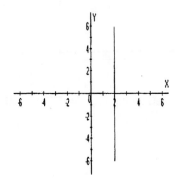

3. _____

Use the graph to find the function value.

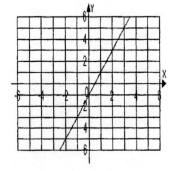

4. $f(-1)$ _____

5. $f(2)$ _____

6. $f(0)$ _____

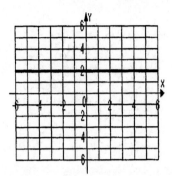

7. $f(-2)$ _____

8. $f(0)$ _____

9. $f(2)$ _____

Express each interval in set-builder notation and graph the interval on a number line.

10. $(-1, 5]$ 10. _____

-6 -5 -4 -3 -2 -1 0 1 2 3 4 5 6

11. $[2, \infty)$ 11. _____

-6 -5 -4 -3 -2 -1 0 1 2 3 4 5 6

Use the graph to identify the following:

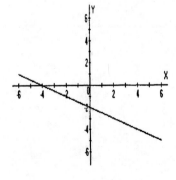

12.   domain   _____

13.   range   _____

The function $r(x) = 1.5x$ models the total revenue in dollars for a hot dog vendor selling x hot dogs.

14. Find $R(100)$, the revenue in selling 100 hot dogs.   14. _____

15. Find $R(225)$, the revenue in selling 225 hot dogs.   15. _____

Name _____ Date _____

Additional Exercises 8.2
Form II
Graphs of Functions

Use the vertical line test to determine whether or not the graph is a graph of a function.

1.

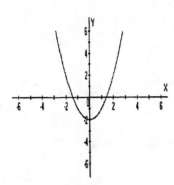

2.

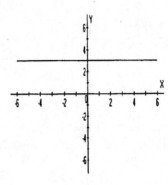

1. _____

2. _____

3.

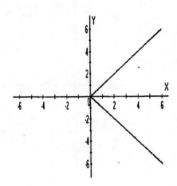

3. _____

Use the graph to find the function value.

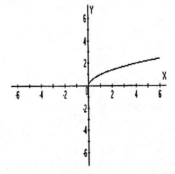

4. $f(0)$ _____

5. $f(1)$ _____

6. $f(4)$ _____

AE-303

Name _____   Date _____

7. $f(-2)$ _____

8. $f(0)$ _____

9. $f(2)$ _____

Express each interval in set-builder notation and graph the interval on a number line.

10. $(-\infty, 4]$

10. _____

-6 -5 -4 -3 -2 -1 0 1 2 3 4 5 6

11. $[2, 6)$

11. _____

-6 -5 -4 -3 -2 -1 0 1 2 3 4 5 6

Use the graph to identify the following:

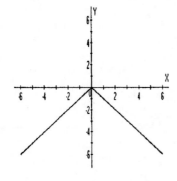

12.   domain   _____

13.   range   _____

The function $P(x) = 0.90x - 52$ models the relationship between the number of pretzels x that a certain vendor sells and the profit the vendor makes.

14. Find $P(100)$, the profit the vendor makes   14. _____
     from selling 100 pretzels.

15. Find $P(500)$, the profit the vendor makes   15. _____
     from selling 500 pretzels.

Name _____ Date _____

Additional Exercises 8.2
Form III
Graphs of Functions

Use the vertical line test to determine whether or not the graph is a graph of a function.

1.

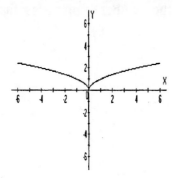

2.

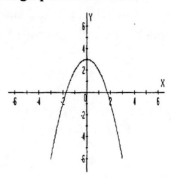

1. _____

2. _____

3.

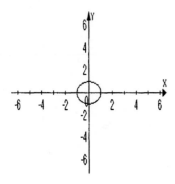

3. _____

Use the graph to find the function value.

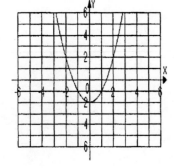

4.　　$f(0)$　　_____

5.　　$f(1)$　　_____

6.　　$f(-2)$　　_____

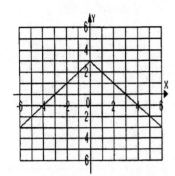

7. $f(-2)$ _____

8. $f(0)$ _____

9. $f(1)$ _____

10. $(-\infty, 5]$

10. _____

-6 -5 -4 -3 -2 -1 0 1 2 3 4 5 6

11. $(-3, 8]$

11. _____

-6 -5 -4 -3 -2 -1 0 1 2 3 4 5 6

Use the graph to identify the following:

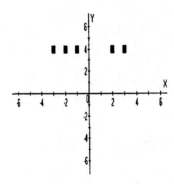

12.   domain   _____

13.   range   _____

Name _____   Date _____

The total cost in dollars for a certain company to produce x empty jars to be used by a jelly producer is given by the polynomial equation $C(x) = 0.6x + 17{,}000$.

14. Find $C(50{,}000)$, the cost of producing 50,000 jars.   14. _____

15. Find $C(100{,}000)$, the cost of producing 100,000 jars.   15. _____

Additional Exercises 8.3
Form I
The Algebra of Functions

Find the domain of the function.

1. $f(x) = 2x - 1$ 1. _____

2. $g(x) = -3x + 2$ 2. _____

3. $f(x) = \dfrac{1}{x + 3}$ 3. _____

4. $g(x) = \dfrac{1}{x - 5}$ 4. _____

Given $f(x) = 2x + 3$, $g(x) = 3x - 1$:

5.   find $(f + g)(x)$ 5. _____

6.   find $(f + g)(2)$ 6. _____

Given $f(x) = -5x + 2$, $g(x) = -5x - 4$:

7.   find $(f + g)(x)$ 7. _____

8.   find $(f + g)(4)$ 8. _____

Given $f(x) = x - 2$, $g(x) = -2x^2$:

9.   find $(f + g)(x)$ 9. _____

10.   find $(f + g)(3)$ 10. _____

Name _____   Date _____

For each pair of functions, determine the domain of $f + g$.

11. $f(x) = 2x - 1$, $g(x) = 2x + 5$ 11. _____

12. $f(x) = 3x - 4$, $g(x) = \dfrac{4}{x - 1}$ 12. _____

13. $f(x) = 5x + 2$, $g(x) = \dfrac{3}{x + 8}$ 13. _____

In exercises 14 through 19, let $f(x) = 2x + 1$ and $g(x) = x^2$:

14.   find $(f + g)(x)$ 14. _____

15.   find $(f + g)(2)$ 15. _____

16.   state the domain of $f + g$ 16. _____

17.   find $(f - g)(x)$ 17. _____

18.   find $(f - g)(-3)$ 18. _____

19.   state the domain of $f - g$ 19. _____

20.   A firm making toaster ovens finds that the total cost,   20. _____
       $C(x)$, of producing x units is given by $C(x) = 40x + 580$.
       The revenue, $R(x)$ from selling x units is determined
       by the price per unit times the number of units sold,
       thus $R(x) = 50x$. Find and interpret $(R - C)(92)$.

Name _____   Date _____

Find the domain of the function.

1. $f(x) = \dfrac{1}{x+1}$

1. _____

2. $g(x) = \dfrac{2}{x-7}$

2. _____

3. $f(x) = \dfrac{2x}{3-x}$

3. _____

4. $g(x) = x + \dfrac{3}{x-4}$

4. _____

Given $f(x) = 3x^2$, $g(x) = x - 5$:

5.   find $(f+g)(x)$

5. _____

6.   find $(f+g)(2)$

6. _____

Given $f(x) = 2x^2 - x + 3$, $g(x) = 3x - 7$:

7.   find $(f+g)(x)$

7. _____

8.   find $(f+g)(-4)$

8. _____

Given $f(x) = 4x^2 + x - 5$, $g(x) = -2x + 4$:

9.   find $(f+g)(x)$

9. _____

10.   find $(f+g)(-3)$

10. _____

For each pair of functions, determine the domain of $f + g$.

11.　$f(x) = \dfrac{1}{x}, \; g(x) = \dfrac{3}{x+2}$　　　　　　　　　11. _____

12.　$f(x) = \dfrac{3x}{x-4}, \; g(x) = \dfrac{7}{x+4}$　　　　　　　12. _____

13.　$f(x) = \dfrac{9x}{x+7}, \; g(x) = \dfrac{1}{x-3}$　　　　　　　13. _____

In exercises 14 through 19, let $f(x) = \dfrac{3x}{x+2}$ and $g(x) = \dfrac{2}{x+2}$:

14.　find $(f + g)(x)$　　　　　　　　　　　　　　14. _____

15.　find $(f + g)(2)$　　　　　　　　　　　　　　15. _____

16.　state the domain of $f + g$　　　　　　　　　16. _____

17.　find $(f - g)(x)$　　　　　　　　　　　　　　17. _____

18.　find $(f - g)(-3)$　　　　　　　　　　　　　18. _____

19.　state the domain of $f - g$　　　　　　　　　19. _____

20.　A firm making microwave ovens finds that the　　20. _____
　　total cost, $C(x)$, of producing x units is given by
　　$C(x) = 90x + 850$. The revenue, $R(x)$, from
　　selling x units is determined by the price per unit
　　times the number of units sold, thus $R(x) = 100x$.
　　Find and interpret $(R - C)(82)$.

Name _____   Date _____

Find the domain of the function.

1. $f(x) = \dfrac{3x}{2-x}$ 1. _____

2. $g(x) = x + \dfrac{4}{x+2}$ 2. _____

3. $f(x) = \dfrac{1}{x+5} + \dfrac{3}{x-6}$ 3. _____

4. $g(x) = \dfrac{1}{x-4} + \dfrac{1}{x+1}$ 4. _____

Given $f(x) = x^2 + 3x + 6$, $g(x) = -x^2 - 5x - 4$:

5. find $(f+g)(x)$ 5. _____

6. find $(f+g)(0)$ 6. _____

Given $f(x) = 3x^2 + 2x - 5$, $g(x) = -2x^2 - x + 7$:

7. find $(f+g)(x)$ 7. _____

8. find $(f+g)(2)$ 8. _____

Given $f(x) = -2x^2 + 5x - 8$, $g(x) = -x^2 + 4x - 2$

9. find $(f+g)(x)$ 9. _____

10. find $(f+g)(-4)$ 10. _____

AE-313

For each pair of functions, determine the domain of $f + g$.

11. $f(x) = \dfrac{6x}{x-6}$, $g(x) = \dfrac{x}{x+2}$ 11. _____

12. $f(x) = \dfrac{3}{x-4}$, $g(x) = \dfrac{2x}{4-x}$ 12. _____

13. $f(x) = x^2 + 2$, $g(x) = x^3 - 2$ 13. _____

In exercises 14 through 19, let $f(x) = x^2 + 3x$ and $g(x) = x + 5$:

14.   find $(f + g)(2)$ 14. _____

15.   find $(f + g)(-1)$ 15. _____

16.   find $\left(\dfrac{f}{g}\right)(x)$ 16. _____

17.   find $\left(\dfrac{f}{g}\right)(1)$ 17. _____

18.   state the domain of $\dfrac{f}{g}$ 18. _____

A firm is considering a new product. The accounting department estimates the total cost, $C(x)$, of producing x lamps will be $C(x) = 85x + 4000$. The sales department estimates that the revenue, $R(x)$, from selling x lamps will be $R(x) = 95x$. Find and interpret $(R - C)(415)$.

19.   Find $(R - C)(x)$.   19. _____

20.   Find $(R - C)(415)$.   20. _____

Additional Exercises 8.4
Form I
Composite and Inverse Functions

Find the composition.

1. If $f(x) = x^2 + 5x$ and $g(x) = x + 2$, find $(f \circ g)(3)$.   1. _____

2. If $f(x) = 3x - 4$ and $g(x) = x + 5$, find $(g \circ f)(x)$.   2. _____

3. If $f(x) = 3x^2 - 4x$ and $g(x) = 2x$, find $(g \circ f)(x)$.   3. _____

4. If $f(x) = 2x^2 + x$ and $g(x) = 3x$, find $(f \circ g)(x)$.   4. _____

5. If $f(x) = \dfrac{x - 8}{3}$ and $g(x) = -3x + 8$, find $(g \circ f)(x)$.   5. _____

6. If $f(x) = \dfrac{x - 8}{3}$ and $g(x) = 3x + 8$, find $(f \circ g)(x)$.   6. _____

7. If $f(x) = \dfrac{x - 8}{3}$ and $g(x) = -3x + 8$, find $(g \circ f)(5)$.   7. _____

8. If $f(x) = \sqrt{x + 6}$ and $g(x) = 8x - 10$, find $(g \circ f)(x)$.   8. _____

Determine whether the pair of functions f and g are inverses of each other.

9. $f(x) = 6x$ and $g(x) = \dfrac{x}{6}$ 9. _____

10. $f(x) = \dfrac{x + 2}{5}$ and $g(x) = \dfrac{5}{x + 2}$ 10. _____

Name _____   Date _____

11. $f(x) = x + 1$ and $g(x) = x - 1$ 11. _____

12. $f(x) = 2x - 5$ and $g(x) = \dfrac{x + 5}{2}$ 12. _____

13. $f(x) = \dfrac{x - 3}{4}$ and $g(x) = 4x + 3$ 13. _____

14. $f(x) = 3x + 1$ and $g(x) = -3x - 1$ 14. _____

Find the inverse of each one-to-one function. Write the inverse function using $f^{-1}(x)$ notation.

15. $f(x) = -5x - 7$ 15. _____

16. $f(x) = -2x$ 16. _____

17. $f(x) = \dfrac{x - 3}{4}$ 17. _____

18. $f(x) = \dfrac{1}{3}x + 1$ 18. _____

Graph each function and its inverse.

19. $f(x) = -3x$

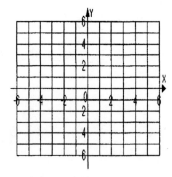

20. $g(x) = \dfrac{1}{2}x + 2$

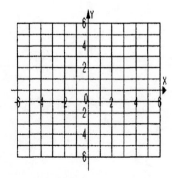

Additional Exercises 8.4
Form II
Composite and Inverse Functions

Find the composition.

1.   If $f(x) = x^2 - 3$ and $g(x) = 2x + 5$, find $(f \circ g)(3)$.   1. _____

2.   If $f(x) = 5x + 2$ and $g(x) = x + 3$, find $(g \circ f)(x)$.   2. _____

3.   If $f(x) = 5x^2 - 2x$ and $g(x) = 3x$, find $(g \circ f)(x)$.   3. _____

4.   If $f(x) = 5x^2 - 2x$ and $g(x) = 3x$, find $(f \circ g)(x)$.   4. _____

5.   If $f(x) = 3x - 9$ and $g(x) = -2x + 4$, find $(g \circ f)(x)$.   5. _____

6.   If $f(x) = \dfrac{2x - 3}{5}$ and $g(x) = \dfrac{5x + 3}{2}$, find $(f \circ g)(x)$.   6. _____

7.   If $f(x) = \sqrt{x + 4}$ and $g(x) = -x^2 - 4$, find $(g \circ f)(x)$.   7. _____

8.   If $f(x) = \sqrt{x + 4}$ and $g(x) = x^2 - 4$, find $(g \circ f)(x)$.   8. _____

Determine whether the pair of functions f and g are inverses of each other.

9. $f(x) = 3x - 1$ and $g(x) = \dfrac{x + 1}{3}$ 9. _____

10. $f(x) = \dfrac{x - 3}{4}$ and $g(x) = \dfrac{4}{x + 3}$ 10. _____

Name _____   Date _____

11. $f(x) = x + 1$ and $g(x) = -x - 1$ 11. _____

12. $f(x) = x^2$ and $g(x) = \sqrt{x}$ 12. _____

13. $f(x) = 8x$ and $g(x) = \dfrac{1}{8}x$ 13. _____

14. $f(x) = \dfrac{1}{\sqrt{x}}$ and $g(x) = x^2$ 14. _____

Find the inverse of each one-to-one function. Write the inverse function using $f^{-1}(x)$ notation.

15. $f(x) = \dfrac{x - 7}{2}$ 15. _____

16. $f(x) = \dfrac{x}{3}$ 16. _____

17. $f(x) = (x + 3)^2$ 17. _____

18. $f(x) = \sqrt[3]{x - 6}$ 18. _____

Graph each function and its inverse.

19. $f(x) = 4$

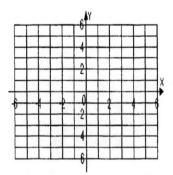

20. $g(x) = 3^x$

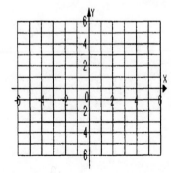

Name _____   Date _____

Additional Exercises 8.4
Form III
Composite and Inverse Functions

Find the composition.

1. If $f(x) = x^2 + 3$ and $g(x) = -x + 1$, find $(f \circ g)(4)$.   1. _____

2. If $f(x) = \sqrt{x + 6}$ and $g(x) = 8x - 10$, find $(f \circ g)(x)$.   2. _____

3. If $f(x) = x^2 - 4$ and $g(x) = x^2 + 12$, find $(g \circ f)(x)$.   3. _____

4. If $f(x) = -\dfrac{7}{x}$ and $g(x) = \dfrac{3}{x}$, find $(f \circ g)(x)$.   4. _____

5. If $f(x) = \sqrt{x + 3}$ and $g(x) = x^2 + 5$, find $(g \circ f)(x)$.   5. _____

6. If $f(x) = x^2 + 2$ and $g(x) = \sqrt{x - 4}$, find $(f \circ g)(6)$.   6. _____

7. If $f(x) = x - 3$ and $g(x) = \dfrac{x + 3}{5x}$, find $(g \circ f)(x)$.   7. _____

8. If $f(x) = x - 4$ and $g(x) = \dfrac{x + 4}{4x}$, find $(g \circ f)(6)$.   8. _____

Determine whether the pair of functions f and g are inverses of each other.

9. $f(x) = \dfrac{x}{2} + 2$ and $g(x) = 2x - 4$ 9. _____

10. $f(x) = \dfrac{x + 3}{5}$ and $g(x) = \dfrac{5}{3}x$ 10. _____

AE-319

11. $f(x) = 2x - 10$ and $g(x) = \dfrac{x}{2} + 5$ 11. _____

12. $f(x) = -2$ and $g(x) = -2$ 12. _____

13. $f(x) = \sqrt{x-5}$ and $g(x) = x^2 - 25$ 13. _____

14. $f(x) = \dfrac{\sqrt{x}}{6}$ and $g(x) = 36x^2$ 14. _____

Find the inverse of each one-to-one function. Write the inverse function using $f^{-1}(x)$ notation.

15. $f(x) = 4 - 3x$ 15. _____

16. $f(x) = \dfrac{-x}{3} + 1$ 16. _____

17. $f(x) = \dfrac{x+6}{2x}$ 17. _____

18. $f(x) = \dfrac{\sqrt{x}}{x}$ 18. _____

Graph each function and its inverse.

19. $f(x) = -2x + 1$

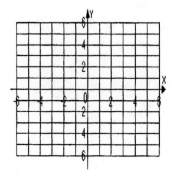

20. $g(x) = 4^x$

Name _____   Date _____

Additional Exercises 9.1
Form I
Reviewing Linear Inequalities and Using Inequalities in Business Applications

Solve each linear inequality. Other then Ø, graph the solution set on a number line.

1. $2x + 9 \leq 11$

    1. _____

2. $4x + 5 \geq -11$

    2. _____

3. $-3x - 5 > 4$

    3. _____

4. $-2x + 7 < 15$

    4. _____

5. $5x + 2 \geq 3x + 10$

    5. _____

6. $-7x < -4x - 3$

    6. _____

7. $8x \leq 4(x + 2)$

    7. _____

8. $6(x - 5) > 4(x - 5)$

    8. _____

9. Let $f(x) = 2x + 5$ and $g(x) = 4x - 3$. Find all values of x for which $f(x) > g(x)$.

    9. _____

In exercises 10 – 11, cost and revenue functions for producing and selling x units of a product are given. Cost and revenue are expressed in dollars. (a) Write the profit function from producing and selling x units of the product. (b) More than how many units must be produced and sold for the business to make money?

10. $C(x) = 12,500 + 12x$ 10a. _____

         $R(x) = 32x$ b. _____

11. $C(x) = 15,000 + 11x$ 11a. _____

         $R(x) = 23x$ b. _____

Name _____   Date _____

Additional Exercises 9.1
Form II
Reviewing Linear Inequalities and Using Inequalities in Business Applications

Solve each linear inequality. Other then Ø, graph the solution set on a number line.

1. $-3(2x+11) < -9x - 27$

          -6 -5 -4 -3 -2 -1 0 1 2 3 4 5 6   1. _____

2. $8x + 10 - 3x < 6 + 3x + 4$

          -6 -5 -4 -3 -2 -1 0 1 2 3 4 5 6   2. _____

3. $3(2x - 4) \geq 5(x - 2)$

          -6 -5 -4 -3 -2 -1 0 1 2 3 4 5 6   3. _____

4. $9x \geq 3(4x-1)$

          -6 -5 -4 -3 -2 -1 0 1 2 3 4 5 6   4. _____

5. $8(x + 1) - 3x \geq 5x + 8$

          -6 -5 -4 -3 -2 -1 0 1 2 3 4 5 6   5. _____

6. $3x - 6 > 3(x + 9)$

          -6 -5 -4 -3 -2 -1 0 1 2 3 4 5 6   6. _____

7. $\dfrac{3}{4}x + 1 < 10$

          -6 -5 -4 -3 -2 -1 0 1 2 3 4 5 6   7. _____

8. $\dfrac{-1}{6}x > \dfrac{1}{3}$

          -6 -5 -4 -3 -2 -1 0 1 2 3 4 5 6   8. _____

9.   Let $f(x) = 5x + 9$ and $g(x) = 2x + 11$. Find all values of x for   9. _____
     which $f(x) > g(x)$.

In exercises 10 – 11, cost and revenue functions for producing and selling x units of a product are given. Cost and revenue are expressed in dollars. (a) Write the profit function from producing and selling x units of the product. (b) More than how many units must be produced and sold for the business to make money?

10. $C(x) = 21{,}500 + 15x$ 10a. _____
      $R(x) = 21x$ b. _____

11. $C(x) = 17{,}500 + 27x$ 11a. _____
      $R(x) = 52x$ b. _____

Name _____   Date _____

Reviewing Linear Inequalities and Inequalities in Business Application

Solve each linear inequality. Other then Ø, graph the solution set on a number line.

1. $4x + 7 \geq 4(x + 2)$ $\xleftarrow{\ -6\ -5\ -4\ -3\ -2\ -1\ 0\ 1\ 2\ 3\ 4\ 5\ 6\ }\rightarrow$ 1. _____

2. $7x + 11 \leq 7(x + 2)$ $\xleftarrow{\ -6\ -5\ -4\ -3\ -2\ -1\ 0\ 1\ 2\ 3\ 4\ 5\ 6\ }\rightarrow$ 2. _____

3. $\dfrac{3}{4}(8x - 4) > \dfrac{2}{3}(6x + 9)$ $\xleftarrow{\ -6\ -5\ -4\ -3\ -2\ -1\ 0\ 1\ 2\ 3\ 4\ 5\ 6\ }\rightarrow$ 3. _____

4. $9 - \dfrac{3}{5}x + 6 > 12$ $\xleftarrow{\ -6\ -5\ -4\ -3\ -2\ -1\ 0\ 1\ 2\ 3\ 4\ 5\ 6\ }\rightarrow$ 4. _____

5. $\dfrac{4}{5}x - 5 \leq 15$ $\xleftarrow{\ -6\ -5\ -4\ -3\ -2\ -1\ 0\ 1\ 2\ 3\ 4\ 5\ 6\ }\rightarrow$ 5. _____

6. $3 < \dfrac{2x}{7} + \dfrac{4}{7} - 3$ $\xleftarrow{\ -6\ -5\ -4\ -3\ -2\ -1\ 0\ 1\ 2\ 3\ 4\ 5\ 6\ }\rightarrow$ 6. _____

7. $\dfrac{3x}{5} - \dfrac{1}{3} < \dfrac{4}{15}$ $\xleftarrow{\ -6\ -5\ -4\ -3\ -2\ -1\ 0\ 1\ 2\ 3\ 4\ 5\ 6\ }\rightarrow$ 7. _____

8. $\dfrac{x - 4}{20} \geq \dfrac{x - 5}{24} + \dfrac{1}{120}$ $\xleftarrow{\ -6\ -5\ -4\ -3\ -2\ -1\ 0\ 1\ 2\ 3\ 4\ 5\ 6\ }\rightarrow$ 8. _____

9.   Let $f(x) = \dfrac{1}{4}x + 5$ and $g(x) = \dfrac{1}{3}x + 6$. Find all values of x for   9. _____

which $f(x) > g(x)$.

In exercises 10 – 11, cost and revenue functions for producing and selling x units of a product are given. Cost and revenue are expressed in dollars. (a) Write the profit function from producing and selling x units of the product. (b) More than how many units must be produced and sold for the business to make money?

10. $C(x) = 25{,}200 + 18x$ 10a. _____
       $R(x) = 30x$ b. _____

11. $C(x) = 18{,}800 + 15x$ 11a. _____
       $R(x) = 31x$ b. _____

Additional Exercises 9.2
Form I
Compound Inequalities

In exercises 1–7 , use the following sets to find the union or intersection.

$$A = \{1, 3, 5, 7, 9, 11\}$$
$$B = \{1, 2, 3, 4, 5, 6\}$$
$$C = \{2, 4, 6, 8\}$$
$$D = \varnothing$$

1. $A \cup B$ 1. _____

2. $B \cap C$ 2. _____

3. $C \cup D$ 3. _____

4. $A \cap C$ 4. _____

5. $B \cap D$ 5. _____

6. $A \cap B$ 6. _____

7. $B \cup C$ 7. _____

(a) Solve the inequalities and write in set builder notation the (b) express the answer in interval notation.

8. $x > 2$ and $x > 4$ 8a. _____

                                                           b. _____

9. $x > 1$ or $x > 3$ 9a. _____

                                                           b. _____

10. $x \leq 5$ and $x \leq 2$ 10a. _____

                                                           b. _____

11. $x < 3$ or $x \geq -4$ 11a. _____

                                                              b. _____

12. $x < 3$ and $x \geq 0$ 12a. _____

                                                              b. _____

13. $x \geq 4$ or $x < -2$ 13a. _____

                                                              b. _____

14. $x > 5$ and $x < -3$ 14a. _____

                                                              b. _____

15. $8 < x + 2 < 10$ 15a. _____

                                                              b. _____

16. $4x < -16$ and $3x > -21$ 16a. _____

                                                              b. _____

17. $2x < -4$ or $2x > 10$ 17a. _____

                                                              b. _____

Name _____ Date _____

Solve. Use interval notation to express the range.

18. The formula for converting Celsius temperature,
C, to Fahrenheit temperature, F, is $F = 1.8C + 32$.
If Celsius temperature ranges from 45° to 115°,
inclusive, what is the range for the Fahrenheit
temperature? Round to the nearest whole number
if necessary.

18. _____

19. On the first four exams, your grades are 75, 87, 62,
and 76. There is still a final exam, and it counts as
two grades. You are hoping to earn a C in the course.
This will occur if the average of the six exam grades
is greater than or equal to 70 and less then 80. What
range of grades on the final will result in earning a C?

19. _____

20. Parts for an automobile repair cost $468. The mechanic
charges $26 per hour. If you receive an estimate for at
least $546 and the most $624 for fixing the car, what
is the time interval that the mechanic will be working
on the job?

20. _____

Name _____   Date _____

Additional Exercises 9.2
Form II
Compound Inequalities

In exercises 1–7, use the following sets to find the union or intersection.

$A = \{1, 3, 5, 7,\}$
$B = \{-3, -1, 1, 3\}$
$C = \{-5, -4, -3, -2, -1, 0\}$
$D = \{0, 1, 2, 3, 4, 5\}$
$E = \emptyset$

1. $A \cup B$ 1. _____

2. $C \cap E$ 2. _____

3. $B \cup D$ 3. _____

4. $A \cap D$ 4. _____

5. $C \cap D$ 5. _____

6. $B \cap C$ 6. _____

7. $A \cup E$ 7. _____

(a) Solve the inequalities and write in set builder notation the (b) express the answer in interval notation.

8. $x > 1$ and $x > 7$ 8a. _____

                                                                           b. _____

9. $x \leq 3$ or $x \leq 0$ 9a. _____

                                                                           b. _____

10. $x > 5$ and $x < -3$ 10a. _____

                                        b. _____

11. $x \geq 4$ or $x < -2$ 11a. _____

                                        b. _____

12. $2x \leq 8$ and $3x > -12$ 12a. _____

                                        b. _____

13. $3x + 1 \leq 7$ or $4x - 3 \geq 9$ 13a. _____

                                        b. _____

14. $9 < x + 3 < 15$ 14a. _____

                                        b. _____

15. $-8 < 2x - 2 \leq 4$ 15a. _____

                                        b. _____

16. $-23 \leq -4x + 1 \leq -7$ 16a. _____

                                        b. _____

17. $-5x > -10$ or $x + 5 > 3$ 17a. _____

                                        b. _____

Name _____   Date _____

Solve. Use interval notation to express the range.

18.   The formula for converting Celsius temperature,   18. _____
        C, to Fahrenheit temperature, F, is $F = 1.8C + 32$.
        If Celsius temperature ranges from 30° to 90°,
        inclusive, what is the range for the Fahrenheit
        temperature? Round to the nearest whole number
        if necessary.

19.   On the first four exams, your grades are 66, 72, 70,   19. _____
        and 80. There is still a final exam , and it counts as
        two grades. You are hoping to earn a C in the course.
        This will occur if the average of the six exam grades
        is greater than or equal to 70 and less then 80. What
        range of grades on the final will result in earning a C?

20.   Parts for an automobile repair cost $471. The mechanic   20. _____
        charges $35 per hour. If you receive an estimate for at
        least $576 and the most $646 for fixing the car, what
        is the time interval that the mechanic will be working
        on the job?

Additional Exercises 9.2
Form III
Compound Inequalities

In exercises 1–7, use the following sets to find the union or intersection.

$$A = \{q, s, y\}$$
$$B = \{q, s, y\; z, w\}$$
$$C = \{r, y, z\}$$
$$D = \{m, n, o, p, q\}$$
$$E = \varnothing$$

1. $A \cap C$ 1. _____

2. $B \cup D$ 2. _____

3. $D \cup E$ 3. _____

4. $A \cap D$ 4. _____

5. $B \cap C$ 5. _____

6. $C \cap E$ 6. _____

7. $C \cap D$ 7. _____

(a) Solve the inequalities and write in set builder notation the (b) express the answer in interval notation.

8. $x + 5 < 3$ or $-5x < -10$.   8a. _____

                                               b. _____

9. $12 - 8 < 4x$ and $-4x \le -12$ 9a. _____

                                               b. _____

10. $-6x < 30$ and $x + 6 < 9$ 10a. _____

    b. _____

11. $-7x + 1 \geq 15$ or $6x + 3 \geq -21$ 11a. _____

    b. _____

12. $-4 \leq \dfrac{x}{3} + 1 \leq 7$ 12a. _____

    b. _____

13. $3(x + 2) > 9$ and $\dfrac{x - 2}{3} \leq 1$ 13a. _____

    b. _____

14. $4x + 1 < -3$ or $2x - 4 \geq 6$ 14a. _____

    b. _____

15. $-1 \leq \dfrac{x}{4} + 3 < 2$ 15a. _____

    b. _____

16. $2x + 5 < -1$ or $2x - 1 \geq -11$ 16a. _____

    b. _____

17. $4(x - 2) > 12$ and $\dfrac{x - 2}{3} \leq -5$ 17a. _____

    b. _____

Solve. Use interval notation to express the range.

18.   The formula for converting Celsius temperature,   18. _____
       C, to Fahrenheit temperature, F, is $F = 1.8C + 32$.
       If Celsius temperature ranges from 10° to 85°,
       inclusive, what is the range for the Fahrenheit
       temperature? Round to the nearest whole number
       if necessary.

19.   On the first four exams, your grades are 75, 72, 71,   19. _____
       and 50. There is still a final exam , and it counts as
       two grades. You are hoping to earn a C in the course.
       This will occur if the average of the six exam grades
       is greater than or equal to 70 and less then 80. What
       range of grades on the final will result in earning a C?

20.   Parts for an automobile repair cost $592. The mechanic 20. _____
       charges $42 per hour. If you receive an estimate for at
       least $760 and the most $802 for fixing the car, what
       is the time interval that the mechanic will be working
       on the job?

Name _____   Date _____

Find the solution set for each equation.

1. $|x| = 5$ 1. _____

2. $|x - 3| = 8$ 2. _____

3. $|x + 2| = 4$ 3. _____

4. $|3x - 1| = 5$ 4. _____

5. $|x| = -7$ 5. _____

6. $|x + 4| = 0$ 6. _____

7. $|x - 6| = 0$ 7. _____

8. $3|x + 2| = 9$ 8. _____

9. $2|3x + 5| = 10$ 9. _____

(a) Solve the inequality and then (b) graph the solution set.

10. $|x| > 2$ 10. _____

11. $|x| \le 3$ 11. _____

12. $|x - 2| < 3$

12. _____

13. $|x - 4| > 0$

13. _____

14. $|x - 6| \geq 2$

14. _____

15. $|3x - 4| < 1$

15. _____

16. $|2x - 4| \geq 2$

16. _____

17. $|2x + 5| \leq 3$

17. _____

18. $|5x + 2| > 7$

18. _____

The following table gives the percent of the viewing public that watched five television programs last week. Use the information in the table to answer exercises 19-20.

Program	Viewing Percentage
The Winstons	38.30%
Guess Who?	42.50%
Four to Go	27.90%
Inside and Out	16.40%
Union Street	11.80%

19. Express the percentage of the viewing public, x, that watched *Inside and Out* last week as an absolute value inequality. The margin of error is ±2.4%.

19. _____

20. Express the percentage of the viewing public, x, that watched *Guess Who?* last week as a compound inequality. The margin of error is ±3.6%.

20. _____

Name _____   Date _____

Additional Exercises 9.3
Form II
Equation and Inequalities Involving Absolute Value

Find the solution set for each equation.

1. $\left|\dfrac{3x-1}{4}\right| = 2$

    1. _____

2. $|x| = -8$

    2. _____

3. $|x - 5| = 0$

    3. _____

4. $4|2x - 1| = 20$

    4. _____

5. $|x| - 1 = 9$

    5. _____

6. $|x - 12| = -14$

    6. _____

7. $|5x - 2| - 9 = 14$

    7. _____

8. $|4x| = |2x - 1|$

    8. _____

9. $|x - 2| = |3 - x|$

    9. _____

(a) Solve the inequality and then (b) graph the solution set.

10. $|x + 3| \le 6$

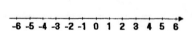

10. _____

11. $|2x - 1| \ge 5$

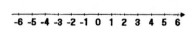

11. _____

12. $|4x + 2| < 9$

-6 -5 -4 -3 -2 -1 0 1 2 3 4 5 6

12. _____

13. $|3x - 5| > 10$

-6 -5 -4 -3 -2 -1 0 1 2 3 4 5 6

13. _____

14. $|2(x - 3) + 1| \le 5$

-6 -5 -4 -3 -2 -1 0 1 2 3 4 5 6

14. _____

15. $|3(x + 2) - 4| \ge 2$

-6 -5 -4 -3 -2 -1 0 1 2 3 4 5 6

15. _____

16. $\left|\dfrac{2x - 1}{4}\right| < 3$

-6 -5 -4 -3 -2 -1 0 1 2 3 4 5 6

16. _____

17. $\left|\dfrac{3x + 2}{5}\right| > 1$

-6 -5 -4 -3 -2 -1 0 1 2 3 4 5 6

17. _____

18. $|x - 4| < -4$

-6 -5 -4 -3 -2 -1 0 1 2 3 4 5 6

18. _____

The following table gives the percent of the viewing public that watched five television programs last week. Use the information in the table to answer exercises 19-20.

Program	Viewing Percentage
The Winstons	38.30%
Guess Who?	42.50%
Four to Go	27.90%
Inside and Out	16.40%
Union Street	11.80%

19. Express the percentage of the viewing public, x, that watched *Union Street* last week as an absolute value inequality. The margin of error is ±1.8%.

19. _____

20. Express the percentage of the viewing public, x, that watched *Four to Go* last week as a compound inequality. The margin of error is ±2.9%.

20. _____

Name _____   Date _____

Find the solution set for each equation.

1. $3\,|\,4x\,|\,-2 = 7$ 1. _____

2. $5\,|\,2x\,|\,+4 = 24$ 2. _____

3. $|\,4x+2\,|\,+5 = 8$ 3. _____

4. $|\,3x-1\,|\,+6 = 2$ 4. _____

5. $|\,5x-9\,|\,=|\,x-2\,|$ 5. _____

6. $|\,x-2\,|\,=|\,2-x\,|$ 6. _____

7. $\left|\dfrac{1}{2}x+2\right| = \left|\dfrac{3}{4}x-2\right|$ 7. _____

8. $|\,6x-8\,|\,=|\,3x+4\,|$ 8. _____

9. $\left|\dfrac{x}{3}-2\right| = \left|\dfrac{2x}{3}+\dfrac{1}{2}\right|$ 9. _____

(a) Solve the inequality and then (b) graph the solution set.

10. $\left|4-\dfrac{x}{2}\right| < 3$ 10. _____

-6 -5 -4 -3 -2 -1 0 1 2 3 4 5 6

11. $\left|\dfrac{3}{4}x+1\right| > -2$ 11. _____

-6 -5 -4 -3 -2 -1 0 1 2 3 4 5 6

12. $|x+2|+7 \leq 9$

-6 -5 -4 -3 -2 -1 0 1 2 3 4 5 6

12. _____

13. $|8x-7|+4 < -2$

-6 -5 -4 -3 -2 -1 0 1 2 3 4 5 6

13. _____

14. $|5x-5|-5 < 1$

-6 -5 -4 -3 -2 -1 0 1 2 3 4 5 6

14. _____

15. $|8x-7|+4 < -2$

-6 -5 -4 -3 -2 -1 0 1 2 3 4 5 6

15. _____

16. $3|4x-1|+3 > 12$

-6 -5 -4 -3 -2 -1 0 1 2 3 4 5 6

16. _____

17. $-4|1-x| < -8$

-6 -5 -4 -3 -2 -1 0 1 2 3 4 5 6

17. _____

18. $-2|4-x| \geq -10$

-6 -5 -4 -3 -2 -1 0 1 2 3 4 5 6

18. _____

The following table gives the percent of the viewing public that watched five television programs last week. Use the information in the table to answer exercises 19-20.

Program	Viewing Percentage
The Winstons	38.30%
Guess Who?	42.50%
Four to Go	27.90%
Inside and Out	16.40%
Union Street	11.80%

19. Express the percentage of the viewing public, x, that watched *Inside and Out* last week as an absolute value inequality. The margin of error is ±3.1%.

19. _____

20. Express the percentage of the viewing public, x, that watched *The Winstons* last week as a compound inequality. The margin of error is ±1.5%.

20. _____

Name _____ Date _____

Additional Exercises 9.4
Form I
Linear Inequalities in Two Variables

Graph the inequality.

1. $x + y < -5$

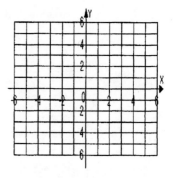

2. $y \geq x - 4$

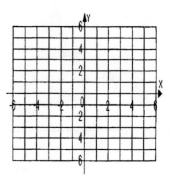

3. $y - 3 \leq x$

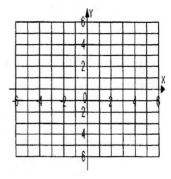

4. $y \geq 2$

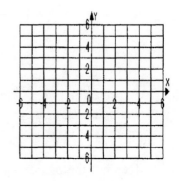

Name _____   Date _____

Graph the solution set of the system of inequalities.

5. $y > x + 2$
      $y < -x - 3$

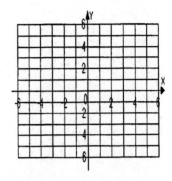

6. $x + y > 3$
      $x + y < -2$

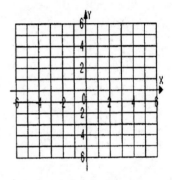

7. $2x + y < 4$
      $2x + y > -1$

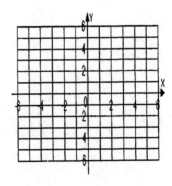

8. $2x + 2y > -4$
      $-4x + 2y < 8$

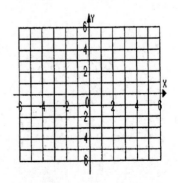

9. $2x + 5y \geq 10$
     $2x - 3y < 6$

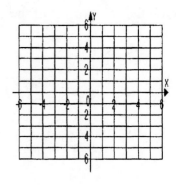

10. $2x - 4y \leq 0$
      $4x + 4y \geq -8$

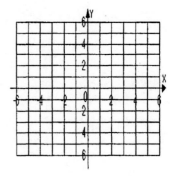

11. $-3 \leq x < 4$

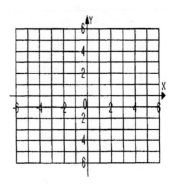

12. $x \leq 2$
      $y < -2$

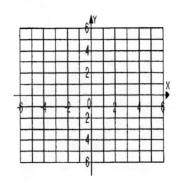

Name _____   Date _____

Graph the inequality.

1. $x - y < -4$

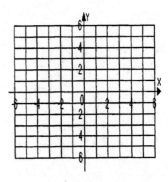

2. $x \leq 0$

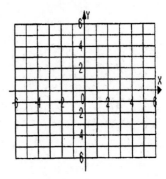

3. $x - y > -2$

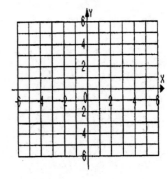

4. $3x + 4y > 12$

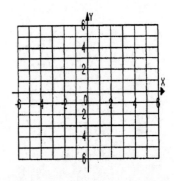

Graph the solution set of the system of inequalities.

5. $x \le 1$
       $y \ge -3$

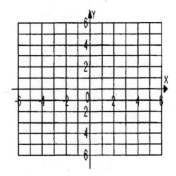

6. $x \ge -2$
       $-x + 2y < -6$

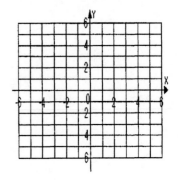

7. $x + y > 1$
       $x + y < -3$

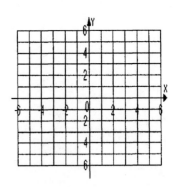

8. $-1 < y \le 4$

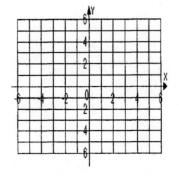

9. $3x + 2y > 6$
        $4x - 3y \leq 12$

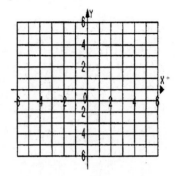

10. $2x - 3y > -6$
      $x \geq -1$

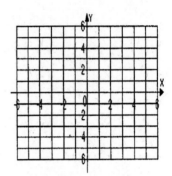

11. $3x - 2y < 4$
      $4x - y > -3$

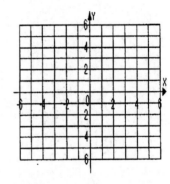

12. $x - y < -2$
      $2x - 3y < 9$

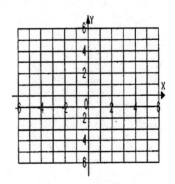

Name _____   Date _____

Additional Exercises 9.4
Form III
Linear Inequalities in Two Variables

Graph the inequality.

1. $-2x + 5y \leq 10$

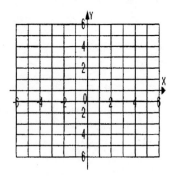

2. $-3x - 5y \leq -15$

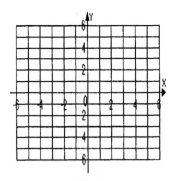

3. $x \geq \dfrac{1}{2}$

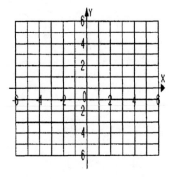

4. $\dfrac{x}{2} - \dfrac{y}{3} > 1$

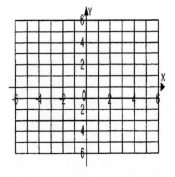

Name _____   Date _____

Graph the solution set of the system of inequalities.

5. $x < 2$
     $y \geq 4$

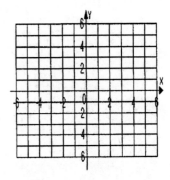

6. $-3 \leq x \leq 4$

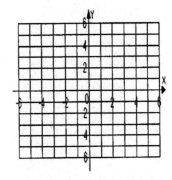

7. $4x + 5y \leq 20$
     $x \geq -2$

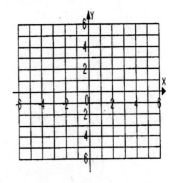

8. $3x - 2y \geq 8$
     $x + 4y \leq -4$

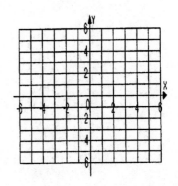

9. $x + y > 2$
       $x + y < -2$

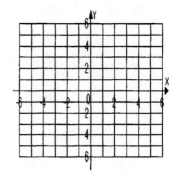

10. $2x - 3y \leq 6$
       $y < -x - 2$

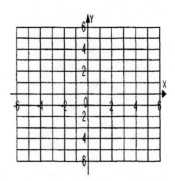

11. $3x + 2y \geq 6$
       $-x - y \leq 1$

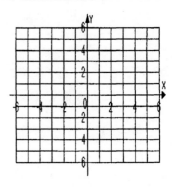

12. $2x + 5y \leq 10$
       $3x + 4y \leq 12$

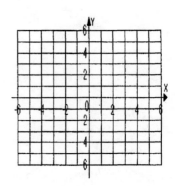

Name _____   Date _____

Additional Exercises 10.1
Form I
Rational Expressions and Functions

Find the indicated root or state that the expression is not a real number.

1. $\sqrt{49}$ 1. _____

2. $\sqrt{-64}$ 2. _____

3. $\sqrt[3]{-27}$ 3. _____

4. $\sqrt[3]{64}$ 4. _____

5. $\sqrt[4]{16}$ 5. _____

6. $\sqrt[4]{-16}$ 6. _____

7. $\sqrt[6]{64}$ 7. _____

8. $\sqrt[5]{-243}$ 8. _____

Simplify each expression. Include absolute value bars where necessary.

9. $\sqrt{(-3)^2}$ 9. _____

10. $\sqrt{(x+4)^2}$ 10. _____

11. $\sqrt[3]{(a+7)^3}$ 11. _____

12. $\sqrt[5]{m^5}$ 12. _____

13. $\sqrt{4x^2}$ 13. _____

14. $\sqrt[4]{(x+6)^4}$ 14. _____

15. $\sqrt[3]{-27x^3}$ 15. _____

16. $-\sqrt[3]{-64}$ 16. _____

Find the indicated function values for each function. If necessary round to two decimal places. If the function value is not a real number and does not exist, so state.

17. $f(x)=\sqrt{x-8}$; $f(44)$ 17. _____

18. $g(x)=\sqrt{x-25}$; $g(25)$ 18. _____

19. $h(x)=\sqrt[3]{5x-12}$; $h(4)$ 19. _____

20. $p(x)=\sqrt[3]{2x-19}$; $p(-4)$ 20. _____

Additional Exercises 10.1
Form II
Rational Expressions and Functions

Find the indicated root or state that the expression is not a real number.

1. $\sqrt{-196}$

1. _____

2. $-\sqrt{400}$

2. _____

3. $\sqrt[3]{-64}$

3. _____

4. $\sqrt[4]{625}$

4. _____

5. $\sqrt[4]{-256}$

5. _____

6. $\sqrt[3]{-1000}$

6. _____

7. $-\sqrt[5]{-32}$

7. _____

8. $\sqrt[4]{81}$

8. _____

Simplify each expression. Include absolute value bars where necessary.

9. $\sqrt{(x+9)^2}$

9. _____

10. $\sqrt[3]{(x-4)^3}$

10. _____

11. $\sqrt[5]{a^5 b^5}$ 11. _____

12. $\sqrt{(x-3)(x-3)}$ 12. _____

13. $\sqrt{x^2 - 8x + 16}$ 13. _____

14. $\sqrt[3]{27(x+1)^3}$ 14. _____

15. $-\sqrt{x^2 + 4x + 4}$ 15. _____

16. $\sqrt{\dfrac{25}{100}x^2}$ 16. _____

Find the indicated function values for each function. If necessary round to two decimal places. If the function value is not a real number and does not exist, so state.

17. $f(x) = \sqrt[3]{x^3 - 19}\,;\ f(-2)$ 17. _____

18. $g(x) = \sqrt{x^2 + 13}\,;\ g(-6)$ 18. _____

19. $h(x) = -\sqrt{4x - x^2}\,;\ h(2)$ 19. _____

20. $m(x) = \sqrt[5]{x^5 + 6x^4 + 8x^3 + 5x^2 + 31}\,;\ m(2)$ 20. _____

Name _____   Date _____

Additional Exercises 10.1
Form III
Rational Expressions and Functions

Find the indicated root or state that the expression is not a real number.

1. $\sqrt{361}$ 1. _____

2. $\sqrt[3]{-1728}$ 2. _____

3. $-\sqrt[4]{81}$ 3. _____

4. $\sqrt{121-242}$ 4. _____

5. $\sqrt{\dfrac{16}{25}}$ 5. _____

6. $\sqrt[3]{\dfrac{-8}{1000}}$ 6. _____

7. $-\sqrt[5]{-1}$ 7. _____

8. $3\sqrt{-0.125}$ 8. _____

Simplify each expression. Include absolute value bars where necessary.

9. $\sqrt{(x-8)^2}$ 9. _____

10. $\sqrt{x^2+10x+25}$ 10. _____

11. $\sqrt[3]{(x+1)^2(x+1)}$ 11. _____

12. $\sqrt[4]{81(x+3)^4}$ 12. _____

13. $\sqrt[5]{-243y^5}$ 13. _____

14. $\sqrt[3]{(-8)^3}$ 14. _____

15. $\sqrt[6]{-64x^6}$ 15. _____

16. $\sqrt[4]{256(y+4)^4}$ 16. _____

Find the indicated function values for each function. If necessary round to two decimal places. If the function value is not a real number and does not exist, so state.

17. $f(x)=\sqrt[3]{x-32}$; $f(-32)$ 17. _____

18. $g(x)=\sqrt{3x^2+3x}$; $g(-4)$ 18. _____

19. $h(x)=\sqrt[5]{-18x^4-15x^3+3x^2+2}$; $h(-3)$ 19. _____

20.   The formula $v=\sqrt{2.5r}$ models the safe maximum speed,   20. _____
      v, in miles per hour, at which a car can travel on a curved
      road with a radius of curvature, r, in feet. A highway crew
      measures the radius of curvature at an exit ramp as 490 feet.
      What is the maximum safe speed?

Additional Exercises 10.2
Form I
Rational Exponents

Use radical notation to rewrite each expression. Simplify if possible.

1. $64^{\frac{1}{2}}$

1. _____

2. $27^{\frac{1}{3}}$

2. _____

3. $(5xy)^{\frac{1}{2}}$

3. _____

4. $32^{\frac{2}{5}}$

4. _____

Rewrite the expression with a rational exponent.

5. $\sqrt{10}$

5. _____

6. $\sqrt[5]{4x}$

6. _____

7. $\sqrt[3]{8^2}$

7. _____

8. $\left(\sqrt[4]{16}\right)^5$

8. _____

Rewrite the expression with a positive rational exponent. Simplify, if possible.

9. $49^{-\frac{1}{2}}$

9. _____

10. $16^{-\frac{3}{4}}$

10. _____

11. $(-27)^{-\frac{2}{3}}$ 11. _____

12. $100^{-\frac{3}{2}}$ 12. _____

Use the properties of rational exponents to simplify each expression. Assume that all variables represent positive numbers.

13. $x^{\frac{1}{8}}x^{\frac{7}{8}}$ 13. _____

14. $\dfrac{a^{\frac{4}{5}}}{a^{\frac{1}{5}}}$ 14. _____

15. $(100x^8 y^4)^{\frac{1}{2}}$ 15. _____

16. $\left(x^{\frac{-3}{4}} y^{\frac{-2}{3}}\right)^{-12}$ 16. _____

Use rational exponents to simplify each expression. If rational exponents appear after simplifying, write the answer in radical notation.

17. $\sqrt[10]{x^5}$ 17. _____

18. $\sqrt[20]{(3y)^4}$ 18. _____

19. $\sqrt[3]{x} \cdot \sqrt[9]{x}$ 19. _____

20. $\dfrac{\sqrt{10}}{\sqrt[3]{10}}$ 20. _____

Name _____   Date _____

Additional Exercises 10.2
Form II
Rational Exponents

Use radical notation to rewrite each expression. Simplify if possible.

1. $196^{\frac{1}{2}}$ 1. _____

2. $(-125)^{\frac{1}{3}}$ 2. _____

3. $(4xy^4)^{\frac{1}{5}}$ 3. _____

4. $(81)^{\frac{3}{4}}$ 4. _____

Rewrite the expression with a rational exponent.

5. $\sqrt{21}$ 5. _____

6. $\sqrt[9]{9x}$ 6. _____

7. $\sqrt[7]{x^6 y}$ 7. _____

8. $\left(\sqrt[3]{-27y}\right)^4$ 8. _____

Rewrite the expression with a positive rational exponent. Simplify, if possible.

9. $81^{\frac{-3}{2}}$ 9. _____

10. $(-27)^{\frac{-1}{3}}$ 10. _____

11. $(4xy^2)^{\frac{-3}{4}}$ 11. _____

12. $4x^{\frac{-1}{3}}$ 12. _____

Use the properties of rational exponents to simplify each expression. Assume that all variables represent positive numbers.

13. $a^{\frac{2}{3}}a^{\frac{4}{3}}$ 13. _____

14. $\dfrac{y^{\frac{5}{6}}}{y^{\frac{2}{6}}}$ 14. _____

15. $(-27x^9y^{12})^{\frac{1}{3}}$ 15. _____

16. $\left(x^{\frac{-9}{8}}y^{\frac{6}{5}}\right)^{\frac{1}{3}}$ 16. _____

Use rational exponents to simplify each expression. If rational exponents appear after simplifying, write the answer in radical notation.

17. $\sqrt[12]{(4x)^3}$ 17. _____

18. $\sqrt[4]{y}\cdot\sqrt[5]{y^2}$ 18. _____

19. $\dfrac{\sqrt[3]{12}}{\sqrt[6]{12}}$ 19. _____

20. $\sqrt[9]{\sqrt[6]{xy}}$ 20. _____

Additional Exercises 10.2
Form III
Rational Exponents

Use radical notation to rewrite each expression. Simplify if possible.

1. $1000^{\frac{1}{3}}$ 1. _____

2. $(-216)^{\frac{2}{3}}$ 2. _____

3. $(9x^2 y^3)^{\frac{3}{5}}$ 3. _____

4. $16^{\frac{3}{2}} + 4^{\frac{1}{2}}$ 4. _____

Rewrite the expression with a rational exponent.

5. $\sqrt[3]{30}$ 5. _____

6. $\sqrt[8]{10x^5}$ 6. _____

7. $\left(\sqrt{14xy}\right)^5$ 7. _____

8. $\left(\sqrt[4]{16y^2}\right)^3$ 8. _____

Rewrite the expression with a positive rational exponent. Simplify, if possible.

9. $8x^{\frac{-1}{2}}$ 9. _____

10. $(-125)^{\frac{-2}{3}}$ 10. _____

11. $(3xy^2)^{\frac{-1}{2}}$ 11. _____

12. $25^{\frac{-1}{2}} + 125^{-\frac{1}{3}}$ 12. _____

Use the properties of rational exponents to simplify each expression. Assume that all variables represent positive numbers.

13. $y^{\frac{3}{4}} y^{\frac{1}{8}}$ 13. _____

14. $\dfrac{a^{\frac{3}{4}}}{a^{\frac{1}{3}}}$ 14. _____

15. $(-125x^6 y^{12})^{\frac{2}{3}}$ 15. _____

16. $\left(16x^{-4} y^8 z^4\right)^{\frac{-1}{4}}$ 16. _____

Use rational exponents to simplify each expression. If rational exponents appear after simplifying, write the answer in radical notation.

17. $\sqrt[5]{x^3} \cdot \sqrt[3]{x^2}$ 17. _____

18. $\sqrt[18]{(6x)^6}$ 18. _____

19. $\sqrt[8]{\sqrt[5]{xy}}$ 19. _____

20. $\dfrac{\sqrt[6]{20}}{\sqrt[10]{20}}$ 20. _____

Name _____   Date _____

Use the product rule to multiply.

1. $\sqrt{6} \cdot \sqrt{5}$ 1. _____

2. $\sqrt[3]{4} \cdot \sqrt[3]{3}$ 2. _____

3. $\sqrt{(x+4)} \cdot \sqrt{(x-4)}$ 3. _____

4. $\sqrt[3]{3x} \cdot \sqrt[3]{2x}$ 4. _____

Simplify. Assume that any variable in the radicand represents a positive real number.

5. $\sqrt{90}$ 5. _____

6. $\sqrt{108}$ 6. _____

7. $\sqrt{45x}$ 7. _____

8. $\sqrt[3]{2xy^2} \cdot \sqrt[3]{2xy^2} \cdot \sqrt[3]{20xy^2}$ 8. _____

9. $\sqrt[3]{24x^{12}}$ 9. _____

10. $\sqrt[3]{48x^6 y^7}$ 10. _____

11. $\sqrt[4]{x^4 y^8 z^{10}}$ 11. _____

12. $\sqrt[5]{(a+b)^7}$ 12. _____

Express the function in simplified form. Assume that x can be any real number.

13. $f(x) = \sqrt{(x-1)^4}$ 13. _____

14. $f(x) = \sqrt{100(x+3)^8}$ 14. _____

15. $f(x) = \sqrt{x^2 + 4x + 4}$ 15. _____

Multiply and simplify. Assume that all variables in a radicand represent positive real numbers.

16. $\sqrt{5} \cdot \sqrt{12}$ 16. _____

17. $\sqrt{18} \cdot \sqrt{6}$ 17. _____

18. $\sqrt{7x} \cdot \sqrt{12y^2}$ 18. _____

19. $\sqrt[3]{12x^2} \cdot \sqrt[3]{4xy^5}$ 19. _____

20. $\sqrt[4]{5x^5 y^5} \cdot \sqrt[4]{32xy^3}$ 20. _____

Name _____   Date _____

Use the product rule to multiply.

1. $\sqrt[4]{7} \cdot \sqrt[4]{4}$ 1. _____

2. $\sqrt{(x+4)} \cdot \sqrt{(x-2)}$ 2. _____

3. $\sqrt[3]{5x} \cdot \sqrt[3]{3x}$ 3. _____

4. $\sqrt[5]{4xy^2} \cdot \sqrt[5]{2x^2y^2}$ 4. _____

Simplify. Assume that any variable in the radicand represents a positive real number.

5. $\sqrt{75}$ 5. _____

6. $\sqrt{150}$ 6. _____

7. $\sqrt[3]{72}$ 7. _____

8. $\sqrt[3]{48x^6y^2}$ 8. _____

9. $\sqrt[4]{96x^3y^5}$ 9. _____

10. $\sqrt[3]{48x^6y^7}$ 10. _____

11. $\sqrt[5]{256x^{12}}$ 11. _____

12. $\sqrt[11]{(x+y)^{12}}$ 12. _____

Express the function in simplified form. Assume that x can be any real number.

13. $f(x) = \sqrt{100(x-1)^8}$ 13. _____

14. $f(x) = \sqrt[3]{3000(x+1)^6}$ 14. _____

15. $f(x) = \sqrt{3x^2 + 30x + 75}$ 15. _____

Multiply and simplify. Assume that all variables in a radicand represent positive real numbers.

16. $\sqrt{18} \cdot \sqrt{9}$ 16. _____

17. $\sqrt{12x} \cdot \sqrt{4x^3} \cdot \sqrt{2x^2}$ 17. _____

18. $\sqrt[3]{18} \cdot \sqrt[3]{6}$ 18. _____

19. $\sqrt[4]{8} \cdot \sqrt[4]{4} \cdot \sqrt[4]{5}$ 19. _____

20. Racing cyclists use the function $r(x) = 4\sqrt{x}$ to determine the   20. _____
     maximum rate, $r(x)$, in miles per hour, to turn a corner of
     radius x, in feet, without tipping over. What is the maximum rate
     a cyclist should travel around a corner of radius 18 feet without
     tipping over? Give the solution in simplified radical form, and
     then give the answer rounded to the nearest mile per hour.

Name _____   Date _____

Additional Exercises 10.3
Form III
Multiplying and Simplifying Radical Expressions

Use the product rule to multiply.

1.　　$\sqrt[5]{3} \cdot \sqrt[5]{6} \cdot \sqrt[5]{5}$ 　　　　　　　　　　　1. _____

2.　　$\sqrt{x-5} \cdot \sqrt{x+7}$ 　　　　　　　　　　2. _____

3.　　$\sqrt[3]{2xy} \cdot \sqrt[3]{3x}$ 　　　　　　　　　　3. _____

4.　　$\sqrt[5]{\dfrac{x}{81}} \cdot \sqrt[4]{\dfrac{81}{y^4}}$ 　　　　　　　　4. _____

Simplify. Assume that any variable in the radicand represents a positive real number.

5.　　$\sqrt{180}$ 　　　　　　　　　　　　5. _____

6.　　$\sqrt[3]{96}$ 　　　　　　　　　　　　6. _____

7.　　$\sqrt[4]{80x^4}$ 　　　　　　　　　　　7. _____

8.　　$\sqrt{x^{13}}$ 　　　　　　　　　　　　8. _____

9.　　$\sqrt[3]{8x^3 y^9 z^4}$ 　　　　　　　　　9. _____

10.　　$\sqrt[5]{64x^4 y^5 z^6}$ 　　　　　　　　10. _____

11. $\sqrt[3]{(x+1)^2(x+1)}$ 11. _____

12. $\sqrt[6]{(x-3)^8}$ 12. _____

Express the function in simplified form. Assume that x can be any real number.

13. $f(x) = \sqrt[3]{1000(x+4)^6}$ 13. _____

14. $f(x) = \sqrt{4x^2 + 32x + 64}$ 14. _____

15. $f(x) = \sqrt{64x^2 + 320x + 400}$ 15. _____

Multiply and simplify. Assume that all variables in a radicand represent positive real numbers.

16. $\sqrt{24} \cdot \sqrt{5}$ 16. _____

17. $\sqrt{3x} \cdot \sqrt{6x^2} \cdot \sqrt{4x^3}$ 17. _____

18. $\sqrt[4]{9} \cdot \sqrt[4]{27}$ 18. _____

19. $\sqrt[3]{6x^{10}y} \cdot \sqrt[3]{4x^{16}y^{13}}$ 19. _____

20. $\sqrt[9]{x+1} \cdot \sqrt[9]{(x+1)^{37}}$ 20. _____

Additional Exercises 10.4
Form I
Adding, Subtracting, and Dividing Radical Expressions

Add or subtract as indicated. Assume all variables represent positive real numbers.

1. $5\sqrt{5} + 3\sqrt{5}$

1. _____

2. $6\sqrt{7} - \sqrt{7} + 2\sqrt{7}$

2. _____

3. $4\sqrt[3]{6} - 2\sqrt[3]{6}$

3. _____

4. $2\sqrt{5} + 4\sqrt[3]{5} - 6\sqrt{5}$

4. _____

5. $3\sqrt{5} + 4\sqrt{125}$

5. _____

6. $\sqrt[3]{8y} - \sqrt[3]{27y}$

6. _____

7. $5\sqrt{8x^3 y} + 2x\sqrt{32xy}$

7. _____

8. $4\sqrt{12} - 2\sqrt{48}$

8. _____

Use the quotient rule to simplify. Assume all variables represent positive real numbers.

9. $\sqrt{\dfrac{25}{4}}$

9. _____

10. $\sqrt{\dfrac{13}{25}}$

10. _____

11.　$\sqrt[3]{\dfrac{3}{8}}$　　　　　　　　　　　　　　11. _____

12.　$\sqrt{\dfrac{14}{x^2}}$　　　　　　　　　　　　　12. _____

13.　$\sqrt{\dfrac{50}{49}}$　　　　　　　　　　　　　13. _____

14.　$\sqrt{\dfrac{12}{81}}$　　　　　　　　　　　　　14. _____

15.　$\sqrt[3]{\dfrac{16}{y^6}}$　　　　　　　　　　　　15. _____

Divide and simplify. Assume that all variables represent positive real numbers.

16.　$\dfrac{\sqrt{100}}{\sqrt{4}}$　　　　　　　　　　　　16. _____

17.　$\dfrac{\sqrt{121}}{\sqrt{11}}$　　　　　　　　　　　　17. _____

18.　$\dfrac{\sqrt{80}}{\sqrt{5}}$　　　　　　　　　　　　18. _____

19.　$\dfrac{\sqrt{32x^7}}{\sqrt{4x}}$　　　　　　　　　　　19. _____

20.　$\dfrac{\sqrt{150x^{11}}}{\sqrt{3x^5}}$　　　　　　　　　　20. _____

Name _____ Date _____

Additional Exercises 10.4
Form II
Adding, Subtracting, and Dividing Radical Expressions

Add or subtract as indicated. Assume all variables represent positive real numbers.

1. $19\sqrt{19} + 8\sqrt{19}$

1. _____

2. $17\sqrt{10} - 3\sqrt{10} + \sqrt{10}$

2. _____

3. $6x\sqrt[4]{20} - 3x\sqrt[4]{20}$

3. _____

4. $5\sqrt{6} - 6\sqrt[3]{6} + 3\sqrt{6}$

4. _____

5. $7\sqrt{28} + 3\sqrt{63}$

5. _____

6. $\sqrt[3]{64y^2} - \sqrt[3]{125y^2}$

6. _____

7. $4a\sqrt{12a^2b} + 3a^2\sqrt{27b}$

7. _____

8. $3\sqrt{45x^3} - \sqrt{5x^3}$

8. _____

Use the quotient rule to simplify. Assume all variables represent positive real numbers.

9. $\sqrt{\dfrac{13}{16}}$

9. _____

10. $\sqrt{\dfrac{16x^2y}{49}}$

10. _____

11. $\sqrt{\dfrac{9}{49}}$ 11. _____

12. $\sqrt[3]{\dfrac{4}{27}}$ 12. _____

13. $\sqrt{\dfrac{18}{y^4}}$ 13. _____

14. $\sqrt[3]{\dfrac{32x}{2}}$ 14. _____

15. $\sqrt{\dfrac{50x^2}{100x}}$ 15. _____

Divide and simplify. Assume that all variables represent positive real numbers.

16. $\dfrac{\sqrt{144}}{\sqrt{4}}$ 16. _____

17. $\dfrac{\sqrt{72}}{\sqrt{3}}$ 17. _____

18. $\dfrac{\sqrt{90}}{\sqrt{10}}$ 18. _____

19. $\dfrac{\sqrt{32x^9}}{\sqrt{2x}}$ 19. _____

20. $\dfrac{\sqrt[3]{200y^{10}}}{\sqrt[3]{5y^4}}$ 20. _____

Name _____   Date _____

Add or subtract as indicated. Assume all variables represent positive real numbers.

1. $12\sqrt{10x} - 10\sqrt{10x}$ 1. _____

2. $11\sqrt{11} + 3\sqrt{11} - 5\sqrt{11}$ 2. _____

3. $6\sqrt{14} - 3\sqrt[3]{14} + 2\sqrt{14}$ 3. _____

4. $3\sqrt[3]{y} + \sqrt[3]{8y}$ 4. _____

5. $5\sqrt{80} - 4\sqrt{45}$ 5. _____

6. $10\sqrt[4]{x^7} - 3x\sqrt[4]{x^3} + 5\sqrt[4]{x^5}$ 6. _____

7. $5\sqrt[3]{x^{16}y^2} + 2x^3\sqrt[3]{x^7x^2}$ 7. _____

8. $\sqrt{16x - 32} + \sqrt{x - 2}$ 8. _____

Use the quotient rule to simplify. Assume all variables represent positive real numbers.

9. $\sqrt{\dfrac{36}{100}}$ 9. _____

10. $\sqrt{\dfrac{25}{x^8}}$ 10. _____

11. $\sqrt[3]{\dfrac{24}{27}}$ 11. _____

12. $\sqrt[4]{\dfrac{48}{81}}$ 12. _____

13. $\sqrt[3]{\dfrac{16}{x^9}}$ 13. _____

14. $\sqrt{\dfrac{20x^4}{36x^2}}$ 14. _____

15. $\sqrt{\dfrac{32x^2y}{49}}$ 15. _____

Divide and simplify. Assume that all variables represent positive real numbers.

16. $\dfrac{\sqrt{196}}{\sqrt{36}}$ 16. _____

17. $\dfrac{\sqrt[3]{125}}{\sqrt[3]{216}}$ 17. _____

18. $\dfrac{\sqrt{225x^{11}}}{\sqrt{3x^9}}$ 18. _____

19. $\dfrac{\sqrt{420x^5y^6}}{\sqrt{7xy}}$ 19. _____

20. $\dfrac{\sqrt{360a^3b^2}}{\sqrt{9a^3}}$ 20. _____

Name _____   Date _____

Multiply as indicated and then simplify if possible. Assume that all variables represent positive real numbers.

1. $\sqrt{3}(\sqrt{7} + \sqrt{5})$ 1. _____

2. $\sqrt{5}(\sqrt{6} - \sqrt{5})$ 2. _____

3. $\sqrt[3]{4}(\sqrt[3]{3} + \sqrt[3]{2}$ 3. _____

4. $3\sqrt{3}(\sqrt{7} - 2\sqrt{2})$ 4. _____

5. $(\sqrt{11} + 5)(\sqrt{11} - 5)$ 5. _____

6. $(\sqrt{5} + 2)^2$ 6. _____

7. $(\sqrt{15} + \sqrt{6})(\sqrt{15} - \sqrt{6})$ 7. _____

Rationalize each denominator. Simplify if possible. Assume that all variables represent positive real numbers.

8. $\dfrac{1}{\sqrt{5}}$ 8. _____

9. $\sqrt{\dfrac{6}{x}}$ 9. _____

10. $\sqrt[3]{\dfrac{2}{3}}$ 10. _____

11. $\sqrt[3]{\dfrac{5x}{16x^2}}$ 11. _____

12. $\sqrt[3]{\dfrac{1}{4x}}$ 12. _____

13. $\dfrac{3}{5-\sqrt{7}}$ 13. _____

14. $\dfrac{5}{8-\sqrt{3}}$ 14. _____

15. $\dfrac{4}{\sqrt{3}-\sqrt{2}}$ 15. _____

16. $\dfrac{2\sqrt{5}}{\sqrt{5}+2}$ 16. _____

Rationalize each numerator. Assume that all variables represent positive real numbers.

17. $\dfrac{\sqrt{7}}{\sqrt{5}}$ 17. _____

18. $\sqrt{\dfrac{5}{2}}$ 18. _____

19. $\dfrac{3\sqrt{2}}{\sqrt{3}}$ 19. _____

20. $\dfrac{\sqrt{11}}{7a}$ 20. _____

Name _____   Date _____

Additional Exercises 10.5
Form II
Multiplying with More Than One Term and Rationalizing Denominators

Multiply as indicated and then simplify if possible. Assume that all variables represent positive real numbers.

1. $\sqrt{5}(\sqrt{7} - \sqrt{3})$ 1. _____

2. $(\sqrt{10} - \sqrt{5})(\sqrt{10} + \sqrt{5})$ 2. _____

3. $\sqrt[3]{5}(\sqrt[3]{7} + \sqrt[3]{2})$ 3. _____

4. $(\sqrt{7} - 3)^2$ 4. _____

5. $\sqrt[3]{x}(3\sqrt[3]{x} - 4\sqrt[3]{x^2})$ 5. _____

6. $(\sqrt{15} + \sqrt{2})^2$ 6. _____

7. $(\sqrt{14} + 3\sqrt{5})(\sqrt{6} - 2\sqrt{5})$ 7. _____

Rationalize each denominator. Simplify if possible. Assume that all variables represent positive real numbers.

8. $\dfrac{1}{\sqrt{7}}$ 8. _____

9. $\sqrt{\dfrac{6x}{3y}}$ 9. _____

10. $\sqrt[3]{\dfrac{2}{9x}}$ 10. _____

11. $\sqrt[5]{\dfrac{7}{y^6}}$

11. _____

12. $\sqrt[3]{\dfrac{5x}{6x^2y}}$

12. _____

13. $\dfrac{5}{8-\sqrt{5}}$

13. _____

14. $\dfrac{\sqrt{3}}{\sqrt{6}+2}$

14. _____

15. $\dfrac{\sqrt{7}+\sqrt{2}}{\sqrt{7}-\sqrt{2}}$

15. _____

16. $\dfrac{3\sqrt{10}}{\sqrt{6}-\sqrt{4}}$

16. _____

Rationalize each numerator. Assume that all variables represent positive real numbers.

17. $\dfrac{\sqrt{6}}{\sqrt{5x}}$

17. _____

18. $\sqrt{\dfrac{17}{2}}$

18. _____

19. $\dfrac{8\sqrt{3}}{\sqrt{10}}$

19. _____

20. $\dfrac{\sqrt{15x}}{3x}$

20. _____

Additional Exercises 10.5
Form III
Multiplying with More Than One Term and Rationalizing Denominators

Multiply as indicated and then simplify if possible. Assume that all variables represent positive real numbers.

1. $\sqrt[3]{6}(\sqrt[3]{3} + \sqrt[3]{2})$ 1. _____

2. $(4\sqrt{2} - 7)^2$ 2. _____

3. $(\sqrt{19} + \sqrt{7})(\sqrt{5} - \sqrt{7})$ 3. _____

4. $(\sqrt{5} + \sqrt{3})^2$ 4. _____

5. $\sqrt[4]{6}(\sqrt[4]{8} - \sqrt[4]{3})$ 5. _____

6. $(2\sqrt{6} + 3\sqrt{5})(2\sqrt{6} - 3\sqrt{5})$ 6. _____

7. $\sqrt[3]{x}(\sqrt[3]{2000x^2} - \sqrt[3]{x})$ 7. _____

Rationalize each denominator. Simplify if possible. Assume that all variables represent positive real numbers.

8. $\dfrac{6}{\sqrt{7y}}$ 8. _____

9. $\sqrt[3]{\dfrac{7}{9x^2}}$ 9. _____

10. $\dfrac{xy\sqrt[3]{2}}{\sqrt[3]{xy^2}}$ 10. _____

11. $\sqrt[4]{\dfrac{2x}{9x^2}}$ 11. _____

12. $\sqrt{\dfrac{16}{13y}}$ 12. _____

13. $\dfrac{4}{\sqrt{6}-2}$ 13. _____

14. $\dfrac{\sqrt{3}}{\sqrt{5}+\sqrt{2}}$ 14. _____

15. $\dfrac{2\sqrt{10}-\sqrt{6}}{3\sqrt{5}-4\sqrt{2}}$ 15. _____

16. $\dfrac{6\sqrt{x}+\sqrt{y}}{\sqrt{y}-6\sqrt{x}}$ 16. _____

Rationalize each numerator. Assume that all variables represent positive real numbers.

17. $\dfrac{7\sqrt{x}}{\sqrt{5y}}$ 17. _____

18. $\dfrac{3\sqrt{6}}{2\sqrt{2}}$ 18. _____

19. $\dfrac{7-\sqrt{2}}{4+6\sqrt{2}}$ 19. _____

20. $\dfrac{2+\sqrt{5}}{2-\sqrt{5}}$ 20. _____

Additional Exercises 10.6
Form I
Radical Equations

Solve each radical equation.

1. $\sqrt{x} = 5$

    1. _____

2. $\sqrt{x+3} = 6$

    2. _____

3. $\sqrt{y+1} = 9$

    3. _____

4. $\sqrt{x-1} - 1 = 7$

    4. _____

5. $\sqrt{y-4} = 5$

    5. _____

6. $\sqrt{5x-4} = 4$

    6. _____

7. $\sqrt{2x+1} = 19$

    7. _____

8. $\sqrt{6x+1} - 11 = 0$

    8. _____

9. $\sqrt{8x+3} = -6$

    9. _____

10. $\sqrt{x} + 4 = 9$

    10. _____

11. $\sqrt{3x+1} - 3 = 1$ 11. _____

12. $(4x+8)^{\frac{1}{2}} = 4$ 12. _____

13. $(a-3)^{\frac{1}{2}} + 6 = 7$ 13. _____

14. $\sqrt[3]{3x} + 4 = 7$ 14. _____

15. $\sqrt[3]{5x+2} = 3$ 15. _____

16. $\sqrt[4]{4x+1} = 3$ 16. _____

17. $\sqrt{a-3} = a-3$ 17. _____

18. $(5x+1)^{\frac{1}{2}} = x+1$ 18. _____

19. $x + 7 = \sqrt{2x+13}$ 19. _____

20. $\sqrt{x+5} = \sqrt{x-3} + 2$ 20. _____

Name _____   Date _____

Additional Exercises 10.6
Form II
Radical Equations

Solve each radical equation.

1. $\sqrt[3]{x} = 4$

   1. _____

2. $\sqrt{3x+1} = 4$

   2. _____

3. $\sqrt{x} + 8 = 7$

   3. _____

4. $\sqrt{4x+6} = 9$

   4. _____

5. $(3x-6)^{\frac{1}{3}} - 8 = -5$

   5. _____

6. $3\sqrt{4x+5} = 27$

   6. _____

7. $\sqrt{2x-3} + 9 = 14$

   7. _____

8. $\sqrt[3]{2x-5} = 1$

   8. _____

9. $(3x+1)^{\frac{1}{4}} = 2$

   9. _____

10. $\sqrt{2x+7} = 4 - x$

    10. _____

11. $(4x+1)^{\frac{1}{2}} = x - 5$ 11. _____

12. $\sqrt[3]{4x+9} = \sqrt[3]{3-2x}$ 12. _____

13. $\sqrt{3x+1} = x - 3$ 13. _____

14. $(2x+7)^{\frac{1}{3}} = -1$ 14. _____

15. $\sqrt{x^2-15} = 7$ 15. _____

16. $\sqrt{6y-9} = \sqrt{3y+3}$ 16. _____

17. $4\sqrt{2x-4} = 24$ 17. _____

18. $\sqrt{8a-3} = \sqrt{7a+3}$ 18. _____

19. $\sqrt{3a+1} = \sqrt{a-4} + 3$ 19. _____

20. $\sqrt{2x+5} - \sqrt{x-2} = 3$ 20. _____

Name _____   Date _____

Additional Exercises 10.6
Form III
Radical Equations

Solve each radical equation.

1. $\sqrt{2x+4} = 6$

                                                                                 1. _____

2. $\sqrt{x+7} + 8 = 12$

  2. _____

3. $\sqrt{3x+5} + 4 = 2$

  3. _____

4. $(3x+1)^{\frac{1}{2}} - 4 = 1$

  4. _____

5. $\sqrt[3]{2x-1} = 1$

  5. _____

6. $y - 4 = \sqrt{2y-8}$

  6. _____

7. $\sqrt{x^2 - 5x + 64} = x + 3$

  7. _____

8. $\sqrt{x^2 - 15} - \sqrt{x+5} = 0$

  8. _____

9. $(3x-2)^{\frac{1}{3}} + 2 = 3$

  9. _____

10. $\sqrt{2x^2 - 7} = x$

  10. _____

11.　$(5x-4)^{\frac{1}{4}} - 4 = -2$　　　　　　　　　　　　　　　11. _____

12.　$(3x+4)^{\frac{1}{2}} = (4x-1)^{\frac{1}{2}}$　　　　　　　　　　12. _____

13.　$\sqrt{2x+3} - \sqrt{x+1} = 1$　　　　　　　　　　　　13. _____

14.　$\sqrt{x+8} - 2 = \sqrt{x-4}$　　　　　　　　　　　　14. _____

15.　$\sqrt{x+6} + \sqrt{2-x} = 4$　　　　　　　　　　　　15. _____

16.　$2 + \sqrt{x-2} = (2x-5)^{\frac{1}{2}}$　　　　　　　　　　16. _____

17.　$\sqrt{2x+5} - \sqrt{x-1} = \sqrt{x+2}$　　　　　　　　17. _____

18.　$\sqrt{3x+3} - \sqrt{2x-3} = \sqrt{3x-2}$　　　　　　　18. _____

Solve.

19.　The formula $v = \sqrt{2.5r}$ can be used to estimate the maximum　　19. _____
safe velocity v, in miles per hour, at which a car can travel
along a curved road with a radius of curvature r, in feet. To
the nearest whole number, find the radius of curvature if the
maximum safe velocity is 20.

20.　The function $f(x) = 6.75\sqrt{x} + 12$ the models the amount, $f(x)$,　　20. _____
in billions of dollars of new student loans x years after 1993.
According to the model, in what year is the amount loaned
expected to reach $25.5 billion?

Name _____   Date _____

Additional Exercises 10.7
Form I
Complex Numbers

Express each number in terms of i and simplify if possible.

1. $\sqrt{-25}$ 1. _____

2. $\sqrt{-121}$ 2. _____

3. $\sqrt{-32}$ 3. _____

4. $\sqrt{-50}$ 4. _____

5. $7 + \sqrt{-18}$ 5. _____

Perform the indicated operations. Write the results in the form $a + bi$.

6. $(8 + 2i) + (2 + 8i)$ 6. _____

7. $6i - (8 - 3i)$ 7. _____

8. $(10 - 3i) - (4 - 6i)$ 8. _____

9. $5(2 - 3i)$ 9. _____

10. $3i(4 - 8i)$ 10. _____

11. $(2 - 9i)(8 + 4i)$ 11. _____

12. $(4 - 5i)^2$ 12. _____

Divide and simplify to the form $a + bi$.

13. $\dfrac{5 + 8i}{4 - 2i}$ 13. _____

14. $\dfrac{3 + 2i}{2 - 5i}$ 14. _____

15. $\dfrac{3 - 4i}{i}$ 15. _____

16. $\dfrac{6 - 5i}{3i}$ 16. _____

Simplify each expression.

17. i^6 17. _____

18. i^{20} 18. _____

19. i^{27} 19. _____

20. $(-i)^5$ 20. _____

Additional Exercises 10.7
Form II
Complex Numbers

Express each number in terms of i and simplify if possible.

1. $\sqrt{-196}$ 1. _____

2. $\sqrt{-40}$ 2. _____

3. $\sqrt{-75}$ 3. _____

4. $8 - \sqrt{-49}$ 4. _____

Perform the indicated operations. Write the results in the form $a + bi$.

5. $8i + (-8 - i)$ 5. _____

6. $(7 - 5i) + (6 + 9i)$ 6. _____

7. $(12 + 2i) - (6 - 6i)$ 7. _____

8. $3i(5i - 3)$ 8. _____

9. $(7 + 3i)(2 - 5i)$ 9. _____

10. $(3 + i\sqrt{6})(3 - i\sqrt{6})$ 10. _____

11. $(4+3i)^2$ 11._____

Divide and simplify to the form $a+bi$.

12. $\dfrac{7-3i}{5+3i}$ 12._____

13. $\dfrac{5+4i}{3+6i}$ 13._____

14. $\dfrac{4-3i}{4+3i}$ 14._____

15. $\dfrac{6-5i}{2i}$ 15._____

16. $\dfrac{2}{2-5i}$ 16._____

Simplify each expression.

17. i^{12} 17._____

18. i^{30} 18._____

19. $6i^7$ 19._____

20. $(-i)^8$ 20._____

Name _____   Date _____

Express each number in terms of i and simplify if possible.

1. $\sqrt{-289}$ 1. _____

2. $\sqrt{-180}$ 2. _____

3. $15 + \sqrt{-25}$ 3. _____

4. $6 + \sqrt{-60}$ 4. _____

Perform the indicated operations. Write the results in the form $a + bi$.

5. $6i - (-3 - 2i)$ 5. _____

6. $(8 - 12i) - (4 - 7i)$ 6. _____

7. $5i(3 - 2i)$ 7. _____

8. $(6 - 5i)(2 - 7i)$ 8. _____

9. $(1 + i)^2$ 9. _____

10. $(3i + \sqrt{6})(4i - \sqrt{6})$ 10. _____

11. $\sqrt{-10} \cdot \sqrt{-4}$ 11. _____

Divide and simplify to the form $a + bi$.

12. $\dfrac{1+i}{1-i}$ 12. _____

13. $\dfrac{4}{2-3i}$ 13. _____

14. $\dfrac{2+3i}{2-i}$ 14. _____

15. $\dfrac{3-4i}{4-3i}$ 15. _____

16. $\dfrac{5+i}{4i}$ 16. _____

Simplify each expression.

17. i^{47} 17. _____

18. i^{82} 18. _____

19. $10i^{10}$ 19. _____

20. $(-i)^{12}$ 20. _____

Name _____   Date _____

Solve the equation by the square root property. If possible, simplify radicals or rationalize denominators. Express imaginary solutions in the form $a + bi$.

1. $4x^2 = 400$ 1. _____

2. $8x^2 = 48$ 2. _____

3. $16x^2 + 49 = 0$ 3. _____

4. $(x + 2)^2 = 20$ 4. _____

5. $\left(x - \dfrac{1}{2}\right)^2 = \dfrac{121}{4}$ 5. _____

Complete the square for the binomial. Then factor the resulting perfect square trinomial.

6. $x^2 + 10x$ 6. _____

7. $x^2 - 12x$ 7. _____

8. $x^2 + 16x$ 8. _____

9. $x^2 - 18x$ 9. _____

Solve the quadratic equation by completing the square.

10. $x^2 - 8x + 15 = 0$ 10. _____

11. $x^2 + 14x + 34 = 0$ 11. _____

12. $x^2 - 4x + 2 = 0$ 12. _____

13. $x^2 + 6y = 1$ 13. _____

Find the distance between the pair of points.

14.   (−5, −8) and (−13, −2)   14. _____

15.   (1, 4) and (2, 3)   15. _____

Find the midpoint of the line segment whose end points are given.

16.   (2, 4) (2, 8)   16. _____

17.   (5, 1) (3, 3)   17. _____

Solve.

18.   A square sheet of paper measures 50 centimeters on each side.   18. _____
        What is the length of the diagonal of the paper?

19.   A ladder that is 5 feet long is 3 feet from the base of the wall.   19. _____
        How far up the wall does the ladder reach?

20.   The function $s(t) = 16t^2$ models the distance, $s(t)$, in feet,   20. _____
        that an object falls in t seconds. Find the number of seconds
        a sky diver is in free fall after jumping from a plane and
        falling 704 feet before opening a parachute. Express answers
        in simplified radical form.

Name _____   Date _____

Additional Exercises 11.1
Form II
The Square Root Property and Completing the Square; Distance and Midpoint Formulas

Solve the equation by the square root property. If possible, simplify radicals or rationalize denominators. Express imaginary solutions in the form $a + bi$.

1. $3x^2 - 33 = 0$ 1. _____

2. $9x^2 + 25 = 0$ 2. _____

3. $(x - 3)^2 = -16$ 3. _____

4. $\left(x + \dfrac{1}{2}\right)^2 = \dfrac{5}{4}$ 4. _____

5. $4(x - 3)^2 = 48$ 5. _____

Complete the square for the binomial. Then factor the resulting perfect square trinomial.

6. $x^2 + \dfrac{1}{2}x$ 6. _____

7. $x^2 + \dfrac{1}{3}x$ 7. _____

8. $x^2 - 5x$ 8. _____

9. $x^2 - 9x$ 9. _____

Solve the quadratic equation by completing the square.

10. $x^2 + 2x + 13 = 0$ 10. _____

11. $x^2 + 8x + 19 = 0$

11. _____

12. $x^2 + 3x - 9 = 0$

12. _____

13. $7x^2 - 2x - 3 = 0$

13. _____

Find the distance between the pair of points.

14. $(0, -8)$ and $(0, 5)$

14. _____

15. $(10, 2)$ and $(-3, 8)$

15. _____

Find the midpoint of the line segment whose end points are given.

16. $(7, 6)$ $(0, 3)$

16. _____

17. $(-7, -9)$ $(8, 5)$

17. _____

Solve.

18. A square sheet of paper measures 55 centimeters on each side. What is the length of the diagonal of the paper?

18. _____

19. A ladder that is 10 feet long is 6 feet from the base of the wall. How far up the wall does the ladder reach?

19. _____

20. The function $s(t) = 16t^2$ models the distance, $s(t)$, in feet, that an object falls in t seconds. Find the number of seconds a sky diver is in free fall after jumping from a plane and falling 1584 feet before opening a parachute. Express answers in simplified radical form.

20. _____

Additional Exercises 11.1
Form III
The Square Root Property and Completing the Square; Distance and Midpoint Formulas

Solve the equation by the square root property. If possible, simplify radicals or rationalize denominators. Express imaginary solutions in the form $a + bi$.

1. $25x^2 + 49 = 0$ 1. _____

2. $2x^2 + 5 = 247$ 2. _____

3. $3(x - 1)^2 = 24$ 3. _____

4. $\left(x - \dfrac{5}{6}\right)^2 = -\dfrac{11}{36}$ 4. _____

5. $(x - 10)^2 + 1 = 0$ 5. _____

Complete the square for the binomial. Then factor the resulting perfect square trinomial.

6. $x^2 - \dfrac{4}{5}x$ 6. _____

7. $x^2 + \dfrac{2}{7}x$ 7. _____

8. $x^2 + \dfrac{1}{6}x$ 8. _____

9. $x^2 - \dfrac{2}{13}x$ 9. _____

Name _____   Date _____

Solve the quadratic equation by completing the square.

10. $x^2 - 3x + 15 = 0$

10. _____

11. $2x^2 - 6x - 10 = 0$

11. _____

12. $4x^2 - 4x = 1$

12. _____

13. $x^2 - 5x + 20 = 0$

13. _____

Find the distance between the pair of points.

14. (5, 6) and (9, 10)

14. _____

15. (6, –7) and (4, –1)

15. _____

Find the midpoint of the line segment whose end points are given.

16. (–3, 5) and (2, 6)

16. _____

17. $(2, 4\sqrt{2})$ and $(4, 2\sqrt{2})$

17. _____

Solve.

18. A square sheet of paper measures 62 centimeters on each side. What is the length of the diagonal of the paper?

18. _____

19. A ladder that is 17 feet long is 8 feet from the base of the wall. How far up the wall does the ladder reach?

19. _____

20. The function $s(t) = 16t^2$ models the distance, $s(t)$, in feet, that an object falls in t seconds. Find the number of seconds a sky diver is in free fall after jumping from a plane and falling 1920 feet before opening a parachute. Express answers in simplified radical form.

20. _____

Name _____   Date _____

Additional Exercises 11.2
Form I
The Quadratic Formula

Solve the equation by using the quadratic formula. Simplify solutions, if possible.

1. $x^2 - 14x + 40 = 0$ 1. _____

2. $2x^2 + x - 21 = 0$ 2. _____

3. $x^2 - 8x = -10$ 3. _____

4. $3x^2 = 7$ 4. _____

Compute the discriminant. Then determine whether the following equation has solutions that are two rational solutions; two irrational solutions; one real solution; or two imaginary solutions.

5. $x^2 - 4x + 4 = 0$ 5. _____

6. $x^2 - 5x + 6 = 0$ 6. _____

7. $x^2 + 6x + 10 = 0$ 7. _____

8. $2x^2 - 7x + 1 = 0$ 8. _____

Solve the equation by the method of your choice. Simplify solutions, if possible.

9. $(x - 6)^2 = 17$ 9. _____

10. $x^2 + 4x = 0$ 10. _____

11. $4x^2 + 6x + 1 = 0$ 11. _____

12. $11x^2 = -704$ 12. _____

Write a quadratic equation in standard form with the given solution set.

13. $\{8, 3\}$ 13. _____

14. $\{-4, 10\}$ 14. _____

15. $\left\{\dfrac{3}{4}, \dfrac{1}{8}\right\}$ 15. _____

16. $\left\{0, \dfrac{-4}{5}\right\}$ 16. _____

17. $\left\{-2\sqrt{3}, 2\sqrt{3}\right\}$ 17. _____

18. $\{-7i, 7i\}$ 18. _____

Solve the problem.

19.   The hypotenuse of an isosceles triangle is 7 feet longer   19. _____
       than either of its legs. Find the length of each side. Round
       to the nearest tenth of an inch.

20.   A rectangular sign must have an area of 45 yards. Its   20. _____
       length must be 4 yards more than its width. Find the
       dimensions of the sign. Round to the nearest tenth of
       a yard.

Additional Exercises 11.2
Form II
The Quadratic Formula

Solve the quadratic equation by using the quadratic formula. Simplify solutions, if possible.

1. $3x^2 + 36 = -31x$ 1. _____

2. $7x^2 + 12x + 1 = 0$ 2. _____

3. $x^2 + 3x + 4 = 0$ 3. _____

4. $5x^2 - 320$ 4. _____

Compute the discriminant. Then determine whether the following equation has solutions that are two rational solutions; two irrational solutions; one real solution; or two imaginary solutions.

5. $5x^2 = 6x$ 5. _____

6. $x^2 + 6x + 4 = 0$ 6. _____

7. $4x^2 - 4x + 1 = 0$ 7. _____

8. $x^2 - 4x = -5$ 8. _____

Solve the equations by the method of your choice. Simplify solutions, if possible.

9. $(x + 9)^2 = 18$ 9. _____

10. $(3x - 5)^2 = 21$ 10. _____

11. $(2x+1)(3x-5)=3$ 11. _____

12. $\dfrac{1}{3}x^2+\dfrac{2}{3}x=\dfrac{-1}{3}$ 12. _____

Write a quadratic equation in standard form with the given solution set.

13. $\left\{\dfrac{-3}{7},\dfrac{-2}{5}\right\}$ 13. _____

14. $\{-9i,9i\}$ 14. _____

15. $\{-10i,10i\}$ 15. _____

16. $\left\{-3\sqrt{5},3\sqrt{5}\right\}$ 16. _____

17. $\left\{-2\sqrt{7},2\sqrt{7}\right\}$ 17. _____

18. $\left\{1+\sqrt{5}\right\}\left\{1-\sqrt{5}\right\}$ 18. _____

Solve the problem.

19. The hypotenuse of an isosceles right triangle is 9 feet   19. _____
     longer than either of its legs. Find the length of each side.
     Round to the nearest tenth of an inch.

20. A rectangular sigh must have an area of 34 square yards.   20. _____
     Its length must be 6 yards more than its width. Find the
     dimensions of the sign. Round to the nearest tenth of a
     yard.

Name _____   Date _____

Solve the equation using the quadratic formula. Simplify solutions, if possible.

1. $3x^2 - 10x = 0$ 1. _____

2. $2x^2 + 8x = 1$ 2. _____

3. $x^2 + x + 5 = 0$ 3. _____

4. $16x^2 - 8x + 1 = 0$ 4. _____

Compute the discrimianat. Then determine whether the following equation has solutions that are two rational solutions; two irrational solutions; one real solution; or two imaginary solutions.

5. $x^2 - 18x = -81$ 5. _____

6. $x^2 - 3x = 8$ 6. _____

7. $x^2 + x - 6 = 0$ 7. _____

8. $8 + 4x^2 = 8x$ 8. _____

Solve the equation by the method of your choice. Simplify solutions, if possible.

9. $(x - 11)^2 = 24$ 9. _____

10. $\dfrac{x^2}{3} + 2x - \dfrac{4}{5} = 0$ 10. _____

11. $\dfrac{1}{x} + \dfrac{1}{x+1} = \dfrac{1}{5}$ 11. _____

12. $(3x+1)(2x-5) = -9(x^2 - 2x) - 3x$ 12. _____

Write a quadratic equation in standard form with the given solution set.

13. $\left\{ \dfrac{2}{7}, \dfrac{-1}{5} \right\}$ 13. _____

14. $\{-12i, 12i\}$ 14. _____

15. $\left\{-7\sqrt{2}, 7\sqrt{2}\right\}$ 15. _____

16. $\left\{-5\sqrt{3}i, 5\sqrt{3}i\right\}$ 16. _____

17. $\left\{2 - \sqrt{3}, 2 + \sqrt{3}\right\}$ 17. _____

18. $\{10 + i, 10 - i\}$ 18. _____

Solve the problem.

19.   The hypotenuse of an isosceles triangle is 10 feet longer   19. _____
       than either of it legs. Find the length of each side. Round
       to the nearest tenth of an inch.

20.   A rectangular sign must have an area of 55 square yards.   20. _____
       Its length must be 5 yards more than its width. Find the
       dimensions of the sign.

Name _____   Date _____

Additional Exercises 11.3
Form I
Quadratic Functions and Their Graphs

The graph of a quadratic function is given. Choose from the following options the function's equation.

$$f(x) = (x+1)^2 \qquad g(x) = x^2 + 1 \qquad h(x) = (x-1)^2 \qquad j(x) = x^2 - 1$$

1.

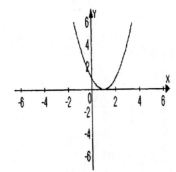

1. _____

2.

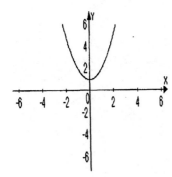

2. _____

3.

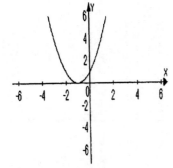

3. _____

4.

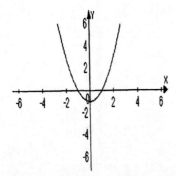

4. _____

Name _____   Date _____

Find the coordinates of the vertex for the parabola defined by the given quadratic equation.

5. $f(x) = x^2$ 5. _____

6. $f(x) = (x+3)^2 + 3$ 6. _____

7. $f(x) = x^2 + 3$ 7. _____

8. $f(x) = (x+9)^2 - 5$ 8. _____

9. $f(x) = -x^2 + 2x + 2$ 9. _____

10. $f(x) = -6x^2 + 12x + 3$ 10. _____

Use the vertex and intercepts to sketch the graph of each quadratic function.

11. $f(x) = x^2 - 4$

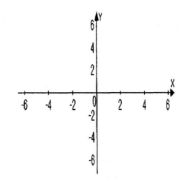

12. $f(x) = x^2 - 4x + 3$

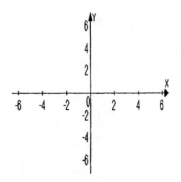

Name _____   Date _____

Determine whether the given quadratic function has a (a) minimum value or maximum value. (b) Find the coordinates of the minimum or maximum point. (c) Identify the function's domain and range.

13. $f(x) = x^2 + 2x - 2$ 13a. _____

                                                  b. _____

                                                  c. _____

14. $f(x) = -x^2 + 4x$ 14a. _____

                                                  b. _____

                                                  c. _____

15. $f(x) = x^2 - 8x + 16$ 15a. _____

                                                  b. _____

                                                  c. _____

Solve the problem.

16.   You have 52 feet of fencing to enclose a rectangular   16. _____
        region. Find the dimensions of the rectangle that
        maximize the enclosed area.

17.   The profit that a vendor makes per day by selling   17. _____
        x pretzels is given by the function
        $P(x) - 0.003x^2 + 1.2x + 25$. Find the number of
        pretzels that must be sold to maximize profit.

18.   Among all pairs of numbers whose sum is 30, find a pair   18. _____
        whose product is as large as possible.

19.   A person standing close to the edge on top of a 88-foot   19. _____
        building throws a baseball vertically upward. The
        quadratic function $s(t) = -16t^2 + 64t + 88$ models the
        ball's height above the ground, $s(t)$, in feet, t seconds
        after it was thrown. How many seconds does it take until
        the ball finally hits the ground? Round to the nearest tenth
        of a second if necessary.

Name _____   Date _____

Additional Exercises 11.3
Form II
Quadratic Functions and Their Graphs

The graph of a quadratic function is given. Choose from the following options the function's equation.

$$f(x) = -(x-3)^2 + 2 \qquad\qquad g(x) = -(x-3)^2 - 2$$
$$h(x) = (x+3)^2 + 2 \qquad\qquad j(x) = (x-3)^2 - 2$$

1.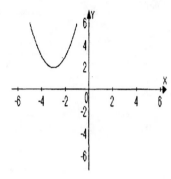

1. _____

2.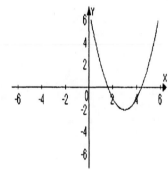

2. _____

3.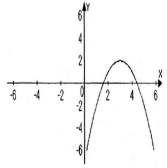

3. _____

4.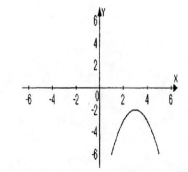

4. _____

Name _____   Date _____

Find the coordinates of the vertex for the parabola defined by the given quadratic equation.

5. $f(x) = x^2 - 6$ 5. _____

6. $f(x) = -(x - 4)^2 - 4$ 6. _____

7. $f(x) = 2x^2 + 8$ 7. _____

8. $f(x) = \dfrac{1}{2}(x + 7) + 3$ 8. _____

9. $f(x) = 2x^2 + 4x - 3$ 9. _____

10. $f(x) = x^2 - 2x - 2$ 10. _____

Use the vertex and intercepts to sketch the graph of each quadratic function.

11. $f(x) = -x^2 - 2x + 3$

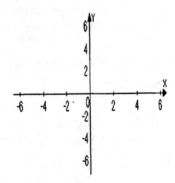

12. $f(x) = x^2 + 7x + 10$

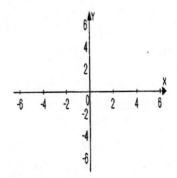

Name _____   Date _____

Determine whether the given quadratic function has a (a) minimum value or maximum value. (b) Find the coordinates of the minimum or maximum point. (c) Identify the function's domain and range.

13. $f(x) = -x^2 - 6x$ 13a. _____

                                                       b. _____

                                                       c. _____

14. $f(x) = x^2 + 6x + 4$ 14a. _____

                                                       b. _____

                                                       c. _____

15. $f(x) = x^2 - 2x - 6$ 15a. _____

                                                       b. _____

                                                       c. _____

Solve the problem.

16.   You have 72 feet of fencing to enclose a rectangular   16. _____
        region. Find the dimensions of the rectangle that
        maximize the enclosed area.

17.   You have 100 feet of fencing to enclose a rectangular   17. _____
        region. What is the maximum area?

18.   The profit that a vendor makes per day by selling x 18. _____
        pretzels is given by the function
        $P(x) - 0.002x^2 + 1.2x + 250$. Find the number of
        pretzels that must be sold to maximize profit.

19.   Among all pairs of numbers whose sum is 32, find a pair   19. _____
        whose product is as large as possible.

20.   A person standing close to the edge on top of a 105-foot   20. _____
        building throws a baseball vertically upward. The
        quadratic function $s(t) = -16t^2 + 64t + 105$ models the
        ball's height above the ground, $s(t)$, in feet, t seconds
        after it was thrown. How many seconds does it take until
        the ball finally hits the ground? Round to the nearest tenth
        of a second if necessary.

Name _____   Date _____

Additional Exercises 11.3
Form III
Quadratic Functions and Their Graphs

The graph of a quadratic function is given. Choose from the following options the function's equation.

$$f(x) = (x-2)^2 - 2 \qquad g(x) = -(x+2)^2 + 2$$
$$h(x) = -(x-2)^2 + 2 \qquad j(x) = (x+2)^2 - 2$$

1.

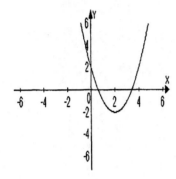

1. _____

2.

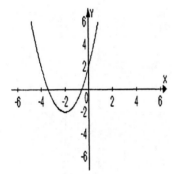

2. _____

3.

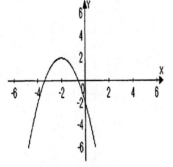

3. _____

4.

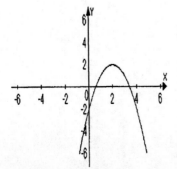

4. _____

Name _____   Date _____

Find the coordinates of the vertex for the parabola defined by the given quadratic equation.

5. $f(x) = \dfrac{3}{4}x^2 + 11$

5. _____

6. $f(x) = -\dfrac{1}{2}(x+3)^2 - 5$

6. _____

7. $f(x) = -5x^2 - 4$

7. _____

8. $f(x) = (x+4)^2 - 2$

8. _____

9. $f(x) = -x^2 - 14x - 5$

9. _____

10. $f(x) = x^2 + 8x + 15$

10. _____

Use the vertex and intercepts to sketch the graph of each quadratic function.

11. $f(x) = -x^2 + 9$

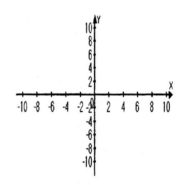

12. $f(x) = x^2 - 4x$

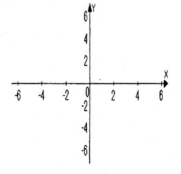

AE-412

Name _____   Date _____

Determine whether the given quadratic function has a (a) minimum value or maximum value.
(b) Find the coordinates of the minimum or maximum point. (c) Identify the function's domain
and range.

13.　　$f(x) = -x^2 - 4x + 5$　　　　　　　　　　　　　13a. _____

　　　　　　　　　　　　　　　　　　　　　　　　　　　b. _____

　　　　　　　　　　　　　　　　　　　　　　　　　　　c. _____

14.　　$f(x) = 4x^2 - 2x - 6$　　　　　　　　　　　　　14a. _____

　　　　　　　　　　　　　　　　　　　　　　　　　　　b. _____

　　　　　　　　　　　　　　　　　　　　　　　　　　　c. _____

15.　　$f(x) = -4x^2 + 8x$　　　　　　　　　　　　　　15a. _____

　　　　　　　　　　　　　　　　　　　　　　　　　　　b. _____

　　　　　　　　　　　　　　　　　　　　　　　　　　　c. _____

Solve the problem.

16.　　You have 104 feet of fencing to enclose a rectangular　　16. _____
　　　　region. Find the dimensions of the rectangle that
　　　　maximize the enclosed area.

17.　　You have 128 feet of fencing to enclose a rectangular　　17. _____
　　　　region. What is the maximum area?

18.　　The profit that the vendor makes per day by selling　　18. _____
　　　　x pretzels is given by the function
　　　　$P(x) - 0.001x^2 + 1.2x + 250$. Find the number of
　　　　pretzels that must be sold to maximize profit.

19.　　A person standing close to the edge on top of a 208-foot　　19. _____
　　　　building throws a baseball vertically upward. The
　　　　quadratic function $s(t) = -16t^2 + 64t + 208$ models the
　　　　ball's height above the ground, $s(t)$, in feet, t seconds
　　　　after it was thrown. How many seconds does it take until
　　　　the ball finally hits the ground? Round to the nearest tenth
　　　　of a second if necessary.

Additional Exercises 11.4
Form I
Equations Quadratic in Form

Solve the equation by making an appropriate substitution.

1. $x^4 - 40x + 144 = 0$ 1. _____

2. $x - 4\sqrt{4} - 32 = 0$ 2. _____

3. $x - 16x^{\frac{1}{2}} - 512 = 0$ 3. _____

4. $(x-4)^2 + 3(x-4) - 18 = 0$ 4. _____

5. $x^4 - 9x^2 + 20 = 0$ 5. _____

6. $x^{-2} + x^{-1} - 1 = 0$ 6. _____

7. $2x^{-2} - x^{-1} - 1 = 0$ 7. _____

8. $6x^4 + x^2 - 5 = 0$ 8. _____

9. $(2a-3)^2 - 9(2a-3) + 20 = 0$ 9. _____

10. $x - 3\sqrt{x} + 2 = 0$ 10. _____

Name _____   Date _____

11. $x - 7\sqrt{x} = -10$ 11. _____

For exercises 12-15 , Match the graph to the appropriate equation.

a.

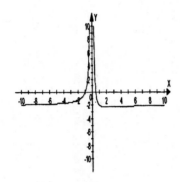

b.

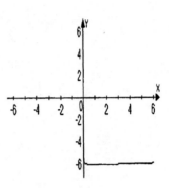

c.

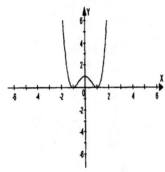

d.

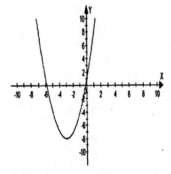

12. $f(x) = x^4 - 2x^2 + 1$ 12. _____

13. $f(x) = x^{-2} - x^{-1} - 2$ 13. _____

14. $f(x) = x^{\frac{1}{3}} - 2x^{\frac{1}{6}} - 5$ 14. _____

15. $f(x) = (x+2)^2 + 2(x-2) + 1$ 15. _____

Additional Exercises 11.4
Form II
Equations Quadratic in Form

Solve the equation by making an appropriate substitution.

1. $x^4 - 4x^2 + 3 = 0$ 1. _____

2. $x - 12\sqrt{x} + 35 = 0$ 2. _____

3. $x^{\frac{2}{3}} - 6x^{\frac{1}{3}} + 5 = 0$ 3. _____

4. $(2x - 2)^2 - 2(2x - 2) - 3 = 0$ 4. _____

5. $4x^4 - 19x^2 + 12 = 0$ 5. _____

6. $x^{-2} - 6x^{-1} + 5 = 0$ 6. _____

7. $7x^{-2} + 8x^{-1} + 1 = 0$ 7. _____

8. $9x^4 - 49 = 0$ 8. _____

9. $2(x + 4)^2 + 5(x + 4) = 12$ 9. _____

10. $3x + \sqrt{x} - 2 = 0$ 10. _____

11. $x - 2\sqrt{x} = 15$

11. _____

For exercises 12-15, Match the graph to the appropriate equation.

a.
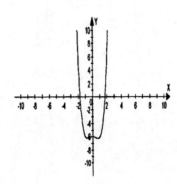

b.
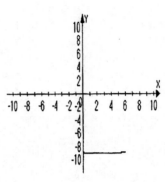

c.
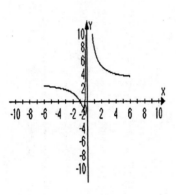

d.
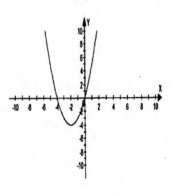

12. $f(x) = x^4 - 2x^2 - 6$

12. _____

13. $f(x) = x^{-2} + 4x^{-1} + 3$

13. _____

14. $f(x) = x^{\frac{1}{3}} + 2x^{\frac{1}{6}} - 8$

14. _____

15. $f(x) = (x+1)^2 + 2(x+1) - 3$

15. _____

Additional Exercises 11.4
Form III
Equations Quadratic in Form

Solve the equation by making an appropriate substitution.

1. $9x^4 - 14x^2 + 5 = 0$ 1. _____

2. $2x - 3\sqrt{x} - 54 = 0$ 2. _____

3. $x^{\frac{2}{5}} - x^{\frac{1}{5}} - 20 = 0$ 3. _____

4. $(x^2 - 4x)^2 - 17(x^2 - 4x) + 60 = 0$ 4. _____

5. $x^4 - 9x^2 + 8 = 0$ 5. _____

6. $4x^{-2} + x^{-1} - 5 = 0$ 6. _____

7. $4x^{-2} + x^{-1} - 1 = 0$ 7. _____

8. $x^4 + 9x^2 + 20 = 0$ 8. _____

9. $(x - 3)^2 + 3(x - 3) = -2$ 9. _____

10. $6x + 11\sqrt{x} - 2 = 0$ 10. _____

Name _____   Date _____

11. $x - \sqrt{x} - 2 + 0$ 11. _____

For exercises 12–15, match the graph to the appropriate equation.

a.

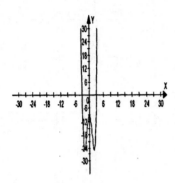

b.

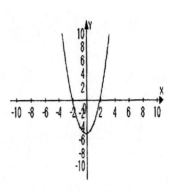

c.

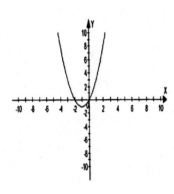

d.

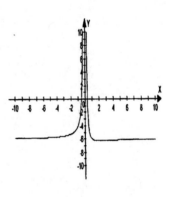

12. $f(x) = x^{-2} - x^{-1} - 6$ 12. _____

13. $f(x) = (x - 1)^2 + 4(x - 1) + 3$ 13. _____

14. $f(x) = 4x^{\frac{2}{3}} + x^{\frac{1}{3}} - 5$ 14. _____

15. $f(x) = x^4 - 8x^2 - 9$ 15. _____

Additional Exercises 11.5
Form I
Polynomial and Rational Inequalities

(a) Solve the quadratic inequality and (b) graph the solution set on a number line. Express the solution set in interval notation.

1. $x^2 - 13x + 42 > 0$

1a. _____

b. ![number line from -6 to 6]

2. $(x+1)(x-4) < 0$

2a. _____

b. ![number line from -6 to 6]

3. $x^2 - 2x - 3 \leq 0$

3a. _____

b. ![number line from -6 to 6]

4. $x^2 - 4x \geq -3$

4a. _____

b. ![number line from -6 to 6]

5. $(x-3)(x+4) > 0$

5a. _____

b. ![number line from -6 to 6]

6. $x^2 - 6x + 9 > 0$

6a. _____

b. ![number line from -6 to 6]

7. $x^2 + 18x + 81 < 0$

7a. _____

b. ![number line from -6 to 6]

8. $x^2 + 4x + 4 \geq 0$

8a. _____

b. ![number line from -6 to 6]

Name _____   Date _____

(a) Solve the rational inequality and (b) graph the solution set on a real number line.

9. $\dfrac{x-2}{x+3} < 0$

9a. _____

b. ![number line from -6 to 6]

10. $\dfrac{x-5}{x+4} > 0$

10a. _____

b. ![number line from -6 to 6]

11. $\dfrac{x+2}{x+5} < 0$

11a. _____

b. ![number line from -6 to 6]

12. $\dfrac{x+6}{x+3} < 0$

12a. _____

b. ![number line from -6 to 6]

13. $\dfrac{-x+3}{x-4} \ge 0$

13a. _____

b. ![number line from -6 to 6]

14. $\dfrac{x}{x-2} > 0$

14a. _____

b. ![number line from -6 to 6]

15. $\dfrac{x+6}{x} > 0$

15a. _____

b. ![number line from -6 to 6]

16. $\dfrac{x+2}{x-1} < 0$

16a. _____

b. ![number line from -6 to 6]

Name _____   Date _____

(a) Solve the quadratic inequality and (b) graph the solution set on a number line. Express the solution set in interval notation.

1. $x^2 + 2x - 15 > 0$

     1a. _____

     b.

2. $(5x - 2)(x + 7) < 0$

     2a. _____

     b.

3. $6x^2 - 5x + 1 \le 0$

     3a. _____

     b.

4. $15x^2 + 19x \ge -6$

     4a. _____

     b.

5. $(4x - 3)(2x - 1) > 0$

     5a. _____

     b.

6. $x^2 + 2x \ge -6$

     6a. _____

     b.

7. $8x^2 - 9x - 14 < 0$

     7a. _____

     b.

8. $x^2 + 10x + 25 < 0$

     8a. _____

     b.

Name _____   Date _____

(a) Solve the rational inequality and (b) graph the solution set on a real number line.

9. $\dfrac{x+2}{x+4} < 2$

9a. _____

b.

10. $\dfrac{x}{x-4} > 2$

10a. _____

b.

11. $\dfrac{x+10}{x+4} < 5$

11a. _____

b.

12. $\dfrac{x+6}{x-4} \geq 0$

12a. _____

b.

13. $\dfrac{x-3}{x+3} \leq 3$

13a. _____

b.

14. $\dfrac{x}{x+1} \geq 4$

14a. _____

b.

15. $\dfrac{2}{x-2} < 1$

15a. _____

b.

16. $\dfrac{x}{x+2} \geq 2$

16a. _____

b.

Additional Exercises 11.5
Form III
Polynomial and Rational Inequalities

(a) Solve the quadratic inequality and (b) graph the solution set on a number line. Express the solution set in interval notation.

1. $7x^2 + 48x - 7 > 0$

1a. _____

b.

2. $6x^2 + 7x + 2 < 0$

2a. _____

b.

3. $10x^2 + 9x + 2 \leq 0$

3a. _____

b.

4. $8x^2 - 14x \geq 15$

4a. _____

b.

5. $(5x - 1)(6x - 5) > 0$

5a. _____

b.

6. $(8x - 1)(x - 2) > 0$

6a. _____

b.

7. $x^2 + 22 + 121 < 0$

7a. _____

b.

8. $x^2 + 2x + 1 \geq 0$

8a. _____

b.

Name _____   Date _____

(a) Solve the rational inequality and (b) graph the solution set on a real number line.

9. $\dfrac{x}{x+3} > -1$

9a. _____

b.

10. $\dfrac{x+4}{x} \le -3$

10a. _____

b.

11. $\dfrac{1}{x+5} < 2$

11a. _____

b.

12. $\dfrac{x-5}{x+5} \le 5$

12a. _____

b.

13. $\dfrac{10-5x}{6x+5} \le 0$

13a. _____

b.

14. $\dfrac{9x+8}{12-4x} \ge 0$

14a. _____

b.

15. $\dfrac{2x+7}{3-4x} \ge 0$

15a. _____

b.

16. $\dfrac{2-x}{3x+5} \le 0$

16a. _____

b.

Name _____   Date _____

Additional Exercises 12.1
Form I
Exponential Functions

Approximate each number using a calculator. Round your answer to three decimal places.

1. $2^{1.5}$ 1. _____

2. $4^{2.3}$ 2. _____

3. $5^{-1.2}$ 3. _____

Graph each function by making a table of coordinates.

4. $f(x) = 2^x$

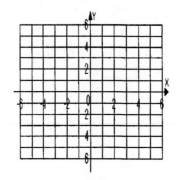

5. $g(x) = -2^x$

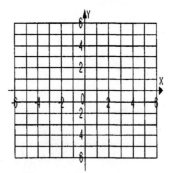

6. $h(x) = \left(\dfrac{1}{3}\right)^x$

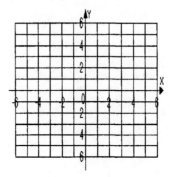

7. $f(x) = 2^x - 3$

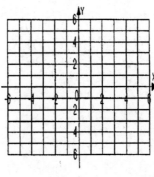

8. $g(x) = 4^{x-2}$

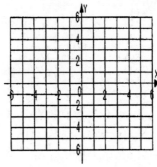

Graph each function on the same rectangular coordinate system. Then describe how the graph of g is related to the graph of f.

9. $f(x) = 3^x$ and $g(x) = 3^{x-1}$

9. _____

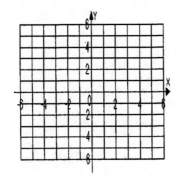

10. $f(x) = 3^x$ and $g(x) = 3^{x-3}$

10. _____

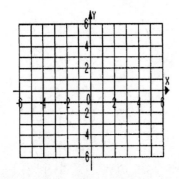

Name _____   Date _____

11. $f(x) = 3^x$ and $g(x) = 3^{x+2}$

11. _____

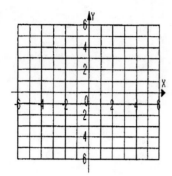

Use the compound interest formulas $A = P\left(1 + \dfrac{r}{n}\right)^{nt}$ and $A = Pe^{rt}$ to solve.

12. Find the accumulated value of an investment of $14,000
at 8% compounded annually for 11 years.

12. _____

13. Find the accumulated value of an investment of $14,000
at 8% compounded semiannually for 11 years.

13. _____

14. Find the accumulated value of an investment of $14,000
at 8% compounded continuously for 11 years.

14. _____

15. Find the accumulated value of an investment of $20,000
for 10 years at an interest rate of 4%, if the money is
compounded annually.

15. _____

16. Find the accumulated value of an investment of $17,000
for 2 years at an interest rate of 6%, if the money is
compounded quarterly.

16. _____

17. Find the accumulated value of an investment of $5,000
for 5 years at an interest rate of 4%, if the money is
compounded monthly.

17. _____

18. Find the accumulated value of an investment of $12,000
for 10 years at an interest rate of 3.5%, if the money is
compounded semiannually.

18. _____

Name _____   Date _____

Additional Exercises 12.1
Form II
Exponential Functions

Approximate each number using a calculator. Round your answer to three decimal places.

1. $3^{-2.1}$

1. _____

2. $5^{-3.4}$

2. _____

3. $e^{2.3}$

3. _____

Graph each function by making a table of coordinates.

4. $f(x) = 4^x$

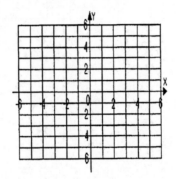

5. $g(x) = -1.5^x$

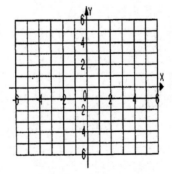

6. $h(x) = \left(-\dfrac{1}{2}\right)^x$

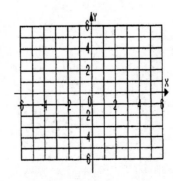

7. $f(x) = 3 \cdot 2^x - 2$

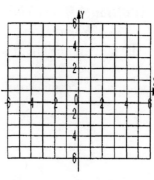

8. $g(x) = 3^{x-5}$

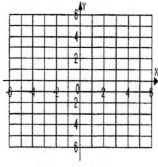

Graph each function on the same rectangular coordinate system. Then describe how the graph of g is related to the graph of f.

9. $f(x) = 4^x$ and $g(x) = 4^{x-2}$

9. _____

10. $f(x) = 4^x$ and $g(x) = 4^{x-2}$

10. _____

11. $f(x) = 4^x$ and $g(x) = -4^{x-2}$ 11. _____

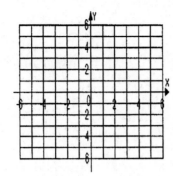

Use the compound interest formulas $A = P\left(1 + \dfrac{r}{n}\right)^{nt}$ and $A = Pe^{rt}$ to solve.

12.   Find the accumulated value of an investment of $20,000   12. _____
        for 7 years at an interest rate of 6%, if the money is
        compounded annually..

13.   Find the accumulated value of an investment of $20,000   13. _____
        for 7 years at and interest rate of 6%, if the money is
        compounded monthly.

14.   Find the accumulated value of an investment of $4,000   13. _____
        for 12 years at and interest rate of 8%, if the money is
        compounded semi-annually.

15.   Find the accumulated value of an investment of $1,000   15. _____
        invested at 8% for 6years and compounded continuously.

16.   Find the accumulated value of an investment of $750   16. _____
        for 2 years at an interest rate of 3.5%, if the money is
        compounded quarterly.

17.   The rabbit population in the forest area grows at the rate   17. _____
        of 5% monthly. If there are 200 rabbits in July, find out
        how many rabbits (rounded to the nearest whole number)
        should be expected by next July. Use $y = 200(2.7)^{0.05t}$.

18.   A small lake is stocked with 200 rainbow trout in March.   18. _____
        The growth in the number of fish can be estimated by the
        function $f(t) = 200e^{0.06t}$. How many trout will be in the
        lake in 2 years?

Name _____   Date _____

Additional Exercises 12.1
Form III
Exponential Functions

Approximate each number using a calculator. Round your answer to three decimal places.

1. $4^{-2.5}$ 1. _____

2. $7^{\sqrt{5}}$ 2. _____

3. $e^{-0.81}$ 3. _____

Graph each function by making a table of coordinates.

4. $f(x) = -2.5^x$

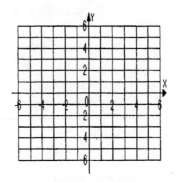

5. $g(x) = \left(\dfrac{2}{3}\right)^x$

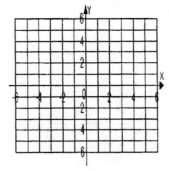

6. $h(x) = (0.4)^x$

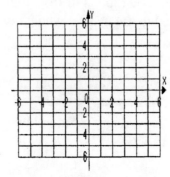

Name _____   Date _____

7. $f(x) = 2^{\sqrt{x}+1}$

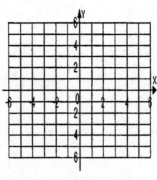

8. $g(x) = 3^{x-2} + 2^y$

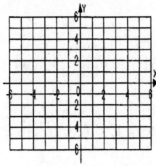

Graph each function on the same rectangular coordinate system. Then describe how the graph of g is related to the graph of f.

9. $f(x) = 3^{x-1}$ and $g(x) = 3^{x+1}$ 9. _____

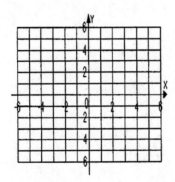

10. $f(x) = 3^{x-1}$ and $g(x) = 3^x - 2$ 10. _____

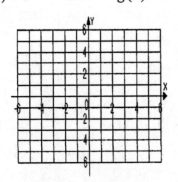

Name _____   Date _____

11. $f(x) = 3^{x-1}$ and $g(x) = 3^{-x}$ 11. _____

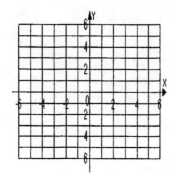

Use the compound interest formulas $A = P\left(1 + \dfrac{r}{n}\right)^{nt}$ and $A = Pe^{rt}$ to solve.

12.   Find the accumulated value of an investment of $9,000   12. _____
       for 2 years at an interest rate of 4%, if the money is
       compounded semi-annually.

13.   Find the accumulated value of an investment of $690   13. _____
       for 13 years at and interest rate of 3%, if the money is
       compounded annually.

14.   Find the accumulated value of an investment of $12,000   13. _____
       for $5\dfrac{1}{2}$ years at and interest rate of 4.5%, if the money is
       compounded monthly.

15.   Find the accumulated amount of an loan debt of $1250   15. _____
       for 4 years at an interest rate of 9.5%, if the loan
       amount is compounded continuously.

16.   Suppose you have $5000 to invest. At one banking   16. _____
       Institution your money will earn 5% and be compounded
       monthly. At a second bank, your money will be
       compounded quarterly at 4.5%. At which bank and rate
       should your money be invested in order to make the
       most money?

17. Find out how long it would take for a $6000 investment to   17. _____
     double if it is invested at 8% interest and the money is
     compounded semi-annually.

18. Find out how long it would take for a $10,000 investment   18. _____
     to triple in value if it is invested in an account paying 4%
     interest compounded continuously.

19. The function $D(h) = 8e^{-0.4h}$ can be used to determine the   19. _____
     the milligrams $D(h)$ of a certain drug in a patients
     bloodstream h hours after the drug has be administered.
     How many milligrams (round to two decimal places)
     would be present after 10 hours?

20. A sample of 900 grams of lead-210 decays to   20. _____
     polonium-210 according to the function given by
     $A(t) = 900e^{-0.032t}$, where t is the time in years. What
     is the amount of the sample after 20 years (to the
     nearest gram)?

Name _____   Date _____

Additional Exercises 12.2
Form I
Logarithmic Functions

Write the equation in its equivalent exponential form.

1. $\log_4 16 = 2$ 1. _____

2. $\log_2 8 = 3$ 2. _____

3. $\log_5 x = 2$ 3. _____

4. $\log_2 16 = x$ 4. _____

Write the equation in its equivalent logarithmic form.

5. $3^2 = 9$ 5. _____

6. $4^3 = 64$ 6. _____

7. $5^2 = x$ 7. _____

8. $6^y = 32$ 8. _____

Evaluate the expression without using a calculator.

9. $\log_{10} 10$ 9. _____

10. $\log_7 1$ 10. _____

11. $\log_{10} 1000$ 11. _____

12. $\log_{36} 6$ 12. _____

13. $\log_2 \sqrt{2}$ 13. _____

Graph 14 and 15 on the same coordinate plane.

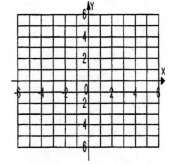

14. $f(x) = 3^x$

15. $g(x) = \log_3 x$

16.   Find the domain of $f(x) = \log_6 (x + 5)$.   16. _____

Use inverse properties of logarithms to simplify each expression.

17. $\ln e^2$ 17. _____

18. $\ln e^{15x}$ 18. _____

19. $10^{\log \sqrt{5x}}$ 19. _____

Solve.

20.   Use the formula $R = \log\left(\dfrac{a}{T}\right) + B$ to find the intensity R on   20. _____

the Richter scale, given that amplitude a is 346 micrometers, time T between waves is 2 seconds, and B is 2.2. Round your answer to one decimal place.

Additional Exercises 12.2
Form II
Logarithmic Functions

Write the equation in its equivalent exponential form.

1. $\log_5 25 = 2$ 1. _____

2. $\log_x 16 = 2$ 2. _____

3. $\log_6 x = 4$ 3. _____

4. $\log_b 512 = 3$ 4. _____

Write the equation in its equivalent logarithmic form.

5. $3^4 = 81$ 5. _____

6. $10^{-3} = 0.01$ 6. _____

7. $5^{-2} = \dfrac{1}{25}$ 7. _____

8. $e^y = 18$ 8. _____

Evaluate the expression without using a calculator.

9. $\log_{25} 25$ 9. _____

10. $\log_{18} 1$ 10. _____

11. $\log_3 81$ 11. _____

Name _____   Date _____

12. $\log_{27} 9$ 12. _____

13. $\ln e^5$ 13. _____

Graph 14 and 15 on the same coordinate plane.

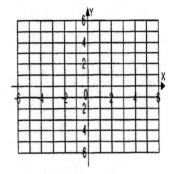

14. $f(x) = 4^x$

15. $g(x) = \left(\dfrac{1}{4}\right)^x$

16.   Find the domain of $f(x) = \ln(4 = x)$ 16. _____

Use inverse properties of logarithms to simplify each expression.

17. $\ln e^{2y}$ 17. _____

18. $10^{\log \sqrt{10x}}$ 18. _____

19. $e^{\ln 4x^3}$ 19. _____

Solve.

20.   Use the formula $R = \log\left(\dfrac{a}{T}\right) + B$ to find the intensity R on   20. _____

       the Richter scale, given that amplitude a is 450 micrometers,
       time T between waves is 1.5 seconds, and B is 3.6. Round your
       answer to one decimal place.

AE-439

Additional Exercises 12.2
Form III
Logarithmic Functions

Write the equation in its equivalent exponential form.

1. $\log_4 x = 2$

1. _____

2. $\log_b 216 = 3$

2. _____

3. $\log_{16} 8 = x$

3. _____

4. $\log_x 0.1 = -1$

4. _____

Write the equation in its equivalent logarithmic form.

5. $5^3 = 125$

5. _____

6. $3^{-4} = \dfrac{1}{81}$

6. _____

7. $9^x = 287$

7. _____

8. $4^{-1} = 0.25$

8. _____

Evaluate the expression without using a calculator.

9. $\log_8 8$

9. _____

10. $\log_3 \sqrt{3}$

10. _____

11. $\log_{64} 8$

11. _____

12. $\log_{125} 5$ 12. _____

13. $\ln e^9$ 13. _____

Graph 14 and 15 on the same coordinate plane.

14. $f(x) = 2^x$

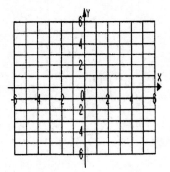

15. $g(x) = 2^{x-2}$

16.   Find the domain of $f(x) = \ln(1-x)$.   16. _____

Use inverse properties of logarithms to simplify each expression.

17. $\ln e^{\sqrt{3x}}$ 17. _____

18. $10^{\log \sqrt{13x}}$ 18. _____

19. $e^{\ln 2x^3}$ 19. _____

Solve.

20.   The pH of a solution ranges from 0 to 14. An acid has a pH   20. _____
       less than 7. Pure water is neutral and has a pH of 7. The pH
       of a solution is given by $pH = -\log x$ where x represents the
       concentration of the hydrogen ions in the solution in moles per
       liter. Find the pH if the hydrogen ion concentration is 1×10^{-2}.

Additional Exercises 12.3
Form I
Properties of Logarithms

Use the properties of logarithms to expand the logarithmic expression as much as possible. Where possible, evaluate logarithmic expressions without using a calculator.

1. $\log_5(7\cdot 11)$ 1. _____

2. $\log_2 3x$ 2. _____

3. $\log_4 16x$ 3. _____

4. $\log_7 \dfrac{5}{x}$ 4. _____

5. $\log_8 \dfrac{8}{x}$ 5. _____

6. $\log_5 \dfrac{125}{x}$ 6. _____

7. $\log_7 x^6$ 7. _____

8. $\ln(4x)$ 8. _____

9. $\ln y^4$ 9. _____

10. $\log_b \dfrac{xy}{z^2}$ 10. _____

Use the properties of logarithms to condense the logarithmic expression. Write the expression as a single logarithm whose coefficient is 1. Where possible, evaluate logarithmic expressions.

11. $\log_4 108 - \log_4 9$ 11. _____

12. $\log_5 1250 - \log_5 2$ 12. _____

13. $\log_6 2 + \log_6 x$ 13. _____

14. $\log_6 9 + \log_6 4$ 14. _____

15. $\log_7 (x-1) - \log_7 (x+3)$ 15. _____

16. $\log_b (x+2) - \log_b (x-2)$ 16. _____

17. $2\log_5 x - 4\log_5 y$ 17. _____

18. $6\log_3 x + 2\log_3 y$ 18. _____

Use common logarithms or natural logarithms and a calculator to evaluate to four decimal places.

19. $\log_4 17$ 19. _____

20. $\log_6 14$ 20. _____

Name _____   Date _____

Use the properties of logarithms to expand the logarithmic expression as much as possible. Where possible, evaluate logarithmic expressions without using a calculator.

1. $\log_4 3x$ 1. _____

2. $\log_2 8x$ 2. _____

3. $\log_9 \dfrac{x}{9}$ 3. _____

4. $\log_b yz^9$ 4. _____

5. $\ln y^z$ 5. _____

6. $\log_b \dfrac{xy^6}{z^4}$ 6. _____

7. $\log_b \dfrac{x^2}{yz^2}$ 7. _____

8. $\log_2 \left(\dfrac{\sqrt{y}}{8} \right)$ 8. _____

9. $\ln \sqrt{\dfrac{x}{y}}$ 9. _____

10. $\ln \sqrt[5]{xy}$ 10. _____

Use the properties of logarithms to condense the logarithmic expression. Write the expression as a single logarithm whose coefficient is 1. Where possible, evaluate logarithmic expressions.

11. $\log_3 486 - \log_3 18$ 11. _____

12. $\log_b (x-4) - \log_b (x+2)$ 12. _____

13. $\log_4 8 + \log_4 32$ 13. _____

14. $\ln x - 4\ln y$ 14. _____

15. $2\ln x - 5\ln y$ 15. _____

16. $3\ln(x-4) - 9\ln x$ 16. _____

17. $8\log_b y + 4\log_b z$ 17. _____

18. $\dfrac{1}{2}\log x - \dfrac{1}{3}\log y$ 18. _____

Use common logarithms or natural logarithms and a calculator to evaluate to four decimal places.

19. $\log_9 27$ 19. _____

20. $\log_{0.4} 20$ 20. _____

Name _____   Date _____

Additional Exercises 12.3
Form III
Properties of Logarithms

Use the properties of logarithms to expand the logarithmic expression as much as possible. Where possible, evaluate logarithmic expressions without using a calculator.

1. $\log_5 x^2 y^3$ 1. _____

2. $\log_8 x^8 y^8 z^8$ 2. _____

3. $\log_{10}\left(\dfrac{2x}{y}\right)$ 3. _____

4. $\log_b\left(\dfrac{x^2}{y^3 z^4}\right)$ 4. _____

5. $\log_3\left(\dfrac{x}{9}\right)$ 5. _____

6. $\log_5\left(\dfrac{x-1}{x+2}\right)$ 6. _____

7. $\ln\left(\dfrac{e^4}{7}\right)$ 7. _____

8. $\log\left(\dfrac{\sqrt[3]{x}}{\sqrt{y}}\right)$ 8. _____

9. $\log\left(\dfrac{\sqrt{x}}{\sqrt[3]{yz^4}}\right)$ 9. _____

10. $\log_3\left(\dfrac{9}{\sqrt{x+2}}\right)$ 10. _____

Use the properties of logarithms to condense the logarithmic expression. Write the expression as a single logarithm whose coefficient is 1. Where possible, evaluate logarithmic expressions.

11. $\log_4 1280 - \log_4 5$ 11. _____

12. $\log_6 (x+2)^2 - \log_6 (x+2)$ 12. _____

13. $8\log_b y + \dfrac{1}{4}\log_b z$ 13. _____

14. $5\ln(x+4) - 2\ln x$ 14. _____

15. $\log_3 x + \log_3 (x-2)$ 15. _____

16. $2\log_2 x + \dfrac{1}{2}\log_2 z$ 16. _____

17. $\dfrac{1}{3}\log_b x - \dfrac{1}{3}\log_b x$ 17. _____

18. $3\log_5 x + \dfrac{1}{2}\log_5 y - 4\log_5 z$ 18. _____

Use common logarithms or natural logarithms and a calculator to evaluate to four decimal places.

19. $\log_5 24$ 19. _____

20. $\ln 0.0345$ 20. _____

Additional Exercises 12.4
Form I
Exponential and Logarithmic Equations

Solve the exponential equation by expressing each side as a power of the same base and then equating the exponents.

1. $5^x = 125$ 1. _____

2. $4^x = 4096$ 2. _____

3. $3^{3x-1} = 9$ 3. _____

Solve each exponential equation by taking the logarithm on both sides. Express the solution set in terms of logarithms.

4. $7^x = 343$ 4. _____

5. $2^x = 90$ 5. _____

6. $3^3 = 15$ 6. _____

7. $e^{1.4x} = 10$ 7. _____

8. $10^x = 9$ 8. _____

Solve each exponential equation by taking the logarithm on both sides. Use a calculator to obtain a decimal approximation correct to two decimal places for the solution.

9. $3^{x+6} = 4$ 9. _____

10. $e^x = 72$ 10. _____

Solve each logarithmic equation. Be sure to reject any value that produces the logarithm of a non-positive number in the original equation.

11. $\log_2(x-4) = -3$ 11. _____

12. $\log_4(2x+6) = 3$ 12. _____

13. $\log_3(2x-1) = 2$ 13. _____

14. $\log_6 x + \log_6(x-1) = 1$ 14. _____

15. $\log(x-2) - \log x = 3$ 15. _____

Solve the equation by isolating the natural logarithm and exponentiating both sides. Express the answer in terms of e.

16. $\ln x = 2$ 16. _____

17. $\ln x = 24$ 17. _____

18. $\ln 2x = 5$ 18. _____

19. $6 + 5\ln x = 3$ 19. _____

20. $6\ln 9x = 12$ 20. _____

Additional Exercises 12.4
Form II
Exponential and Logarithmic Equations

Solve the exponential equation by expressing each side as a power of the same base and then equating the exponents.

1. $4^x = 8$ 1. _____

2. $25^x = 5$ 2. _____

3. $9^{x+1} = 27^x$ 3. _____

Solve each exponential equation by taking the logarithm on both sides. Express the solution set in terms of logarithms.

4. $5^x = 32$ 4. _____

5. $3^x = 5.2$ 5. _____

6. $e^{2.8} = 7$ 6. _____

7. $e^x = 42$ 7. _____

8. $-4e^x = -16$ 8. _____

Solve each exponential equation by taking the logarithm on both sides. Use a calculator to obtain a decimal approximation correct to two decimal places for the solution.

9. $e^x = 7$ 9. _____

10. $5e^{2x} = 8$ 10. _____

Solve each logarithmic equation. Be sure to reject any value that produces the logarithm of a non-positive number in the original equation.

11. $\log_5(x-1) = 1$ 11. _____

12. $\log_3(2x+1) = 3$ 12. _____

13. $\log_{1024} x = \dfrac{1}{5}$ 13. _____

14. $\log_3 x + \log_3(x+6) = 3$ 14. _____

15. $\log_2(x-2) + \log_2(x+4) = 4$ 15. _____

Solve the equation by isolating the natural logarithm and exponentiating both sides. Express the answer in terms of e.

16. $\ln x = 5$ 16. _____

17. $\ln 3x = 5.5$ 17. _____

18. $\ln(x+1) = 3$ 18. _____

19. $2\ln x + 3 = 0$ 19. _____

20. $6\ln 4x = 12$ 20. _____

Additional Exercises 12.4
Form III
Exponential and Logarithmic Equations

Solve the exponential equation by expressing each side as a power of the same base and then equating the exponents.

1. $27^x = 9$ 1. _____

2. $3^{a-2} = 9^9$ 2. _____

3. $2^{3x-1} = 32$ 3. _____

Solve each exponential equation by taking the logarithm on both sides. Express the solution set in terms of logarithms.

4. $9^x = 4$ 4. _____

5. $7^x = 13.8$ 5. _____

6. $e^{-2x} = 4$ 6. _____

7. $\dfrac{1}{3}e^x = 5$ 7. _____

8. $4^{x+7} = 5^x$ 8. _____

Solve each exponential equation by taking the logarithm on both sides. Use a calculator to obtain a decimal approximation correct to two decimal places for the solution.

9. $5e^{2x} = 1560$ 9. _____

10. $(2.7)^x = 3$ 10. _____

Name _____   Date _____

Solve each logarithmic equation. Be sure to reject any value of x that is not in the domain of the original logarithm expressions. Give the exact answer. Then, where necessary, use a calculator to obtain a decimal approximation, correct to two decimal places.

11. $\log_3 x = -2$ 11. _____

12. $\log_{729} x = \dfrac{1}{6}$ 12. _____

13. $\log_2 (x^2 + 2x) = 3$ 13. _____

14. $\log_4 (x + 5) - \log_4 (x - 1) = 2$ 14. _____

15. $6 + 5 \ln x = 3$ 15. _____

16. $\log_9 x + \log_9 (x - 8) = 1$ 16. _____

17. $\log_2 (x - 3) + \log_2 (x + 4) = 3$ 17. _____

18. $\ln(x + 1) + \ln(x - 1) = 0$ 18. _____

19. $\ln(3x + 1) = \ln(x + 7)$ 19. _____

20. $\ln(x^2 + 3x - 4) - \ln(x + 4) = 3$ 20. _____

Additional Exercises 13.1
Form I
The Circle

Write the standard form of the equation of the circle with the given center and radius.

1.   center $(0, 0)$, $r = 5$ 1. _____

2.   center $(0, 2)$, $r = 6$ 2. _____

3.   center $(4, 0)$, $r = 3$ 3. _____

4.   center $(1, 3)$, $r = 4$ 4. _____

Find the (a) center and the (b) radius of the circle.

5. $x^2 + y^2 = 81$ 5a. _____

                                                                       b. _____

6. $(x - 3)^2 + y^2 = 36$ 6a. _____

                                                                       b. _____

7. $x^2 + (y - 4)^2 = 25$ 7a. _____

                                                                       b. _____

Complete the square and write the equation in standard form.

8. $x^2 + y^2 + 6x + 20y + 28 = 8$ 8. _____

Name _____   Date _____

9. $x^2 + y^2 + 8x - 16y + 44 = 0$ 9. _____

10. $x^2 + y^2 + 20x + 19 = 0$ 10. _____

Graph the circle.

11. $x^2 + y^2 = 9$ 11.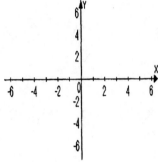

12. $x^2 + (y-2)^2 = 4$ 12.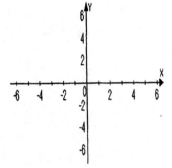

13. $(x-4)^2 + y^2 = 1$ 13.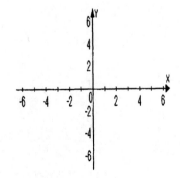

Name _____   Date _____

Additional Exercises 13.1
Form II
The Circle

Find the distance between the pair of points.

1.   (0, –8) and (0, 5)   1. _____

2.   (10, 2) and (–3, 8)   2. _____

3.   (0, 0) and (–5, –8)   3. _____

4.   (6, –2) and (4, 5)   4. _____

Find the midpoint of the line segment whose end points are given.

5.   (7, 6) (0, 3)   5. _____

6.   (–7, –9) (8, 5)   6. _____

7.   (9, 9) and (7, 1)   7. _____

Write the standard form of the equation of the circle with the given center and radius.

8.   center (5, –9), r = 12   8. _____

9.   center (0, 9), r = 11   9. _____

10.   center (0, 8), r = $\sqrt{3}$ 10. _____

11.   center (0, 0), r = $\sqrt{6}$ 11. _____

Find the (a) center and the (b) radius of the circle.

12. $(x+5)^2 + (y+9)^2 = 4$ 12a. _____

                                                                            b. _____

13. $x^2 + 10x + 25 + y^2 - 10y + 25 = 16$ 13a. _____

                                                                      b. _____

14. $x^2 + y^2 = 100$ 14a. _____

                                                                      b. _____

Complete the square and write the equation in standard form.

15. $x^2 - 2x + y^2 - 6y = 26$ 15. _____

16. $x^2 + 2x + y^2 - 16y = -61$ 16. _____

17. $x^2 + y^2 - 6x + 10y + 30 = 0$ 17. _____

Graph the circle.

18. $(x+1)^2 + (y-4)^2 = 16$ 18.

19. $x^2 + (y+2)^2 = 25$ 19.

20. $(x-4)^2 + (y+2)^2 = 9$ 20.

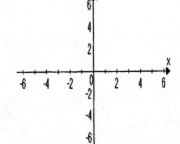

Name _____   Date _____

Write the standard form of the equation of the circle with the given center and radius.

1.   center $(-2, 3)$, $r = \sqrt{7}$ 1. _____

2.   center $(1, -5)$, $r = 8$ 2. _____

3.   center $(-4, -6)$, $r = \sqrt{5}$ 3. _____

4.   center $(-3, 0)$, $r = \sqrt{17}$ 4. _____

Find the (a) center and the (b) radius of the circle.

5. $(x-4)^2 + (y+4)^2 = 16$ 5a. _____

                                                          b. _____

6. $x^2 + 6x + 9 + y^2 - 6y + 9 = 9$ 6a. _____

                                                          b. _____

7. $(x+5)^2 + y^2 = 121$ 7a. _____

                                                          b. _____

Complete the square and write the equation in standard form.

8. $x^2 + 4x + y^2 = 6y$ 8. _____

9. $x^2 + y^2 - 2x - 4y = 3$ 9. _____

10. $x^2 + y^2 - 8x + 10y = 0$ 10. _____

Graph the circle.

11. $(x-4)^2 + (y-3)^2 = 16$ 11.

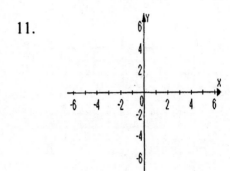

12. $(x-3)^2 + (y-5)^2 = 25$ 12.

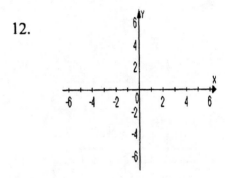

13. $\left(x + \dfrac{1}{2}\right)^2 + \left(y - \dfrac{1}{4}\right)^2 = \dfrac{1}{9}$ 13.

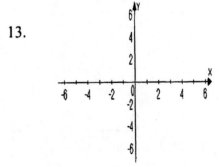

Additional Exercises 13.2
Form I
The Ellipse

Graph the ellipse.

1. $\dfrac{x^2}{25} + \dfrac{y^2}{4} = 1$

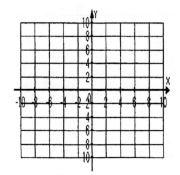

2. $\dfrac{x^2}{4} + \dfrac{y^2}{25} = 1$

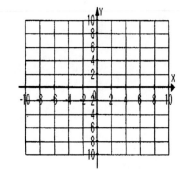

3. $\dfrac{x^2}{9} + \dfrac{y^2}{4} = 1$

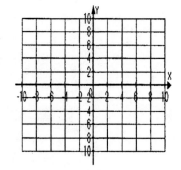

4. $\dfrac{x^2}{9} + \dfrac{y^2}{16} = 1$

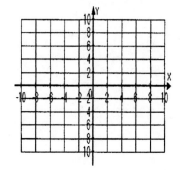

5. $\dfrac{x^2}{4} + y^2 = 1$

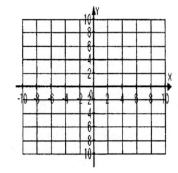

6. $x^2 + \dfrac{y^2}{9} = 1$

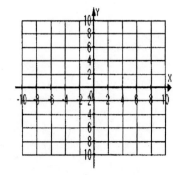

7. $\dfrac{X^2}{36}+\dfrac{Y^2}{25}=1$

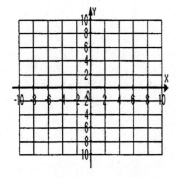

8. $\dfrac{x^2}{25}+\dfrac{y^2}{49}=1$

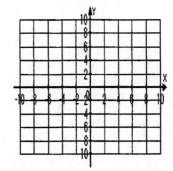

9. $4x^2+16y^2=64$

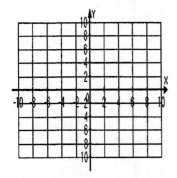

10. $25x^2+y^2=25$

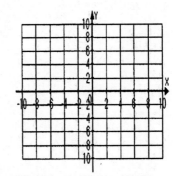

11. $9x^2+4y^2=36$

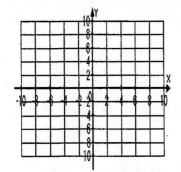

12. $4x^2+9y^2=36$

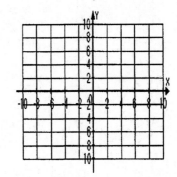

13. $\dfrac{(x-1)^2}{9}+\dfrac{(y-3)^2}{4}=1$

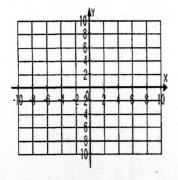

14. $\dfrac{(x+1)^2}{25}+\dfrac{(y-2)^2}{16}=1$

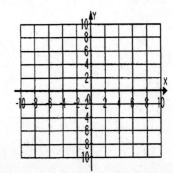

AE-461

Name _____   Date _____

Graph the ellipse.

1. $\dfrac{x^2}{4} + \dfrac{y^2}{9} = 1$

2. $\dfrac{x^2}{16} + \dfrac{y^2}{4} = 1$

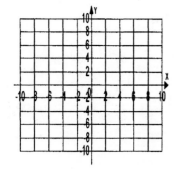

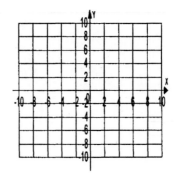

3. $\dfrac{x^2}{16} + \dfrac{y^2}{25} = 1$

4. $\dfrac{x^2}{49} + y^2 = 1$

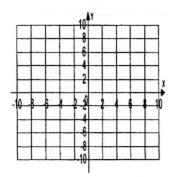

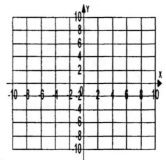

5. $\dfrac{x^2}{12} + \dfrac{y^2}{9} = 1$

6. $\dfrac{x^2}{4} + \dfrac{y^2}{16} = 1$

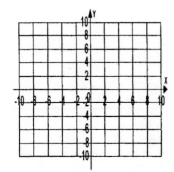

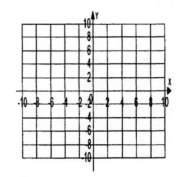

7. $\dfrac{x^2}{16} + \dfrac{y^2}{6} = 1$

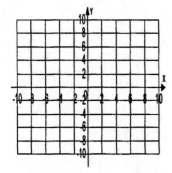

8. $\dfrac{x^2}{2} + \dfrac{y^2}{8} = 1$

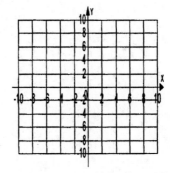

9. $15x^2 + 9y^2 = 135$

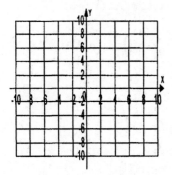

10. $12x^2 + 24y^2 = 24$

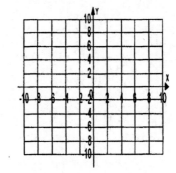

11. $9x^2 + 12y^2 = 108$

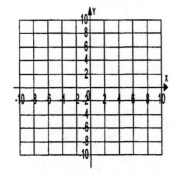

12. $3x^2 + y^2 = 21$

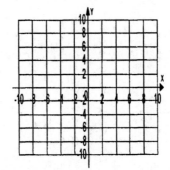

13. $x^2 + 5y^2 = 10$

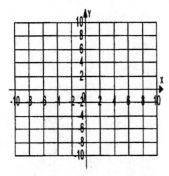

14. $\dfrac{(x-2)^2}{16} + \dfrac{(y+1)^2}{4} = 1$

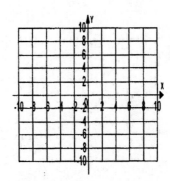

Name _____   Date _____

Additional Exercises 13.2
Form III
The Ellipse

Graph the ellipse.

1. $x^2 + \dfrac{y^2}{25} = 1$

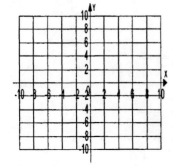

2. $\dfrac{x^2}{49} + y^2 = 1$

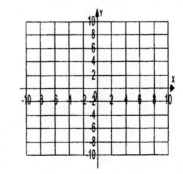

3. $\dfrac{x^2}{7} + \dfrac{y^2}{9} = 1$

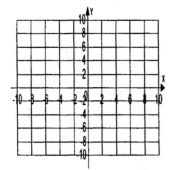

4. $\dfrac{x^2}{8} + \dfrac{y^2}{4} = 1$

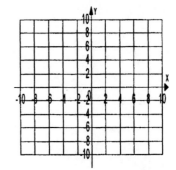

5. $\dfrac{x^2}{12} + \dfrac{y^2}{20} = 1$

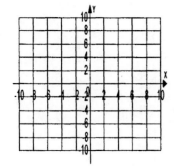

6. $\dfrac{x^2}{15} + \dfrac{y^2}{36} = 1$

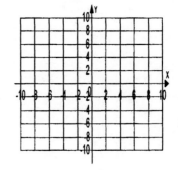

7. $\dfrac{x^2}{11} + \dfrac{y^2}{20} = 1$

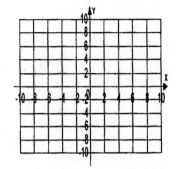

8. $\dfrac{x^2}{3} + \dfrac{y^2}{24} = 1$

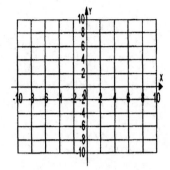

9. $9x^2 + 7y^2 = 63$

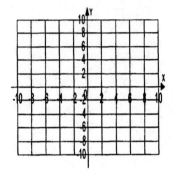

10. $4x^2 + 6y^2 = 24$

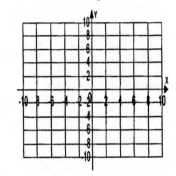

11. $5x^2 + 8y^2 = 40$

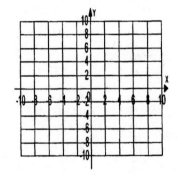

12. $7x^2 + y^2 = 42$

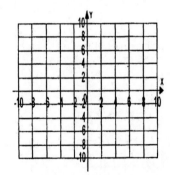

13. $9(x-2)^2 + 16(y-1)^2 = 144$

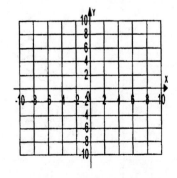

14. $16(x-2)^2 + 4(y+1)^2 = 64$

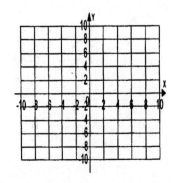

Name _____   Date _____

Find the vertices for the hyperbola.

1. $\dfrac{x^2}{1} - \dfrac{y^2}{4} = 1$

   1. _____

2. $\dfrac{y^2}{16} - \dfrac{x^2}{9} = 1$

   2. _____

3. $\dfrac{y^2}{25} - \dfrac{x^2}{1} = 1$

   3. _____

4. $\dfrac{x^2}{100} - \dfrac{y^2}{16} = 1$

   4. _____

5. $\dfrac{x^2}{4} - \dfrac{y^2}{81} = 1$

   5. _____

Graph the hyperbola.

6. $\dfrac{x^2}{9} - \dfrac{y^2}{4} = 1$

7. $\dfrac{x^2}{4} - \dfrac{y^2}{25} = 1$

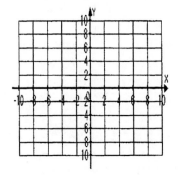
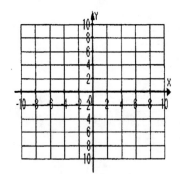

8. $\dfrac{x^2}{4} - \dfrac{y^2}{9} = 1$

9. $\dfrac{x^2}{9} - \dfrac{y^2}{36} = 1$

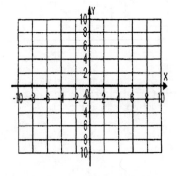
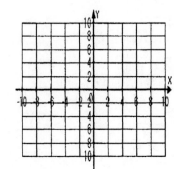

10. $\dfrac{y^2}{9} - \dfrac{x^2}{36} = 1$

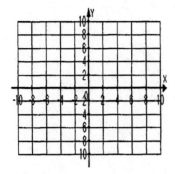

11. $36x^2 - 4y^2 = 144$

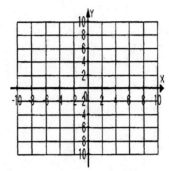

12. $4y^2 - 9x^2 = 36$

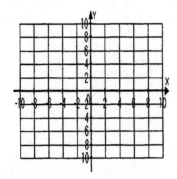

13. $4y^2 - x^2 = 4$

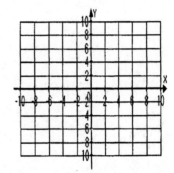

14. $4y^2 - 9x^2 = 36$

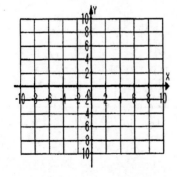

15. $25y^2 = 4x^2 + 100$

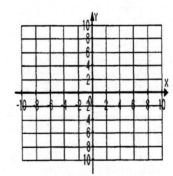

Name _____   Date _____

Find the vertices for the hyperbola.

1. $\dfrac{x^2}{9} - \dfrac{y^2}{4} = 1$ 1. _____

2. $\dfrac{y^2}{25} - \dfrac{x^2}{16} = 1$ 2. _____

3. $\dfrac{y^2}{49} - \dfrac{x^2}{64} = 1$ 3. _____

4. $\dfrac{x^2}{81} - \dfrac{y^2}{36} = 1$ 4. _____

5. $\dfrac{y^2}{100} - \dfrac{x^2}{64} = 1$ 5. _____

Graph the hyperbola.

6. $\dfrac{y^2}{81} - \dfrac{x^2}{36} = 1$ 7. $\dfrac{x^2}{64} - \dfrac{y^2}{100} = 1$

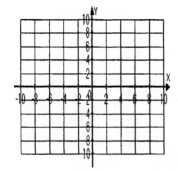   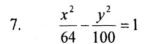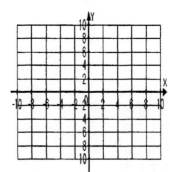

8. $\dfrac{y^2}{64} - \dfrac{x^2}{49} = 1$ 9. $y^2 - x^2 = 1$

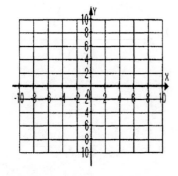   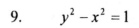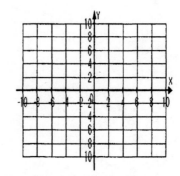

AE-468

10. $x^2 - y^2 = 1$

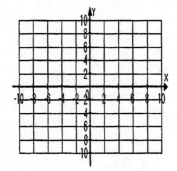

11. $25x^2 - 9y^2 = 225$

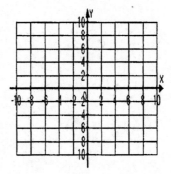

12. $16x^2 - 9y^2 = 144$

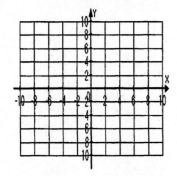

13. $9y^2 - 16x^2 = 144$

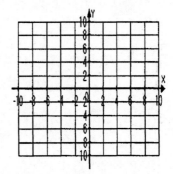

14. $4x^2 - y^2 = 4$

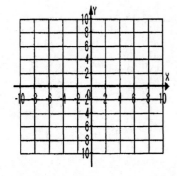

15. $4y^2 - 25x^2 = 100$

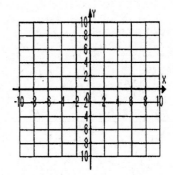

Name _____   Date _____

Additional Exercises 13.3
Form III
The Hyperbola

Find the vertices for the hyperbola.

1. $\dfrac{x^2}{16} - \dfrac{y^2}{121} = 1$ 1. _____

2. $\dfrac{y^2}{16} - \dfrac{x^2}{10} = 1$ 2. _____

3. $\dfrac{x^2}{121} - \dfrac{y^2}{144} = 1$ 3. _____

4. $\dfrac{y^2}{100} - \dfrac{x^2}{64} = 1$ 4. _____

5. $\dfrac{x^2}{25} - \dfrac{y^2}{144} = 1$ 5. _____

Graph the hyperbola.

6. $\dfrac{y^2}{10} - \dfrac{x^2}{20} = 1$ 7. $\dfrac{y^2}{24} - \dfrac{x^2}{3} = 1$

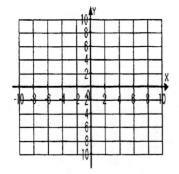   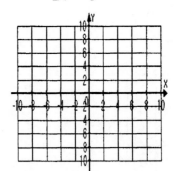

8. $\dfrac{y^2}{5} - \dfrac{x^2}{20} = 1$ 9. $\dfrac{x^2}{9} - \dfrac{y^2}{6} = 1$

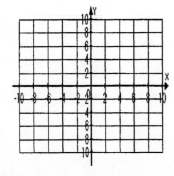   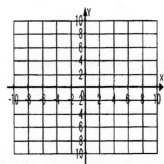

AE-470

10. $\dfrac{x^2}{5} - \dfrac{y^2}{16} = 1$

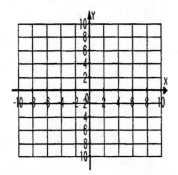

11. $121x^2 - 49y^2 = 5929$

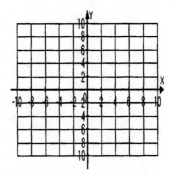

12. $144y^2 - 25x^2 = 3600$

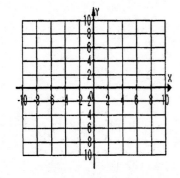

13. $81x^2 - 4y^2 = 324$

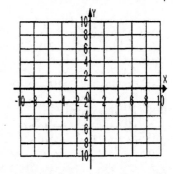

14. $9x^2 - 18y^2 = 18$

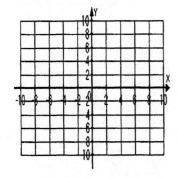

15. $64y^2 - 144x^2 = 9216$

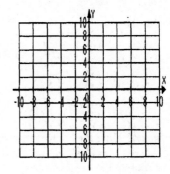

Name _____   Date _____

Determine (a) the direction the parabola opens and (b) if the parabola is horizontal or vertical.

1. $x = (y - 10)^2 - 5$ 1a. _____

                                                               b. _____

2. $y = -(x + 4)^2 + 3$ 2a. _____

                                                               b. _____

3. $x = -(y - 6)^2 - 6$ 3a. _____

                                                               b. _____

4. $y = (x - 2)^2 - 1$ 4a. _____

                                                               b. _____

Determine the vertex of each parabola.

5. $x = 3y^2$ 5. _____

6. $y = 3(x - 1)^2 + 4$ 6. _____

Graph the parabola.

7. $x = \dfrac{-1}{4} y^2$ 8. $y = -5x^2$

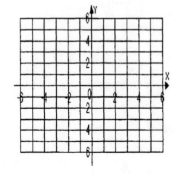   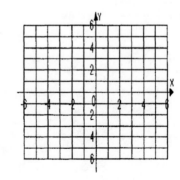

9. $x = (y+2)^2 + 3$

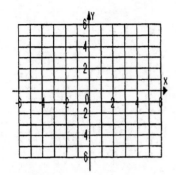

10. $y = (x-1)^2 - 1$

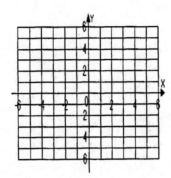

Give the equation for the parabola's axis of symmetry.

11. $x = (y-2)^2 - 2$ 11._____

12. $x = -(y-3)^2 - 2$ 12._____

Determine whether the graph of the equation is an ellipse, hyperbola, circle, or parabola.

13. $x^2 + y^2 + x + y = 0$ 13._____

14. $8x^2 - 4y^2 = 4$ 14._____

15. $5x^2 + 8y^2 = 36$ 15._____

Name _____   Date _____

Additional Exercises 13.4
Form II
The Parabola: Identifying Conic Sections

Determine (a) the direction the parabola opens and (b) if the parabola is horizontal or vertical.

1. $x = -(y+4)^2 - 1$ 1a. _____

                                          b. _____

2. $y = (x-2)^2 + 6$ 2a. _____

                                          b. _____

3. $x = (y-1)^2 + 3$ 3a. _____

                                          b. _____

4. $y = -(x+3)^2 - 5$ 4a. _____

                                          b. _____

Determine the vertex of each parabola.

5. $x = -2y^2$ 5. _____

6. $y = 4(x+3)^2 - 4$ 6. _____

Graph the parabola.

7. $y = 6x^2$ 8. $x - \dfrac{-1}{7} y^2$

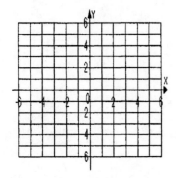

9. $y = -(x-2)^2 - 1$ 10. $x = (y-3)^2 - 1$

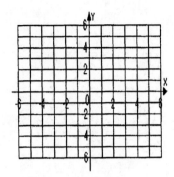   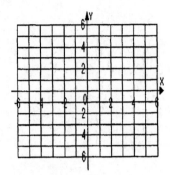

Give the equation for the parabola's axis of symmetry.

11. $x = (y+1)^2 - 4$ 11. _____

12. $x = -(y-2)^2 + 6$ 12. _____

Determine whether the graph of the equation is an ellipse, hyperbola, circle, or parabola.

13. $x^2 - 2y^2 = 6$ 13. _____

14. $2y^2 + 3x - 5y = 2$ 14. _____

15. $4x^2 = 36 - 4y^2$ 15. _____

Additional Exercises 13.4
Form III
The Parabola: Identifying Conic Sections

Determine (a) the direction the parabola opens and (b) if the parabola is horizontal or vertical.

1. $y = -(x+5)^2 - 3$ 1a. _____

                                                                              b. _____

2. $x = -(y+3)^2 - 5$ 2a. _____

                                                                              b. _____

3. $y = (x-1)^2 - 1$ 3a. _____

                                                                              b. _____

4. $x = -(y+3)^2 - 5$ 4a. _____

                                                                              b. _____

Determine the vertex of each parabola.

5. $y = x^2 - 4x + 7$ 5. _____

6. $x = y^2 + 10y + 21$ 6. _____

Graph the parabola.

7. $x = 4y^2$ 8. $y = -3(x-1)^2 + 5$

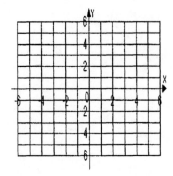   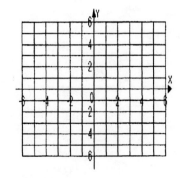

9. $y = \dfrac{1}{2}x^2$ 10. $x = -(y+1)^2 - 4$

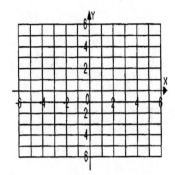   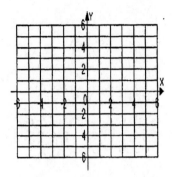

Give the equation for the parabola's axis of symmetry.

11. $x = 2(y-4)^2 + 2$ 11. _____

12. $x = 2(y+1)^2 - 2$ 12. _____

Determine whether the graph of the equation is an ellipse, hyperbola, circle, or parabola.

13. $7x^2 - y^2 = 32$ 13. _____

14. $3x^2 + 8x - y = 72$ 14. _____

15. $9x^2 = 36 - 4y^2$ 15. _____

Name _____   Date _____

Additional Exercises 13.5
Form I
Systems of Nonlinear Equations in Two Variables

Solve the system by the substitution method.

1. $x^2 + y^2 = 100$ 1. _____

       $x + y = 2$

2. $xy = 20$ 2. _____

       $x + y = 9$

3. $x^2 + y^2 = 34$ 3. _____

       $x - y = -2$

Solve the system by the addition method.

4. $2x^2 + y^2 = 17$ 4. _____

       $3x^2 - 2y^2 = -6$

5. $2x^2 + y^2 = 66$ 5. _____

       $x^2 + y^2 = 41$

Solve the system by the method of your choice.

6. $xy = -63$ 6. _____

       $x^2 + y^2 = 130$

7. $xy = -40$ 7. _____

       $x + y = 6$

8. $x^2 + y^2 = 25$ 8. _____

       $x - y = -1$

Let x represent one number and let y represent the other number. Use the given conditions to write a system of nonlinear equations. Solve the system and find the numbers.

9. The sum of the square of two numbers is 82. The sum of of the two numbers is 10. Find the two numbers.

9. _____

10. The sum of the squares of two numbers is 130. The difference of the two numbers is 16. Find the two numbers.

10. _____

11. The sum of two numbers is 13 and their product is 36. Find the numbers.

11. _____

12. The difference between the squares of two numbers 55. Twice the square of the second number subtracted from the square of the first number is 46. Find the numbers.

12. _____

13. The perimeter of a rectangle is 28 inches and its area is 45 square inches. What are the dimensions?

13. _____

14. A rectangular piece of tin has an area of 840 square inches. A square of 2 inches is cut from each corner, and an open box is made by turning up the ends and sides. If the volume of the box is 1216 cubic inches, what were the original dimensions of the piece of tin?

14. _____

15. The area of a garden is 4860 square feet and the length of its diagonal is 117 feet. Find the dimensions of the garden.

15. _____

Name _____   Date _____

Additional Exercises 13.5
Form II
Systems of Nonlinear Equations in Two Variables

Solve the system by the substitution method.

1. $y = x - 2$ 1. _____
    $y = -x^2 + 4$

2. $x^2 + y^2 = 1$ 2. _____
    $x - y = -1$

3. $x^2 + y^2 = 61$ 3. _____
    $x^2 = y^2 + 11$

Solve the system by the addition method.

4. $x^2 + y^2 = 10$ 4. _____
    $x^2 + 9y^2 = 18$

5. $x^2 - 2y^2 = 2$ 5. _____
    $3x^2 + 2y^2 = 14$

Solve the system by the method of your choice.

6. $x^2 + y^2 = 16$ 6. _____
    $x^2 + y = -4$

7. $25x^2 + 4y^2 = 100$ 7. _____
    $25x^2 - 4y^2 = 100$

8. $x^2 - y^2 = 25$ 8. _____
    $x^2 + 25y^2 = 100$

Name _____   Date _____

Let x represent one number and let y represent the other number. Use the given conditions to write a system of nonlinear equations. Solve the system and find the numbers.

9.   The sum of the square of two numbers is 58. The sum of of the two numbers is 10. Find the two numbers.

9. _____

10.   The sum of the squares of two numbers is 89. The difference of the two numbers is 3. Find the two numbers.

10. _____

11.   The sum of two numbers is 12 and their product is 32. Find the numbers.

11. _____

12.   The difference between the squares of two numbers 96. Twice the square of the second number subtracted from the square of the first number is 92. Find the numbers.

12. _____

13.   The perimeter of a rectangle is 22 inches and its area is 24 square inches. What are the dimensions?

13. _____

14.   A rectangular piece of tin has an area of 600 square inches. A square of 2 inches is cut from each corner, and an open box is made by turning up the ends and sides. If the volume of the box is 832 cubic inches, what were the original dimensions of the piece of tin?

14. _____

15.   The area of a garden is 4440 square feet and the length of its diagonal is 126 feet. Find the dimensions of the garden.

15. _____

Additional Exercises 13.5
Form III
Systems of Nonlinear Equations in Two Variables

Solve the system by the substitution method.

1. $x^2 + y^2 = 169$ 1. _____
     $x + y = 17$

2. $xy - x^2 = -20$ 2. _____
     $x - 2y = 3$

3. $x + y = -9$ 3. _____
     $(x - 2)^2 + (y + 5)^2 = 20$

Solve the system by the addition method.

4. $x^2 + y^2 = 4$ 4. _____
     $-x^2 + 3y = 0$

5. $x^2 + y^2 = 8$ 5. _____
     $x^2 - y^2 = 2$

Solve the system by the method of your choice.

6. $x^2 + xy + y^2 - 3 = 0$ 6. _____
     $2x - y = -5$

7. $2x + 2y = 3$ 7. _____
     $xy = -1$

8. $x^2 + y^2 - 2x + 8y + 13 = 0$ 8. _____
     $x^2 - y - 2 - 8y - 19 = 0$

Name _____   Date _____

Let x represent one number and let y represent the other number. Use the given conditions to write a system of nonlinear equations. Solve the system and find the numbers.

9.   The sum of the square of two numbers is 41. The sum of of the two numbers is 9. Find the two numbers.

9. _____

10.   The sum of the squares of two numbers is 49. The difference of the two numbers is 3. Find the two numbers.

10. _____

11.   The sum of two numbers is 14 and their product is 45. Find the numbers.

11. _____

12.   The difference between the squares of two numbers 65. Twice the square of the second number subtracted from the square of the first number is 49. Find the numbers.

12. _____

13.   The perimeter of a rectangle is 20 inches and its area is 24 square inches. What are the dimensions?

13. _____

14.   A rectangular piece of tin has an area of 396 square inches. A square of 2 inches is cut from each corner, and an open box is made by turning up the ends and sides. If the volume of the box is 504 cubic inches, what were the original dimensions of the piece of tin?

14. _____

15.   The area of a garden is 5980 square feet and the length of its diagonal is 126 feet. Find the dimensions of the garden.

15. _____

Name _____   Date _____

Additional Exercises 14.1
Form I
Sequences and Summation Notation

Write the first four terms of the sequence whose general term is given.

1. $a_n = n+1$ 1. _____

2. $a_n = 9n$ 2. _____

3. $a_n = 2^n$ 3. _____

4. $a_n = \dfrac{n+1}{zn}$ 4. _____

Find the indicated sum.

5. $\displaystyle\sum_{i=1}^{5}(2i+7)$ 5. _____

6. $\displaystyle\sum_{i=1}^{10} i$ 6. _____

7. $\displaystyle\sum_{i=1}^{7} 2^i$ 7. _____

8. $\displaystyle\sum_{i=1}^{5} 2\cdot 4^i$ 8. _____

9. $\displaystyle\sum_{i=1}^{3} 1.02i$ 9. _____

Name _____   Date _____

Express the sum using summation notation.

10. $2^4 + 3^4 + 4^4 + ... + 8^4$

    10. _____

11. $1 + 4 + 9 + ... + 36$

    11. _____

12. $2 + 4 + 6 + ... + 10$

    12. _____

13. $5 + 8 + 11 + ... + 20$

    13. _____

14. The finite sequence whose general term is
    $a_n = 0.18n^2 - 1.08n + 6.62$ where $n = 1, 2, 3, ..., 9$ models
    the total operating costs, in millions of dollars, for a
    company from 1999 through 2007. Find $\sum_{i=1}^{4} a_i$.

    14. _____

15. A deposit of $7000 is made in an account that earns 6%
    interest compounded quarterly. The balance in the account
    after n quarters is given by the sequence $a_n = 7000\left(1 + \dfrac{0.06}{4}\right)^n$,
    $n = 1, 2, 3, ...$ Find the balance in the account after one year
    by computing a_4.

    15. _____

Additional Exercises 14.1
Form II
Sequences and Summation Notation

Write the first four terms of the sequence whose general term is given.

1. $a_n = n - 4$ 1. _____

2. $a_n = n^2 - n$ 2. _____

3. $a_n = 3^n$ 3. _____

4. $a_n = \dfrac{n!}{n+1}$ 4. _____

Find the indicated sum.

5. $\displaystyle\sum_{i=1}^{6} i^2 + 1$ 5. _____

6. $\displaystyle\sum_{i=1}^{6} i^2 + 1$ 6. _____

7. $\displaystyle\sum_{i=4}^{8} 9$ 7. _____

8. $\displaystyle\sum_{i=1}^{5} \dfrac{(-1)i + 1}{(i-1)!}$ 8. _____

9. $\displaystyle\sum_{i=1}^{5} \dfrac{(i-1)!}{(i+1)!}$ 9. _____

Name _____   Date _____

Express the sum using summation notation.

10. $\dfrac{1}{3}+\dfrac{2}{4}+\dfrac{3}{5}+...+\dfrac{12}{14}$ 10. _____

11. $9+10+11+12+...+38$ 11. _____

12. $\dfrac{1}{2}+\dfrac{1}{4}+\dfrac{1}{8}+...+\dfrac{1}{64}$ 12. _____

13. $16+-64+256+...+4096$ 13. _____

14.   The finite sequence whose general term is   14. _____
        $a_n = 0.18n^2 - 1.08n + 6.62$ where $n = 1, 2, 3, ..., 9$ models
        the total operating costs, in millions of dollars, for a
        company from 1999 through 2007. Find $\displaystyle\sum_{i=1}^{5} a_i$.

15.   A deposit of $7000 is made in an account that earns 6%   15. _____
        interest compounded quarterly. The balance in the account
        after n quarters is given by the sequence $a_n = 7000\left(1+\dfrac{0.06}{4}\right)^n$,
        $n = 1, 2, 3, ...$ Find the balance in the account after one year
        and a half by computing a_6 .

Additional Exercises 14.1
Form III
Sequences and Summation Notation

Write the first four terms of the sequence whose general term is given.

1. $a_n = 2n + 1$ 1. _____

2. $a_n = (-4)^n$ 2. _____

3. $a_n = \left(-\dfrac{3}{4}\right)^n$ 3. _____

4. $a_n = 3(n + 2)!$ 4. _____

Find the indicated sum.

5. $\displaystyle\sum_{i=3}^{4} (3i - 2)$ 5. _____

6. $\displaystyle\sum_{i=1}^{4} 3i$ 6. _____

7. $\displaystyle\sum_{i=1}^{4} \dfrac{1}{i}$ 7. _____

8. $\displaystyle\sum_{i=1}^{5} (-1)^i (2i + 3)$ 8. _____

9. $\displaystyle\sum_{i=2}^{4} i(i + 5)$ 9. _____

Express the sum using summation notation.

10. $1 + 8 + 27 + \ldots + 512$ 10. _____

11. $\dfrac{1}{2} + \dfrac{1}{4} + \dfrac{1}{8} + \ldots + \dfrac{1}{64}$ 11. _____

12. $1 + 2 + 6 + \ldots + 5040$ 12. _____

13. $a + ar + ar^2 + \ldots + ar^{10}$ 13. _____

14. The finite sequence whose general term is   14. _____
$a_n = 0.18n^2 - 1.08n + 6.62$ where $n = 1, 2, 3, \ldots, 9$ models
the total operating costs, in millions of dollars, for a
company from 1999 through 2007. Find $\displaystyle\sum_{i=1}^{6} a_i$.

15. A deposit of $7000 is made in an account that earns 6%   15. _____
interest compounded quarterly. The balance in the account
after n quarters is given by the sequence $a_n = 7000\left(1 + \dfrac{0.06}{4}\right)^n$,
$n = 1, 2, 3, \ldots$ Find the balance in the account after two years
by computing a_8 .

Additional Exercises 14.2
Form I
Arithmetic Sequences

Find the common difference.

1. 8, 12, 16, 20, ...   1. _____

2. 2, −1, −4, −7, ...   2. _____

Write the first five terms of the arithmetic sequence whose first term, a_1, and common difference, d, are given.

3. $a_1 = 10; d = 4$ 3. _____

4. $a_1 = 6; d = -1$ 4. _____

5. $a_1 = 1; d = 5$ 5. _____

6. $a_1 = 2; d = 0.5$ 6. _____

Find the indicated term.

7. Find a_5 when $a_1 = -3, d = -3$ 7. _____

8. Find a_7 when $a_1 = -5, d = -\dfrac{1}{3}$ 8. _____

9. Find a_{10} when $a_1 = 1, d = 6$ 9. _____

Write a formula for the general term (the nth term) of the arithmetic sequence.

10. 4, 20, 36, 52, 68, ...   10. _____

11.   −13, −22, −31, −40, …   11. _____

12. $a_1 = 6, d = -3$ 12. _____

13. $a_1 = -5, d = -7$ 13. _____

Use the partial sum formula to find the partial sum of the given arithmetic sequence.

14.   Find the sum of the first eight terms of the arithmetic sequence   14. _____
       3, 8, 13, …

15.   Find the sum of the first 10 terms of the arithmetic sequence   15. _____
       −7, −3. 1. 5. …

16.   Find the sum of the even integers between 17 and 45.   16. _____

Solve.

17. $\sum_{i=1}^{10} (2i - 1)$ 17. _____

       Find the indicated sum.

18. $\sum_{i=1}^{40} -2i$ 18. _____

       Write out the first three terms and the last term.

Solve the problem.

19.   Jacie is considering a job that offers a monthly starting salary   19. _____
       of $4000 and guarantees her a monthly raise of $110 during
       her first year on the job. Find the general term of the
       arithmetic sequence and her monthly salary at the end of her
       first year.

20.   A theater has 12 rows with 25 seats in the first row, 29 in the   20. _____
       second row, 33 in the third row, and so forth. How many
       seats are in the theater?

Additional Exercises 14.2
Form II
Arithmetic Sequences

Find the common difference.

1.   6, 8, 10, 12, …   1. _____

2.   5, 3, 1, –1, …   2. _____

Write the first five terms of the arithmetic sequence whose first term, a_1, and common difference, d, are given.

3. $a_1 = 15; d = 3$ 3. _____

4. $a_1 = 100; d = 25$ 4. _____

5. $a_1 = 2.2; d = 0.4$ 5. _____

6. $a_1 = \dfrac{1}{2}; d = \dfrac{1}{2}$ 6. _____

Find the indicated term.

7.   Find a_8 when $a_1 = -3, d = -3$ 7. _____

8.   Find a_{12} when $a_1 = -5, d = -\dfrac{1}{3}$ 8. _____

9.   Find a_{13} when $a_1 = 1, d = 6$ 9. _____

Write a formula for the general term (the nth term) of the arithmetic sequence.

10.   1, –7, –15, –23, –31, …   10. _____

11. $100, 99\frac{1}{2}, 99, 98\frac{1}{2}, 98, \ldots$ 11. _____

12. $a_1 = \frac{1}{2}, d = \frac{1}{2}$ 12. _____

13. $a_1 = .5, d = .2$ 13. _____

Use the partial sum formula to find the partial sum of the given arithmetic sequence.

14.   Find the sum of the first twelve terms of the arithmetic sequence   14. _____
       $3, 8, 13, \ldots$

15.   Find the sum of the first 17 terms of the arithmetic sequence   15. _____
       $-7, -3. 1. 5. \ldots$

16.   Find the sum of the even integers between 21 and 53.   16. _____

Solve.

17. $\displaystyle\sum_{i=1}^{15}(2i-1)$ 17. _____
       Find the indicated sum.

18. $\displaystyle\sum_{i=1}^{40}-2i+5$ 18. _____
       Write out the first three terms and the last term.

Solve the problem.

19.   Jacie is considering a job that offers a monthly starting salary   19. _____
       of $3500 and guarantees her a monthly raise of $90 during
       her first year on the job. Find the general term of the
       arithmetic sequence and her monthly salary at the end of her
       first year.

20.   A theater has 15 rows with 25 seats in the first row, 29 in the   20. _____
       second row, 33 in the third row, and so forth. How many
       seats are in the theater?

Additional Exercises 14.2
Form III
Arithmetic Sequences

Find the common difference.

1.   24, 30, 36, 42, ...   1. _____

2.   8, 4, 0, –4, ...   2. _____

Write the first five terms of the arithmetic sequence whose first term, a_1, and common difference, d, are given.

3. $a_1 = \dfrac{-3}{4}; d = \dfrac{1}{4}$ 3. _____

4. $a_1 =$ 4. _____

5. $a_1 = \dfrac{7}{5}; d = 1$ 5. _____

6. $a_1 = 1.5; d = 1.6$ 6. _____

Find the indicated term.

7.   Find a_{14} when $a_1 = -3, d = -3$ 7. _____

8.   Find a_{16} when $a_1 = -5, d = -\dfrac{1}{3}$ 8. _____

9.   Find a_{17} when $a_1 = 1, d = 6$ 9. _____

Write a formula for the general term (the nth term) of the arithmetic sequence.

10.   2, 7, 12, 17, 22, ...   10. _____

Name _____   Date _____

11.   −8, −1, 6, 13, 20, …   11. _____

12. $a_1 = \dfrac{3}{4}, d = \dfrac{1}{2}$ 12. _____

13. $a_1 = 8, d = -0.3$ 13. _____

Use the partial sum formula to find the partial sum of the given arithmetic sequence.

14.   Find the sum of the first sixteen terms of the arithmetic sequence   14. _____
        3, 8, 13, …

15.   Find the sum of the first 30 terms of the arithmetic sequence   15. _____
        −7, −3. 1. 5. …

16.   Find the sum of the even integers between 15 and 59.   16. _____

Solve.

17. $\displaystyle\sum_{i=1}^{24}(2i-1)$ 17. _____

        Find the indicated sum.

18. $\displaystyle\sum_{i=1}^{40} -2i^2$ 18. _____

        Write out the first three terms and the last term.

Solve the problem.

19.   Jacie is considering a job that offers a monthly starting salary   19. _____
        of $3250 and guarantees her a monthly raise of $95 during
        her first year on the job. Find the general term of the
        arithmetic sequence and her monthly salary at the end of her
        first year.

20.   A theater has 20 rows with 25 seats in the first row, 29 in the   20. _____
        second row, 33 in the third row, and so forth. How many
        seats are in the theater?

AE-495

Name _____   Date _____

Additional Exercises 14.3
Form I
Geometric Sequences and Series

Find the common ratio for the geometric sequence.

1.   4, –12, 36, –108, 324, ...   1. _____

2. $10, 5, \dfrac{5}{2}, \dfrac{5}{4}, \dfrac{5}{8}, \ldots$ 2. _____

3.   2. 0.2, 0.02, 0.002, 0.0002, ...   3. _____

Write the first four terms of the geometric sequence whose first term, a_1, and common ratio, r, are given.

4. $a_1 = -2;\ r = 3$ 4. _____

5. $a_1 = -4;\ r = -3$ 5. _____

Find the indicated term of the sequence.

6.   Find a_4 when $a_1 = 6$, $r = 4$ 6. _____

7.   Find a_5 when $a_1 = 4$, $r = 3$ 7. _____

Find a formula for the general term, a_n, of the given sequence.

8.   5, 10, 20, 40, 80, ...   8. _____

9. $3, \dfrac{3}{2}, \dfrac{3}{4}, \dfrac{3}{8}, \dfrac{3}{16}, \ldots$ 9. _____

10.   2, 4, 8, 16, 32, ...   10. _____

11.   0.1, 0.5, 2.5, 12.5, 62.5, ...   11. _____

Name _____ Date _____

Use the formula for the sum of the first n terms of a geometric sequence to solve.

12.   Find the sum of the first five terms of the geometric   12. _____

sequence $\dfrac{1}{3}, \dfrac{2}{3}, \dfrac{4}{3}, \ldots$

13.   Find the sum of the first six terms of the geometric   13. _____
        sequence, $-5, -10, -20, \ldots$

14. $\displaystyle\sum_{i=1}^{6} (2)^i$ 14. _____

Find the sum, if it exists.

15. $4, 2, 1, \dfrac{1}{2}, \ldots$ 15. _____

16. $\dfrac{3}{4}, \dfrac{9}{16}, \dfrac{27}{64}, \dfrac{81}{256}, \ldots$ 16. _____

Express the repeating decimal as a fraction in lowest terms.

17.   Write 0.444 … as an infinite geometric series and use the   17. _____
        formula for S_∞ to write it as a rational number.

18.   Write 0.5757 … as an infinite geometric series and use the   18. _____
        formula for S_∞ to write it as a rational number.

Determine whether the given sequence is arithmetic, geometric, or neither. If arithmetic, find the common difference. If geometric, find the common ratio.

19. $a_n = \left(\dfrac{3}{5}\right)^n$ 19. _____

20. $a_n = n + 4$ 20. _____

AE-497

Name _____   Date _____

Additional Exercises 14.3
Form II
Geometric Sequences and Series

Find the common ratio for the geometric sequence.

1.   8, 16, 32, 64, 128, ...   1. _____

2.   40, 20, 10, 5, 2.5, ...   2. _____

3.   −.6, −6, 60, −600, −6000, ...   3. _____

Write the first four terms of the geometric sequence whose first term, a_1, and common ratio, r, are given.

4. $a_1 = 36$; $r = \dfrac{1}{3}$ 4. _____

5. $a_1 = -8$; $r = 4$ 5. _____

Find the indicated term of the sequence.

6.   Find a_7 when $a_1 = 6$, $r = 4$ 6. _____

7.   Find a_8 when $a_1 = 4$, $r = 3$ 7. _____

Find a formula for the general term, a_n, of the given sequence.

8.   4, 16, 64, 256, 1024, ...   8. _____

9. $\dfrac{1}{5}, \dfrac{1}{35}, \dfrac{1}{245}, \dfrac{1}{1715}, \ldots$ 9. _____

10. $-\dfrac{1}{6}, \dfrac{1}{30}, -\dfrac{1}{150}, \dfrac{1}{750}, \ldots$ 10. _____

11.   0.0009, 0.18, 3.6, 72, ...   11. _____

Name _____   Date _____

Use the formula for the sum of the first n terms of a geometric sequence to solve.

12.   Find the sum of the first five terms of the geometric   12. _____
      sequence $\frac{1}{2}$, 1, 2, ...

13.   Find the sum of the first six terms of the geometric   13. _____
      sequence, 3, –12, 48, ...

14. $\sum_{i=1}^{6} (-3)^i$ 14. _____

Find the sum, if it exists.

15. $\frac{1}{2}, \frac{1}{4}, \frac{1}{8}, \frac{1}{16}, \dots$ 15. _____

16. $\frac{2}{5}, \frac{4}{25}, \frac{8}{125}, \frac{16}{625}, \dots$ 16. _____

Express the repeating decimal as a fraction in lowest terms.

17.   Write 0.333 ... as an infinite geometric series and use the   17. _____
      formula for S_∞ to write it as a rational number.

18.   Write 0.4545 ... as an infinite geometric series and use the   18. _____
      formula for S_∞ to write it as a rational number.

Determine whether the given sequence is arithmetic, geometric, or neither. If arithmetic, find the common difference. If geometric, find the common ratio.

19. $a_n = n + 7$ 19. _____

20. $a_n = n^2 + 1$ 20. _____

Name _____   Date _____

Find the common ratio for the geometric sequence.

1.   20, 40, 80, 160, 320, ...   1. _____

2. $-5, \dfrac{5}{3}, \dfrac{-5}{9}, \dfrac{5}{27}, \dfrac{-5}{81}, \ldots$ 2. _____

3.   3, −1.2, 0.48, −0.192, ...   3. _____

Write the first four terms of the geometric sequence whose first term, a_1, and common ratio, r, are given.

4. $a_1 = \dfrac{1}{3}; r = 2$ 4. _____

5. $a_1 = \dfrac{-1}{7}; r = -3$ 5. _____

Find the indicated term of the sequence.

6.   Find a_9 when $a_1 = 6, r = 4$ 6. _____

7.   Find a_{10} when $a_1 = 4, r = 3$ 7. _____

Find a formula for the general term, a_n, of the given sequence.

8.   −5, 25, −125, 625, −3125, ...   8. _____

9. $2, \dfrac{2}{3}, \dfrac{2}{9}, \dfrac{2}{27}, \dfrac{2}{81}, \ldots$ 9. _____

10. $\dfrac{1}{4}, \dfrac{1}{8}, -\dfrac{1}{16}, \dfrac{1}{32}, \dfrac{1}{64}, \ldots$ 10. _____

11.   0.032, 0.48, 7.2, 108, 1620, ...   11. _____

Use the formula for the sum of the first n terms of a geometric sequence to solve.

12.   Find the sum of the first five terms of the geometric   12. _____
       sequence $\frac{1}{8}, \frac{1}{4}, \frac{1}{2}, \ldots$

13.   Find the sum of the first six terms of the geometric   13. _____
       sequence, $\frac{2}{5}, \frac{6}{5}, \frac{18}{5}, \ldots$

14. $\displaystyle\sum_{i=1}^{6} \left(\frac{2}{3}\right)^{i}$ 14. _____

Find the sum, if it exists.

15. $2, -\frac{2}{3}, \frac{2}{9}, -\frac{2}{27}, \ldots$ 15. _____

16. $108, 18, 3, \frac{1}{2}, \ldots$ 16. _____

Express the repeating decimal as a fraction in lowest terms.

17.   Write 0.666 ... as an infinite geometric series and use the   17. _____
       formula for S_{∞} to write it as a rational number.

18.   Write 0.6969 ... as an infinite geometric series and use the 18. _____
       formula for S_{∞} to write it as a rational number.

Determine whether the given sequence is arithmetic, geometric, or neither. If arithmetic, find the
common difference. If geometric, find the common ratio.

19. $a_{n} = 4n^2 - 5$ 19. _____

20. $a_{n} = \left(\frac{5}{4}\right)^{n}$ 20. _____

Additional Exercises 14.4
Form I
The Binomial Theorem

Evaluate.

1. $\dbinom{10}{4}$

1. _____

2. $\dbinom{7}{7}$

2. _____

3. $\dbinom{7}{1}$

3. _____

4. $\dbinom{12}{4}$

4. _____

Use the binomial formula to expand the binomial.

5. $(x + y)^5$

5. _____

6. $(x + 2)^4$

6. _____

7. $(2x - 3)^5$

7. _____

8. $(x + 3y)^3$

8. _____

Write the first three terms of the expansion.

9. $(x + 2)^9$

9. _____

10. $(x - y)^{10}$

10. _____

11. $(x+1)^{15}$ 11. _____

12. $(x+2y)^{10}$ 12. _____

Write the indicated term of the binomial expansion.

13. $(x-3y)^{11}$; 4th term   13. _____

14. $(x-y)^{15}$; 12th term   14. _____

15. $(x+3y)^{12}$; 4th term   15. _____

Additional Exercises 14.4
Form II
The Binomial Theorem

Evaluate.

1. $\binom{8}{5}$

1. _____

2. $\binom{9}{7}$

2. _____

3. $\binom{12}{6}$

3. _____

4. $\binom{15}{11}$

4. _____

Use the binomial formula to expand the binomial.

5. $(2x+1)^5$

5. _____

6. $(x-2y)^5$

6. _____

7. $(3x-2)^4$

7. _____

8. $(x^2+2)^4$

8. _____

Write the first three terms of the expansion.

9. $(x+2)^{20}$

9. _____

10. $(x-4)^{17}$

10. _____

11. $(x^2 + 6)^9$ 11. _____

12. $(x + 2)^{14}$ 12. _____

Write the indicated term of the binomial expansion.

13. $(x^3 - 5)^6$; 3rd term   13. _____

14. $(4x + 5)^5$; 5th term   14. _____

15. $(x^2 + y^3)^6$; 3rd term   15. _____

Name _____   Date _____

Evaluate.

1. $\begin{pmatrix} 20 \\ 12 \end{pmatrix}$ 1. _____

2. $\begin{pmatrix} 24 \\ 18 \end{pmatrix}$ 2. _____

3. $\begin{pmatrix} 103 \\ 2 \end{pmatrix}$ 3. _____

4. $\begin{pmatrix} 145 \\ 143 \end{pmatrix}$ 4. _____

Use the binomial formula to expand the binomial.

5. $(3x - 4y)^3$ 5. _____

6. $(2x - 2)^4$ 6. _____

7. $(2x + 3)^5$ 7. _____

8. $(x^5 + 2y)^4$ 8. _____

Write the first three terms of the expansion.

9. $(x^2 + y^2)^3$ 9. _____

10. $\left(\dfrac{1}{2}x - 4 \right)^3$ 10. _____

11. $(2x+3y)^8$ 11. _____

12. $\left(\dfrac{1}{3}x+\dfrac{1}{2}y\right)^4$ 12. _____

Write the indicated term of the binomial expansion.

13. $(x+y)^{34}$; 17th term   13. _____

14. $(x-y)^{12}$; 13th term   14. _____

15. $(3x^2-2y^3)^7$; 4th term   15. _____

Additional Exercises Answers

1.1 Form I

1. 13   2. –5   3. 14   4. 32   5. 12   6. $x+12$ 7. $x-9$ 8. $6x+15$ 9. $\dfrac{2x}{7}$ 10. $3x+5$
11. No   12. Yes   13. No   14. Yes   15. Yes   16. $6x=42$ 17. $3x=24$ 18. $x-8=3x$
19. $x-14=15$ 20. $\dfrac{x}{10}=4$

1.1 Form II

1. 11   2. 9   3. 5   4. 115   5. 6   6. $x-10$ 7. $\dfrac{x}{16}$ 8. $5x+4$ 9. $7x+8$ 10. $2(x+17)$
11. Yes   12. Yes   13. No   14. No   15. Yes   16. $x+17=40$ 17. $2x+13=59$ 18. $\dfrac{x}{16}=48$
19. $x-8=12$ 20. $4(x+9)=54$

1.1 Form III

1. 48   2. 4   3. 4   4. 36   5. 3   6. $3x-9$ 7. $2(x+32)$ 8. $\dfrac{x}{8}+2x$ 9. $2x-63$ 10. $x-14$
11. Yes   12. No   13. Yes   14. $2(x-18)=4$ 15. $\dfrac{3x}{15}=2x-7$ 16. $x-21=12$
17. $3(10+x)=45$ 18. $x+25=2x-19$ 19. 85   20. 7

1.2 Form I

1. $\dfrac{10}{3}$ 2. $\dfrac{47}{8}$ 3. $\dfrac{43}{4}$ 4. $2\dfrac{2}{3}$ 5. $4\dfrac{2}{5}$ 6. $21\dfrac{1}{2}$ 7. $\dfrac{5}{9}$ 8. $\dfrac{2}{3}$ 9. $\dfrac{3}{7}$ 10. $\dfrac{2}{35}$ 11. $\dfrac{2}{7}$
12. 8   13. $\dfrac{15}{16}$ 14. $\dfrac{3}{4}$ 15. $7\dfrac{7}{8}$ 16. $3\dfrac{69}{85}$ 17. $\dfrac{6}{7}$ 18. $\dfrac{11}{12}$ 19. $\dfrac{23}{30}$ 20. $\dfrac{2}{11}$ 21. $\dfrac{2}{15}$
22. $\dfrac{11}{15}$ 23. $5\dfrac{1}{2}$ 24. $4\dfrac{9}{16}$ 25. Yes

1.2 Form II

1. $\dfrac{53}{12}$ 2. $\dfrac{123}{10}$ 3. $\dfrac{250}{16}$ 4. $14\dfrac{1}{3}$ 5. $13\dfrac{5}{7}$ 6. $11\dfrac{2}{3}$ 7. $\dfrac{5}{8}$ 8. $\dfrac{4}{15}$ 9. $\dfrac{23}{24}$ 10. $\dfrac{3}{10}$ 11. $\dfrac{2}{9}$
12. 160   13. $\dfrac{9}{4}$ 14. 32   15. $2\dfrac{33}{34}$ 16. $23\dfrac{3}{5}$ 17. $\dfrac{4}{5}$ 18. $\dfrac{2}{3}$ 19. $1\dfrac{7}{8}\,or\,\dfrac{25}{18}$ 20. $\dfrac{1}{7}$
21. $\dfrac{13}{72}$ 22. $\dfrac{13}{28}$ 23. $5\dfrac{4}{5}$ 24. $6\dfrac{13}{24}$ 25. Yes

1.2 Form III

1. $\dfrac{83}{8}$ 2. $\dfrac{284}{17}$ 3. $\dfrac{5089}{108}$ 4. $9\dfrac{5}{9}$ 5. $8\dfrac{4}{7}$ 6. $4\dfrac{10}{13}$ 7. $\dfrac{40}{71}$ 8. $\dfrac{3}{4}$ 9. $\dfrac{19}{75}$ 10. $\dfrac{25}{64}$ 11. 280

12. $25\dfrac{4}{5}$ 13. $\dfrac{33}{8}\,or\,4\dfrac{1}{8}$ 14. $\dfrac{72}{95}$ 15. $1\dfrac{34}{35}$ 16. $\dfrac{19}{24}$ 17. $\dfrac{7}{20}$ 18. $10\dfrac{1}{2}$ 19. $\dfrac{2}{3}$ 20. $\dfrac{25}{36}$

21. $\dfrac{7}{36}$ 22. $8\dfrac{1}{2}$ 23. $29\dfrac{2}{15}$ 24. Yes 25. Yes

1.3 Form I

1. –371 feet 2. –$420 3. 4.

5. 0.2 6. 0.8 7. 7.25 8. 10.125 9a. 0, 2 b. $-16, -7, 0, 2, 14\dfrac{1}{2}$ c. $\sqrt{10}$ 10a. $-14, 0, 10$

b. $3\pi, \sqrt{5}$ c. 10 11. < 12. > 13. < 14. < 15. 11 16. 11 17. False 18. False
19. False 20. True

1.3 Form II

1. 7042 feet 2. –$62.53 3. 4. 0.6 5. $0.8\overline{3}$ 6. 1.375

7. 19.45 8a. 3 b. $-11, 0, 3$ c. $-11, -\dfrac{5}{9}, 0, 3, 12.6$ 9a. 1, 9 b. $4\pi, \sqrt{6}$

c. $-6.8, -4, -\dfrac{1}{2}, 1, 4\pi, \sqrt{6}, 9$ 10. 4.5 11. 4.5 12. < 13. > 14. < 15. > 16. False
17. False 18. True 19. False 20. False

1.3 Form III

1. –$12.82 2. 3050 feet 3. –6° 4. 0.375 5. $0.4\overline{5}$ 6. 16.75 7. $25.8\overline{3}$ 8a. 0, 15
b. $-9, -3.7, 0, 2\dfrac{7}{9}, \sqrt{16}, 15$ c. $-9, 0, \sqrt{16}, 15$ 9a. $\dfrac{\pi}{2}, -\sqrt{15}$ b. $-8.1, -\dfrac{3}{11}, -2, 6, 7\dfrac{5}{9}$

c. $-8.1, -\sqrt{15}, -\dfrac{3}{11}, -2, 6, \dfrac{\pi}{2}, 7\dfrac{5}{9}$ 10. $8\dfrac{3}{5}$ 11. 6.47 12. < 13. < 14. > 15. <
16. False 17. True 18. True 19. True 20. False

1.4 Form I

1a. 2 terms b. 4, 5 c. 5 d. None 2a. 3 terms b. 6, 3 c. 10 d. None 3a. 4 terms
b. 3, 1, 5, 7 c. Not one d. $3x$ and $5x$ 4. $8 + 6x$ 5. $7y$ 6. $x + (12 + 18)$ 7. $(6 \cdot 3)a$
8. $5x + 35$ 9. $18x - 27$ 10. $4x + 8y + 12$ 11. $2a + 5$ 12. $17x$ 13. $16y + 5x$ 14. $16a + 6$
15. $6x + 2y$ 16. $17y + 18$ 17. $10m + 2$ 18. $8x + 10$ 19. $8x + 16$ 20. $3x + x$; $4x$
21. $4x - x$; $3x$ 22. $5(x \cdot 8)$; $40x$ 23. $6(x + 12)$; $6x + 72$ 24. $9(7 - x)$; $63 - 9x$

1.4 Form II

1a. 3 terms b. 12, 3 c. 8 d. $12x$ and $3x$ 2a. 4 terms b. 7, $\frac{1}{4}$, 2 c. 5 d. $7x$ and $2y$

3a. 4 terms b. $\frac{1}{5}$, $\frac{1}{3}$, $\frac{3}{5}$, $\frac{1}{6}$ c. Not one d. $\frac{1}{5}x$ and $\frac{3}{5}y$ 4. $4x+9$ 5. $12a$

6. $y+(25+15)$ 7. $(7\cdot15)a$ 8. $12x+9$ 9. $36x-42$ 10. $9x+9y+45$ 11. $x-2y-3$
12. $17x$ 13. $18y+9$ 14. $6a+1$ 15. $3.4x+4.7y+13$ 16. $15x+53$
17. $2(x+10)$; $2x+20$ 18. $8(6x)$; $48x$ 19. $14+2x(10)$; $14+20x$
20. $5(x+8)+3(x-3)$; $8x+31$

1.4 Form III

1a. 3 terms b. 8, 3 c. -15 d. None 2a. 4 terms b. 12, 10, -3 c. 12 d. $10y$ and $-3y$

3a. 5 terms b. $\frac{1}{4}$, $\frac{3}{4}$, $\frac{1}{8}$, $\frac{1}{2}$ c. 8 d. $\frac{1}{4}a$ and $\frac{1}{8}a$; $\frac{3}{4}b$ and $\frac{1}{2}b$ 4. $5x+12y$ 5. $21a$

6. $(3x+4x)+19$ 7. $(32\cdot5)y$ 8. $35+42y$ 9. $36-24x$ 10. $15a-15b-15c$
11. $9x+12y+3$ 12. $9x+2$ 13. $0.2a+0.3b$ 14. $7x+17$ 15. $2x+6$ 16. $15x+12$

17. $7(x+3)+4(x-1)$; $11x+17$ 18. $5x+\frac{1}{2}(8x)$; $9x$ 19. $0.9x+36{,}000$ 20. $\$90{,}000$

1.5 Form I

1. 6 2. 5 3. -4 4. 20 5. 13 6. -30 7. -59 8. -41 9. $-\frac{1}{11}$ 10. -17.9 11. $-\frac{1}{2}$

12. $-\frac{3}{5}$ 13. -37 14. 7 15. -17 16. $-7x$ 17. $-13a$ 18. $16y$ 19. $-5x$ 20. $4m+11$

1.5 Form II

1. -3 2. 64 3. 39 4. -14 5. -62 6. -213 7. $\frac{4}{13}$ 8. $-\frac{1}{2}$ 9. -2.797 10. -20 11. 21

12. -3.1 13. $-25\frac{2}{3}$ 14. -62 15. $-8x$ 16. $10b+5$ 17. $-4y+40$ 18. $10y+6$ 19. $13°$
20. -52 feet

1.5 Form III

1. 32 2. 28 3. -43 4. 28 5. -88 6. -494 7. $-\frac{13}{15}$ 8. 26.4 9. $\frac{1}{8}$ 10. $-\frac{3}{4}$ 11. 1.52
12. -13 13. 10 14. $4a$ 15. $-12y+15$ 16. $4x+(-6)$ 17. $-12m+(-30)$ 18. $-\$2$ billion
19. 8 under par 20. He took home $\$54$.

1.6 Form I

1. -3 2. -29 3. 29 4. -50 5. 5 6. $-\frac{1}{2}$ 7. -10.1 8. 74 9. 1 10. -0.65 11. 7.321

12. -113 13. -5 14. -6 15. 4 16. $-6x$ 17. $16-7x$ 18. $-3a-30$ 19. 5 inches 20. $38°$

1.6 Form II

1. 77 2. 8 3. 26 4. –36 5. –89 6. 73 7. –1 8. $-\dfrac{5}{7}$ 9. 6.494 10. –10.5 11. –24.4
12. –21.3 13. –5 14. –22 15. –19 16. $-15y-15x$ 17. $-2a-20$ 18. $-6y-2$
19. 1966 feet 20. 5° F.

1.6 Form III

1. –84 2. –48 3. –16 4. 0 5. $-\dfrac{11}{12}$ 6. 11.6 7. –10.537 8. –2 9. –4.09 10. –77
11. -13π 12. $\dfrac{1}{6}$ 13. 6 14. 19 15. $\dfrac{7}{8}$ 16. –22.23 17. $-17a+9$ 18. $-2x+38$
19. $3x-5y+5$ 20. 30,466 feet

1.7 Form I

1. –24 2. –42 3. 20 4. $-\dfrac{1}{20}$ 5. 3 6. –0.052 7. 24 8. –720 9. –5 10. Undefined
11. 9 12. 0 13. $\dfrac{1}{6}$ 14. –126 15. 8.2 16. –64 17. $-18x$ 18. y 19. $-15x+10$ 20. No

1.7 Form II

1. 35 2. –72 3. –63 4. 3.45 5. $-\dfrac{15}{44}$ 6. 288 7. –200 8. –4 9. 12 10. Undefined
11. 36 12. –80 13. –1 14. 7.3 15. x 16. $-18x+24$ 17. $-7x+7$ 18. $2x-12$
19. Yes 20. No

1.7 Form III

1. 72 2. –200 3. 21 4. –14 5. 21.142 6. $-\dfrac{9}{20}$ 7. –25 8. 45 9. Undefined 10. –320
11. $\dfrac{15}{2}$ or $7\dfrac{1}{2}$ 12. 0 13. $\dfrac{27}{16}$ 14. x 15. $32x-56$ 16. $2x+18$ 17. $x+1$ 18. $4x-4$
19. Yes 20. No

1.8 Form I

1. 64 2. 64 3. –64 4. $16x^2$ 5. $10x^4$ 6. $13x^3$ 7. 6 8. –1 9. –38 10. 8 11. 16
12. 27 13. –144 14. –12 15. 0 16. 62 17. –6 18. 2 19. 5 20. $21x-91$

1.8 Form II

1. –81 2. 81 3. –343 4. $12x^3$ 5. $16x^2$ 6. can't be simplified 7. –16 8. –44 9. 1
10. 198 11. 64 12. –81 13. 77 14. 24 15. 192 16. –300 17. –3 18. –5
19. $-10x+36$ 20. $16x+84$

1.8 Form III

1. 121 2. –196 3. –512 4. can't be simplified 5. $5x^3$ 6. $5x^2$ 7. 6 8. –18 9. 3
10. –3 11. –228 12. –4 13. –4 14. –46 15. –2 16. –2 17. $-45x+60$
18. $35x-80$ 19. 68° 20. 39.23 seconds

Additional Exercises Answers

2.1 Form I

1. linear 2. not linear 3. not linear 4. not linear 5. {12} 6. {11} 7. {13} 8. {23}
9. {0} 10. {0.8} 11. {22} 12. {−17} 13. {−26.7} 14. {13} 15. {−8.8} 16. $74
17. $53,865 18. $11.95 19. 80 ounces 20. 4982 feet

2.1 Form II

1. linear 2. not linear 3. not linear 4. linear 5. {−14} 6. {19} 7. $\left\{\dfrac{1}{3}\right\}$ 8. $\left\{\dfrac{14}{5}\right\}$

9. {1.2} 10. $\left\{-\dfrac{3}{20}\right\}$ 11. {17.9} 12. $\left\{-\dfrac{15}{4}\right\}$ 13. {310} 14. {14.2} 15. {0} 16. $101
17. $67,290 18. $13.35 19. 45 ounces 20. 6382 feet

2.1 Form III

1. linear 2. not linear 3. not linear 4. not linear 5. $\left\{\dfrac{7}{5}\right\}$ 6. $\left\{-\dfrac{7}{12}\right\}$ 7. {−1315}

8. {5.7} 9. {−13.5} 10. {−20} 11. {6} 12. {−61} 13. {−2} 14. {−3} 15. {0}
16. $221 17. $112,935 18. $18.95 19. 31 ounces 20. 9882 feet

2.2 Form I

1. {20} 2. {−21} 3. {3} 4. {8} 5. $\left\{-\dfrac{1}{4}\right\}$ 6. {−11} 7. {10} 8. {6} 9. {4}

10. {−6} 11. {7} 12. {−7} 13. {0} 14. {1} 15. {−1} 16. 150 miles 17. 14 miles
18. 7.0 meters 19. 6000 joules 20. 288 ft/sec

2.2 Form II

1. {−24} 2. {−44} 3. {22} 4. $\left\{-\dfrac{1}{3}\right\}$ 5. {5} 6. $\left\{\dfrac{2}{5}\right\}$ 7. {36} 8. $\left\{-\dfrac{16}{5}\right\}$ 9. {15}

10. $\left\{\dfrac{8}{5}\right\}$ 11. {10} 12. $\left\{-\dfrac{4}{5}\right\}$ 13. $\left\{-\dfrac{11}{2}\right\}$ 14. $\left\{-\dfrac{9}{7}\right\}$ 15. $\left\{\dfrac{1}{2}\right\}$ 16. 247.5 miles
17. 15.0 meters 18. 7.9 meters 19. 6600 joules 20. 256 ft/sec

2.2 Form III

1. {91} 2. {0} 3. {−32} 4. {−9} 5. $\left\{\dfrac{25}{4}\right\}$ 6. $\left\{\dfrac{3}{5}\right\}$ 7. {−35} 8. {3} 9. {12}

10. {5} 11. $\left\{\dfrac{33}{4}\right\}$ 12. {−3} 13. {−4} 14. {−1} 15. $\left\{\dfrac{16}{5}\right\}$ 16. 437.5 miles 17. 22.4
meters 18. 8.2 meters 19. 8250 joules 20. 384 ft/sec

2.3 Form I

1. $\left\{\dfrac{1}{4}\right\}$ 2. $\left\{\dfrac{5}{4}\right\}$ 3. $\left\{-\dfrac{5}{2}\right\}$ 4. {1} 5. {6} 6. $\left\{\dfrac{3}{2}\right\}$ 7. {5} 8. {4} 9. {25} 10. {45}

11. {21} 12. $\left\{\dfrac{6}{5}\right\}$ 13. {5} 14. {10} 15. {1} 16. 201.25 cm 17. 4 18. 89 mph
19. 5.5% 20. 30°

2.3 Form II

1. $\{-4\}$ 2. $\{-8\}$ 3. $\{9\}$ 4. $\left\{\dfrac{89}{70}\right\}$ 5. $\{47\}$ 6. $\{22\}$ 7. $\{x \mid x \text{ is a real number}\}$ 8. $\varnothing$

9. $\{3\}$ 10. $\left\{\dfrac{1}{2}\right\}$ 11. $\{-14\}$ 12. $\{28\}$ 13. $\{75\}$ 14. $\left\{\dfrac{1}{2}\right\}$ 15. $\{12\}$ 16. 196.77 cm

17. 3 18. 85 mph 19. 6.5% 20. 35°

2.3 Form III

1. $\varnothing$ 2. $\{2\}$ 3. $\{-5\}$ 4. $\{4\}$ 5. $\{x \mid x \text{ is a real number}\}$ 6. $\{-12\}$ 7. $\{37\}$ 8. $\{1\}$

9. $\{-2\}$ 10. $\{-10\}$ 11. $\{4\}$ 12. $\{3\}$ 13. $\left\{\dfrac{1}{2}\right\}$ 14. $\{-1\}$ 15. $\left\{\dfrac{11}{18}\right\}$ 16. 187.81 cm

17. 5 18. 91 mph 19. 7.5% 20. 25°

2.4 Form I

1. $t = \dfrac{I}{\text{Pr}}$ 2. $h = \dfrac{3V}{B}$ 3. $s_3 = P - s_1 - s_2$ 4. $b = y - mx$ 5. 88% 6. 10% 7. 230%

8. 0.9% 9. 0.72 10. 0.032 11. 1 12. 0.0004 13. 20.52 14. 7.37 15. 250 16. 25%

17. $45.60 18. 23% 19. 34,650 people 20. 560 students

2.4 Form II

1. $A = \dfrac{C - By}{x}$ 2. $B = \dfrac{3V}{h}$ 3. $C = \dfrac{5}{9}(F - 32)$ 4. $w = \dfrac{P - 2l}{2}$ 5. 21% 6. 70% 7. 0.91%

8. 400% 9. 0.81 10. 0.046 11. 6 12. 0.0009 13. 95.2 14. 72 15. 60 16. 120%

17. $63.75 18. 77.8% 19. 24,150 people 20. 1225 students

2.4 Form III

1. $h = \dfrac{S - 2\pi r^2}{2\pi r}$ 2. $B = \dfrac{C - Ax}{y}$ 3. $a = 2s - b - c$ 4. $R = \dfrac{PV}{nT}$ 5. 15.2% 6. 50%

7. 980% 8. 205% 9. 0.925 10. 0.0317 11. 1.5 12. 0.00011 13. 95.2 14. 72 15. 85

16. 120% 17. $74.63 18. 26.5% 19. 31,115 people 20. 1040 students

2.5 Form I

1. $11x + 13$ 2. $7x - 59$ 3. $\dfrac{42}{-7x}$ 4. $-27(x + 25)$ 5. $2(x + -41)$ 6. $\dfrac{25x}{-8}$

7a. $4x + 7x = 44$ b. 4 8a. $\dfrac{3}{4}x = \dfrac{1}{2}$ b. $\dfrac{2}{3}$ 9a. $\dfrac{x}{42} + 7 = 13$ b. 252 10a. $x + 3x = 180000$

b. $45,000, $135,000 11a. $x + 3x + 2x = 30$ b. 5, 15, 10 marbles 12a. $15 + 0.05x = 55$

b. 800 minutes

2.5 Form II

1. $3x + 11$ 2. $8x - 9$ 3. $\dfrac{7}{9x}$ 4. $14(x - 5)$ 5. $\dfrac{x}{8} - 2$ 6. $\dfrac{2}{5}x + 3$ 7a. $7x - 3x = 44$ b. 11

8a. $4x + 7 = 2x - 8$ b. $-\dfrac{15}{2}$ 9a. $9x - 6 = 3x$ b. 1 10a. $x + 3x - 2 = 90$ b. $23°, 67°$

11a. $2x = 120$ b. 60 sq ft   12a. $2x + 2(2x) = 120$ b. 20 meters, 40 meters

2.5 Form III

1. $\dfrac{3}{7}x + 4$ 2. $13 - 4x$ 3. $\dfrac{19}{-2x}$ 4. $-11(x - 8)$ 5. $2(x + 9)$ 6. $3x + 40$ 7a. $5x + -6 = 11x$

b. -1 8a. $6(x + 2) = 48$ b. 6 9a. $7x + 5 = 2x + 10$ b. 1 10a. $x + x + (x - 45) = 180$

b. $75°, 75°, 30°$ 11a. $x + (x + 18) = 108$ b. 45 juniors, 63 sophomores   12a. $2x + 2(5x) = 144$

b. 12 inches, 60 inches

2.6 Form I

1a. 22 inches   b. 28 in.^{2} 2a. 24 inches   b. 24 ft.^{2} 3a. 54 inches   b. 216 in.^{2}
4. 64π square centimeters; 113 cm.^{2} 5. 36π square inches; 113 in.^{2} 6. 8π square ft.; 25 feet
7. 20π cm.; 63 cm.   8. 12π cubic inches; 38 in.^{3} 9. 64π cubic centimeters; 201 cm.^{3}
10. 20π cubic inches; 63 in.^{3} 11. 105 cubic inches   12. $138°$ 13. $53°$
14. Width 7 feet; length 11 feet   15. 5 inches, 11 inches and 15 inches   16. $55°, 57°,$ and $68°$

2.6 Form II

1a. 37 inches   b. 78 sq. in.   2a. 40 cm.   b. 64 sq. cm.   3. 296 sq. in.
4. 49π square inches; 154 in.^{2} 5. 20.25π square centimeters; 64 cm.^{2} 6. 4.8π feet; 15 feet
7. 16π cubic centimeters; 50 cm.^{3} 8. 4608π cubic inches; 147 in.^{3}
9. 4.5π cubic decimeters; 14 dm.^{3} 10. 3 meters   11. $34°$ and $56°$
12. Width 5.5 feet; length 11 feet   13. 240 cubic feet   14. $38°, 59°$ and $83°$
15. $36.2°, 41.2°$ and $102.6°$ 16. 17 inches by 92 inches

2.6 Form III

1a. 34.08 in.   b. 58.752 in.^{2} 2a. 38.63 cm.   b. 63.44 cm^2 3. 331.2 in.^{2}
4. 331.24π mm^2; 1041 mm^2 5. 24.8π inches; 78 inches   6. 8π cubic inches; 25 in.^{3}
7. 370.301π cubic centimeters   8. 47.916π in.^{3} 9. 1444 ft.^{2} 10. 14 meters   11. 8 inches
12. 39.68 ft.^{3} 13. $65°$ and $115°$ 14. $39°$ and $102°$ 15. $20.5°, 41°$ and $118.5°$
16. 979 square feet

1.

2.

3.

4.

5.

6. $\{x \mid x > 1\}$ 7. $\{x \mid x \geq 2\}$

8. $\{x \mid x \leq -1\}$ 9. $\{x \mid x < 1\}$ 10. $\{x \mid x > -2\}$

11. $\{x \mid x > 2\}$

12. $\{x \mid x > -4\}$

13. $\{x \mid x > 3\}$

14. $\{x \mid x > -2\}$

15. $\varnothing$

2.7 Form II

1.
2.
3.
4.
5.
6. $\{x \mid x > -2\}$ 7. $\{x \mid x \geq 0\}$

8. $\{x \mid x \leq -3\}$ 9. $\{x \mid x \leq 4\}$ 10. $\{x \mid x < -5\}$

11. $\{x \mid x \leq 4\}$ 12. $\{x \mid x \leq -3\}$

13. $\{x \mid x < -2\}$ 14. $\{x \mid x < 5\}$

15. $\{x \mid x \text{ is a real number}\}$

2.7 Form III

1.
2.
3.
4.
5.

6. $\{x \mid x > -4\}$ 7. $\{x \mid x \geq -2\}$ 8. $\{x \mid x < 3\}$ 9. $\{x \mid x \leq -2\}$

10a. $\{x \mid x < 4\}$ b.

-6 -5 -4 -3 -2 -1 0 1 2 3 4 5 6

11a. $\{x \mid x \geq -5\}$ b.

-6 -5 -4 -3 -2 -1 0 1 2 3 4 5 6

12a. $\{x \mid x \leq 6\}$ b.

-6 -5 -4 -3 -2 -1 0 1 2 3 4 5 6

13a. $\{x \mid x \geq -2\}$ b.

-6 -5 -4 -3 -2 -1 0 1 2 3 4 5 6

14a. $\{x \mid x \geq 2\}$ b.

-6 -5 -4 -3 -2 -1 0 1 2 3 4 5 6

15a. $\{x \mid x \text{ is a real number}\}$ b.

-6 -5 -4 -3 -2 -1 0 1 2 3 4 5 6

Additional Exercises Answers

3.1 Form I

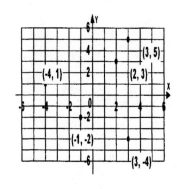

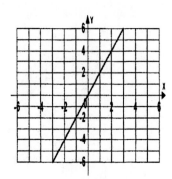

1. I 2. II 3. III 4. I 5. IV

6. yes 7. yes 8. no 9. (6, 42) 10. (2, 17) 11. (−1, −1)

12.

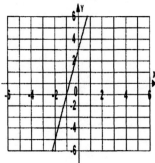

13.

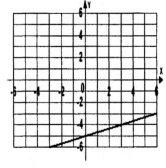

14.

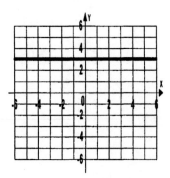

15.

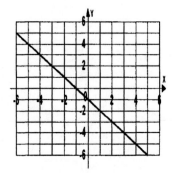

16.

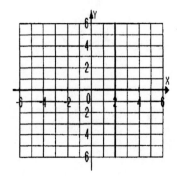

17.

AE-518

18. $193.50   19. 96 ft.   20. 100 ounces

3.1 Form II

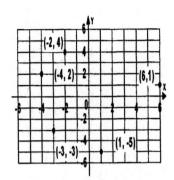

1. IV   2. II   3. III   4. I   5. II

6. no   7. no   8. yes   9. (5, –41)   10. (4, –35)   11. (–1, 7)

12.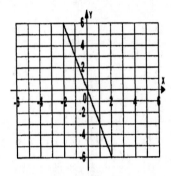

13.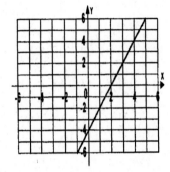

14.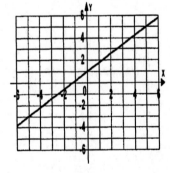

15.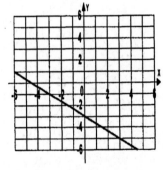

16.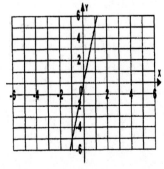

17.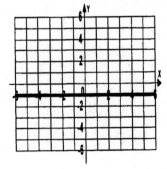

18. $46   19. $23.20   20. 3993 ft.

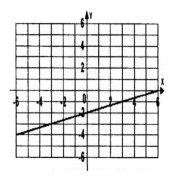

1. IV 2. III 3. I 4. IV 5. II

6. yes 7. no 8. no 9. $\left(-4, -\dfrac{8}{3}\right)$ 10. (5, 1) 11. $\left(\dfrac{1}{2}, -4\right)$

12.

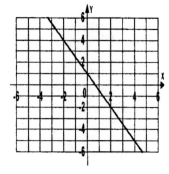

13.

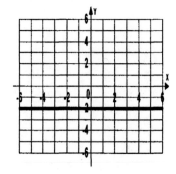

14.

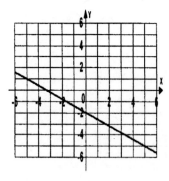

15.

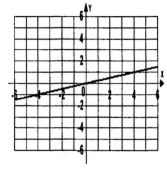

16.

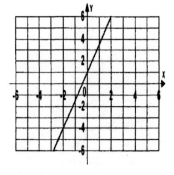

17.

17. $\left.\right.$

18. $203.75 19. $75 20. 134 feet

3.2 Form I

1. *x*-int (6, 0) ; *y*-int (0, 6)   2. *x*-int (4, 0) ; *y*-int (0, 2)   3. *x*-int (4, 0) ; *y*-int (0, –3)
4. *x*-int none ; *y*- int (0, 5)   5. *x*-int (3, 0) ; *y*-int (0, 3)   6. *x*-int (–3, 0) ; *y*-int (0, –6)
7. *x*-int (5, 0) ; *y*-int (0, –2)   8. *x*-int (2, 0) ; *y*-int (0, –2)

9a. *x*-int (–4, 0) ; *y*-int (0, 1)   10a. *x*- int (–1, 0) ; *y*- int none

b. 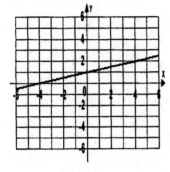   b.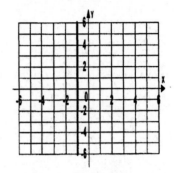

11a. *x*-int (3, 0) ; *y*- int (0,1)   12a. *x*-int (0, 0) ; *y*-int (0,0)

b. 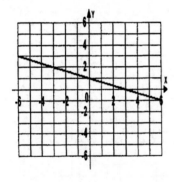   b.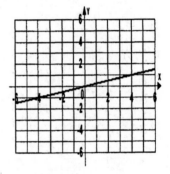

13. *y* = –2   14. *x* = –3

3.2 Form II

1. *x*-int (1, 0) ; *y*-int (0, 2)   2. *x*-int (2, 0) ; *y*-int (0, –6)   3. *x*-int (3, 0) ; *y*-int none
4. *x*-int (0, 0) ; *y*- int (0, 0)   5. *x*-int (6, 0) ; *y*-int (0, 6)   6. *x*-int (4, 0) ; *y*-int (0, –8)
7. *x*-int (–10, 0) ; *y*-int (0, –6)   8. *x*-int $\left(\frac{9}{2},\ 0\right)$; *y*-int (0, –6)

9a. *x*-int (3, 0) ; *y*-int (0, –2)   10a. *x*- int none ; *y*- int (0, –2)

b. 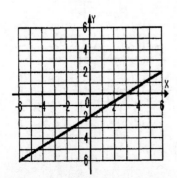   b.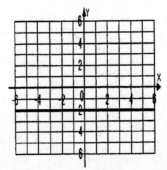

AE-521

11a. x-int $\left(\dfrac{5}{2},\ 0\right)$; y- int $(0,-1)$

12a. x-int $(0,\ 0)$; y-int $(0,0)$

b.

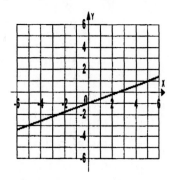

b.

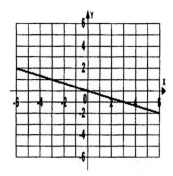

13. $x = 3$ 14. $y = 4$

3.2 Form III

1. x-int $(0, 0)$; y-int $(0, 0)$ 2. x-int $(-3, 0)$; y-int $(0, -3)$ 3. x-int $(-4, 0)$; y-int none

4. x-int $(5, 0)$; y- int $(0, -4)$ 5. x-int $\left(\dfrac{15}{2},\ 0\right)$; y-int $(0, -5)$ 6. x-int $(3, 0)$; y-int $\left(0,\ \dfrac{9}{4}\right)$

7. x-int $\left(\dfrac{12}{5},\ 0\right)$; y-int $(0, 4)$ 8. x-int $\left(4,\ 0\right)$; y-int $\left(0,\ -\dfrac{24}{5}\right)$

9a. x-int $\left(-\dfrac{3}{4},\ 0\right)$; y-int $(0, 3)$

10a. x- int none ; y- int $(0, -2)$

b.

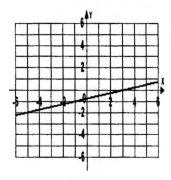

b.

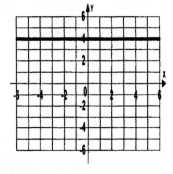

11a. x-int $\left(\dfrac{8}{5},\ 0\right)$; y- int $(0,-2)$

12a. x-int $(0, 0)$; y-int $(0,0)$

b.

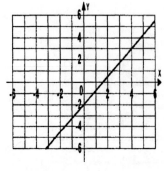

b.

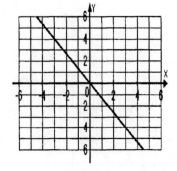

13. $x = 1$ 14. $y = -2$

3.3 Form I

1a. $m = \dfrac{2}{11}$ b. rises 2a. $m = \dfrac{21}{5}$ b. rises 3a. $m = -\dfrac{3}{7}$ b. falls
4a. m is undefined b. vertical 5a. $m = 0$ b. horizontal 6. $m = 1$ 7. $m = 3$ 8. $m = -4$
9. $m = 0$ 10. m is undefined 11. parallel 12. perpendicular 13. neither 14. 43% 15. 3 ft.

3.3 Form II

1a. $m = \dfrac{1}{2}$ b. rises 2a. m is undefined b. vertical 3a. $m = \dfrac{3}{5}$ b. rises 4a. $m = -\dfrac{3}{5}$ b. falls

5a. $m = 0$ b. horizontal 6. $m = \dfrac{2}{3}$ 7. m is undefined 8. $m = -\dfrac{3}{5}$ 9. $m = 0$ 10. $m = -3$

11. neither 12. parallel 13. perpendicular 14. $m = \dfrac{4}{3}$ 15. 55%

3.3 Form III

1a. m is undefined b. vertical 2a. $m = -\dfrac{1}{5}$ b. falls 3a. $m = -3$ b. falls

4a. $m = 0$ b. horizontal 5a. $m = \dfrac{4}{13}$ b. rises 6. $m = 0$ 7. $m = -\dfrac{3}{2}$ 8. m is undefined

9. $m = 2$ 10. $m = -\dfrac{5}{3}$ 11. neither 12. perpendicular 13. parallel 14. 50% 15. 58%

3.4 Form I

1. $m = -8$ 2. $m = 6$ 3. $m = 0$ 4. $m = -1$ 5. $m = 7$ 6. $m = -3$ 7. y-intercept $(0, 0)$
8. y-intercept $(0, -7)$ 9. y-intercept $(0, 2)$ 10. y-intercept $(0, 4)$

11.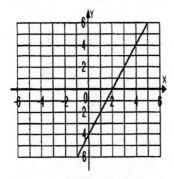

12.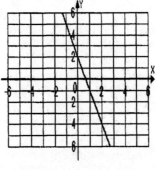

13.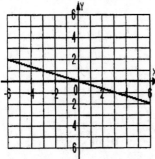

14. 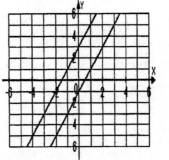 parallel

15. $m = 3$; The cost of the service increases \$3 every mile the car is towed. b = 65; The cost of the service is \$65 if the car is not towed.

3.4 Form II

1. $m = -\dfrac{2}{3}$ 2. $m = \dfrac{3}{5}$ 3. $m = 0$ 4. $m = \dfrac{7}{2}$ 5. $m = -\dfrac{3}{5}$ 6. $m = -\dfrac{3}{4}$

7. y-intercept $\left(0, -\dfrac{3}{2}\right)$ 8. y-intercept $\left(0, -\dfrac{5}{2}\right)$ 9. y-intercept $(0, -3)$

10. y-intercept $\left(0, -\dfrac{1}{2}\right)$

11.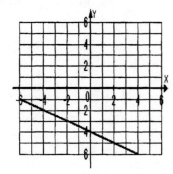

12.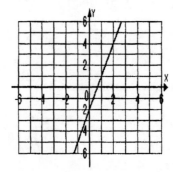

13.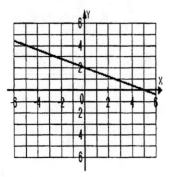

14. 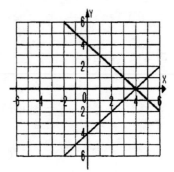   perpendicular

15. $m = -3$; The amount of water in the bucket decreases 3 ounces every minute. $b = 110$; at $x = 0$, the amount of water in the bucket was 110 ounces.

3.4 Form III

1. $m = \dfrac{4}{3}$ 2. $m = 0$ 3. $m = \dfrac{2}{5}$ 4. $m = \dfrac{7}{2}$ 5. $m = \dfrac{1}{5}$ 6. $m = 2$

7. y-intercept $\left(0, -\dfrac{5}{3}\right)$ 8. y-intercept $\left(0, -\dfrac{7}{4}\right)$ 9. y-intercept $\left(0, \dfrac{1}{3}\right)$

10. y-intercept $(0, 1)$

11.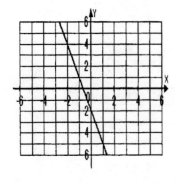

12.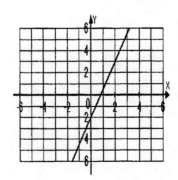

13.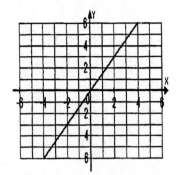

14.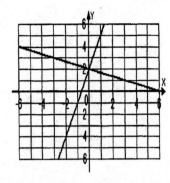

15. $m = 32$; The speed of the ball increases 32 feet per second every second. $b = 0$; The speed of the ball was 0 the moment it was dropped.

3.5 Form I

1a. $y - 1 = 1(x - 2)$ b. $y = x - 1$ 2a. $y - 4 = -2(x - 4)$ b. $y = -2x + 12$

3a. $y - 2 = 4(x - 0)$ b. $y = 4x + 2$ 4a. $y - 2 = 8(x - 4)$ b. $y = 8x - 30$

5a. $y - 3 = -9(x - 4)$ b. $y = -9x + 39$ 6a. $y + 4 = 5(x + 3)$ b. $y = 5x + 11$

7a. $y - 1 = 1(x - 0)$ or $y - 5 = 1(x - 4)$ b. $y = x + 1$

8a. $y - 8 = -1(x - 0)$ or $y - 6 = -1(x - 2)$ b. $y = -x + 8$

9a. $y - 0 = 1(x - 2)$ or $y - 2 = 1(x - 4)$ b. $y = x - 2$

10a. $y - 1 = 1(x + 4)$ or $y - 4 = 1(x + 1)$ b. $y = x + 5$

11a. $y - 1 = -2(x + 3)$ b. $y = -2x - 5$

12a. $y + 6 = 1(x + 4)$ b. $y = x - 2$

13a. $y + 2 = -3(x - 2)$ b. $y = -3x + 4$ 14. $y = 4x + 2$ 15. $y = -40x + 175$

3.5 Form II

1a. $y - 5 = \frac{5}{3}(x - 0)$ b. $y = \frac{5}{3}x + 5$ 2a. $y - 2 = -\frac{2}{3}(x - 0)$ b. $y = -\frac{2}{3}x + 2$

3a. $y - 3 = -\frac{3}{5}(x - 10)$ b. $y = -\frac{3}{5}x + 9$ 4a. $y - 5 = \frac{5}{3}(x - 0)$ b. $y = \frac{5}{3}x + 5$

5a. $y - 10 = -\frac{4}{5}(x + 5)$ b. $y = -\frac{4}{5}x + 6$ 6a. $y + 8 = \frac{3}{4}(x - 8)$ b. $y = \frac{3}{4}x - 14$

7a. $y + 5 = -1(x - 1)$ or $y - 1 = -1(x + 5)$ b. $y = -x - 4$

8a. $y + 3 = 3(x - 0)$ or $y - 6 = 3(x - 3)$ b. $y = 3x - 3$

9a. $y + 9 = 3(x + 1)$ or $y + 15 = 3(x + 3)$ b. $y = 3x - 6$

10a. $y - 3 = \frac{1}{4}(x - 2)$ or $y - 1 = \frac{1}{4}(x + 6)$ b. $y = \frac{1}{4}x + \frac{5}{2}$

11a. $y - 6 = \frac{1}{2}(x - 4)$ b. $y = \frac{1}{2}x + 4$

12a. $y - 5 = \frac{1}{3}x + 6$ b. $y = \frac{1}{3}x + 6$

13a. $y - 4 = -\frac{1}{2}(x - 4)$ b. $y = -\frac{1}{2}x + 6$ 14. $y = 0.2x + 0.45$ 15. $y = -52x + 198$

1a. $y + 5 = -\dfrac{1}{3}(x-1)$ b. $y = -\dfrac{1}{3}x + \dfrac{16}{3}$ 2a. $y - 4 = -\dfrac{2}{7}(x-2)$ b. $y = -\dfrac{2}{7}x + \dfrac{32}{7}$

3a. $y - 2 = -\dfrac{4}{5}(x+1)$ b. $y = -\dfrac{4}{5}x + \dfrac{6}{5}$ 4a. $y - 0 = \dfrac{3}{4}(x-1)$ b. $y = \dfrac{3}{4}x - \dfrac{3}{4}$

5a. $y + 5 = \dfrac{1}{2}(x-2)$ b. $y = \dfrac{1}{2}x - 6$ 6a. $y - 4 = \dfrac{3}{5}(x+1)$ b. $y = \dfrac{3}{5}x + \dfrac{23}{5}$

7a. $y - 2 = -\dfrac{3}{4}(x-1)$ or $y - 5 = -\dfrac{3}{4}(x+3)$ b. $y = -\dfrac{3}{4}x + \dfrac{11}{4}$

8a. $y - 7 = \dfrac{1}{5}(x-4)$ or $y - 6 = \dfrac{1}{5}(x+1)$ b. $y = \dfrac{1}{5}x + \dfrac{31}{5}$

9a. $y - 5 = \dfrac{1}{6}(x+2)$ or $y - 6 = \dfrac{1}{6}(x-4)$ b. $y = \dfrac{1}{6}x + \dfrac{16}{3}$

10a. $y - 3 = -\dfrac{1}{2}(x-3)$ or $y - 7 = -\dfrac{1}{2}(x+5)$ b. $y = -\dfrac{1}{2}x + \dfrac{9}{2}$

11a. $y + 2 = \dfrac{2}{3}(x-3)$ b. $y = \dfrac{2}{3}x - 4$

12a. $y = \dfrac{5}{4}(x+1)$ b. $y = \dfrac{5}{4}x + \dfrac{5}{4}$

13a. $y + 4 = \dfrac{5}{2}(x+8)$ b. $y = \dfrac{5}{2}x + 16$ 14. $y = -2860x + 13{,}440$ 15. $y = 397x + 2342$

Additional Exercises Answers

4.1 Form I

1. Yes 2. No 3. No

4.

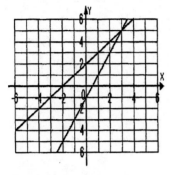

$\{(3, 5)\}$

5.

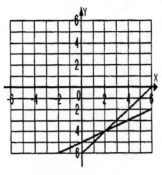

$\{(2, -4)\}$

6.

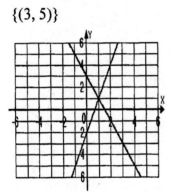

$\{(1, 1)\}$

7.

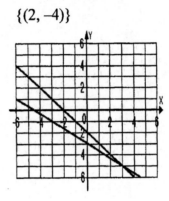

$\{3, -5\}$

8.

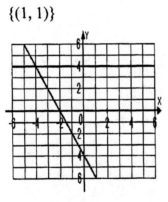

$\{(-4, 4)\}$

9.

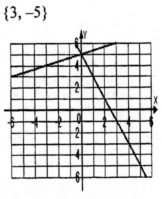

$\{(0, 5)\}$

10.

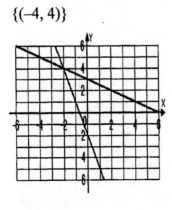

$\{(-2, 4)\}$

11.

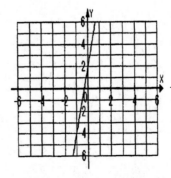

Infinitely many solutions
$\{(x, \ y) \mid y - 6x = 2\}$ $\{(x, \ y) \mid 2y = 12x + 4\}$

12.

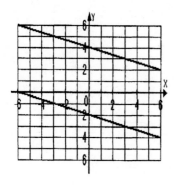

No Solution; Ø

4.1 Form II

1. No   2. Yes   3. Yes

4.

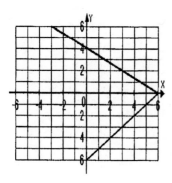

{(6, 0)}

5.

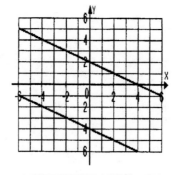

No Solution; Ø

6.

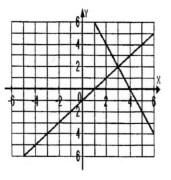

{(3, 2)}

7.

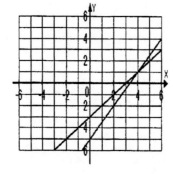

{(4, 1)}

8.

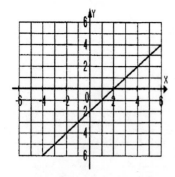

Infinitely many solutions
$\{(x, \ y) \mid y = x - 2\}$

9.

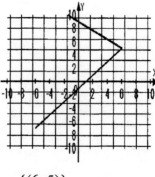

{(6, 5)}

10.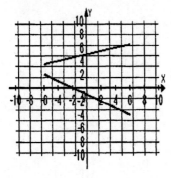

{(–4, 1)}

11.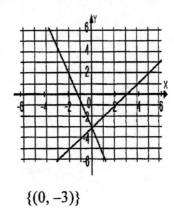

{(0, –3)}

12.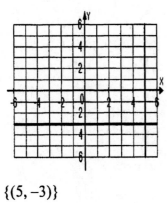

{(5, –3)}

4.1 Form III

1. No 2. Yes 3. No

4.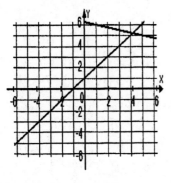

{(4, 5)}

5.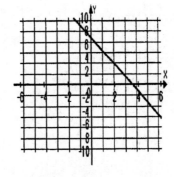

Infinitely many solutions

$\{(x,\ y)\mid 2x + y = 7\}$ $\{(x,\ y)\mid 6x + 3y = 21\}$

6.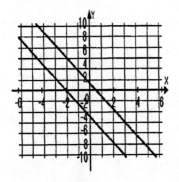

No Solution; Ø

7.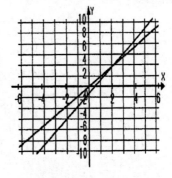

{(2, 3)}

8.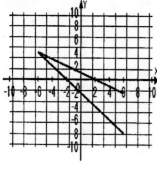

$\{(-6, 4)\}$

9.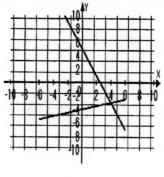

$\{(4, -3)\}$

10.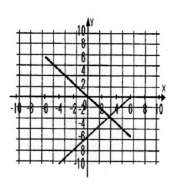

$\{3, -3\}$

11.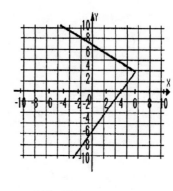

$\{(6, 3)\}$

12.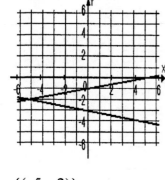

$\{(-5, -2)\}$

4.2 Form I

1. $\{(4, 7)\}$ 2. $\{(-3, -4)\}$ 3. $\{(1, -3)\}$ 4. $\{(10, 5)\}$ 5. Infinitely many solutions;
$\{(x, y) \mid 3x + 3y = 12\}$ or $\{(x, y) \mid x = 4 - y\}$ 6. $\{(2, 4)\}$ 7. $\{(5, -6)\}$ 8. No Solution; Ø
9. $\{(2, 0)\}$ 10. $\{(0, -7)\}$ 11. $\{(-4, 3)\}$ 12. $\{(5, -5)\}$ 13. $\{(-3, 5)\}$ 14. No Solution, Ø
15. $\{(-2, 2)\}$ 16. $\{(-2, -1)\}$

4.2 Form II

1. $\{(7, -1)\}$ 2. $\{(4, 16)\}$ 3. Infinitely many solutions; $\{(x, y) \mid 6x - 2y = 14\}$ or
$\{(x, y) \mid 3x - y = 7\}$ 4. $\{(8, 2)\}$ 5. $\{(-4, 12)\}$ 6. No Solution; Ø   7. $\{(1, 0)\}$ 8. $\{(5, 4)\}$
9. $\{(5, -2)\}$ 10. $\left\{\left(\dfrac{1}{2}, 4\right)\right\}$ 11. $\left\{\left(\dfrac{4}{5}, -\dfrac{1}{5}\right)\right\}$ 12. $\left\{\left(1, \dfrac{1}{3}\right)\right\}$ 13. No Solution; Ø
14. $\{(8, 6)\}$ 15. $\{(11, 15)\}$ 16. $\{(-9, 5)\}$

4.2 Form III

1. $\{(5, -3)\}$ 2. $\{(-2, -7)\}$ 3. $\{(-2, -1)\}$ 4. $\{(-5, 6)\}$ 5. Infinitely many solutions; $\{(x, y) \mid 2x + y = 14\}$ or $\{(x, y) \mid 4x + 2y = 28\}$ 6. $\{(-2, 2)\}$ 7. $\{(12, 10)\}$

8. No Solution; $\emptyset$ 9. $\{(-4, 9)\}$ 10. $\left\{\left(\dfrac{1}{8}, -\dfrac{3}{8}\right)\right\}$ 11. $\left\{\left(\dfrac{2}{3}, -4\right)\right\}$ 12. $\{(5, 4)\}$

13. $\{(7, -7)\}$ 14. $\{(14, 12)\}$ 15. After 2 ½ years, 869 thousand of Product A and 869 thousand of Product B would be sold. 16. The numbers are 7 and 8.

4.3 Form I

1. $\{(-4, 3)\}$ 2. $\{(4, 2)\}$ 3. $\{(5, -4)\}$ 4. No Solution; $\emptyset$ 5. $\{(-5, -6)\}$ 6. $\{(1, 2)\}$
7. $\{(0, 2)\}$ 8. $\{(8, 3)\}$ 9. $\{(-2, -2)\}$ 10. $\{(6, 1)\}$ 11. $\{(-3, 10)\}$

12. Infinitely many solutions; $\{(x, y) \mid 4x - 6y = 10\}$ or $\{(x, y) \mid 6x - 9y = 15\}$ 13. $\left\{\left(\dfrac{1}{3}, -2\right)\right\}$

14. $\{(8, 14)\}$ 15. $\left\{\left(\dfrac{2}{5}, -\dfrac{3}{5}\right)\right\}$ 16. $\{(1, -3)\}$

4.3 Form II

1. $\{(4, 4)\}$ 2. $\{(-3, -2)\}$ 3. $\{(1, -6)\}$ 4. $\{(0, 4)\}$ 5. $\{(-2, -5)\}$
6. Infinitely many solutions; $\{(x, y) \mid 6x + 3y = 27\}$ or $\{(x, y) \mid 2x + y = 9\}$ 7. $\{(5, -12)\}$

8. $\left\{\left(\dfrac{1}{5}, 2\right)\right\}$ 9. $\left\{\left(\dfrac{1}{4}, -\dfrac{7}{4}\right)\right\}$ 10. No Solution; $\emptyset$ 11. $\left\{\left(-\dfrac{1}{3}, -\dfrac{5}{4}\right)\right\}$ 12. $\{(-5, 3)\}$
13. $\{(-4, -7)\}$ 14. No Solution; $\emptyset$ 15. $\{(1, 2)\}$ 16. $\{(20, -16)\}$

4.3 Form III

1. $\{(36, -9)\}$ 2. $\{(-7, -10)\}$ 3. No Solution; $\emptyset$ 4. Infinitely many solutions; $\{(x, y) \mid 6x - 4y = -4\}$ or $\{(x, y) \mid 12x - 8y = -8\}$ 5. $\{(-1, 3)\}$ 6. $\{(13, 0)\}$ 7. No Solution; $\emptyset$

8. $\{(6, 4)\}$ 9. $\left\{\left(-\dfrac{2}{9}, \dfrac{14}{9}\right)\right\}$ 10. $\left\{\left(-\dfrac{4}{5}, \dfrac{3}{8}\right)\right\}$ 11. $\{(5, -1)\}$ 12. $\{(-4, -16)\}$
13. $\{(10, 4)\}$ 14. $\{(-15, -2)\}$ 15. $\{(3, 1)\}$ 16. $\{(-4, -1)\}$

4.4 Form I

1. 4 and 8 2. 24 and 28 3. 8 and 12 4. 30 and 126 5. Bath towels are $7. Washcloths are $4.
6. A shirt costs $26. Pants cost $32. 7. 50 bracelets and 30 necklaces 8. 35 geraniums and 45 daisies 9. The width is 7 inches. The length is 11 inches. 10. The width is 121 cm. The length is 363 cm. 11. 29° and 111° 12. The current is 3 mph.

4.4 Form II

1. −4 and 8 2. 17 and 24 3. 14 and −6 4. 18 adult tickets and 15 children's tickets
5. 98 dimes; 14 nickels 6. 382 hardback books and 451 paperback books 7. 8°, 40°, and 132°
8. The width is 5 inches. The length is 16 inches 9. The width is 7 feet. The length is 40 feet.
10. Popcorn, $1.50, Juice, $1.25 11. 9 hours 12. 1 mph

4.4 Form III

1. 22 and 70   2. 6 and −5   3. 12 and 15   4. Hot dogs, $4.50; Sodas, $3.00   5. 13 nickels, 52 quarters   6. 1272 adult tickets; 526 children's tickets   7. 47° and 90°   8. 40°, 40° and 100° 9. The width is 15.8 feet. The length is 24.2 feet.   10. Ken's rate is 5.6 mph. Hector's rate is 7 mph.   11. Still water speed is 6.25 mph. The current is 1.25 mph.   12. After driving 50 miles the plan would be equal. The cost would be $33.00.

4.5 Form I

1.
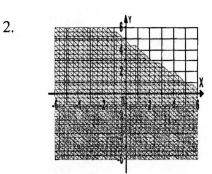

2.

3.

4.

5.

6.
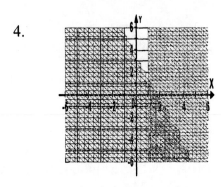

7.
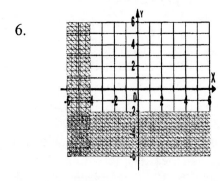

8.
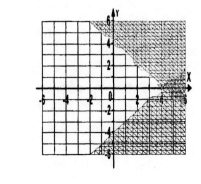

9.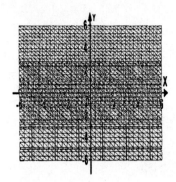

10.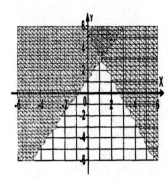

4.5 Form II

1.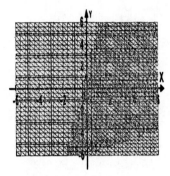

2.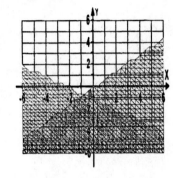

3.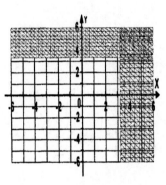

4.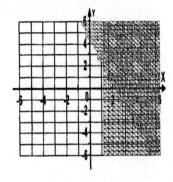

5.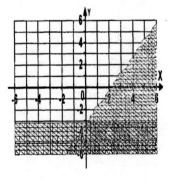

6.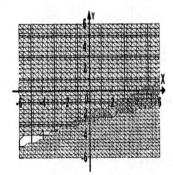

7.

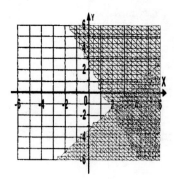

8.

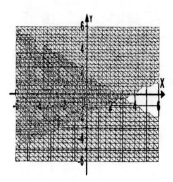

9.

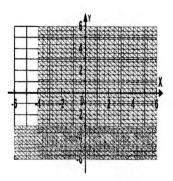

10.

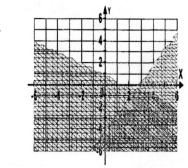

4.5 Form III

1.

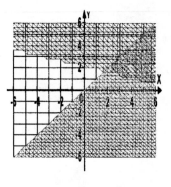

2.

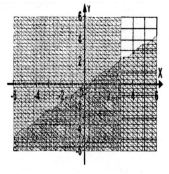

3.

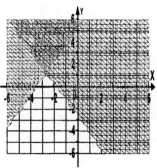

4.

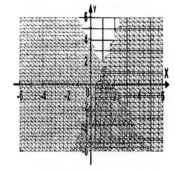

5.

6.

7.

8.

9.

10.

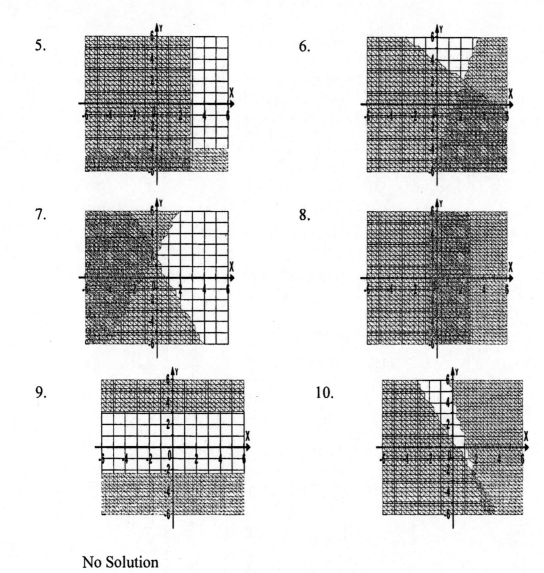

No Solution

11. Yes   12. No

Additional Exercises Answers

5.1 Form I

1. monomial, 1   2. trinomial, 4   3. trinomial, 5   4. monomial, 0   5. $5y^5 - 15y^3$

6. $12y^7 + 8y^6 + 13y$ 7. $14y^6 + 6y^3 - 7$ 8. $12y^5 + 2y^3$ 9. $21y^4 - 2y^3 + y^2 - y$

10. $-12x + 6$ 11. $7y^3 - 13y^2$ 12. $-4x^5 - 11x^4 - 3$ 13. $-12x^4 + 3x^2$

14. $-4y^5 - 5y^3 + 35$ 15. \$6700

5.1 Form II

1. binomial, 3   2. monomial, 0   3. trinomial, 6   4. binomial, 2   5. $3x^3 - 2x^2 - 5$

6. $4x^5 - 4x^3 + 2x + 1$ 7. $4x^4 - x^3 - 5x - 4$ 8. $-3x^5 + 6x^4 + x^3 + 1$ 9. $12x^3 - x^2 + x + 2$

10. $-4x^2 + 2x - 4$ 11. $5x^5 - x^2 - 9x + 5$ 12. $6x^4 - 2x^3 - 5x^2 - 2x - 7$ 13. $-14x^3 - x^2$

14. $5x^4 + 7x^3 - 9x^2$ 15. 360 newtons

5.1 Form III

1. binomial, 9   2. trinomial, 3   3. monomial, 0   4. trinomial, 5   5. $-\dfrac{1}{2}x^3 + \dfrac{2}{7}x^2 + \dfrac{7}{9}$

6. $\dfrac{1}{7}x^3 + \dfrac{1}{3}x^2 - \dfrac{3}{4}x + \dfrac{1}{5}$ 7. $\dfrac{1}{5}x^2 + \dfrac{3}{4}x + \dfrac{31}{20}$ 8. $\dfrac{5}{7}x^2 - x + \dfrac{4}{5}$ 9. $\dfrac{3}{5}x^2 + \dfrac{4}{15}x - 1$

10. $4x^5 - 11x^4 - 2x^3 + 25$ 11. $\dfrac{1}{4}x^4 + \dfrac{3}{5}x^3 - \dfrac{1}{7}$ 12. $\dfrac{1}{2}x^3 + \dfrac{1}{3}x^2 - \dfrac{1}{5}x - \dfrac{3}{8}$

13. $\dfrac{7}{8}x^3 + \dfrac{4}{5}x^2 + x - 8$ 14. $2y^6 - 9y^4 - 2y$ 15. 3215

5.2 Form I

1. y^8 2. 3^{14} 3. x^{16} 4. 5^{24} 5. y^{48} 6. $9x^2$ 7. $-64x^{18}$ 8. $-14x^{13}$ 9. $-\dfrac{1}{56}x^{12}$

10. $x^2 + 11x$ 11. $-12x^3 - 48x^2$ 12. $56x^{10} + 49x^8$ 13. $32x^9 + 80x^8 + 88x^2$

14. $3x^2 - 23x - 110$ 15. $x^2 - 4x - 32$ 16. $x^3 + 6x - 20$ 17. $x^4 + 2x^3 - 16x^2 - 17x + 70$

18. $7x^3 + 62x^2 + 62x + 12$ 19. $y(2y + 7) = 2y^2 + 7y$ 20. $(24x^2 + 12x)\text{ in}^2$

5.2 Form II

1. x^{10} 2. 4^{10} 3. y^{16} 4. 6^{12} 5. y^{36} 6. $-8x^3$ 7. $25x^8$ 8. $-18x^{14}$ 9. $-\dfrac{9}{14}x^9$

10. $2x^2 - 5x$ 11. $-6x^4 - 15x^3$ 12. $15x^{10} + 10x^9$ 13. $14x^8 + 28x^7 + 98x^3$

14. $4x^2 + 25x - 21$ 15. $x^2 + 6x - 27$ 16. $2x^3 - 11x^2 + 24x - 18$

17. $x^4 + x^3 + 4x^2 + 21x - 27$ 18. $15x^3 - 13x^2 + 22x - 4$ 19. $x(3x + 4) = 3x^2 + 4x$

20. $(18x^2 + 6x)\text{ in}^2$

5.2 Form III

1. x^{14} 2. 4^{13} 3. x^{16} 4. 6^{40} 5. y^{48} 6. $-64x^3$ 7. $25x^{10}$ 8. $-24x^{11}$ 9. $-\dfrac{6}{35}x^9$

10. $x^3 - 8x^2$ 11. $-18x^4 - 108x^3$ 12. $20x^{13} + 30x^7$ 13. $27x^9 + 63x^8 - 90x^4$

14. $6x^2 - 32x + 32$ 15. $x^2 + 3x - 40$ 16. $3x^3 - 10x^2 - 16x + 32$

17. $x^4 + 15x^2 + 16x - 55$ 18. $4x^3 - 5x^2 - x + 35$ 19. $y(3y + 8) = 3y^2 + 8y$

20. $(12x^2 + 28x)\,\text{in}^2$

5.3 Form I

1. $x^2 + x - 12$ 2. $2x^2 + 7x - 4$ 3. $12x^2 + x - 35$ 4. $35 - 17x + 2x^2$ 5. $x^3 + 5x^2 - 25x - 125$

6. $a^2 - 4$ 7. $9 - m^2$ 8. $25 - 49r^2$ 9. $9x^2 - \dfrac{1}{9}$ 10. $x^4 - 1$ 11. $17n^2 + 22n + 121$

12. $w^2 - 16w + 64$ 13. $9a^2 - 42a + 49$ 14. $4x^2 + 2x + \dfrac{1}{4}$ 15. $49x^2 - 2x + \dfrac{1}{49}$

16. $64 - 64x + 16m^2$ 17. $n^6 + 18n^3 + 81$ 18. $\left(18x^2 + 9x - 20\right)\text{units}^2$ 19. $(6x + 10)\,\text{units}^2$

20. $(6x^3 - 35x^2 + 50x)\ \text{units}^3$

5.3 Form II

1. $x^2 + 10x + 16$ 2. $4x^2 - 15x - 54$ 3. $12x^2 - 26x - 88$ 4. $8x^2 - 40x + 42$

5. $x^3 + 3x^2 - 9x - 27$ 6. $a^2 - 1$ 7. $16 - m^2$ 8. $9 - 100r^2$ 9. $25x^2 - \dfrac{1}{25}$ 10. $x^4 - 25$

11. $n^2 + 32n + 256$ 12. $w^2 - 20w + 100$ 13. $64a^2 - 144a + 81$ 14. $9x^2 + 2x + \dfrac{1}{9}$

15. $25x^2 - 2x + \dfrac{1}{25}$ 16. $100m^2 - 220m + 121$ 17. $n^6 + 24n^3 + 144$

18. $\left(32x^2 - 120x + 100\right)\text{units}^2$ 19. $(-2x + 2)\,\text{units}^2$ 20. $(4x^3 - 38x^2 + 84x)\ \text{units}^3$

5.3 Form III

1. $x^2 + 13x + 36$ 2. $5x^2 - 27x - 56$ 3. $12x^2 + 8x - 84$ 4. $72 - 69x + 15x^2$

5. $x^3 + 5x^2 - 7x - 35$ 6. $a^2 - 169$ 7. $49 - m^2$ 8. $25 - 121r^2$ 9. $64x^2 - \dfrac{1}{64}$ 10. $x^4 - 49$

11. $n^2 + 42n + 441$ 12. $w^2 - 28w + 196$ 13. $81a^2 - 198a + 121$ 14. $49x^2 + 2x + \dfrac{1}{49}$

15. $81x^2 - 2x + \dfrac{1}{81}$ 16. $144 - 192m + 64m^2$ 17. $n^6 + 30n^3 + 225$

18. $\left(45x^2 - 73x + 22\right)\text{units}^2$ 19. $(17x - 1)\,\text{units}^2$ 20. $(3x^3 - 50x^2 + 75x)\ \text{units}^3$

5.4 Form I

1. -33 2. 28 3. 12 4. 18 5. -95 6. $4x^2 y^2 + 4y^4$ 7. $5x^4 + 25x^2 y^2 + 2y^4$

8. $4x^2 + xy + 3y^2$ 9. $8x^2 + 3xy + 7y^2$ 10. $x^5 + 8x^4 y + 12y^2$ 11. $6x^7 y^8$ 12. $-12x^4 y^9$

13. $-12a^2b^8 + 32ab^7$ 14. $3x^2 + 26xy + 35y^2$ 15. $20x^2 - 32xy - 16y^2$

16. $4x^2 + 28xy + 49y^2$ 17. $25x^2 - 20xy + 4y^2$ 18. $15x^2 + 10x - 42xy + 24y^2 - 8y$

19. $4a^2 - b^2$ 20. $4x^2 - 4xy + y^2 - 1$

5.4 Form II

1. -44 2. 35 3. 18 4. 32 5. -125 6. $5x^2y^2 + 10y^4$ 7. $-8x^4 + 36x^2y^2$

8. $5x^2 + 5xy + 10y^2$ 9. $10x^2 + 6xy + 8y^2$ 10. $-3x^5 + 10x^4y + 20y^2$ 11. $64x^7y^7$

12. $-32x^3y^8$ 13. $-36a^2b^{11} + 66ab^9$ 14. $4x^2 + 50xy + 66y^2$ 15. $35x^2 - 50xy - 40y^2$

16. $9x^2 + 30xy + 25y^2$ 17. $49x^2 - 126xy + 81y^2$ 18. $42x^2 - 156xy + 7x + 144y^2 - 12y$

19. $16a^2 - b^2$ 20. $9x^2 - 6xy + y^2 - 25$

5.4 Form III

1. 30 2. 53 3. 9 4. 41 5. 65 6. $23x^2y^2 + 13y^4$ 7. $9x^4 + 51x^2y^2 + 32y^4$

8. $11x^2 + 7xy + 9y^2$ 9. $8x^2 + 4xy + 4y^2$ 10. $x^5 + 12x^4y + 18y^2$ 11. $81x^7y^8$ 12. $-48x^3y^9$

13. $-42a^3b^{10} + 84ab^8$ 14. $3x^2 + 59xy + 38y^2$ 15. $30x^2 - 101xy + 77y^2$

16. $16x^2 + 64xy + 64y^2$ 17. $64x^2 - 144xy + 81y^2$ 18. $20x^2 + 28x - 107xy + 143y^2 - 77y$

19. $25a^2 - 4b^2$ 20. $16x^2 - 16xy + 4y^2 - 36$

5.5 Form I

1. 2^2 or 4 2. x^2 3. x^2y^4 4. 1 5. -1 6. 1 7. 7 8. 1 9. $\dfrac{4}{a^2}$ 10. $\dfrac{27x^6}{y^3}$ 11. $\dfrac{4p^2v^4}{s^6}$

12. $-4x^4$ 13. $5x^3yz$ 14. $-6x^5y^3$ 15. $-\dfrac{x}{3}$ 16. $\dfrac{7}{15}$ 17. $3r^6 - 2r^3$ 18. $x^5 - 2x^2$

19. $3x^4 + 4x^3$ 20. $2x^2y - 3x^4y^2 + 4$

5.5 Form II

1. 4^2 or 16 2. x^5 3. $x^{11}y^4$ 4. 1 5. -1 6. 1 7. 12 8. 1 9. $\dfrac{9}{a^2}$ 10. $\dfrac{256x^{12}}{y^8}$

11. $\dfrac{4p^6v^8}{s^8}$ 12. $-9x^9$ 13. $5x^8y^9z$ 14. $-8x^{10}y^3$ 15. $-\dfrac{x^4}{4}$ 16. $\dfrac{8}{11}$ 17. $3r^7 - 5r^4$

18. $4x^6 - 2x^3$ 19. $4x^8 + 10x^4$ 20. $4x^4y^4 - 8x^2y^2 - 9$

5.5 Form III

1. 11^6 2. x^4 3. x^2y^3 4. 1 5. -1 6. 1 7. 18 8. 1 9. $\dfrac{49}{a^{10}}$ 10. $\dfrac{625x^{20}}{y^{12}}$

11. $\dfrac{25p^{12}v^{16}}{s^{14}}$ 12. $8x^{12}$ 13. $3x^{11}y^8z^{11}$ 14. $-2x^3y^3$ 15. $-\dfrac{7x^5}{12}$ 16. $\dfrac{17}{23}$ 17. $2x^8 - 3x^5$

18. $7x^4 - 6x^2$ 19. $5x^6 + 3x^3$ 20. $5x^4y^4 - 4x^2y^2 - 9$

5.6 Form I

1. $x+5$ 2. $x-5$ 3. $x+2$ 4. $x+3$ 5. $x-2$ 6. $x+4$ 7. $x-9$ 8. $x+8$ 9. $x+5$
10. $x-1$ 11. $3x-2$ 12. $7m-7$ 13. $7m^2-3m+8$ 14. $6r^2+5r+4$ 15. $5x^2-3x-4$

5.6 Form II

1. $x-3-\dfrac{8}{x-1}$ 2. $x-5-\dfrac{50}{x-5}$ 3. $x-2-\dfrac{2}{x+6}$ 4. $x^2+3x+15+\dfrac{36}{x-3}$ 5. x^2-2x+4

6. $9x^2-12x+16$ 7. $p-4+\dfrac{5}{p+8}$ 8. $x+8-\dfrac{3}{x+3}$ 9. $2x+5$ 10. $3y^2+6y+8+\dfrac{37}{2y-4}$

11. $x^3+2x^2+4x+6+\dfrac{17}{x-2}$ 12. $3x^2+x+4+\dfrac{7}{x+1}$ 13. y^2-y+1 14. r^3-2r^2+4r-8

15. x^2+2x+3

5.6 Form III

1. $x-2+\dfrac{12}{5x-2}$ 2. $2y^2-7y+4$ 3. y^3-6 4. a^2+5 5. $y^3+3y^2+3y+9+\dfrac{36}{y-3}$

6. y^2-3y+1 7. x^3-2x^2+x-6 8. $x^2-3x+2+\dfrac{4}{x+3}$ 9. x^2+1 10. y^3-1

11. x^2-x+1 12. $2x^2-4x+2+\dfrac{17}{3x+2}$ 13. $x^2+4x+16$ 14. a^2-a+1

15. $-5x^2+5x+4+\dfrac{18}{-3x+2}$

5.7 Form I

1. $-\dfrac{1}{9}$ 2. $\dfrac{5}{6}$ 3. $\dfrac{16}{27}$ 4. $\dfrac{x^2}{2}$ 5. $\dfrac{1}{x^5}$ 6. $\dfrac{2}{x}$ 7. $\dfrac{6}{5p^6}$ 8. $\dfrac{x^4}{y^{10}}$ 9. $8x^2$ 10. 1250

11. 0.03957 12. 0.00020351 13. 4.7 14. 3.418×10^1 15. 1.9×10^4 16. 1.4×10^{-3}
17. 3×10^2 18. 2×10^{-1} 19. 9×10^4 20. 2.51×10^{-7}

5.7 Form II

1. $-\dfrac{1}{16}$ 2. $\dfrac{16}{23}$ 3. $\dfrac{25}{16}$ 4. $\dfrac{x^3}{3}$ 5. $\dfrac{1}{x^2}$ 6. $\dfrac{2}{x^4}$ 7. $\dfrac{5}{2p^{10}}$ 8. $\dfrac{x^2}{y^{12}}$ 9. $\dfrac{27}{x^3}$

10. $11,800,000$ 11. 0.000736 12. 0.00000010483 13. 4.48 14. 6.9735×10^2
15. 6.5×10^7 16. 7.948×10^{-5} 17. 4×10^{-3} 18. 8×10^{-3} 19. 4×10^6 20. 8.96×10^{-8}

5.7 Form III

1. $-\dfrac{1}{216}$ 2. $\dfrac{19}{88}$ 3. $\dfrac{343}{125}$ 4. $\dfrac{x^6}{8}$ 5. $\dfrac{1}{x^2}$ 6. $\dfrac{6}{x^4}$ 7. $\dfrac{7}{3p^{11}}$ 8. $\dfrac{x^6}{y^8}$ 9. $125x^6$ 10. 30500

11. 0.00918 12. 0.000000011936 13. 5.7 14. 1.0457×10^3 15. 2.9×10^{10} 16. 5.7×10^{-6}
17. 4×10^{-2} 18. 1.8×10^3 19. 6.25×10^{-10} 20. 7.7×10^{-7}

Additional Exercises Answers

6.1 Form I

1. $5x$ 2. $4y^2$ 3. $8a^2$ 4. $3x^2$ 5. $5(x^2+4)$ 6. $6a^2(a+3)$ 7. $y(3y^2+5y+6)$

8. $6x(4x^3+3x-2)$ 9. $4xy(4x^3y^2-5x^2y+3)$ 10. $2x^3y^2(2x^2+5xy^2-7y)$

11. $(y+14)(x+6)$ 12. $(b-7)(a-3)$ 13. $(x+10)(11-y)$ 14. $(x+4)(y+2)$

15. $(a+3)(b-6)$ 16. $(x-5)(y+1)$ 17. $(x-2)(x^2+2)$ 18. $(3a+1)(2b+3)$

19. $(5x+2)(y-2)$ 20. $(x^3+2)(x-1)$

6.1 Form II

1. $4x$ 2. $9xy$ 3. $8a^5b^2$ 4. $6m^3n^2$ 5. $7x^2(2x+3)$ 6. $x^5(6-5x^2)$

7. $3a^3(8a^6-10a^2+5)$ 8. $4x^3y^3(5x^3-11x^2y+9y^3)$ 9. $4x^3y^4(10x^5y^4-4y^2-5x^3)$

10. $5x^2y^3(3x^4y^2-5x^2+11xy-12y)$ 11. $(y-7)(x-2)$ 12. $(b+3)(a^2+4)$

13. $(8+b)(4a-1)$ 14. $(x-2)(x^2-3)$ 15. $(x+5)(y+4)$ 16. $(b+2a)(b^2+4)$

17. $(3x+2)(2y+5)$ 18. $(7y-1)(2x-3)$ 19. $(x-2)(4x^3-3)$ 20. $(5a^2-4b^2)(4a+3b)$

6.1 Form III

1. $4x^2$ 2. $3x^4$ 3. $6x^5y^2$ 4. $3y(7y^2-3y+4)$ 5. $8x(4x^4+3x^2y-12y^3)$

6. $5a(4a^2-3a+1)$ 7. $8x^4y^3(6x^4y^6+5x^2y^3+8)$ 8. $16mn(m^2n^2-3m-4n)$

9. $(x-3)(x^2+6)$ 10. $(x+7)(y-1)$ 11. $(2x-7)(6x^2+1)$ 12. $(x-3)(x^3-4x)$

13. $(a-4b)(b+6)$ 14. $(5x+8)(2y-1)$ 15. $(3m+1)(2n-9)$ 16. $(3x^2+5)(3x-2)$

17. $(5x^3+3x)(4x-5)$ 18. $(4a^2-3)(3a-4)$ 19. $2x+4y$ 20. $4x^3+2x^2y-10x-5y$

6.2 Form I

1. $(x+4)(x+1)$ 2. $(x+3)(x+4)$ 3. $(y+2)(y+6)$ 4. $(a-4)(a-2)$ 5. $(x-5)(x-3)$

6. $(y-7)(y-1)$ 7. $(a+3)(a-2)$ 8. $(x+5)(x-8)$ 9. $(m+1)(m-4)$ 10. $(x+2y)(x+5y)$

11. $(a+7b)(a-3b)$ 12. $(x+3y)(x-9y)$ 13. $(a-5)(a-6)$ 14. $(x+7)(x+4)$

15. $2(x+1)(x-3)$ 16. $3(a-2)(a-3)$ 17. $x(x+6)(x+1)$ 18. $xy(x+7)(x-5)$

19. $4(x-2)(x-6)$ 20. $8a(a+3)(a+4)$

6.2 Form II

1. $(x+8)(x+2)$ 2. $(x-4)(x-6)$ 3. $(x+5)(x-6)$ 4. $(a+3)(a+7)$ 5. $(y+12)(y-3)$

6. $(x-6)(x-9)$ 7. $(x+9)(x-4)$ 8. $(a+11)(a+3)$ 9. Prime   10. $(x-1)(x-10)$

11. $(y+7)(y-6)$ 12. $(a+5)(a+4)$ 13. Prime   14. $(y-8)(y-4)$ 15. $5(x+3)(x-1)$

16. $4(x+4)(x+3)$ 17. $x^2(x-6)(x+8)$ 18. $2a(a+4)(a+5)$ 19. $xy^2(x-5)(x+8)$

20. $6y(y+4)(y+7)$

6.2 Form III

1. $(x+9)(x+5)$ 2. $(a-8)(a+3)$ 3. $(y+7)(y+2)$ 4. $(x-16)(x-2)$ 5. $(x-1)(x-12)$
6. $(y+8)(y-11)$ 7. $(a-b)(a+16b)$ 8. Prime 9. $(y-13)(y-3)$ 10. $(a-17)(a-8)$
11. $(x+18y)(x+3y)$ 12. $(y-6)(y-2)$ 13. Prime 14. $(x-15y)(x+4y)$
15. $4x(x^2-2x+4)$ 16. $5(x-8)(x+2)$ 17. $3a(a+4)(a+5)$ 18. $x^2y(x+6)(x-4)$
19. $6y(y-9)(y+4)$ 20. $8x(x^2+7xy+12y^2)$

6.3 Form I

1. $(x+4)(2x+1)$ 2. $(3x+1)(x+5)$ 3. $(4a+3)(a+2)$ 4. $(x+8)(3x-2)$ 5. $(2y+5)(y-3)$
6. $(3x+1)(x-5)$ 7. $(4a-5)(a-2)$ 8. $(6x-1)(x-3)$ 9. $(2y-3)(3y-2)$
10. $(4x+1)(2x+1)$ 11. $(5x-1)(2x-3)$ 12. $(6y+5)(2y-1)$ 13. $(8a+3)(2a-5)$
14. $2(3x+1)(x+4)$ 15. $3(4x-1)(2x-5)$ 16. $a^2(5a-2)(2a+1)$ 17. $4y(2y+3)(y+2)$
18. $x^2(3x+2)(x-2)$ 19. $2a(4a+3)(a-3)$ 20. $5(2x+5)(x+2)$

6.3 Form II

1. $(3x+1)(2x+3)$ 2. $(4x+3)(x+2)$ 3. $(2x+5)(5x+1)$ 4. $(4x-5)(2x-1)$
5. $(3x-4)(4x-3)$ 6. $(5x+8)(2x-3)$ 7. $(8x+1)(x+4)$ 8. $(7x-2)(2x+3)$
9. $(6x+5)(x-2)$ 10. $(4x-5)(4x+3)$ 11. $(2x+9y)(6x-y)$ 12. $(8x-3)(2x+5)$
13. $(3x+7y)(x-4y)$ 14. $4(2a+1)(a+1)$ 15. $6(3a-1)(a+4)$ 16. $5(4y+1)(y-2)$
17. $6x(2x^2+3x+4)$ 18. $3a(2a+3)(2a-5)$ 19. $2y(8y-3)(2y+5)$ 20. $8(3x-4)(2x+1)$

6.3 Form III

1. $(7x+11)(x+1)$ 2. $(2a+7)(a-4)$ 3. Prime 4. $(3x+2)(5x+6)$ 5. $(9x-4)(x+2)$
6. $(2a-3)(5a+4)$ 7. $(8y-1)(3y+4)$ 8. $(5x+2y)(3x-y)$ 9. $x^2(x+6)(x+1)$
10. $(5b-2)(3b+4)$ 11. $(5x+9)(4x-3)$ 12. $2(2x+y)(x-4y)$ 13. Prime
14. $7(2x+3)(3x-2)$ 15. $(4a+1)(3a+4)$ 16. $6(3y+2)(y-5)$ 17. $5(4x+y)(3x+y)$
18. $(4x-5)(2x-5)$ 19. $xy^4(4x+5y)^2$ 20. $6x+5$

6.4 Form I

1. $(x+8)(x-8)$ 2. $(a+1)(a-1)$ 3. $(y+10)(y-10)$ 4. $(2x+5)(2x-5)$ 5. $(x+5)^2$
6. $(y+3)^2$ 7. $(a-4)^2$ 8. $(a-10)^2$ 9. $(x-1)(x^2+x+1)$ 10. $(y+4)(y^2-4y+16)$
11. $(x-2y)(x^2+2xy+4y^2)$ 12. $(a+3b)(a^2-3ab+9b^2)$ 13. $2(x+1)(x-1)$
14. $3(x-4)^2$ 15. $x(x+4)(x-4)$ 16. $5(y+2)^2$ 17. $7(x+2)(x-2)$
18. $100(x+2y)(x-2y)$ 19. $4(a-5)^2$ 20. $8(x+3)^2$

6.4 Form II

1. $(x+11)(x-11)$ 2. $(2a+9)(2a-9)$ 3. $(4y+13)(4y-13)$ 4. $(x+15)(x-15)$
5. $(x-2)^2$ 6. Prime   7. $(x-5y)^2$ 8. $(2x+3)^2$ 9. $(x-10)(x^2+10x+100)$
10. $(a+2b)(a^2-2ab+4b^2)$ 11. $(y-3)(y^2+3y+9)$ 12. $(5x+3y)^2$ 13. $5(x+2)(x-2)$
14. $3(2x+5)^2$ 15. Prime   16. $ab^2(b+8a)(b-8a)$ 17. $9y(y+1)(y-1)$ 18. $3x(2x+7)^2$
19. $(x^2+4)(x+2)(x-2)$ 20. $5(2x+5)(2x-5)$

6.4 Form III

1. $(7x+8)(7x-8)$ 2. Prime   3. $(x-6)^2$ 4. $18(a+2)(a-2)$ 5. $(3x-5)^2$ 6. $2(4x+3)^2$
7. $(a+5b)(a^2-5ab+25b^2)$ 8. $(7x+1)^2$ 9. $(2x-9y)^2$ 10. $(2-m)(4+2m+m^2)$
11. $2(4x+7)(4x-7)$ 12. $16(x^2+4y^2)$ 13. $5(2x+5y)^2$
14. $2x(3x+4y)(9x-12xy+16y^2)$ 15. Prime   16. $2(2a-3b)(4a^2+6ab+9b^2)$
17. $(9m+13n)^2$ 18. $(x^3+9y^2)(x^3-9y^2)$ 19. $(x+6)(x+10)$ 20. $25(a-3)^2$

6.5 Form I

1. $(x+8)(x-8)$ 2. $(2x+3)(4x-1)$ 3. $(a-7)^2$ 4. $3(x^2-6)$ 5. $(5x+1)(2x+3)$
6. $(x+7)(x+2)$ 7. $x^2(x+6)(x-2)$ 8. $(x+5)(y-4)$ 9. $2(a+1)^2$ 10. $y(y+3)(y-8)$
11. $(3m+4)(2m+3)$ 12. $4(x+4)(x-4)$ 13. $(x^2+4)(x-8)$ 14. $7(x-3)(2x+5)$
15. $2(y-2)(y^2+2y+4)$ 16. Prime   17. $4x^3(x^2-2)$ 18. $3xy(2x+1)(5x-4)$
19. $5(2x-1)(4x^2+2x+1)$ 20. $4(y^2-8)(x^2+4)$

6.5 Form II

1. $(y-4)(y^2+4y+16)$ 2. $3(x+5)(x-5)$ 3. $4(2x+3)(2x-5)$ 4. $(x^2+6)(y-4)$
5. $(7x-8)(3x-4)$ 6. $(6x+5y)(6x-5y)$ 7. $4(a+4)(a^2-4a+16)$ 8. $xy(5x^2-4y)$
9. $6(x+7)^2$ 10. $(3x+8)(4x+3)$ 11. $6(2y-1)(4y^2+2y+1)$ 12. $3(2x+5)(3y-2)$
13. Prime   14. $ab^2(a+b)^2$ 15. $(12x+5)(4x-7)$ 16. Prime
17. $3(a-5b)(a^2+5ab+25b^2)$ 18. $(4x^2+9)(2x+3)(2x-3)$ 19. $2x(3x+1)^2$
20. $x(y^3+4)(x^2-3)$

6.5 Form III

1. $(a^2+9)(a+3)(a-3)$ 2. $(6x-7)(3x+5)$ 3. $(2y-5)(4y^2+10y+25)$
4. $(3x^2-2)(4y^2+3)$ 5. $11(2a+3)(2a-1)$ 6. $(8y+5)(8y-5)$ 7. $xy(5x-6)(x+4)$
8. $2a(4a-5b)(5b+4)$ 9. $(6y-7)^2$ 10. $(9x^2+25)(3x+5)(3x-5)$ 11. $5(3a-4)^2$
12. Prime   13. $xy^2(9x+10y)(2x-5y)$ 14. $2(3a+2)(9a^2-6a+4)$ 15. $25(y+2)(y-2)$
16. $(5x+12)(2x-9)$ 17. $(x+y)(x^2-xy+y^2)(x-y)(x^2+xy+y^2)$ 18. $9(x+4)(5x-2)$
19. $(a^2-2b^2)(a^4+2a^2b^2+4b^4)$ 20. Prime

6.6 Form I

1. $\{-7, 9\}$ 2. $\{-12, -8\}$ 3. $\left\{-\dfrac{1}{3}, \dfrac{1}{2}\right\}$ 4. $\{0, 5\}$ 5. $\left\{-3, 0, \dfrac{4}{5}\right\}$ 6. $\{1, 4\}$

7. $\left\{-\dfrac{2}{3}, 4\right\}$ 8. $(-4, 5\}$ 9. $\{-6, 2\}$ 10. $\left\{-\dfrac{2}{3}, \dfrac{1}{2}\right\}$ 11. $\{-7, 7\}$ 12. $\{4, 5\}$

13. $\left\{-\dfrac{5}{2}, 6\right\}$ 14. $\{-1, 6\}$ 15. $\left\{0, \dfrac{5}{3}\right\}$ 16. $\left\{\dfrac{2}{3}\right\}$ 17. width: 4 meters; length: 10 meters

18. 5 seconds

6.6 Form II

1. $\{7, 10\}$ 2. $\{-12, -4\}$ 3. $\left\{-9, \dfrac{4}{5}\right\}$ 4. $\{-6, 0, 7\}$ 5. $\left\{-3, 0, \dfrac{7}{4}\right\}$ 6. $\{1, 8\}$

7. $\left\{-4, \dfrac{3}{4}\right\}$ 8. $\left\{-\dfrac{2}{5}, 5\right\}$ 9. $\left\{-\dfrac{5}{2}, \dfrac{5}{2}\right\}$ 10. $\left\{-\dfrac{1}{3}, 7\right\}$ 11. $\left\{-\dfrac{7}{2}, \dfrac{1}{4}\right\}$ 12. $\left\{-\dfrac{10}{3}, 8\right\}$

13. $\left\{-\dfrac{3}{5}, -\dfrac{2}{5}\right\}$ 14. $\left\{-\dfrac{7}{4}, 0\right\}$ 15. $\{0, 3, 5\}$ 16. $\left\{0, \dfrac{1}{2}, 4\right\}$

17. width: 9 inches; length 10 inches 18. 2 seconds

6.6 Form III

1. $\left\{-\dfrac{4}{7}, 2\right\}$ 2. $\left\{\dfrac{10}{3}, 8\right\}$ 3. $\{-5, 0\}$ 4. $\{-17, 0\}$ 5. $\left\{0, \dfrac{1}{5}, 8\right\}$ 6. $\left\{-1, \dfrac{9}{5}\right\}$ 7. $\{-1, 25\}$

8. $\left\{0, \dfrac{6}{13}\right\}$ 9. $\left\{-\dfrac{5}{4}, \dfrac{5}{4}\right\}$ 10. $\left\{\dfrac{5}{2}\right\}$ 11. $\left\{-\dfrac{5}{2}, 0, \dfrac{3}{4}\right\}$ 12. $\left\{-\dfrac{7}{3}, 4\right\}$ 13. $\left\{-2, \dfrac{2}{5}\right\}$

14. $\{-5, 0, 5\}$ 15. $\left\{-8, \dfrac{9}{2}\right\}$ 16. $\left\{-\dfrac{2}{5}, 6\right\}$ 17. width: 12 feet; length: 18 feet

18. 6 meters 19. $2\dfrac{1}{2}$ seconds 20. 9 minutes

Additional Exercises Answers

7.1 Form I

1. -1 2. 3 3. none 4. 3 5. ± 4 6. $-1, 5$ 7. defined for all real numbers 8. 0

9. $x + 2$ 10. 3 11. -1 12. $\dfrac{1}{x - 5}$ 13. cannot be simplified 14. $\dfrac{x + 5}{x - 5}$ 15. $80

7.1 Form II

1. 8 2. -6 3. none 4. 6 5. ± 7 6. $-8, -5$ 7. $2, 8$ 8. $2k^2$ 9. $\dfrac{1}{3x + 2}$ 10. $\dfrac{y + 7}{y + 8}$

11. -1 12. $-\dfrac{2}{7}$ 13. $4x - 6$ 14. $\dfrac{7x}{4}$ 15. $48

7.1 Form III

1. ± 5 2. 3 3. $-\dfrac{1}{3}, 2$ 4. $-\dfrac{3}{4}, 7$ 5. $-1, \dfrac{4}{3}$ 6. $4, -\dfrac{1}{5}$ 7. none 8. $\dfrac{x - 3}{x - 5}$ 9. $\dfrac{6}{x - 4}$

10. $\dfrac{x + y}{x^2 + xy + y^2}$ 11. $\dfrac{x - 6}{x + 6}$ 12. $a - b$ 13. $y^2 + 2y + 4$ 14. cannot be simplified

15. $41.25

7.2 Form I

1. $\dfrac{24}{x}$ 2. $18z$ 3. $\dfrac{a}{d}$ 4. $\dfrac{x}{3}$ 5. $\dfrac{2}{x}$ 6. $\dfrac{x^3}{2y}$ 7. $\dfrac{1}{y - 5}$ 8. $\dfrac{x + y}{2}$ 9. $\dfrac{14}{x}$ 10. $\dfrac{27p}{10}$

11. $y - 2$ 12. 15 13. $\dfrac{x - y}{x^2 + y^2}$ 14. $\dfrac{8}{5}$ 15. $\dfrac{1}{(x - 4)(2x - 1)}$

7.2 Form II

1. $\dfrac{12p}{5}$ 2. $\dfrac{a + 4}{a + 5}$ 3. $\dfrac{x + 2}{x + 3}$ 4. $\dfrac{x - 2}{3(x + 4)}$ 5. $5(x - 7)$ 6. $\dfrac{1}{x - 2}$ 7. $(x - 3)(x - 2)$

8. $\dfrac{x + 3}{3}$ 9. -1 10. $x + 2$ 11. 1 12. $\dfrac{x + 5}{x - 5}$ 13. $x(x + 9)$ 14. $\dfrac{(x - 2)^2}{(x - 3)^2}$ 15. $\dfrac{x + 8}{x + 4}$

7.2 Form III

1. $\dfrac{k}{k - 9}$ 2. $\dfrac{k}{k + 9}$ 3. 1 4. $\dfrac{(x - 7)(x - 1)}{(x - 12)(x - 11)}$ 5. $-\dfrac{1}{12}$ 6. $(x + 1)(x - 1)$ 7. $(x + 2)(x - 2)$

8. 1 9. $\dfrac{z + 8}{z}$ 10. $\dfrac{z - 4}{z}$ 11. $-\dfrac{a - 12}{a + 12}$ 12. $\dfrac{7}{2}$ 13. $\dfrac{(x + 1)(x - 1)}{(x + 4)^2}$ 14. $\dfrac{x + 3}{x + 4}$ 15. $\dfrac{x + 3}{x - 2}$

7.3 Form I

1. $\dfrac{11}{14x}$ 2. $\dfrac{5}{13x}$ 3. $\dfrac{4x+5}{5}$ 4. $3b$ 5. $\dfrac{8}{x+2}$ 6. $\dfrac{1}{x-1}$ 7. $\dfrac{4x+1}{x+2}$ 8. $\dfrac{7}{8x^2}$ 9. $\dfrac{2}{x-3}$

10. $\dfrac{17}{x-4}$ 11. $\dfrac{1}{x-2}$ 12. $\dfrac{9}{x-8}$ 13. $\dfrac{13}{x-2}$ 14. $\dfrac{3}{x-5}$ 15. $\dfrac{16}{x-1}$

7.3 Form II

1. 1 2. -1 3. 6 4. $3y$ 5. $\dfrac{8}{q-7}$ 6. $\dfrac{5x+6}{5x-7}$ 7. 1 8. $\dfrac{3x+2}{3x+5}$ 9. $\dfrac{4x+3}{x-3}$ 10. $\dfrac{3}{x-3}$

11. $\dfrac{6x+1}{x-6}$ 12. $\dfrac{x+6}{x-5}$ 13. $m-6$ 14. $\dfrac{14}{x+3}$ 15. $\dfrac{x-1}{x-6}$

7.3 Form III

1. $\dfrac{y+2}{y+4}$ 2. $\dfrac{x+2}{x^2}$ 3. $4x-1$ 4. $x+4$ 5. $\dfrac{2x-1}{x-5}$ 6. $-\dfrac{3}{x+y}$ 7. $\dfrac{y-5}{2y-3}$ 8. $\dfrac{2x+3}{x+1}$

9. 1 10. $\dfrac{2x-10}{x^2-9}$ 11. $\dfrac{19}{x-8}$ 12. $\dfrac{y+4}{3y-8}$ 13. $\dfrac{5y+1}{2y+1}$ 14. $-\dfrac{6}{x+y}$ 15. $\dfrac{x+6}{x-8}$

7.4 Form I

1. $60x^3$ 2. $36x^5$ 3. $10x^2y^2$ 4. $30x^2y$ 5. $t(t-2)$ 6. $(x+2)(x-3)$ 7. $x^2(x+1)$

8. $\dfrac{2y+5}{y^2}$ 9. $\dfrac{4x+1}{x}$ 10. $\dfrac{4x+5}{10x^2}$ 11. $\dfrac{3(2-3z)}{z^2}$ 12. $\dfrac{-6x-35}{15x}$ 13. $\dfrac{x^2+3xy-y^2}{x^2y^2}$

14. $\dfrac{11-5z}{z}$ 15. $x-1$

7.4 Form II

1. $(x-5)(x+3)$ 2. $(x+3)(x-3)$ 3. $3a(a-2)$ 4. $x(x+2)(x-2)$ 5. $(a+1)^2$

6. $8(x-1)$ 7. $(x+2)(x+3)$ 8. $\dfrac{10r-6}{r(r-3)}$ 9. $\dfrac{-81x-35}{9x}$ 10. $\dfrac{7}{w-12}$ 11. $\dfrac{3x-45}{(x+5)(x-5)}$

12. $\dfrac{4x+5}{4(x-3)}$ 13. $\dfrac{2x^2-10x+25}{x(x-5)}$ 14. $\dfrac{3x-5}{(x-1)^2}$ 15. $2x-3$

7.4 Form III

1. $r(r+1)^2$ 2. $m(m+6)(m+3)$ 3. $(x+4)(x+3)^2$ 4. $(x-2)^2(x-3)$

5. $(x+2)(x-2)(x+3)$ 6. $y^2(y+1)(y-1)$ 7. $(x+1)(x-2)(x+2)$ 8. $\dfrac{6m^2+5m+3}{(m+4)(m-1)(m+6)}$

9. $\dfrac{10y-11}{(y-1)(y+1)(y-2)}$ 10. $\dfrac{x^2-5x+24}{(x+4)(x-4)(x+1)}$ 11. $\dfrac{5x+12}{(x-3)(x+3)(x+2)}$

12. $\dfrac{3x+20}{(x+4)(x-4)}$ 13. $\dfrac{2}{7}D$ 14. $\dfrac{7}{24}D$ 15. $3x-5$

7.5 Form I

1. $\dfrac{9}{8}$ 2. $\dfrac{2}{5}$ 3. $\dfrac{1}{y}$ 4. $\dfrac{288}{385}$ 5. $-\dfrac{28}{3}$ 6. $\dfrac{217}{132}$ 7. 10 8. $\dfrac{8+a}{8-a}$ 9. $\dfrac{36}{x}$ 10. $\dfrac{y+x}{y-x}$

11. $\dfrac{2y+x}{2y-2x}$ 12. $\dfrac{16}{x}$ 13. $3s+7t$ 14. $\dfrac{x-3}{x+2}$ 15. Any value but 3.

7.5 Form II

1. $\dfrac{x(x+9)}{28}$ 2. $\dfrac{y(y+9)}{15}$ 3. $\dfrac{2(y+4)}{9y}$ 4. $\dfrac{2(y+7)}{3y}$ 5. $\dfrac{2-5r}{5r}$ 6. $\dfrac{5y+2x}{7xy-9}$ 7. $\dfrac{x-3}{x-2}$

8. $\dfrac{x}{x-2}$ 9. $\dfrac{3+x}{3-x}$ 10. $\dfrac{x+3}{x+2}$ 11. $\dfrac{x}{x^2+1}$ 12. $\dfrac{3a+8}{3a+10}$ 13. $\dfrac{5x+1}{5x-1}$ 14. $\dfrac{2x}{5(x-3)}$

15. Any value but $\dfrac{3}{2}$.

7.5 Form III

1. $\dfrac{x-1}{x+1}$ 2. $\dfrac{1}{(x-2)(x+5)}$ 3. $\dfrac{2y-1}{2y+1}$ 4. $\dfrac{x+2}{x+3}$ 5. $\dfrac{1}{a^2-a+1}$ 6. $\dfrac{x+3}{x-2}$ 7. $\dfrac{x-5}{x+5}$

8. $-\dfrac{1}{3}$ 9. $\dfrac{y}{x}$ 10. x^2+1 11. -2 12. $\dfrac{x-2}{x+8}$ 13. $\dfrac{k-6}{3}$ 14. $\dfrac{2-9r}{9r}$

15. Any value but $-\dfrac{7}{8}$.

7.6 Form I

1. $\{144\}$ 2. $\{6\}$ 3. $\left\{-\dfrac{7}{6}\right\}$ 4. $\{1\}$ 5. $\left\{\dfrac{29}{2}\right\}$ 6. $\{-6\}$ 7. $\{-4,-1\}$ 8. $\{10\}$ 9. $\{3\}$

10. $\{3\}$ 11. $A=P(1+rt)$ 12. $m=\dfrac{Fr}{v^2}$ 13. $p=\dfrac{qf}{q-f}$ 14. $P_2=\dfrac{V_1P_1}{V_2}$ 15. $R_1=\dfrac{RR_2}{R_2-R}$

7.6 Form II

1. $\left\{\dfrac{2}{9}\right\}$ 2. $\varnothing$ 3. $\left\{\dfrac{3}{13}\right\}$ 4. $\{-6\}$ 5. $\left\{\dfrac{1}{2},-3\right\}$ 6. $\{-4\}$ 7. $\{-10,9\}$ 8. $\left\{\dfrac{5}{3},-\dfrac{1}{2}\right\}$

9. $\left\{\dfrac{1}{2}\right\}$ 10. $\{16\}$ 11. $a=\dfrac{b}{bc-1}$ 12. $b=\dfrac{ac}{a-c}$ 13. $t=\dfrac{A-P}{Pr}$ 14. $b=\dfrac{2A-Bh}{h}$

15. $d=\dfrac{Pt}{F}$

7.6 Form III

1. $\{-2\}$ 2. $\varnothing$ 3. $\{2\}$ 4. $\{7\}$ 5. $\varnothing$ 6. $\{2\}$ 7. $\left\{\dfrac{3}{5},-\dfrac{1}{2}\right\}$ 8. $\left\{-\dfrac{5}{6}\right\}$ 9. $\{-5\}$ 10. $\{10\}$

11. $h=\dfrac{3V}{4\pi r^2}$ 12. $n=\dfrac{R-C}{P}$ 13. $b=\dfrac{af}{a-f}$ 14. $m=\dfrac{-VM}{V-v}$ or $\dfrac{VM}{v-V}$ 15. $m_2=\dfrac{Fr^2}{Gm_1}$

7.7 Form I

1. 5 mph 2. 6 mph 3. $84.38 4. $\frac{14}{5}$ minutes 5. $1980 6. 100 trout 7. 28 inches

8. 25 feet 9. 18 10. 24 m

7.7 Form II

1. 20 mph 2. $\frac{150}{7}$ km/h 3. 6 minutes 4. $\frac{44}{7}$ minutes 5. $5500 6. 60 trout 7. 9 yrs.

8. 6 feet 9. 28 10. 11.25 inches

7.7 Form III

1. SUV: 30 km/h; sports car: 70 km/h 2. $\frac{55}{19}$ mph 3. $\frac{12}{5}$ hr.

4. Baker: 15 minutes; assistant: 60 minutes 5. $5625 6. 119 trout 7. 9 inches

8. 10 feet 9. 9 10. 13/5 feet

7.8 Form I

1. $y = 63$ 2. $y = 960$ 3. $s = 144$ 4. $m = 42$ 5. $x = 6$ 6. $x = 36$ 7. $f = 32$ 8. $f = -24$

9. $q = 3$ 10. $h = 6$ 11. 3 gallons 12. 240 milliamperes 13. 60 gallons 14. 88.2 meters

15. 84 pounds per square inch 16. 5 feet per second 17. 60 milliamperes 18. 2.8 quarts

19. $736.00 20. 96 watts

7.8 Form II

1. $y = 99$ 2. $y = 192$ 3. $s = 300$ 4. $m = 108$ 5. $x = 20$ 6. $x = 45$ 7. $f = 24$ 8. $f = -\frac{56}{9}$

9. $q = 8$ 10. $h = 7$ 11. 7.7 gallons 12. 220 milliamperes 13. 91 gallons 14. 161.6 meters

15. 120 pounds per square inch 16. 7 feet per second 17. 60 milliamperes 18. 3.2 quarts

19. $395.20 20. 125 watts

7.8 Form III

1. $y = 192$ 2. $y = 324$ 3. $s = 225$ 4. $m = 270$ 5. $x = 15$ 6. $x = 96$ 7. $f = 1323$

8. $f = -800$ 9. $q = 6$ 10. $h = 4$ 11. 5.6 gallons 12. 350 milliamperes 13. 79.75 gallons

14. 255 meters 15. 132 pound per square inch 16. 8.4 feet per second 17. 50 milliamperes

18. 3.6 quarts 19. $472.50 20. 108 watts

Additional Exercises Answers

8.1 Form I

1a. $\{1, 2, 3\}$ b. $\{4, 5, 6\}$ 2a. (3) b. (5, 7, 9) 3. function 4. function 5. not a function
6. 2 7. 4 8. –4 9. –6 10. –4 11. –12 12. 1 13. 5 14. –11 15. days of the week
16. degrees 17. (5, 85), (M, 90), (T, 95), (W, 80), (R, 75), (F, 75), (S, 70) 18. A function is a correspondence from a first set, called the domain corresponds to exactly one element in the range. 19. yes 20. Each element in the domain corresponds to exactly one element in the range.

.

8.1 Form II

1a. $\{-1, -3, -8\}$ b. $\{2, -6, 4\}$ 2a. (1, –2, –3) b. (4) 3. not a function 4. function
5. not a function 6. $3a + 4$ 7. –2 8. 13 9. $4a - 2$ 10. –10 11. 10 12. $a^2 + a + 1$ 13. 3
14. 13. 15. majors 16. percent of students 17. (education, 25%), (business, 20%), (nursing, 15%), (math/eng, 10%), (pre-major, 10%) 18. A function is a correspondence from a first set, called the domain to a second set, called the range, such that each element in the domain corresponds to exactly one element in the range. 19. yes 20. Each element in the domain corresponds to exactly one element in the range.

8.1 Form III

1a. $\{-8, -5, 2\}$ b. $\{-2, -7, -1\}$ 2a. (3, 2, –6) b. (6, –4, 9) 3. function 4. not a function
5. function 6. 28 7. 4 8. $2a^2 + 4ah + 2h^2 - 4$ 9. 54 10. 12
11. $3a^2 + 6ah + 3h^2 - a - h + 2$ 12. undefined 13. $\dfrac{1}{2}$ 14. $\dfrac{2a + 2h - 1}{a + h + 4}$ 15. number of
year's experience 16. salary
17. (0, \$37,500), (1, \$39,500), (2, \$41,000), (3, \$42,000), (4, \$42,000), (5, \$43,000), (6, \$44,000)
18. A function is a correspondence from a first set, called the domain to a second set, called the range, such that each element in the domain corresponds to exactly one element in the range.
19. yes 20. Each element in the domain corresponds to exactly one element in the range.

8.2 Form I

1. function 2. function 3. not a function 4. –3 5. 3 6. –1 7. 2 8. 2 9. 2

10. $\{x \mid -1 < x \le 5\}$

11. $\{x \mid x \ge 2\}$

12. $\{x \mid x \text{ is a real number}\}$ 13. $\{y \mid y \text{ is a real number}\}$ 14. $R(100) = \$150$
15. $R(225) = \$337.50$

8.2 Form II

1. function   2. function   3. not a function   4. 0   5. 1   6. 2   7. 0   8. 2   9. 4

10. $\{x \mid x \le 4\}$

11. $\{x \mid 2 \le x < 6\}$

12. $\{x \mid x \text{ is a real number}\}$ 13. $\{y \mid y \le 0\}$ 14. $P(100) = 38$ 15. $P(500) = 398$

8.2 Form III

1. function   2. function   3. not a function   4. –2   5. –1   6. 2   7. 1   8. 3   9. 2

10. $\{x \mid x \le 5\}$

11. $\{x \mid -3 < x \le 8\}$

12. $\{-3, -2, -1, 2, 3\}$ 13. $\{4\}$ 14. $C(50,000) = \$47,000$ 15. $C(100,000) = \$77,000$

8.3 Form I

1. $\{x \mid x \text{ is a real number}\}$ 2. $\{x \mid x \text{ is a real number}\}$ 3. $\{x \mid x \text{ is a real number and } x \ne -3\}$
4. $\{x \mid x \text{ is a real number and } x \ne 5\}$ 5. $5x + 2$ 6. 12   7. $-10x - 2$ 8. –42   9. $-2x^2 + x - 2$
10. –17   11. $\{x \mid x \text{ is a real number}\}$ 12. $\{x \mid x \text{ is a real number and } x \ne 1\}$
13. $x \mid x \text{ is a real number and } x \ne -8\}$ 14. $x^2 + 2x + 1$ 15. 9   16. $\{x \mid x \text{ is a real number}\}$
17. $-x^2 + 2x + 1$ 18. –14   19. $\{x \mid x \text{ is a real number}\}$
20. \$340 (The profit when 92 toaster ovens are made and sold is \$340.)

8.3 Form II

1. $\{x \mid x \text{ is a real number and } x \ne -1\}$ 2. $\{x \mid x \text{ is a real number and } x \ne 7\}$ 3.$\{x \mid x \text{ is a real number}$
and $x \ne 3\}$ 4. $\{x \mid x \text{ is a real number and } x \ne 4\}$ 5. $3x^2 + x - 5$ 6. 9   7. $2x^2 + 2x - 4$ 8. 20
9. $4x^2 - x - 1$ 10. 38   11. $\{x \mid x \text{ is a real number and } x \ne 0 \text{ and } x \ne -2\}$
12. $\{x \mid x \text{ is a real number and } x \ne 4 \text{ and } x \ne -4\}$ 13. $\{x \mid x \text{ is a real number and } x \ne -7 \text{ and } x \ne 3\}$
14. $\dfrac{3x + 2}{x + 2}$ 15. 2   16. $\{x \mid x \text{ is a real number and } x \ne -2\}$ 17. $\dfrac{3x - 2}{x + 2}$ 18. 11

19. $\{x \mid x$ is a real number and $x \neq -2\}$ 20. $-\$30$ (The profit when 82 microwave ovens are made and sold is a loss of $\$30$.)

8.3 Form III

1. $\{x \mid x$ is a real number and $x \neq 2\}$ 2. $\{x \mid x$ is a real number and $x \neq -2\}$
3. $\{x \mid x$ is a real number and $x \neq -5$ and $x \neq 6\}$ 4. $\{x \mid x$ is a real number and $x \neq 4$ and $x \neq -1\}$
5. $-2x+2$ 6. 2 7. $x^2 + x + 2$ 8. 8 9. $-3x^2 + 9x - 10$ 10. -94
11. $\{x \mid x$ is a real number and $x \neq 6$ and $x \neq -2\}$ 12. $\{x \mid x$ is a real number and $x \neq 4\}$

13. $\{x \mid x$ is a real number$\}$ 14. 17 15. 2 16. $\dfrac{x^2 + 3x}{x+5}$ 17. $\dfrac{2}{3}$

18. $\{x \mid x$ is a real number and $x \neq -5\}$ 19. $10x - 4000$ 20. $\$150$ (The profit when 415 lamps are made and sold is $\$150$.)

8.4 Form I

1. 50 2. $3x+1$ 3. $6x^2 - 8x$ 4. $18x^2 + 3x$ 5. $-x+16$ 6. $-x$ 7. 11 8. $8\sqrt{x+6} - 10$
9. yes 10. no 11. yes 12. yes 13. yes 14. no 15. $f^{-1}(x) = \dfrac{x+7}{-5}$ 16. $f^{-1}(x) = -\dfrac{1}{2}x$
17. $f^{-1}(x) = 4x+3$ 18. $f^{-1}(x) = 3x-3$

19. 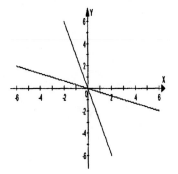 20.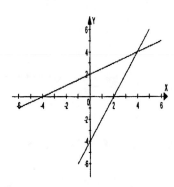

8.4 **Form II**
1. 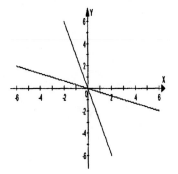 118 2. $5x+5$ 3.
$15x^2 - 6x$ 4. $45x^2 - 6x$
5. $-6x+22$ 6. x 7. $-x-8$ 8. 8
9. yes 10. no 11. no 12. yes 13. yes 14. no 15. $f^{-1}(x) = 2x+7$ 16. $f^{-1}(x) = 3x$
17. $f^{-1}(x) = \sqrt{x} - 3$ 18. $f^{-1}(x) = x^3 + 6$

19. 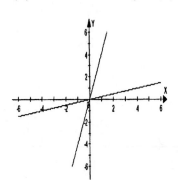 20.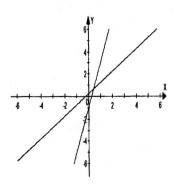

8.4 Form III

1. 12. 2. $2\sqrt{2x-1}$ 3. $x^4 - 8x + 28$ 4. $\dfrac{-7x}{3}$ 5. $x+8$ 6. 4 7. $\dfrac{1}{5}$ 8. $\dfrac{3}{4}$ 9. yes

10. no 11. yes 12. yes 13. no 14. yes 15. $f^{-1}(x) = -\dfrac{1}{3}x + \dfrac{4}{3}$ 16. $f^{-1}(x) = -3x + 3$

17. $f^{-1}(x) = \dfrac{6}{2x-1}$ 18. $f^{-1}(x) = \dfrac{1}{x^2}$

19.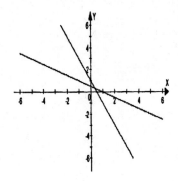

20.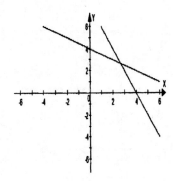

1. $x \le 1$

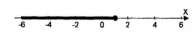

2. $x \ge -4$

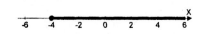

3. $x < -3$

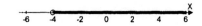

4. $x > -4$

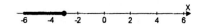

5. $x \ge 4$

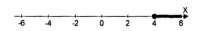

6. $x > 1$

7. $x \le 2$

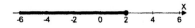

8. $x > 5$

9. $(-\infty, 4)$ 10a. $P(x) = 20x - 12{,}500$ b. more than 625 units   11a. $P(x) = 12x - 15{,}000$
b. more than 1250 units

1. $x < 2$

2. $x < 0$

3. $x \geq 2$

4. $x \leq 1$

5. $\{x \mid x$ is a real number$\}$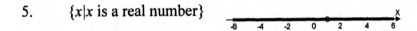

6. $\emptyset$

7. $x < 12$

8. $x < -2$

9. $\left(\dfrac{2}{3}, \ \infty \right)$ 10a. $P(x) = 6x - 21{,}000$ b. more than 3500 units   11a. $P(x) = 25x -$
17,500
b. more than 700 units

1. ∅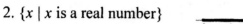

2. $\{x \mid x \text{ is a real number}\}$

3. $x > \dfrac{9}{2}$

4. $x < 5$

5. $x \le 25$

6. $x > 19$

7. $x < 1$

8. $x \ge 0$

9. $(-\infty, -12)$ 10a. $P(x) = 12x - 25,000$ b. more than 2100 units 11a. $P(x) = 16x - 18,000$
b. more than 1175 units

9.2 Form I

1. {1, 2, 3, 4, 5, 6, 7, 9, 11} 2. {2, 4, 6} 3. {2, 4, 6, 8} 4. Ø 5. Ø 6. {1, 3, 5}
7. {1, 2, 3, 4, 5, 6, 8} 8. $\{x \mid x > 4\}$ $(4, \infty)$ 9. $\{x \mid x > 1\}$ $(1, \infty)$ 10. $\{x \mid x \le 2\}$ $(-\infty, 2]$
11. $\{x \mid x$ is a real number$\}$ $(-\infty, \infty)$ 12. $\{x \mid 0 \le x < 3\}$ $[0, 3)$
13. $\{x \mid x < -2$ or $x \ge 4\}$ $(-\infty, -2) \cup [4, \infty)$ 14. Ø 15. $\{x \mid 6 < x < 8\}$ $(6, 8)$
16. $\{x \mid -7 < x < -4\}$ $(-7, -4)$ 17. $\{x \mid x < -2$ or $x > 5\}$ $(-\infty, -2) \cup (5, \infty)$ 18. [113°, 239°]
19. [60, 90) 20. [3, 6]

9.2 Form II

1. {-3, -1, 1, 3, 5, 7} 2. Ø 3. {-3, -1, 0, 1, 2, 3, 4, 5} 4. {1, 3, 5} 5. {0} 6. {-3, -1}
7. {1, 3, 5, 7} 8. $\{x \mid x > 7\}$ $(7, \infty)$ 9. $\{x \mid x \le 3\}$ $(-\infty, 3]$ 10. Ø 11. $\{x \mid x \ge 4$ or $x < -2\}$
12. $\{x \mid -4 < x \le 4\}$ $(-4, 4]$ 13. $\{x \mid -4 < x \le 2\}$ $(-4, 2]$ 14. $\{x \mid 6 < x < 12\}$ $(6, 12)$
15. $\{x \mid -3 < x \le 3\}$ $(-3, 3]$ 16. $\{x \mid 2 \le x \le 6\}$ $[2, 6]$ 17. $\{x \mid x$ is a real number $(-\infty, \infty)$
18. [86, 194] 19. [66, 96) 20. [3, 5]

9.2 Form III

1. {y} 2. {m, n, o, p, q, s, y, z, w} 3. {m, n, o, p, q} 4. {q} 5. {y, z} 6. Ø 7. Ø
8. $\{x \mid x < -2$ and $x > 2\}$ $(-\infty, -2) \cup (2, \infty)$ 9. $\{x \mid x \ge 3\}$ $[3, \infty)$ 10. $\{x \mid -5 < x < 3\}$ $(-5, 3)$
11. $\{x \mid x$ is a real number$\}$ $(-\infty, \infty)$ 12. $\{x \mid -15 < x \le 18\}$ $(-15, 18]$ 13. $\{x \mid 1 < x \le 5\}$ $(1, 5]$
14. $\{x \mid x < -1$ or $x \ge 5\}$ $(-\infty, -1) \cup [5, \infty)$ 15. $\{x \mid -16 \le x < -4\}$ $[-16, 4)$
16. $\{x \mid x$ is a real number$\}$ $(-\infty, \infty)$ 17. Ø 18. [50°, 185°] 19. [76, 106) 20. [4, 5]

9.3 Form I

1. {-5, 5} 2. {-5, 1} 3. {-6, 2} 4. $\left\{\dfrac{-4}{3}, 2\right\}$ 5. Ø 6. {-4} 7. {6} 8. {-5, 1} 9. $\left\{\dfrac{-10}{3}, 0\right\}$

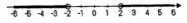

10a. $\{x \mid x < -2$ or $x > 2\}$ b.

11a. $\{x \mid -3 \le x \le 3\}$ b.

12a. $\{x \mid -1 < x < 5\}$ b.

13a. $\{x \mid x < 4 \text{ or } x > 4\}$ b.

14a. $\{x \mid x \leq 4 \text{ or } x \geq 8\}$ b.

15a. $\left\{x \mid 1 < x < \dfrac{5}{3}\right\}$ b.

16a. $\{x \mid x \leq 1 \text{ or } x \geq 3\}$ b.

17a. $\{x \mid -4 \leq x \leq -1\}$ b.

18a. $\left\{x \mid x < \dfrac{-9}{5} \text{ or } x > 1\right\}$ b.

19. $|x - 16.4| \leq 2.4$ 20. $38.9 \leq x \leq 46.1$

9.3 Form II

1. $\left\{\dfrac{-7}{3}, 3\right\}$ 2. $\varnothing$ 3. $\{5\}$ 4. $\{-2, 3\}$ 5. $\{-10, 10\}$ 6. $\varnothing$ 7. $\left\{\dfrac{-21}{5}, 5\right\}$ 8. $\left\{\dfrac{-1}{2}, \dfrac{1}{6}\right\}$

9. $\left\{\dfrac{5}{2}\right\}$

10. $\{x \mid -9 \leq x \leq 3\}$

11. $\{x \mid x \leq -2 \text{ or } x \geq 3\}$

12. $\left\{x \mid \dfrac{-11}{4} < x < \dfrac{7}{4}\right\}$

13. $\{x \mid x < \dfrac{-5}{3} \text{ or } x > 5\}$

14. $\{x \mid 0 \leq x \leq 5\}$

15. $\{x \mid x \leq \dfrac{-4}{3} \text{ or } x \geq 0\}$

16. $\{x \mid \dfrac{-11}{2} < x < \dfrac{13}{2}\}$

17. $\{x \mid x < \dfrac{-7}{3} \text{ or } x > 1\}$

18. $\varnothing$

19. $|x - 11.8| \leq 30.8$ 20. $25 \leq x \leq 30.8$

9.3 Form III

1. $\left\{\dfrac{-3}{4}, \dfrac{3}{4}\right\}$ 2. $\{2, -2\}$ 3. $\left\{\dfrac{1}{4}, \dfrac{-5}{4}\right\}$ 4. $\varnothing$ 5. $\left\{\dfrac{7}{4}, \dfrac{11}{6}\right\}$ 6. $\{2\}$ 7. $\{0, 16\}$ 8. $\left\{\dfrac{4}{9}, 4\right\}$

9. $\left\{\dfrac{-15}{2}, \dfrac{3}{2}\right\}$

10. $\{x \mid 2 < x < 14\}$

11. $\{x \mid x \text{ is a real number}\}$

12. $\{x \mid -4 \le x \le 0\}$

13. $\varnothing$

14. $\{x \mid -\dfrac{1}{5} < x < \dfrac{11}{5}\}$

15. $\varnothing$

16. $\{x \mid x < \dfrac{-1}{2} \text{ or } x > 1\}$

17. $\{x \mid x < -1 \text{ or } x > 3\}$

18. $\{x \mid x < -1 \text{ or } x \ge 9\}$

19. $|x - 16.4| \le 3.1$ 20. $36.8 \le x \le 39.8$

9.4 Form I

1.

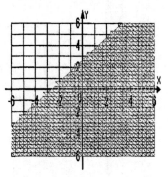

2.

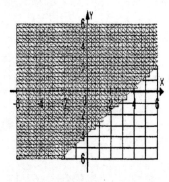

3.

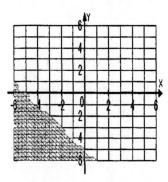

4.

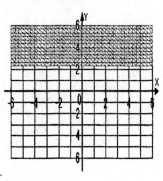

5.

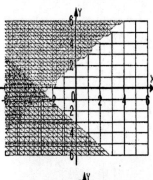

6.

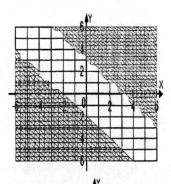

7.

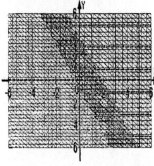

8.

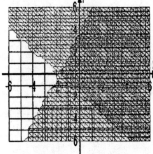

9.

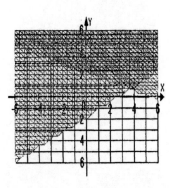

10.

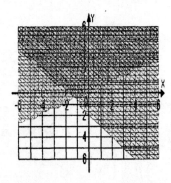

AE-559

11.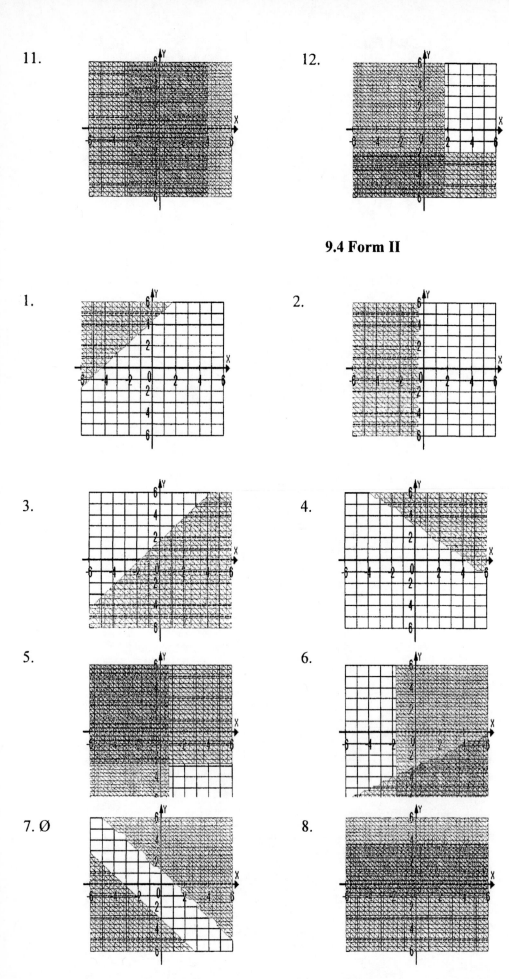

12.

9.4 Form II

1.

2.

3.

4.

5.

6.

7. Ø

8.

AE-560

9.

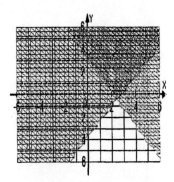

10.

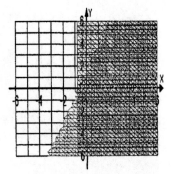

11.

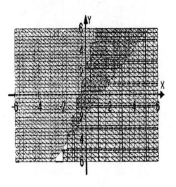

12.

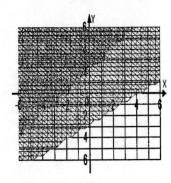

9.4 Form III

1.

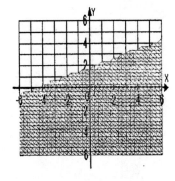

2.

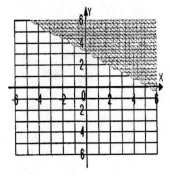

3.

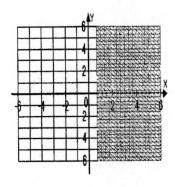

4.

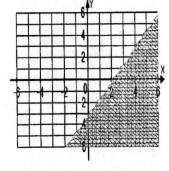

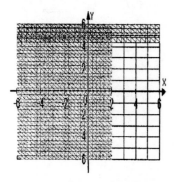

6.

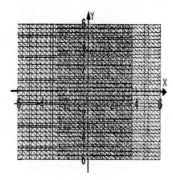

7.

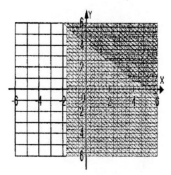

8.

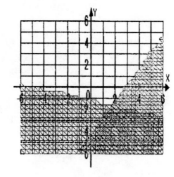

9.

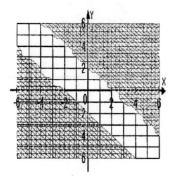

10.

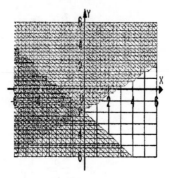

11.

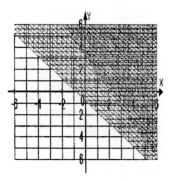

12.

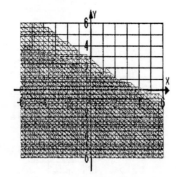

Additional Exercises Answers

10.1 Form I

1. 7 2. Not a real number 3. −3 4. 4 5. 2 6. Not a real number 7. 2 8. −3 9. 3

10. $|x+4|$ 11. $a+7$ 12. m 13. $2|x|$ 14. $|x+6|$ 15. $-3x$ 16. 4 17. 6 18. 0 19. 2

20. −3

10.1 Form II

1. Not a real number 2. −20 3. −4 4. 5 5. Not a real number 6. −10 7. 2 8. 3

9. $|x+9|$ 10. $x-4$ 11. ab 12. $|x-3|$ 13. $|x-4|$ 14. $3(x+1)$ 15. $-|x+2|$ 16. $\frac{1}{2}|x|$

17. −3 18. 7 19. −2 20. 3

10.1 Form III

1. 19 2. −12 3. −3 4. Not a real number 5. $\frac{4}{5}$ 6. $\frac{-1}{5}$ 7. 1 8. −0.5 9. $|x-8|$

10. $|x+5|$ 11. $x+1$ 12. $3|x+3|$ 13. $-3y$ 14. −8 15. Not a real number 16. $4|y+4|$

17. −4 18. 6 19. −4 20. 35 miles per hour

10.2 Form I

1. $\sqrt{64}=8$ 2. $\sqrt[3]{27}=3$ 3. $\sqrt{5xy}$ 4. $\left(\sqrt[5]{32}\right)^2=4$ 5. $10^{\frac{1}{2}}$ 6. $(4x)^{\frac{1}{5}}$ 7. $8^{\frac{2}{3}}$ 8. $16^{\frac{5}{4}}$

9. $\frac{1}{49^{\frac{1}{2}}}=\frac{1}{7}$ 10. $\frac{1}{16^{\frac{3}{4}}}=\frac{1}{8}$ 11. $\frac{1}{(-27)^{\frac{2}{3}}}=\frac{1}{9}$ 12. $\frac{1}{100^{\frac{3}{2}}}=\frac{1}{1000}$ 13. x 14. $a^{\frac{3}{5}}$

15. $10x^4y^2$ 16. x^9y^8 17. $x^{\frac{5}{10}}=\sqrt{x}$ 18. $(3y)^{\frac{1}{5}}=\sqrt[5]{3y}$ 19. $x^{\frac{4}{9}}=\sqrt[9]{x^4}$ 20. $10^{\frac{1}{6}}=\sqrt[6]{10}$

10.2 Form II

1. 14 2. −5 3. $\sqrt[5]{4xy^4}$ 4. $\left(\sqrt[4]{81}\right)^3=27$ 5. $21^{\frac{1}{2}}$ 6. $(9x)^{\frac{1}{9}}$ 7. $\left(x^6y\right)^{\frac{1}{7}}$ 8. $(-27y)^{\frac{4}{3}}$

9. $\frac{1}{81^{\frac{3}{2}}}=\frac{1}{729}$ 10. $\frac{1}{(-27)^{\frac{1}{3}}}=\frac{-1}{3}$ 11. $\frac{1}{\left(4xy^2\right)^{\frac{3}{4}}}=\frac{1}{\left(\sqrt[4]{4xy^2}\right)^3}$ 12. $\frac{4}{x^{\frac{1}{3}}}$ 13. a^2 14. $y^{\frac{1}{2}}$

15. $-3x^3y^4$ 16. $\frac{y^{\frac{2}{5}}}{x^{\frac{3}{8}}}$ 17. $\sqrt[4]{4x}$ 18. $y^{\frac{13}{20}}=\sqrt[20]{y^{13}}$ 19. $12^{\frac{1}{6}}=\sqrt[6]{12}$ 20. $\sqrt[54]{xy}$

10.2 Form III

1. $\sqrt[3]{1000} = 10$ 2. $\left(\sqrt[3]{-216}\right)^2 = 36$ 3. $\left(\sqrt[5]{9x^2 y^3}\right)^3$ 4. $\left(\sqrt{16}\right)^3 + \sqrt{4} = 66$ 5. $30^{\frac{1}{3}}$ 6. $\left(10x^5\right)^{\frac{1}{8}}$

7. $(14xy)^{\frac{5}{2}}$ 8. $\left(16y^2\right)^{\frac{3}{4}}$ 9. $\dfrac{8}{x^{\frac{1}{2}}}$ 10. $\dfrac{1}{(-125)^{\frac{2}{3}}} = \dfrac{1}{25}$ 11. $\dfrac{1}{(3xy)^{\frac{1}{2}}}$ 12. $\dfrac{1}{25^{\frac{1}{2}}} + \dfrac{1}{125^{\frac{1}{3}}} = \dfrac{2}{5}$

13. $y^{\frac{7}{8}}$ 14. $a^{\frac{5}{12}}$ 15. $25x^4 y^8$ 16. $\dfrac{x}{2y^2 z}$ 17. $x^{\frac{19}{15}} = \sqrt[15]{x^{19}}$ 18. $(6x)^{\frac{1}{3}} = \sqrt[3]{6x}$

19. $(xy)^{\frac{1}{40}} = \sqrt[40]{xy}$ 20. $20^{\frac{1}{15}} = \sqrt[15]{20}$

10.3 Form I

1. $\sqrt{30}$ 2. $\sqrt[3]{12}$ 3. $\sqrt{x^2 - 16}$ 4. $\sqrt[3]{6x^2}$ 5. $3\sqrt{10}$ 6. $6\sqrt{3}$ 7. $3\sqrt{5x}$ 8. $2xy^2 \sqrt[3]{5}$
9. $2x^4 \sqrt[3]{3}$ 10. $2x^2 y^2 \sqrt[3]{6y}$ 11. $xy^2 z^2 \sqrt{z^2}$ 12. $(a+b)\sqrt[5]{(a+b)^2}$ 13. $(x-1)^2$
14. $10(x+3)^4$ 15. $x+2$ 16. $2\sqrt{15}$ 17. $6\sqrt{3}$ 18. $2y\sqrt{21x}$ 19. $2xy\sqrt[3]{6y^2}$
20. $2xy^2 \sqrt[4]{10x^2}$

10.3 Form II

1. $\sqrt[4]{28}$ 2. $\sqrt{x^2 + 2x - 8}$ 3. $\sqrt[3]{10x^2}$ 4. $\sqrt[5]{8x^3 y^4}$ 5. $5\sqrt{3}$ 6. $5\sqrt{6}$ 7. $2\sqrt[3]{9}$
8. $2x^2 \sqrt{6y^2}$ 9. $2y\sqrt[4]{6x^3 y}$ 10. $3x^2 y^2 \sqrt[3]{6y}$ 11. $2x^2 \sqrt[5]{8x^2}$ 12. $(x+y)\sqrt[4]{x+y}$
13. $10(x-1)^4$ 14. $10(x+1)^2 \sqrt[3]{3}$ 15. $|x+5|\sqrt{3}$ 16. $9\sqrt{2}$ 17. $4x^3 \sqrt{6}$ 18. $3\sqrt[3]{4}$
19. $2\sqrt[4]{10}$ 20. $12\sqrt{2}$ miles per hour ≈ 17

10.3 Form III

1. $\sqrt[5]{90}$ 2. $\sqrt{x^2 + 2x - 35}$ 3. $\sqrt[3]{6x^2 y}$ 4. $\dfrac{\sqrt[4]{x}}{y}$ 5. $6\sqrt{5}$ 6. $2\sqrt[3]{12}$ 7. $4x\sqrt[4]{5}$ 8. $x^6 \sqrt{x}$

9. $2xy^3 z\sqrt[3]{z}$ 10. $2yz\sqrt[5]{2x^4 z}$ 11. $x+1$ 12. $(x-3)\sqrt[6]{(x-3)^2}$ 13. $10(x+4)^2$ 14. $2(x+4)$
15. $4(2x+5)$ 16. $2\sqrt{30}$ 17. $6x^3 \sqrt{2}$ 18. $3\sqrt[4]{3}$ 19. $2x^8 y^4 \sqrt[3]{3x^2 y^2}$
20. $(x+1)^4 \sqrt[9]{(x+1)^2}$

10.4 Form I

1. $8\sqrt{5}$ 2. $7\sqrt{7}$ 3. $2\sqrt[3]{6}$ 4. $4\sqrt[3]{5} - 4\sqrt{5}$ 5. $23\sqrt{5}$ 6. $-\sqrt[3]{y}$ 7. $18x\sqrt{2xy}$ 8. 0 9. $\dfrac{5}{2}$

10. $\dfrac{\sqrt{13}}{5}$ 11. $\dfrac{\sqrt[3]{3}}{2}$ 12. $\dfrac{\sqrt{14}}{x}$ 13. $\dfrac{5\sqrt{2}}{7}$ 14. $\dfrac{2\sqrt{3}}{9}$ 15. $\dfrac{2\sqrt{2}}{y^2}$ 16. 5 17. $\sqrt{11}$ 18. 4

19. $2x^3 \sqrt{2}$ 20. $5x^3 \sqrt{2}$

10.4 Form II

1. $27\sqrt{19}$ 2. $15\sqrt{10}$ 3. $3x\sqrt[4]{20}$ 4. $8\sqrt{6}-6\sqrt[3]{6}$ 5. $23\sqrt{7}$ 6. $-\sqrt[3]{y^2}$ 7. $17a^2\sqrt{3b}$

8. $8x\sqrt{5x}$ 9. $\dfrac{\sqrt{13}}{4}$ 10. $\dfrac{4x\sqrt{y}}{7}$ 11. $\dfrac{3}{7}$ 12. $\dfrac{\sqrt[3]{4}}{3}$ 13. $\dfrac{3\sqrt{2}}{y^2}$ 14. $2\sqrt[3]{2x}$ 15. $\dfrac{\sqrt{2x}}{2}$ 16. 6

17. $2\sqrt{6}$ 18. 3 19. $4x^4$ 20. $2y^2\sqrt[3]{5}$

10.4 Form III

1. $2\sqrt{10x}$ 2. $9\sqrt{11}$ 3. $8\sqrt{14}-3\sqrt[3]{14}$ 4. $5\sqrt[3]{y}$ 5. $23\sqrt{7}$ 6. $7x\sqrt[4]{x^3}+5x\sqrt[4]{x}$

7. $17a^2\sqrt{3b}$ 8. $5\sqrt{x-2}$ 9. $\dfrac{3}{5}$ 10. $\dfrac{5}{x^4}$ 11. $\dfrac{2\sqrt[3]{3}}{3}$ 12. $\dfrac{2\sqrt[4]{3}}{3}$ 13. $\dfrac{2\sqrt[3]{2}}{x^3}$ 14. $\dfrac{x\sqrt{5}}{3}$

15. $\dfrac{4x\sqrt{2y}}{7}$ 16. $\dfrac{7}{3}$ 17. $\dfrac{5}{6}$ 18. $5x\sqrt{3}$ 19. $2x^2y^2\sqrt{15y}$ 20. $2b\sqrt{10}$

10.5 Form I

1. $\sqrt{21}+\sqrt{15}$ 2. $\sqrt{30}-5$ 3. $\sqrt[3]{12}+2$ 4. $3\sqrt{21}-6\sqrt{6}$ 5. -14 6. $9+4\sqrt{5}$ 7. 9 8. $\dfrac{\sqrt{5}}{5}$

9. $\dfrac{\sqrt{6x}}{x}$ 10. $\dfrac{\sqrt[3]{18}}{3}$ 11. $\dfrac{\sqrt[3]{20x^2}}{4x}$ 12. $\dfrac{\sqrt[3]{2x^2}}{4x}$ 13. $\dfrac{5}{6}+\dfrac{\sqrt{7}}{6}$ 14. $\dfrac{40+5\sqrt{3}}{61}$ 15. $4\sqrt{3}+4\sqrt{2}$

16. $10-4\sqrt{5}$ 17. $\dfrac{7}{\sqrt{35}}$ 18. $\dfrac{5}{\sqrt{10}}$ 19. $\dfrac{6}{\sqrt{6}}$ 20. $\dfrac{11}{7a\sqrt{11}}$

10.5 Form II

1. $\sqrt{35}-\sqrt{15}$ 2. 5 3. $\sqrt[3]{35}+\sqrt[3]{10}$ 4. $16-6\sqrt{7}$ 5. $3\sqrt[3]{x^2}-4x$ 6. $17+2\sqrt{30}$

7. $2\sqrt{21}-2\sqrt{70}+3\sqrt{30}-30$ 8. $\dfrac{\sqrt{7}}{7}$ 9. $\dfrac{\sqrt{2xy}}{y}$ 10. $\dfrac{\sqrt[3]{6x^2}}{3x}$ 11. $\dfrac{\sqrt[5]{7y^4}}{y^2}$ 12. $\dfrac{\sqrt[3]{180xy^2}}{6xy}$

13. $\dfrac{40+5\sqrt{5}}{59}$ 14. $\dfrac{3\sqrt{2}-2\sqrt{3}}{2}$ 15. $\dfrac{9+2\sqrt{14}}{5}$ 16. $3\sqrt{15}+3\sqrt{10}$ 17. $\dfrac{6}{\sqrt{30x}}$ 18. $\dfrac{17}{\sqrt{34}}$

19. $\dfrac{24}{\sqrt{30}}$ 20. $\dfrac{5}{\sqrt{15x}}$

10.5 Form III

1. $\sqrt[3]{18} + \sqrt[3]{12}$ 2. $81 - 56\sqrt{2}$ 3. $\sqrt{95} - \sqrt{133} + \sqrt{35} - 7$ 4. $8 + 2\sqrt{15}$ 5. $2\sqrt[4]{3} - \sqrt[4]{18}$ 6. -21

7. $10x\sqrt[3]{2} - \sqrt[3]{x^2}$ 8. $\dfrac{6\sqrt{7y}}{7y}$ 9. $\dfrac{\sqrt[3]{21x}}{3x}$ 10. $\sqrt[3]{2x^2 y}$ 11. $\dfrac{\sqrt[4]{18x^3}}{3x}$ 12. $\dfrac{4\sqrt{13y}}{13y}$ 13. $2\sqrt{6} + 4$

14. $\dfrac{\sqrt{15} - \sqrt{6}}{3}$ 15. $\dfrac{30\sqrt{2} + 16\sqrt{5} - 3\sqrt{30} - 8\sqrt{3}}{13}$ 16. $\dfrac{36x + y + 12\sqrt{xy}}{y - 36x}$ 17. $\dfrac{7x}{\sqrt{5xy}}$ 18. $\dfrac{9}{4\sqrt{3}}$

19. $\dfrac{47}{40 + 46\sqrt{2}}$ 20. $\dfrac{-1}{9 - 4\sqrt{5}}$

10.6 Form I

1. $\{25\}$ 2. $\{33\}$ 3. $\{80\}$ 4. $\{65\}$ 5. $\{29\}$ 6. $\{4\}$ 7. $\{180\}$ 8. $\{20\}$ 9. No Solution
10. $\{25$ 11. $\{5\}$ 12. $\{2\}$ 13. $\{4\}$ 14. $\{9\}$ 15. $\{5\}$ 16. $\{20\}$ 17. $\{3, 4\}$ 18. $\{0, 3\}$
19. $\{-6\}$ 20. $\{4\}$

10.6 Form II

1. $\{64\}$ 2. $\{5\}$ 3. No Solution   4. $\left\{\dfrac{75}{4}\right\}$ 5. $\{11\}$ 6. $\{19\}$ 7. $\{14\}$ 8. $\{3\}$ 9. $\{5\}$
10. $\{1\}$ 11. $\{12\}$ 12. $\{-1\}$ 13. $\{8\}$ 14. $\{-4\}$ 15. $\{8, -8\}$ 16. $\{4\}$ 17. $\{20\}$ 18. $\{6\}$
19. $\{5, 8\}$ 20. $\{2, 38\}$

10.6 Form III

1. $\{16\}$ 2. $\{9\}$ 3. No Solution   4. $\{8\}$ 5. $\{1\}$ 6. $\{4, 6\}$ 7. $\{5\}$ 8. $\{-4, 5\}$ 9. $\{1\}$
10. $\left\{\sqrt{7}\right\}$ 11. $\{4\}$ 12. $\{5\}$ 13. $\{-1, 3\}$ 14. $\{8\}$ 15. $\{-2\}$ 16. $\{27\}$ 17. $\{2\}$ 18. $\{2\}$
19. 160 feet   20. 1997

10.7 Form I

1. $5i$ 2. $11i$ 3. $4i\sqrt{2}$ 4. $5i\sqrt{2}$ 5. $7 + 3i\sqrt{2}$ 6. $10 + 10i$ 7. $-8 + 9i$ 8. $6 + 3i$
9. $10 - 15i$ 10. $24 + 12i$ 11. $52 - 64i$ 12. $-9 - 40i$ 13. $\dfrac{1}{5} + \dfrac{21}{10}i$ 14. $\dfrac{-4}{29} + \dfrac{19}{29}i$
15. $-4 - 3i$ 16. $\dfrac{-5}{3} - 2i$ 17. -1 18. 1 19. $-i$ 20. $-i$

10.7 Form II

1. $14i$ 2. $2i\sqrt{10}$ 3. $5i\sqrt{3}$ 4. $8 - 7i$ 5. $-8 + 7i$ 6. $13 + 4i$ 7. $6 + 8i$ 8. $-15 - 9i$
9. $29 - 29i$ 10. 15 11. $7 + 24i$ 12. $\dfrac{26}{33} - \dfrac{12}{11}i$ 13. $\dfrac{13}{15} - \dfrac{2}{5}i$ 14. $\dfrac{7}{25} - \dfrac{24}{25}i$ 15. $\dfrac{-5}{2} - 3i$
16. $\dfrac{4}{29} + \dfrac{10}{29}i$ 17. 1 18. -1 19. $-6i$ 20. 1

10.7 Form III

1. $17i$ 2. $6i\sqrt{5}$ 3. $15 - 5i$ 4. $6 + 2i\sqrt{15}$ 5. $3 + 8i$ 6. $4 - 5i$ 7. $10 + 15i$ 8. $-23 - 52i$

9. $2i$ 10. $-18 + i\sqrt{6}$ 11. $-2\sqrt{10}$ 12. i 13. $\dfrac{8}{13} + \dfrac{12}{13}i$ 14. $\dfrac{1}{5} + \dfrac{8}{5}i$ 15. $\dfrac{24}{25} - \dfrac{7}{25}i$

16. $\dfrac{1}{4} - \dfrac{5}{4}i$ 17. $-i$ 18. -1 19. -10 20. 1

Additional Exercises Answers

11.1 Form I

1. $\{\pm 10\}$ 2. $\left\{\pm\sqrt{6}\right\}$ 3. $\left\{\pm\dfrac{7}{4}i\right\}$ 4. $\left\{-2\pm 2\sqrt{5}\right\}$ 5. $\{-5, 6\}$ 6. $25; x^2 + 10x + 25 = (x+5)^2$

7. $36;\ x^2 - 12x + 36 = (x-6)^2$ 8. $64;\ x^2 + 16x + 64 = (x+8)^2$ 9. $81;\ x^2 - 18x + 81 = (x-9)^2$

10. $(3, 5\}$ 11. $\left\{-7\pm\sqrt{15}\right\}$ 12. $\left\{2\pm\sqrt{2}\right\}$ 13. $\left\{-3\pm\sqrt{10}\right\}$ 14. 10 units 15. $\sqrt{2}$ units

16. $(2, 6)$ 17. $(4, 2)$ 18. $50\sqrt{2}$ cm 19. 4 feet 20 $2\sqrt{11}$ seconds

11.1 Form II

1. $\left\{\pm\sqrt{11}\right\}$ 2. $\left\{\pm\dfrac{5}{3}i\right\}$ 3. $\{3\pm 4i\}$ 4. $\left\{\dfrac{-1\pm\sqrt{5}}{2}\right\}$ 5. $\left\{3\pm 2\sqrt{3}\right\}$

6. $\dfrac{1}{16};\ x^2 + \dfrac{1}{2}x + \dfrac{1}{16} = (x+\dfrac{1}{4})^2$ 71. $\dfrac{1}{36};\ x^2 + \dfrac{1}{3}x + \dfrac{1}{36} = (x+\dfrac{1}{6})^2$

8. $\dfrac{25}{4};\ x^2 - 5x + \dfrac{25}{4} = \left(x-\dfrac{5}{2}\right)^2$ 9. $\dfrac{81}{4};\ x^2 - 9x + \dfrac{81}{4} = \left(x-\dfrac{9}{2}\right)^2$

10 $\left\{-1\pm 2\sqrt{3}i\right\}$ 11. $\left\{-4\pm\sqrt{3}i\right\}$ 12. $\left\{\dfrac{-3\pm 3\sqrt{5}}{2}\right\}$ 13. $\left\{\dfrac{1\pm\sqrt{22}}{7}\right\}$ 14. 13 15. $\sqrt{205}$

16. $\left(\dfrac{7}{2}, \dfrac{9}{2}\right)$ 17. $\left(\dfrac{1}{2}, -2\right)$ 18. $55\sqrt{2}$ cm 19. 8 feet 20. $3\sqrt{11}$ seconds

11.1 Form III

1. $\pm\dfrac{7}{5}i$ 2. ± 11 3. $\left\{1\pm 2\sqrt{2}\right\}$ 4. $\left\{\dfrac{5}{6}\pm\dfrac{\sqrt{11}}{6}i\right\}$ 5. $\{10\pm i\}$ 6. $\dfrac{4}{25};\ x^2 - \dfrac{4}{5}x + \dfrac{4}{25} = \left(x-\dfrac{2}{5}\right)^2$

7. $\dfrac{1}{49};\ x^2 + \dfrac{2}{7}x + \dfrac{1}{49} = \left(x+\dfrac{1}{7}\right)^2$ 8. $\dfrac{1}{144};\ x^2 + \dfrac{1}{6}x + \dfrac{1}{144} = \left(x+\dfrac{1}{12}\right)^2$

9. $\dfrac{1}{169};\ x^2 - \dfrac{2}{13}x + \dfrac{1}{169} = \left(x+\dfrac{1}{13}\right)^2$ 10. $\left\{\dfrac{3}{2}\pm\dfrac{\sqrt{51}}{2}i\right\}$ 11. $\left\{\dfrac{3\pm\sqrt{29}}{2}\right\}$ 12. $\left\{\dfrac{1\pm\sqrt{6}}{2}\right\}$

13. $\left\{\dfrac{5}{2}\pm\dfrac{\sqrt{55}}{2}i\right\}$ 14. $4\sqrt{2}$ 15. $2\sqrt{10}$ 16. $\left(\dfrac{-1}{2}, \dfrac{11}{2}\right)$ 17. $(3, 3\sqrt{2})$ 18. $62\sqrt{2}$ cm

19. 15 feet 20. $2\sqrt{30}$ seconds

11.2 Form I

1. $\{4, 10\}$ 2. $\left\{\dfrac{-7}{2}, 3\right\}$ 3. $\left\{4\pm\sqrt{6}\right\}$ 4. $\left\{\pm\dfrac{\sqrt{21}}{3}\right\}$ 5. 0, one real rational solution

6. 1, two real rational solutions 7. −4, two imaginary solutions

8. 41, two real irrational solutions   9. $\left\{6\pm\sqrt{17}\right\}$ 10. $\{-4, 0\}$ 11. $\left\{\dfrac{-3\pm\sqrt{5}}{4}\right\}$ 12. $\{\pm 8i\}$

13. $x^2 - 11x + 24 = 0$ 14. $x^2 - 6x - 40 = 0$ 15. $32x^2 - 28x + 3 = 0$ 16. $5x^2 + 4x = 0$
17. $x^2 - 12 = 0$ 18. $x^2 + 49 = 0$ 19. 16.9 ft.   20. 5 yards by 9 yards

11.2 Form II

1. $\left\{-\dfrac{4}{3}, -9\right\}$ 2. $\left\{\dfrac{-6\pm\sqrt{29}}{7}\right\}$ 3. $\left\{-\dfrac{3}{2}\pm\dfrac{\sqrt{7}}{2}i\right\}$ 4. $\pm 8i$ 5. 36 , two real rational solutions

6. 20, two irrational solutions   7. 0, two real rational solutions   8. −4, two imaginary solutions

9. $\left\{-9\pm 3\sqrt{2}\right\}$ 10. $\left\{\dfrac{5\pm\sqrt{21}}{3}\right\}$ 11. $\left\{\dfrac{7\pm 8\sqrt{3}}{12}\right\}$ 12. $\{-1\}$ 13. $35x^2 + 29x + 6 = 0$

14. $x^2 + 81 = 0$ 15. $x^2 + 100 = 0$ 16. $x^2 - 45 = 0$ 17. $x^2 - 28 = 0$ 18. $x^2 - 2x - 4 = 0$
19. 21.8 feet   20. 3.6 yards by 9.6 yards

11.2 Form III

1. $\left\{0, \dfrac{10}{3}\right\}$ 2. $\left\{\dfrac{-4\pm 3\sqrt{2}}{2}\right\}$ 3. $\left\{-\dfrac{1}{2}\pm\dfrac{\sqrt{19}}{2}i\right\}$ 4. $\left\{\dfrac{1}{4}\right\}$ 5. 0, one real rational solution

6. 41, two real irrational solutions   7. 25, two real rational solutions

8. −64, two imaginary solutions   9. $\left\{11\pm 2\sqrt{6}\right\}$ 10. $\left\{\dfrac{-15\pm\sqrt{285}}{5}\right\}$ 11. $\left\{\dfrac{9\pm\sqrt{101}}{2}\right\}$

12. $\left\{\dfrac{14\pm\sqrt{271}}{15}\right\}$ 13. $35x^2 - 3x - 2 = 0$ 14. $x^2 + 144 = 0$ 15. $x^2 - 98 = 0$ 16.

$x^2 + 75 = 0$
17. $x^2 - 4x + 1 = 0$ 18. $x^2 - 20x + 101 = 0$ 19. 24.1 feet   20. 5.3 yards by 10.3 yards

11.3 Form I

1. $g(x) = x^2 + 1$ 2. $h(x) = (x-1)^2$ 3. $f(x) = (x+1)^2$ 4. $j(x) = x^2 - 1$ 5. $(0, 0)$
6. $(-3, 3)$ 7. $(0, 3)$ 8. $(-9, -5)$ 9. $(1, 3)$ 10. $(1, 9)$
11.

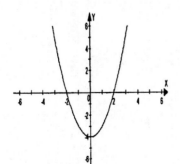

12.

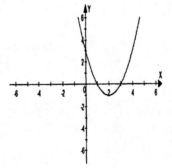

13. a.   minimum b. (−1, −   3) c.
        domain (−∞, ∞) ;   range [−3,
∞)
14. a.   maximum b. (2, 4)   c. domain

$(-\infty, \infty)$; range $[4, -\infty)$

15. a. minimum b. $(4, 0)$ c. domain $(-\infty, \infty)$; range $[0, \infty)$
16. 13 feet by 13 feet   17. 200 pretzels 18. 15 and 15 19. 5.1 seconds

11.3 Form II

1. $h(x) = (x+3)^2 + 2$ 2. $j(x) = (x-3)^2 - 2$ 3. $f(x) = -(x-3)^2 + 2$
4. $g(x) = -(x-3)^2 - 2$ 5. $(0, -6)$ 6. $(4, -4)$ 7. $(0, 8)$ 8. $(-7, 3)$ 9. $(-1, -5)$ 10. $(1, -3)$

11.   12.

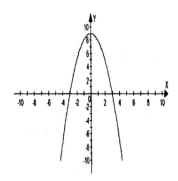 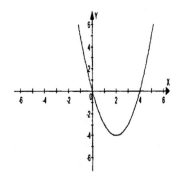

13. a. maximum b. $(-3, 9)$ c. domain $(-\infty, \infty)$; range $[9, -\infty)$
14. a. minimum   b. $(-3, -5)$ c. domain $(-\infty, \infty)$; range $[-5, \infty)$
15. a. minimum   b. $(1, -7)$ c. domain $(-\infty, \infty)$; range $[-7, \infty)$ 16. 18 feet by 18 feet
17. 625 square feet 18. 300 pretzels 19. 16 and 16 20. 5.3 seconds

11.3 Form III

1. $f(x) = (x-2)^2 - 2$ 2. $j(x) = (x+2)^2 - 2$ 3. $g(x) = -(x+2)^2 + 2$
4. $h(x) = -(x-2)^2 + 2$ 5. $(0, 11)$ 6. $(-3, -5)$ 7. $(0, -4)$ 8. $(-4, -2)$ 9. $(-7, 44)$ 10. $(-4, -1)$

11.   12.

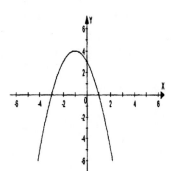

13. a. maximum   b. $(-2, 9)$ c. domain $(-\infty, \infty)$; range $[9, -\infty)$

14. a. minimum   b. $\left(\dfrac{1}{4}, \dfrac{-25}{4}\right)$ c. domain $(-\infty, \infty)$; range $\left[-\dfrac{25}{4}, \infty\right)$

15. a. maximum b. $(1, 4)$ c. domain $(-\infty, \infty)$; range $[4, -\infty)$ 16. 26 feet by 26 feet
17. 1024 square feet   18. 600 pretzels 19. 6.1 seconds

11.4 Form I

1. $\{-2, 2, -6, 6\}$ 2. $\{64\}$ 3. $\{1024\}$ 4. $\{-2, 7\}$ 5. $\left\{-\sqrt{5}, \sqrt{5}, -2, 2\right\}$ 6. $\left\{-\dfrac{1}{6}, \dfrac{1}{5}\right\}$

7. $\{-2, 1\}$ 8. $\left\{\dfrac{-\sqrt{30}}{6}, \dfrac{\sqrt{30}}{6}, -i, i\right\}$ 9. $\left\{\dfrac{7}{2}, 4\right\}$ 10. $\{1, 4\}$ 11. $\{4, 25\}$ 12. c 13. a

14. b 15. d

11.4 Form II

1. $\left\{-1, 1, -\sqrt{3}, \sqrt{3}\right\}$ 2. $\{25, 49\}$ 3. $\{1, 125\}$ 4. $\left\{\dfrac{5}{2}, \dfrac{1}{2}\right\}$ 5. $\left\{\dfrac{-\sqrt{3}}{2}, \dfrac{\sqrt{3}}{2}, -2, 2\right\}$ 6. $\left\{\dfrac{1}{5}, 1\right\}$

7. $\{-7, -1\}$ 8. $\left\{\dfrac{-\sqrt{21}}{3}, \dfrac{\sqrt{21}}{3}, \dfrac{-\sqrt{21}i}{3}, \dfrac{\sqrt{21}i}{3}\right\}$ 9. $\left\{-\dfrac{5}{2}, -8\right\}$ 10. $\left\{\dfrac{4}{9}\right\}$ 11. $\{25\}$

12. a 13. c 14. b 15. d

11.4 Form III

1. $\left\{-\dfrac{\sqrt{5}}{3}, \dfrac{\sqrt{5}}{3}, -1, 1\right\}$ 2. $\{36\}$ 3. $\{3125, -1024\}$ 4. $\{-2, -1, 5, 6\}$ 5. $\left\{-2\sqrt{2}, 2\sqrt{2}, -1, 1\right\}$

6. $\{7, -6\}$ 7. $\left\{-\dfrac{4}{5}, 1\right\}$ 8. $\left\{-2i, 2i, -\sqrt{5}i, \sqrt{5}i\right\}$ 9. $\{5\}$ 10. $\left\{\dfrac{1}{36}\right\}$ 11. $\{4\}$ 12. d 13. c

14. b 15. a

11.5 Form I

1. $(-\infty, 6) \cup (7, \infty)$

2. $(-1, 4)$

3. $[-1, 3]$

4. $(-\infty, 1] \cup [3, \infty)$

5. $(-\infty, -4) \cup (3, \infty)$

6. $(-\infty. 3) \cup (3, \infty)$

7. $\varnothing$

8. $(-\infty, \infty)$

9. $(-3, 2)$

10. $(-\infty, -4) \cup (5, \infty)$

11. $(-5, -2)$

12. $(-6, -3)$

13. $[3, 4)$

14. $(-\infty, 0) \cup (2, \infty)$

15. $(-\infty. -6) \cup (0. \infty)$

16. $(-2, 1)$

11.5 Form II

1. $(-\infty-5) \cup (3, \infty)$

2. $\left(-7, \dfrac{2}{5}\right)$

3. $\left[\dfrac{1}{3}, \dfrac{1}{2}\right]$

4. $\left(-\infty, -\dfrac{2}{3}\right] \cup \left[\dfrac{-3}{5}, \infty\right)$

5. $(-\infty, -2) \cup \left(\dfrac{3}{4}, \infty\right)$

6. $(-\infty, -2] \cup [0, \infty)$

7. $\left(-\dfrac{7}{8}, 2\right)$

8. $\varnothing$

9. $(-6, -4)$

10. $(4, 8)$

11. $(-\infty, -4) \cup \left(-\dfrac{5}{2}, \infty\right)$

12. $(4, 6]$

13. $(-\infty, -6] \cup (3, \infty)$

14. $\left[\dfrac{-4}{3}, -1\right)$

15. $(-\infty, 2) \cup (4, \infty)$

16. $[-4, -2)$

11.5 Form III

1. $(-\infty, -7) \cup \left(\dfrac{1}{7}, \infty\right)$

2. $\left(\dfrac{-2}{3}, \dfrac{-1}{2}\right)$

3. $\left[\dfrac{-1}{2}, \dfrac{-2}{5}\right]$

4. $\left(-\infty, \dfrac{-3}{4}\right] \cup \left[\dfrac{5}{2}, \infty\right)$

5. $\left(-\infty, \dfrac{1}{5}\right) \cup \left(\dfrac{5}{6}, \infty\right)$

6. $\left(-\infty, \dfrac{1}{8}\right) \cup (2, \infty)$

7. $\varnothing$

8. . $(-\infty, \infty)$

9. $(-\infty, -3) \cup \left(\dfrac{-3}{2}, \infty\right)$

10. $[-1, 0)$

11. $(-\infty, -5) \cup \left(\dfrac{-9}{2}, \infty \right)$

12. $(-\infty, -5) \cup \left(\dfrac{-15}{2}, \infty \right)$

13. $\left(-\infty, \dfrac{-5}{6} \right) \cup [2, \infty)$

14. $\left[\dfrac{-8}{9}, 3 \right)$

15. $\left[\dfrac{-7}{2}, \dfrac{3}{4} \right)$

16. $\left(\dfrac{-5}{3}, 2 \right]$

12.1 Form I

1. 2.828   2. 24.251   3. 0.145

4.
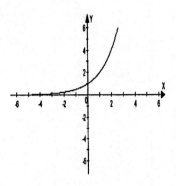

5.
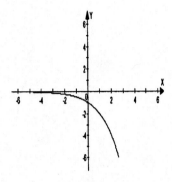

6.
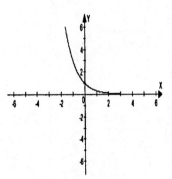

7.
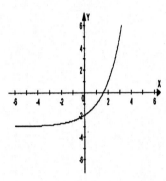

8.
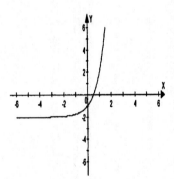

9.
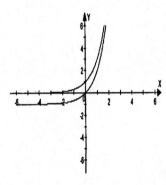

10.
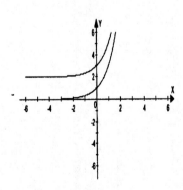

11.
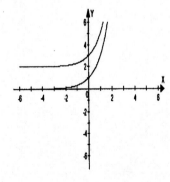

12. $32,642.95   13. $33178.86   14. $33752.60   15. $29604.89   16. $19150.37
17. $6104.9818   18. $16977.34

1. 0.100 2. 0.004 3. 9.974

4.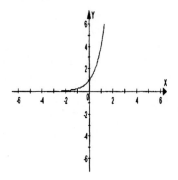

5.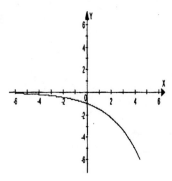

6.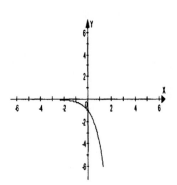

7.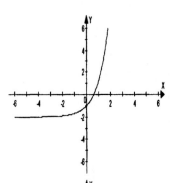

8.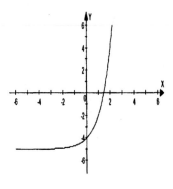

9.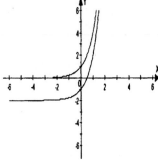

10.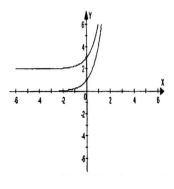

11.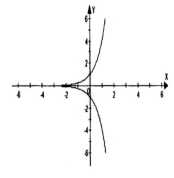

12. $30,072.61 13. $30,407.39 14. $10,253.22 15. $1616.07 16. $804.14
17. 363 rabbits 18. 225 trout

1. 0.031   2. 77.571   3. 0.445

4.

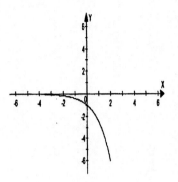

5.

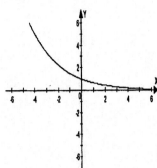

6.

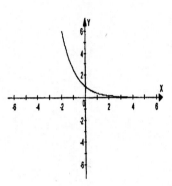

7.

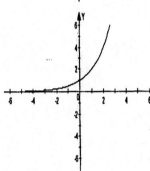

8.

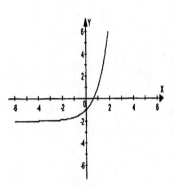

9.

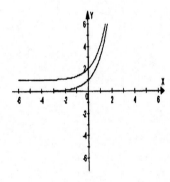

10.

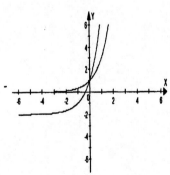

11.

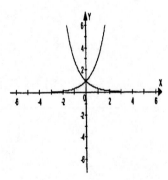

12. $9741.89   13. $1013.29   14. 15362.72   15. $1827.86   16. bank paying 5%

12.2 Form I

1. 50 2. $3x+1$ 3. $6x^2-8x$ 4. $18x^2+3x$ 5. $-x+16$ 6. $-x$ 7. 11 8. $8\sqrt{x+6}-10$

9. yes 10. no 11. yes 12. yes 13. yes 14. no 15. $f^{-1}(x)=\dfrac{x+7}{-5}$ 16. $f^{-1}(x)=-\dfrac{1}{2}x$

17. $f^{-1}(x)=4x+3$ 18. $f^{-1}(x)=3x-3$

19.

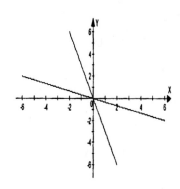

20.

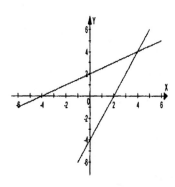

12.2 Form II

1. 118 2. $5x+5$ 3. $15x^2-6x$ 4. $45x^2-6x$ 5. $-6x+22$ 6. x 7. $-x-8$ 8. 8
9. yes 10. no 11. no 12. yes 13. yes 14. no 15. $f^{-1}(x)=2x+7$ 16. $f^{-1}(x)=3x$
17. $f^{-1}(x)=\sqrt{x}-3$ 18. $f^{-1}(x)=x^3+6$

19.

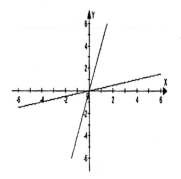

20.

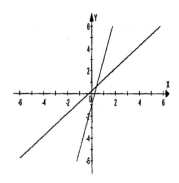

12.2 Form III

1. 12. 2. $2\sqrt{2x-1}$ 3. $x^4-8x+28$ 4. $\dfrac{-7x}{3}$ 5. $x+8$ 6. 4 7. $\dfrac{1}{5}$ 8. $\dfrac{3}{4}$ 9. yes

10. no 11. yes 12. yes 13. no 14. yes 15. $f^{-1}(x)=-\dfrac{1}{3}x+\dfrac{4}{3}$ 16. $f^{-1}(x)=-3x+3$

17. $f^{-1}(x)=\dfrac{6}{2x-1}$ 18. $f^{-1}(x)=\dfrac{1}{x^2}$

19.

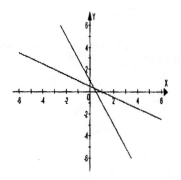

20.

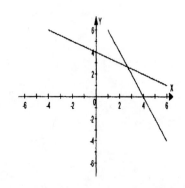

12.3 Form I

1. $4^2 = 16$ 2, $2^3 = 8$ 3. $5^2 = x$ 4. $2^x = 16$ 5. $\log_3 9 = 2$ 6. $\log_4 64 = 3$ 7. $\log_5 x = 2$

8. $\log_6 32 = y$ 9. $x = 1$ 10. $x = 0$ 11. $x = 3$ 12. $x = \dfrac{1}{2}$ 13. $x = \dfrac{1}{2}$

14 - 15.

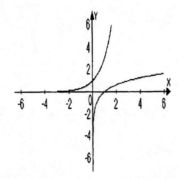

16. $\{x \mid x > -5\}, (-5, \infty)$ 17. 2

18. $15x$ 19. $\sqrt{5x}$ 20. 4.4

12.3 Form II

1. $2^2 = 25$ 2. $x^2 = 16$ 3. $6^4 = x$ 4. $b^3 = 512$ 5. $\log_3 81 = 4$ 6. $\log_{10} 0.01 = -3$

7. $\log_5 \dfrac{1}{25} = -2$ 8. $\log_x 18 = y$ 9. $x = 1$ 10. $x = 0$ 11. $x = 4$ 12. $x = \dfrac{2}{3}$ 13. 5

14.-15

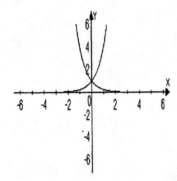

16. $\{x \mid x < 4\}, \{-\infty, 4\}$ 17. $2y$

18. $\sqrt{10x}$ 19. $4x^3$ 20. 2.5

12.3 Form III

1. $4^2 = x$ 2. $x^3 = 216$ 3. $16^x = 8$ 4. $x^{-1} = 0.1$ 5. $\log_5 125 = 3$ 6. $\log_3 \dfrac{1}{81} = -4$

7. $\log_9 287 = 3$ 8. $\log_4 0.25 = -1$ 9. $x = 1$ 10. $x = \dfrac{1}{2}$ 11. $x = \dfrac{1}{2}$ 12. $x = \dfrac{1}{3}$ 13. 9

14. -15.

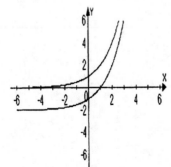

16. $\{x \mid x \neq 1\}, (-\infty, 1)(1, \infty)$ 17. $\sqrt{3x}$

18. $\sqrt{13x}$ 19. $2x^3$ 20. 2

12.4 Form I

1. $\log_5 7 + \log_5 11$ 2. $\log_2 3 + \log_2 x$ 3. $\log_4 16 + \log_4 x; 2 + \log_4 x$ 4. $\log_7 5 - \log_7 x$

5. $\log_8 8 - \log_8 x; 1 - \log_8 x$ 6. $\log_5 125 - \log_5 x; 3 - \log_5 x$ 7. $6\log_7 x$ 8. $\ln 4 + \ln x$

9. $4\ln y$ 10. $\log_b x + \log_b y - 2\log_b z$ 11. $\log_4 12$ 12. $\log_5 625; 4$ 13. $\log_6 2x$

14. $\log_6 36; 2$ 15. $\log_7 \dfrac{x-1}{x+3}$ 16. $\log_6 \dfrac{x+2}{x-2}$ 17. $\log_5 x^2 y^4$ 18. $\log_3 x^6 y^2$ 19. 2.0437

20. 1.4729

12.4 Form II

1. $\log_4 3 + \log_4 x$ 2. $\log_2 8 + \log_2 x$ 3. $\log_9 x - \log_9 9; \log_9 x - 1$ 4. $\log_6 y + 9\log_b z$

5. $z\ln y$ 6. $\log_6 x + 6\log_b y - 4\log_b z$ 7. $2\log_b x - \log_b y - 2\log_b z$ 8. $\dfrac{1}{2}\log_2 y - \log_2 8$

9. $\ln x - \ln y$ 10. $\log_3 \dfrac{486}{18}; 3$ 11. $\log_3 \dfrac{486}{18}; 3$ 12. $\log_{36} \dfrac{(x-4)}{(x+2)}$ 13. $\log_4 (8 \cdot 32); 4$

14. $\ln \dfrac{x}{y^4}$ 15. $\ln \dfrac{x^2}{y^5}$ 16. $\ln \dfrac{(x-4)^3}{x^9}$ 17. $\log_b \dfrac{y^8}{z^4}$ 18. $\log \dfrac{\sqrt{x}}{\sqrt[3]{y}}$ 19. 1.5 20. -3.2694

12.4 Form III

1. $2\log_5 x + 3\log_5 y$ 2. $8\log_8 x + 8\log_8 y + 8\log_8 z$ 3. $\log_{10} 2 + \log_{10} x - \log_{10} y$

4. $2\log_b x - 3\log_b y - 4\log_b z$ 5. $\log_3 x - \log_3 9; \log_3 x - 2$ 6. $\log_5 (x-1) - \log_5 (x+2)$

7. $4\ln e - \ln 7$ 8. $\dfrac{1}{3}\log x - \dfrac{1}{2}\log y$ 9. $\dfrac{1}{2}\log x - \dfrac{1}{3}\log y - 4\log z$

10. $\log_3 9 - \dfrac{1}{2}\log_3 (x+2); 2 - \dfrac{1}{2}\log_3 (x+2)$ 11. $\log_4 \dfrac{1280}{5}; 4$ 12. $\log_6 \dfrac{x+2}{x+4}$ 13. $\log_b \dfrac{y^8}{\sqrt[4]{z}}$

14. $\ln \dfrac{(x+4)^5}{x^2}$ 15. $\log_3 \dfrac{x}{x-2}$ 16. $\log_2 \dfrac{x^2}{\sqrt{z}}$ 17. $\log_b \dfrac{\sqrt[3]{x}}{\sqrt[3]{x}}; \log_b 1; 0$ 18. $\log_5 \dfrac{x\sqrt[3]{y}}{z^4}$

19. 1.9746 20. -3.3668

12.5 Form I

1. 3 2. 6 3. 1 4. 3 5. $\dfrac{\ln 90}{\ln 2}$ 6. $\dfrac{\ln 15}{\ln 3}$ 7. $\dfrac{\ln 10}{1.4}$ 8. $\ln 10$ 9. -4.74 10. 4.277

11. $\dfrac{33}{8}$ 12. 29 13. 5 14. 3 15. No solution   16. 7.39 17. e^{24} 18. 74.2066 19. $e^{\frac{-3}{5}}$

20. $\dfrac{e^2}{9}$

12.5 Form II

1. $\dfrac{3}{2}$ 2. $\dfrac{1}{2}$ 3. 2 4. $\dfrac{\log 32}{\log 5}$ 5. $\dfrac{\log 5.2}{\log 3}$ 6. $\dfrac{\log 7}{\log 2.8}$ 7. 3.74 8. ln4 9. 1.9459

10. 0.235 11. 6 12. 13 13. 4 14. 3 15. 4 16. 148.4132 17. 81.56 18. 19.0855

19. $e^{\frac{-3}{2}}$ 20. 1.85

12.5 Form III

1. $\dfrac{2}{3}$ 2. –2 3. 2 4. $\dfrac{\log 4}{\log 9}$ 5. $\dfrac{\log 13.8}{\log 7}$ 6. $\dfrac{\ln 4}{-2}$ 7. ln15 8. $\dfrac{7\ln 4}{\ln 5 - \ln 4}$ 9. 2.87

10. 1.11 11. $\dfrac{1}{9}$ 12. 3 13. –4, 2 14. $\dfrac{7}{5}$ 15. 0.55 16. 9 17. 4 18. 1.41 19. 3

20. $l + e^3; x \approx 21.09$

Additional Exercises Answers

13.1 Form I

1. $x^2 + y^2 = 25$ 2. $x^2 + (y-2)^2 = 36$ 3. $(x-4)^2 + y^2 = 9$ 4. $(x-1)^2 + (y-3)^3 = 16$
5a. center $(0, 0)$ b. $r = 9$ 6a. center $(3, 0)$ b. $r = 6$ 7a. center $(0, 4)$ b. $r = 5$
8. $(x+3)^2 + (y+10)^2 = 81$ 9. $(x+4)^2 + (y-8)^2 = 36$ 10. $(x+10)^2 + y^2 = 81$

11.

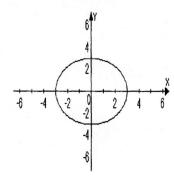

12.

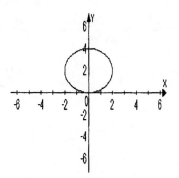

13.

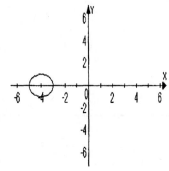

13.1 Form II

1. $(x-5)^2 + (y+9)^2 = 144$ 2. $x^2 + (y-9)^2 = 121$ 3. $x^2 + (y-8)^2 = 3$ 4. $x^2 + y^2 = 6$
5a. center $(-5, -9)$ b. $r = 2$ 6a. center $(-5, 5)$ b. $r = 4$ 7a. center $(-5, 5)$ b. $r = 10$
8. $(x-1)^2 + (y-3)^2 = 36$ 9. $(x+1)^2 + (y-8)^2 = 4$ 10. $(x-3)^3 + (y+5)^2 = 4$

11.

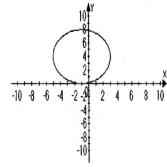

12.

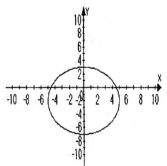

13.

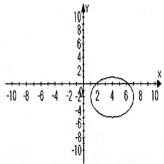

13.1 Form III

1. $(x+2)^2 + (y-3)^2 = 7$ 2. $(x-1)^2 + (y+5)^2 = 64$ 3. $(x+4)^2 + (y+6)^2 = 5$

4. $(x+3)^2 + y^2 = 17$ 5a. center $(4, -4)$ b. $r = 4$ 6a. center $(-3, 3)$ b. $r = 3$

7a. center $(-5, 0)$ b. $r = 11$ 8. $(x+2)^2 + (y-3)^2 = 13$ 9. $(x-1)^2 + (y-2)^2 = 8$

10. $(x-4)^2 + (y+5)^2 = 41$

11.

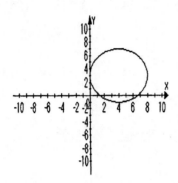

12.

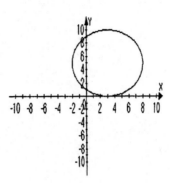

13.

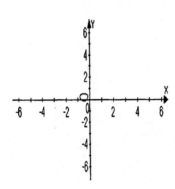

13.2 Form I

1.

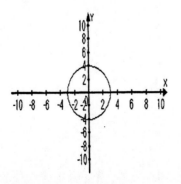

2.

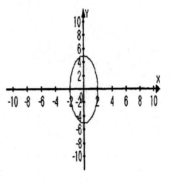

3.

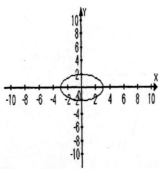

4.

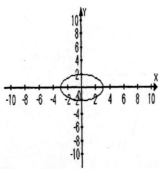

AE-583

5.

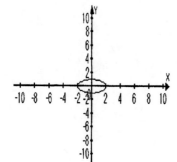

6.

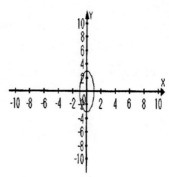

7.

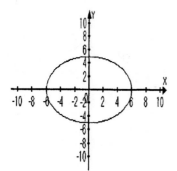

8.

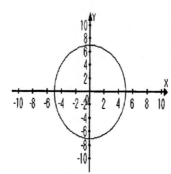

9.

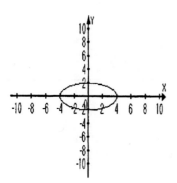

10.

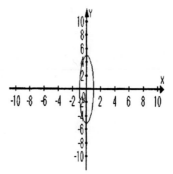

11.

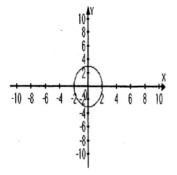

12.

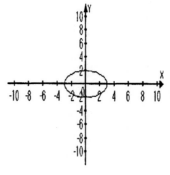

13.

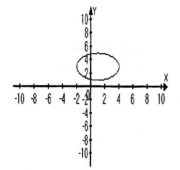

14.

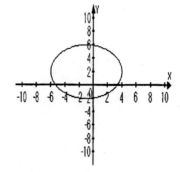

1.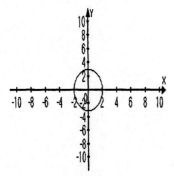

2.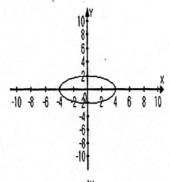

3.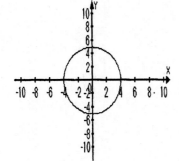

4.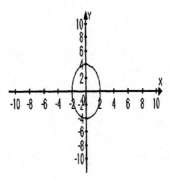

5.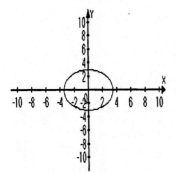

6.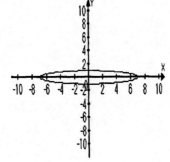

7.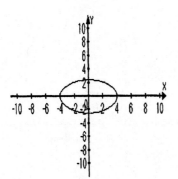

8.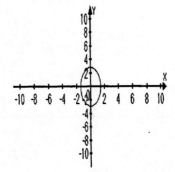

9.

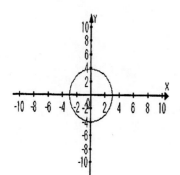

10.

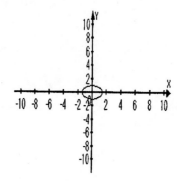

11.

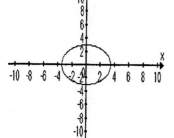

12.

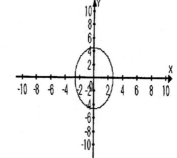

13.

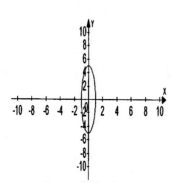

14.

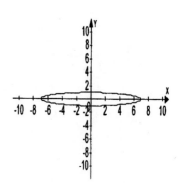

13.2 Form III

1.

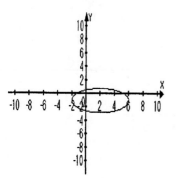

2.

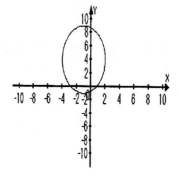

3.

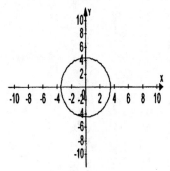

4.

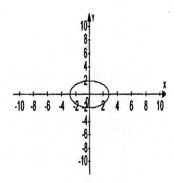

5.

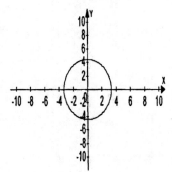

6.

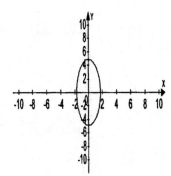

7.

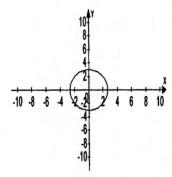

8.

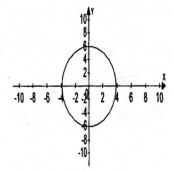

9.

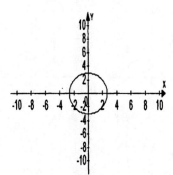

10.

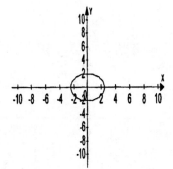

11.

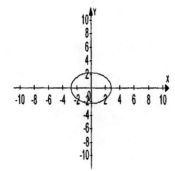

12.

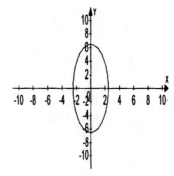

13.

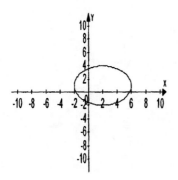

14.

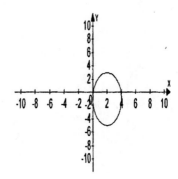

13.3 Form I

1. $(1, 0)$ and $(-1, 0)$ 2. $(0, 4)$ and $(0, -4)$ 3. $(0, 5)$ and $(0, -5)$ 4. $(10, 0)$ and $(-10. 0)$
5. $(2, 0)$ and $(-2, 0)$

6.

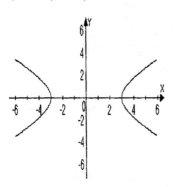

7.

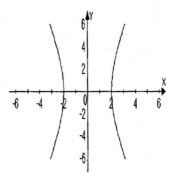

8.

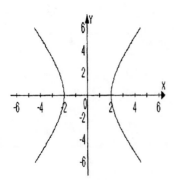

9.

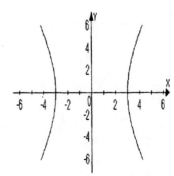

10.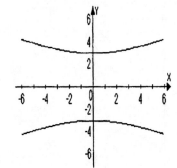

11.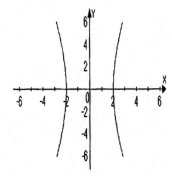

12.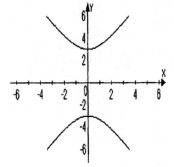

13.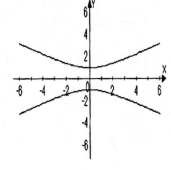

14.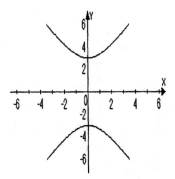

15.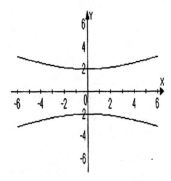

13.3 Form II

1. (3, 0) and (–3, 0)   2. (0, 5) and (0, –5)   3. (0, 7) and (0, –7)   4. (9, 0) and (–9, 0)
5. (0, 10) and (0, –10)

6.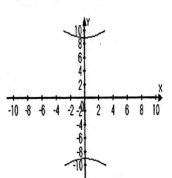

7.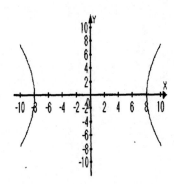

8.

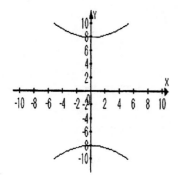

9.

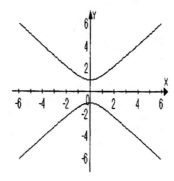

10.

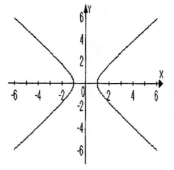

11.

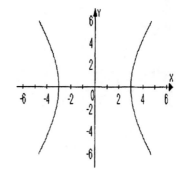

12.

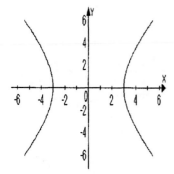

13.

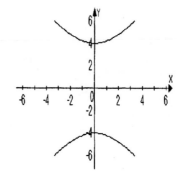

14.

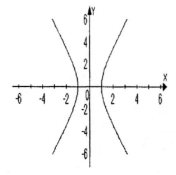

15.

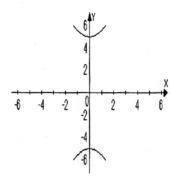

13.3 Form III

1. (4, 0) and (−4, 0) 2. (0, 4) and (0, −4) 3. (11, 0) and (−11, 0) 4. (0, 10) and (0, −10)
5. (5, 0) and (−5, 0)

6.
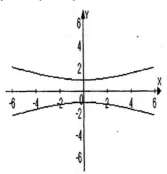

7.
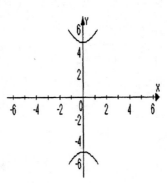

8.
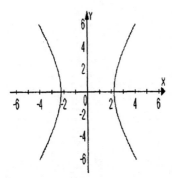

9.
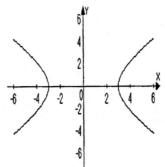

10.
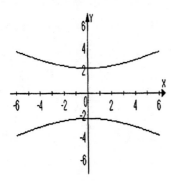

11.
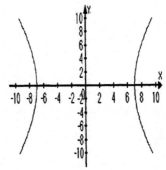

12.
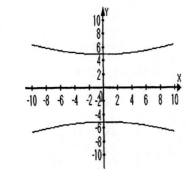

13.
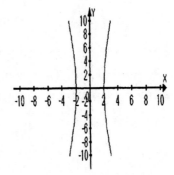

14.

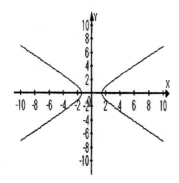

15.

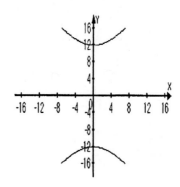

13.4 Form I

1a. opens to right   b. horizontal   2a. opens downward   b. vertical   3a. opens to left
b. horizontal   4a. opens upward   b. vertical   5. (0, 0)   6. (1, 4)

7.

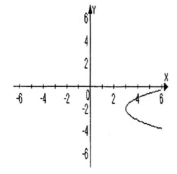

8.

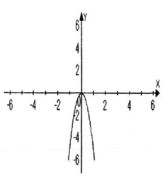

9.

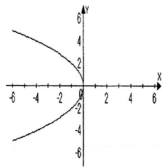

10.

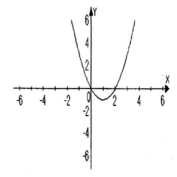

11. $y = 2$ 12. $y = 3$ 13. circle   14. hyperbola   15. ellipse

13.4 Form II

1a. opens to left   b. horizontal   2a. opens upward   b. vertical   3a. opens to right
b. horizontal   4a. opens downward   b. vertical   5. (0, 0)   6. (–3, –4)

7.

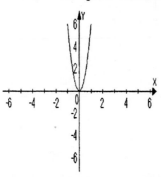

8.

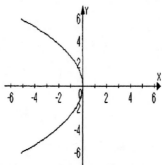

9.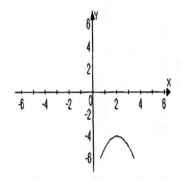

10.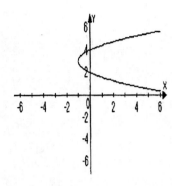

11. $y = -1$ 12. $y = 2$ 13. hyperbola   14. parabola   15. circle

13.4 Form III

1a. opens downward b. vertical 2a. opens to right b. horizontal 3a. opens upward
b. vertical 4a. opens to left b. horizontal 5. (2, 3) 6. (−4, −5)

7.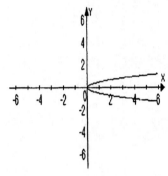

8.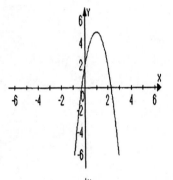

9.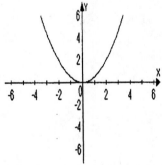

10.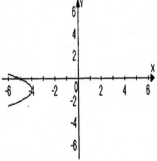

11. $y = 4$ 12. $y = -1$ 13. hyperbola   14. parabola   15. ellipse

13.5 Form I

1. $\{(-6,8)(8,-6)\}$ 2. $\{(5,4)(4,5)\}$ 3. $\{(3,5)(-5,-3)\}$ 4. $\begin{cases}(2,3)(2,-3) \\ (-2,3)(-2,-3)\end{cases}$ 5. $\begin{cases}(5,4)(5,-4) \\ (-5,4)(-5,-4)\end{cases}$

6. $\begin{cases}(7,-9)(-7,9) \\ (9,-7)(-9,7)\end{cases}$ 7. $\{(-4,10)(10,-4)\}$ 8. $\{(-4,3)(3,4)\}$ 9. 1 and 9   10. −7 and 9; −9 and 7

11. 9 and 4 12. 8 and 3,–8 and 3; 8 and –3, –8 and –3 13. 5 by 9 inches 14. 20 by 42 inches
15. 45 by 108 feet

13.5 Form II

1. 1. $\{(2,0)(-3,-5\}$ 2. $\{(-1,0)(0,1)\}$ 3. $\left\{\begin{array}{l}(6,5)(-6,5)\\(-6,-5)(6,-5)\end{array}\right\}$ 4. $\left\{\begin{array}{l}(-3,1)(-3,-1)\\(3,1)(3,-1)\end{array}\right\}$

5. $\left\{\begin{array}{l}(2,1)(2,-1)\\(-2,1)(-2,-1)\end{array}\right\}$ 6. $\{(0,-4)\}$ 7. $\{(2,0)(-2,0)\}$ 8. $\{(5,0)(-5,0)\}$ 9. 3 and 7

10. –8 and 5; –5 and 8 11. 4 and 8 12. 10 and 2, –10 and 2; 10 and –2, –10 and –2
13. 3 by 8 inches 14. 20 by 30 units 15. 37 by 120 feet

13.5 Form III

1. $\{(12,5)(5,12)\}$ 2. $\left\{(5,1)(-8,\dfrac{-11}{2}\right\}$ 3. $\{(-2,-7)(0,-9)\}$ 4. $\{\sqrt{3},1)(-\sqrt{3},1)\}$

5. $\left\{\begin{array}{l}(\sqrt{5},\sqrt{3})(-\sqrt{5},\sqrt{3})\\(-\sqrt{5},-\sqrt{3})(\sqrt{5},-\sqrt{3})\end{array}\right\}$ 6. $\left\{(2,-1)\left(\dfrac{11}{7},\dfrac{-13}{7}\right)\right\}$ 7. $\left\{\left(-\dfrac{1}{2},2\right)\left(2,-\dfrac{1}{2}\right)\right\}$ 8. $\{(3,-4)(-1,-4)\}$

9. 4 and 5 10. –7 and 10; –10 and 7 11. 5 and 9 12. 9 and 4, –9 and 4; 9 and –4, –9 and –4
13. 4 by 6 inches 14. 18 by 22 inches 15. 52 by 115 feet

Additional Exercises Answers

14.1 Form I

1. 2, 3, 4, 5 2. 9, 18, 27, 36 3. 2, 4, 8, 16 4. 1, 3, 6, 10 5. 65 6. 55 7. 254 8. 2728

9. 6.12 10. $\displaystyle\sum_{i=2}^{8} i^4$ 11. $\displaystyle\sum_{i=1}^{6} i^2$ 12. $\displaystyle\sum_{i=1}^{5} 2i$ 13. $\displaystyle\sum_{i=1}^{6} 3i+2$ 14. \$21,08 million 15. \$7429.54

14.1 Form II

1. $-3, -2, -1, 0$ 2. 0, 2, 6, 12 3. 3, 9, 27, 81 4. $\dfrac{1}{2}, \dfrac{2}{3}, \dfrac{3}{2}, \dfrac{24}{5}$ 5. 97 6. 108 7. 279 8. $\dfrac{3}{8}$

9. $\dfrac{5}{6}$ 10. $\displaystyle\sum_{i=1}^{12} \dfrac{i}{i+2}$ 11. $\displaystyle\sum_{i=8}^{37}(i+1)$ 12. $\displaystyle\sum_{i=1}^{6}\left(\dfrac{1}{2}\right)^i$ 13. $\displaystyle\sum_{i=1}^{5}(-4)^{(i+1)}$ 14. \$26.8 million 15. \$8003.73

14.1 Form III

1. 3, 5, 7, 9 2. $-4, 16, -64, 256$ 3. $\dfrac{-3}{4}, \dfrac{9}{16}, \dfrac{-27}{64}, \dfrac{81}{256}$ 4. 18, 72, 360, 2160 5. 22 6. 120

7. $\dfrac{25}{12}$ 8. -9 9. 74 10. $\displaystyle\sum_{i=1}^{8} i^3$ 11. $\displaystyle\sum_{i=1}^{6}\left(\dfrac{1}{2}\right)^x$ 12. $\displaystyle\sum_{i=1}^{7} i!$ 13. $\displaystyle\sum_{i=1}^{11} ar^{(i-1)}$ 14. \$33.42 million

15. \$8882.90

14.2 Form I

1. $d=4$ 2. $d=-3$ 3. 10, 14, 18, 22, 26 4. 6, 5, 4, 3, 2 5. 1, 6, 11, 16, 21 6. 2, 2.5, 3, 3.5, 4
7. -15 8. -3 9. 55 10. $16n-12$ 11. $-9n-4$ 12. $-3n+9$ 13. $7n-12$ 14. 164 15. 110
16. 434 17. 100 18. $-2, -4, -6, \ldots, -170$ 19. $a_n = 3890+110n$; \$5210 20. 564 seats

14.2 Form II

1. $d=2$ 2. $d=-2$ 3. $-15, -12, -9, -6, -3$ 4. 100, 125, 150, 175, 200 5. 2.2, 2.6, 3, 3.4, 3.8
6. $\dfrac{1}{2}, 1, \dfrac{3}{2}, 2, \dfrac{5}{2}$ 7. -24 8. $-1\dfrac{1}{3}$ 9. 73 10. $-8n+9$ 11. $\dfrac{1}{2}n+99\dfrac{1}{2}$ 12. $\dfrac{1}{2}n$ 13. $0.2n+0.3$
14. 366 15. 425 16. 592 17. 225 18. $3, 1, -1, \ldots, -75$ 19. $a_n = 3410+90n$; \$4490
20. 795 seats

14.2 Form III

1. $d=6$ 2. $d=-4$ 3. $-\dfrac{3}{4}, -\dfrac{1}{2}, -\dfrac{1}{4}, 0, \dfrac{1}{4}$ 4. $\dfrac{3}{8}, \dfrac{1}{2}, \dfrac{5}{8}, \dfrac{3}{4}, \dfrac{7}{8}$ 5. $\dfrac{7}{5}, \dfrac{12}{5}, \dfrac{17}{5}, \dfrac{22}{5}, \dfrac{27}{5}$

6. 1.5, 3.1, 4.7, 6.3, 7.9 7. -42 8. 0 9. 97 10. $5n-3$ 11. $7n-15$ 12. $\dfrac{1}{2}n+\dfrac{1}{4}$

13. $-0.3n-7.7$ 14. 648 15. 1530 16. 814 17. 576 18. $-2, -8, -18, \ldots, -3200$
19. $a_n = 3155+95n$; \$4295 20. 1260 seats

14.3 Form I

1. $r = -3$ 2. $r = \dfrac{1}{2}$ 3. $r = 0.1$ 4. $-2, -6, -18, -54 \ldots$ 5. $-4, 12, -36, 108 \ldots$ 6. 384

7. 324 8. $a_n = 5 \cdot 2^{n-1}$ 9. $a_n = 3 \cdot \left(\dfrac{1}{2}\right)^{n-1}$ 10. $a_n = 2^n$ 11. $a_n = 0.1 \cdot (5)^{n-1}$ 12. $\dfrac{31}{3}$

13. -315 14. 126 15. 8 16. $\dfrac{9}{8}$ 17. $\dfrac{4}{9}$ 18. $\dfrac{19}{33}$ 19. geometric; $r = \dfrac{3}{5}$

20. arithmetic; $d = 4$

14.3 Form II

1. $r = 2$ 2. $r = 0.5$ 3. $r = 10$ 4. $36, 12, 4, \dfrac{4}{3}, \ldots$ 5. $-8, -32, -128, -512 \ldots$ 6. $24{,}576$

7. 8748 8. $a_n = 4^n$ 9. $a_n = \dfrac{1}{5} \cdot \left(\dfrac{1}{7}\right)^{n-1}$ 10. $a_n = -\dfrac{1}{6} \cdot \left(-\dfrac{1}{5}\right)^{n-1}$ 11. $a_n = 0.009 \cdot (20)^{n-1}$

12. $\dfrac{31}{2}$ 13. -2457 14. 546 15. 1 16. $\dfrac{2}{3}$ 17. $\dfrac{1}{3}$ 18. $\dfrac{5}{11}$ 19. arithmetic; $d = 7$

20. neither

14.3 III

1. $r = 2$ 2. $r = \dfrac{-1}{3}$ 3. $r = -0.4$ 4. $\dfrac{1}{3}, \dfrac{2}{3}, \dfrac{4}{3}, \dfrac{8}{3}, \ldots$ 5. $-\dfrac{1}{7}, \dfrac{3}{7}, \dfrac{-9}{7}, \dfrac{27}{7}, \ldots$ 6. $393{,}216$

7. $78{,}732$ 8. $a_n = (-5)^n$ 9. $a_n = 2 \cdot \left(\dfrac{1}{3}\right)^{n-1}$ 10. $a_n = \dfrac{1}{4} \cdot \left(\dfrac{1}{2}\right)^{n-1}$ 11. $a_n = 0.032 \cdot (15)^{n-1}$

12. $\dfrac{31}{8}$ 13. $\dfrac{728}{5}$ 14. $\dfrac{1330}{729}$ 15. $\dfrac{3}{2}$ 16. $\dfrac{648}{5}$ 17. $\dfrac{2}{3}$ 18. $\dfrac{23}{33}$ 19. neither

20. geometric; $r = \dfrac{5}{4}$

14.4 Form I

1. 210 2. 1 3. 7 4. 495 5. $x^5 + 5x^4 y + 10x^3 y^2 + 10x^2 y^3 + 5xy^4 + y^5$

6. $a^4 + 8a^3 + 24a^2 + 32a + 16$ 7. $32x^5 - 240x^4 + 720x^3 - 1080x^2 + 810x - 243$

8. $x^3 + 9x^2 y + 27xy^2 + 27y^3$ 9. $x^9 + 18x^8 + 144x^7 \ldots$ 10. $x^{10} - 10x^9 y + 45x^8 y^2 \ldots$

11. $x^{15} + 15x^{14} + 105x^{13} \ldots$ 12. $x^{10} + 20x^9 y + 180x^8 y^2 \ldots$ 13. $-4455x^8 y^3$ 14. $-1365x^4 y^{11}$

15. $5940x^9 y^3$

14.4 Form II

1. 56 2. 36 3. 924 4. 1365 5. $32x^5 + 80x^4 + 80x^4 + 80x^3 + 40x^2 + 10x + 1$

6. $x^5 - 10x^4 y + 40x^3 y^2 - 80x^2 y^3 + 80xy^4 - 32y^5$ 7. $81x^4 - 216x^3 + 216x^2 - 96x + 16$

8. $x^8 + 8x^6 + 24x^4 + 32x^2 + 16$ 9. $x^{20} + 40x^{19} + 760x^{18} \ldots$ 10. $x^{17} - 68x^{16} + 2176x^{15} \ldots$

11. $x^{18} + 54x^{16} + 1296x^{14} \ldots$ 12. $x^{14} + 28x^{13} + 364x^{12} \ldots$ 13. $375x^{12}$ 14. $12{,}500x$ 15. $15x^8 y^6$

14.4 Form III

1. 125,970   2. 134,596   3. 5253   4. 10,440   5. $27x^3 - 108x^2 y + 144xy^2 - 64y^3$

6. $16x^4 - 64x^3 + 96x^2 - 64x + 16$ 7. $32x^5 + 240x^4 + 720x^3 + 1080x^2 + 810x + 243$

8. $x^{20} + 8x^{15}y + 24x^{10}y^2 + 32x^5 y^3 + 16y^4$ 9. $x^6 + 3x^4 y^2 + 3x^2 y^4 \dots$ 10. $\frac{1}{8}x^3 - 3x^2 + 24x \dots$

11. $256x^8 + 3072x^7 y + 16{,}128x^6 y^2 \dots$ 12. $\frac{1}{81}x^4 + \frac{2}{27}x^3 y + \frac{1}{6}x^2 y^2 \dots$

13. $2{,}203{,}961{,}430x^{18}y^{16}$ 14. y^{12} 15. $-22680x^8 y^9$

Chapter 1 Activity
Lightly shade the boxes that are correctly worked or true statements.

$\dfrac{33}{99}$ reduces to $\dfrac{1}{3}$	$2+-4=-2$	The point $(0, 5)$ lies on the x-axis	$-9^2 = -81$	$3x - 2x = -7x + 8x$
$2 \cdot 3 = 3 \cdot 2$ Illustrates the Commutative Property of Multiplication	$(-3)(-3)(-3) = -27$	0 is a natural number	$-3.8 + 3.8 = 0$	$\lvert -5 \rvert = 5$
Evaluate $3x + 2$ if $x = 3$ answer is 7	$\dfrac{0}{9}$ is undefined	$3(x - 2y) = 3x - 6$	$3x + 2y + 7 = 12xy$	$2x$ and $2y$ are like terms
$-3 + -6 = 9$	$3x - -4x = 7x^2$	$1\dfrac{3}{8} = \dfrac{11}{8}$	$2 + -4 + 5 = 11$	$6x \div x = 6x^2$
$\sqrt{3}$ is irrational	$2 \cdot 4 + 7 \cdot 2 = 13$	$9(x + y) = 9x + 9y$ Illustrates the Distributive Property	$\dfrac{1}{8} + \dfrac{1}{2} = \dfrac{2}{16}$	$40 = 2 \cdot 2 \cdot 2 \cdot 5$
The point $(0, 0)$ is called the origin	$\left(\dfrac{-2}{3}\right)\left(\dfrac{-3}{2}\right) = 1$	57 is a prime number	$\dfrac{12 + 4}{-4} = -4$	The x axis runs horizontally
$\dfrac{3}{7} = .37$	$9 + 2 \cdot -3 = 3$	In quadrant III, ordered pairs are (negative, negative)	$\dfrac{-60}{-15} = 4$	$-20 > -10$
$8 - -8 = 0$	$\dfrac{15}{0} = 0$	$\dfrac{15}{4} = 3\dfrac{3}{4}$	$(-5)^2 = 25$	$-2 - 4 - 5 - 8 = -18$

Chapter 2 Activity

Karol is trying to learn to be a smarter shopper. Fill in the table. Round prices to the nearest cent.

	Item	Original Price	Price @ 15% Off	Price @ 25% Off	Price @ 40% Off	Price @ 75% Off
1.	Blouse	$38.00				
2.	Jacket	$72.95				
3.	Shoes	$54.00				
4.	Purse	$120.00				
5.	CD Player	69.90				
6	Necklace	$210.00				

7. How much would Karol save if she purchased a purse and shoes at 40% off their regular prices?

8. Karol has $85.00 to spend. How much would Karol spend if she purchased 2 blouses at 75% off? Would she have enough left to buy a CD player at 15% off?

9. How much would Karol save if she waited to purchase a necklace at 75% off rather than purchasing it at 15% off?

10. How much would Karol spend if she bought all items at 25% off? If she waited and purchased then all at 40% off, how much would she save?

Chapter 3 Activity
Graphing

Graphing doesn't have to be a drag! Have some fun with this one!

Plot the points below (left to right), connecting them as you go.

Begin here:
(0, –1), (1, –1), (1, –3), (3, –3), (3, –1), (5, 0), (8, 0),

(7, 1), (9, 0), (8, 2), (5, 1), (4, 3), (3, 4), (2, 3), (1, 4),

(0, 3), (–1, 4), (–2, 3), (–3, 4), (–4, 3), (–5, 1), (–8,2),

(–5, 2), (–3, –1), (–3, –3), (–1, –3), (–1, –1), (0, –1) The End.

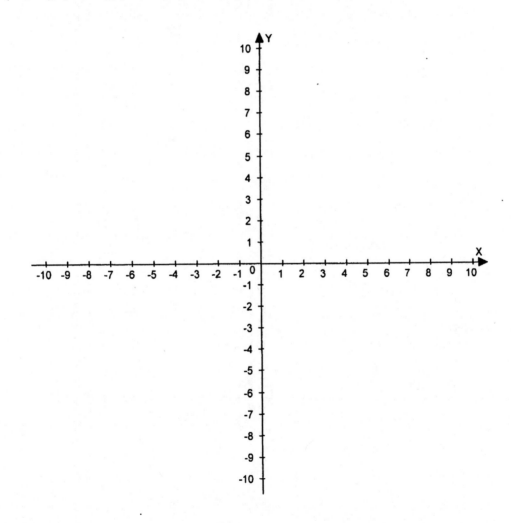

Solve each system of equations by substitution or addition. Plot the solutions to each system on the same coordinate plane on your own graph paper. Connect the points in order 1-10 and back to #1.

1. $x + y = 14$
   $4x - y = -14$

2. $2x - y = -1$
   $x + 2y = 13$

3. $x = 3y$
   $2x - 4y = 10$

4. $2x + 4y = 12$
   $x - 2y = 10$

5. $y = -x - 4$
   $2x + y = 5$

6. *Free Point*
   Plot $(0, -6\frac{1}{4})$

7. $x - y = 4$
   $3x - 2y = -1$

8. $4x - 4y = -13$
   $2x - 4y = -2$

9. $x + 3y = 0$
   $2x + 7y = 5$

10. $5x - 4y = 5$
    $y = 2x + 1$

Chapter 5 Activity
Polynomials

Many people use math daily in their jobs. Graphic artists and designers, architects, landscapers and construction contractors are professions in which math is used extensively. The following problems are similar to some that these professionals might encounter.

1. Jessica is creating new packaging for a new designer fragrance from a 20 inch square piece of cardboard. Squares with side "x" are cut out of the corners and the sides are folded up. The finished box will have a square bottom. Jessica must determine the volume of the box to make sure it will hold the new product. Express the volume of the box as a polynomial in "x". (Hint: draw a picture)

2. Bob has been hired to put a small fence around his client's vegetable garden to keep the neighbor's dog out. The length of the garden is 6 meters longer than the width. The area of the garden is 40 m^2.

    a. How many meters of fencing will Bob need to purchase?
    b. If white fencing costs $2.50 per meter, how much would it cost for the materials for a white fence?
    c. If green fencing costs $3.19 per meter, how much would it cost for the materials for a green fence?
    d. How much would he save by using the white fencing?

3. Patricia is making a giant sized cereal box display and wants the display to be made in the same proportion as the real box. She needs to determine the surface area of the display in order to purchase the materials for its construction. The real box is 6 times as high as it is deep and it is twice as high as it is wide.

    a. Express the surface area of the real box in terms of its depth, "x".
    b. Find the surface area if the depth is 2 inches.

Chapter 6 Activity

Directions: Cut up the grid and align the boxes so that each polynomial matches with its factored form.

$b^2 - 4b + 4$	$b^2 + 2b - 63$		$(b+5)(b-5)$
			$b^2 + 9b - 70$
$b^2 - 2b + 1$ **1.** $b^2 - 3b + 2$	$b^2 - 13b + 30$ **2.** $b^2 - 18b - 40$	$(b+9)(b-1)$ **3.** $(b-7)(b+6)$	$b^2 + 2b - 6$ **4.** $b^2 - 4b - 32$
$b^2 - 7b + 12$	$b^2 - 49$	$(b+14)(b-5)$	$b^2 - 64$
			$(b+13)(b+3)$
$b^2 + 11b + 28$	$b^2 + 11b + 28$	$b^2 + 10b + 21$	
$b^2 + 16b + 15$ **5.** $b^2 - 10b + 16$	$b^2 - 6b + 9$ **6.** $b^2 + 10b - 25$	$b^2 + 6b - 40$ **7.** $b^2 + 27b + 75$	prime **8.** $(b+5)(b-5)$
$b^2 + 27b + 75$	$b^2 - 14b + 49$	$b^2 + 16b + 39$	$(b+1)(b+10)$
$(b-22)(b+2)$	$b^2 - 3b + 3$	$(b+7)(b-7)$	$(b+8)(b-8)$
$(b-8)(b+4)$ **9.** $(b-10)(b-3)$	$b^2 - b - 42$ **10.** $b^2 - 4b - 12$	$(b-2)(b-1)$ **11.** $(b+10)(b-4)$	$(b-9)(b+5)$ **12.** $(b-1)^2$
$(b-2)^2$	$b^2 - 20b - 44$	$(b+7)(b+4)$	$(b+7)(b+4)$
$(b-1)(b+11)$	$(b+10)(b-10)$	$(b-4)(b-3)$	$b^2 - 1$
$(b-6)(b+2)$ **13.** $(b+9)(b-2)$	$(b-20)(b+2)$ **14.** $(b-10)(b-7)$	$(b-2)(b-8)$ **15.** $(b-3)^2$	$b^2 + 7b - 18$ **16.** $b^2 + 13b + 36$
$(b+9)(b-7)$	$(b+7)(b+3)$	$(b-4)^2$	$b^2 - 100$

Chapter 7 Activity

Which one doesn't belong? In each row, circle the item that does not belong.

	A	B	C
1.	$(y+2)^2$	y^2+4y+4	$(y+2)(y-2)$
2.	$(x+5)(x-2)$	$(x-5)(x+2)$	$x^2-3x-10$
3.	$4y^2-9$	$(2y+3)(2y-3)$	$(2y-3)^2$
4.	$5y(1-y)$	$5y-5y^2$	$(5y+1)(y-5y)$
5.	$x-3$	$-x-3$	$-1(3-x)$
6.	$(y-5)(y-3)$	$(y+5)(y+3)$	$y^2+8y+15$
7.	$7(w-9)$	$7(w+9)(w-9)$	$7w^2-63$
8.	$(x-9)(x+4)$	$(x+9)(x-4)$	$x^2+5x-36$
9.	$4w^3(2w-3)$	$8w^4-12w^3$	$(8-12)(w^4-w^3)$
10.	$(x-5)(x+4)$	x^2+x-20	$(x+5)(x-4)$
11.	x^2+2x-3	$(x-3)(x+1)$	$(x-4)(x-1)$
12.	$(3x+1)(2x-1)$	$(3x-1)(2x+1)$	$6x^2+x-1$
13.	$(x+4)(x-3)$	$x^2-7x+12$	$(x-4)(x-3)$
14.	$2y^2-7y-4$	$(2y-1)(y-3)$	$(2y+1)(y-4)$
15.	$(4x+9)(4x-9)$	$16x^2-81$	$(8x+9)(8x-9)$

Chapter 8 Activity

A. Write two ordered pairs using two dates and two dollar values For example:
1. (Year home or car purchased, purchase price) (let the year purchased be zero)
a. (Current year, current value of home or car) (current year be number of years since year of purchase)

B. Using these two ordered pairs, determine the slope and explain the meaning of the slope.

C. Using the point-slope equation, write the equation of the line represented by these two points in slope-intercept form.

D. Name the *y*-intercept and tell what it means.

E. Graph the equation.

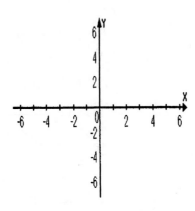

Chapter 9 Activity

In day to day life we are often comparing prices. Advertisements on television and advertisements in print try to lure us as consumers. A wise shopper should not only compare prices but also product quality and applicable warranties.

Locate three printed advertisements comparing cell phone rates, high speed internet cable rates, car rental rates, or something of interest to you. Cut out and paste the ads below. Write out equations or inequalities representing each plan. Tell which plan would best fit your needs and give five reasons to support your answer.

Chapter 10 Activity

Did you ever wonder how meteorologists are able to predict how long a storm will last? Often times, math can be used in real life situations and estimating the length of a storm is just one of those times.

Tornados, hurricanes, and thunderstorms all cover the ground in a circular pattern. Using satellite or radar pictures, forecasters can estimate the diameter of a storm. The formula $t = \sqrt{\dfrac{d^3}{216}}$ where t represents the time the storm will last in hours and d represents the diameter of a storm in miles can be used to estimate how long a storm will last.

1.   Use the formula to estimate how long each storm will last. Round to the nearest hour if necessary.

        a. A hurricane with a diameter of 96 miles.

        b. A tornado with a diameter of 8 miles.

        c. A thunderstorm with a diameter of 24 miles.

2.   If a hurricane lasts 27 hours, what is the diameter of the storm?

Chapter 11 Activity

Use your knowledge of the Pythagorean Theorem formula to answer the following:

1. A baseball diamond is a square, 90 feet on each side. How far is it from 1st to 3rd base?

2. If the left fielder catches the ball on the third base line 40 feet behind third base, how far would the fielder have to throw the ball to first base? (Hint: Draw a picture.)

3. Two trains leave the same city at the same time. One heads due west and one due north. One train travels 5 miles per hour faster than the other. After 2 hours they are 50 miles apart. Find the speed of each train.

4. The diagonal of a square has a length of $6\sqrt{2}$ feet. Find the perimeter of the square.

5. Any three positive integers that can be the lengths of the sides of a right triangle are called Pythagorean Triples. One example is a right triangle that has sides 3 in., 4 in., and 5 in. The Pythagorean Triple is 3, 4, 5. Find three other sets of Pythagorean Triples.

Chapter 12 Activity

Gather population numbers from five different countries. Using the mathematical model for exponential growth or decay outlined in section 9.6 of your text book, $(f(t) = A_0 e^{kt})$, determine a function for each of the five countries that models your data. Predict the population of each country in the year 2015. List five reasons for the different rates of growth that exist among the five countries you chose. With the data gathered and your predictions for 2010, use a line graph on a coordinate plan to graph each function. You may find it convenient to use five different colored pencils to show the five models.

Chapter 13 Activity

Use five paper cones and four index cards. Cut and paste or tape the cones and planes four times to illustrate the intersections of:

1. a cone and a plane in a circular path.
2. a cone and a plane in a ellipse path.
3. a cone and a plane in a parabolic path.
4. two cones and a plane in a hyperbolic path.

Chapter 14 Activity

With a partner, investigate what is known as **Pascal's Triangle** (pg 829). Start with row 0, which is a 1, and build through row 10. Make sure to construct your triangle in neat and defined columns.

1.   What is the pattern formed by the sums of each diagonal?

2.   What is the pattern formed by the sums of each row?

3.   Write three additional comments concerning patterns you see in the triangle.

Activity Answers

Chapter 1

Shaded boxes: Row 1: 1, 2, 4, 5; Row 2: 1, 2, 4, 5; Row 3: none; Row 4: 3
Row 5: 1,3,5; Row 6: 1, 2, 4, 5; Row 7: 2, 3, 4; Row 8: 3

Chapter 2

1.	Blouse	$38.00	$32.30	$28.50	$22.80	$9.50
2.	Jacket	$72.95	$62.01	$54.71	$43.77	$18.24
3.	Shoes	$54.00	$45.90	$40.50	$32.40	$13.50
4.	Purse	$120.00	$102.00	$90.00	$72.00	$30.00
5.	CD Player	$69.90	$59.40	$52.42	$41.94	$17.47
6.	Necklace	$210.00	$178.50	$157.50	$126.00	$52.50

7. She would save $69.60.
8. $19.00, Yes
9. $126.00
10. $423.63; $84.72

Chapter 3

Graph is a stegosaurus.

Chapter 4

1. (0, 14) 2. (3, 5) 3. (15, 5) 4. $\left(5\frac{1}{2}, -2\frac{1}{4}\right)$ 5. (9, –13) 6. Free point 7. (–9, –13)

8. $\left(5\frac{1}{2}, -2\frac{1}{4}\right)$ 9. (–15, 5) 10. (–3, –5) The picture is a five point star.

Chapter 5

1. $4x^3 - 8x^2 + 400$ 2. a. 28 meters b. $70 c. $89.32 d. $19.32 3. a. $54x^2$ b. 216 in.^{2}

Chapter 6

When arranged correctly, boxes will be in the following order:

    3, 10, 13, 16
    4, 9, 2, 14
    12, 1, 11, 7
    5, 15, 6, 8

Chapter 7

1. c 2. a 3. c 4. c 5. b 6. a 7. b 8. a 9. c 10. a 11. b 12. c 13. a 14. b 5. c

Chapter 8

A. Answers will vary
B. The slope represents the increase or decrease per year.
C. Answers will vary.
D. The *y*-intercept represents the original amount the first year.
D. Graphs will vary.

Chapter 9

Activity 9 answers will vary.

Chapter 10

1. a. 64 hours   b. 2 hours   c. 8 hours   2. 54 miles

Chapter 11

1. $90\sqrt{2} \approx 127.28$ feet   2. $50\sqrt{10}$ feet ≈ 158 feet   3. 15 mph and 20 mph   4. 24 feet
5. 6, 8, 10; 5, 12, 13; 10, 24, 26

Chapter 12

Answers will vary.

Chapter 13

Students, with the use of the cones and cards, should be able to visualize more clearly the conic sections outlined in chapter 13.

Chapter 14

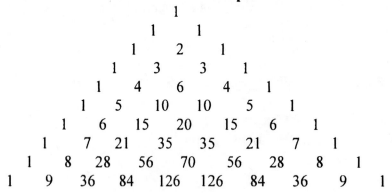

Then,

1. Another row of Pascal's Triangle is formed.
2. The sum of each row is twice the sum of the previous row.
3. Answers will vary.

Name _____   Date _____

Chapter 1
Form A

For problems 1 – 8, perform the indicated operation or operations.

1. $9 - (-2) + (3 - 4)$ 1. _____

2. $-\dfrac{2}{3} - \dfrac{1}{2}$ 2. _____

3. $10 \div -5 \cdot 4$ 3. _____

4. $\left(-\dfrac{2}{3}\right) \div \left(-\dfrac{4}{9}\right)$ 4. _____

5. $7 - 2(4 + 3)^2$ 5. _____

6. -5^2 6. _____

7. $(3 - 6)^3 (4 - 8)^2$ 7. _____

8. $\dfrac{3(2^3 - 4)}{-2 + 3 \cdot 4}$ 8. _____

For problems 9 – 10, simplify each algebraic expression.

9. $4(2a - 3b) - 3(4a - b)$ 9. _____

10. $8x - 4[5 - 3(x + 1)]$ 10. _____

11.   List all the whole numbers in this set: 11. _____
$$\left\{ -\frac{4}{3}, \ -1, \ 0, \ 1.7, \ \pi, \ \sqrt{9} \right\}$$

12. Give an example of a number that is an integer but not a   12. _____
     whole number.

13. Insert either < or > in the boxed area to make a true statement: 13. _____
     –6 ☐ –10

14. Find the absolute value: $|-\sqrt{3}\,|$ 14. _____

15. For problems 15 – 16, plot and label the given point in the rectangular coordinate system
     below. Indicate in which quadrant each point lies.

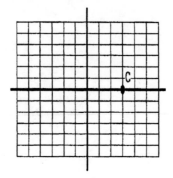

15. $\left(\dfrac{1}{2}, -3\right)$ 15. _____

16. (–4, 4)   16. _____

17. Find the coordinates of point C on the above graph.   17. _____

For problems 18 – 19, evaluate each algebraic expression for the given value of the variable.

18. $-6(x+3);\ x=2$ 18. _____

19. $x^4 - x;\ x = -2$ 19. _____

20. Use the associative property of addition to write an equivalent   20. _____
     algebraic expression. Then simplify the expression. $3+(5+x)$

21.   Use the commutative property of multiplication to write an   21. _____
      equivalent algebraic expression. Then simplify the expression.
      (4x)2

22.   The formula $F = \dfrac{5}{9}C + 32$ expresses the relationship between   22. _____

      Celsius temperature, C, and Fahrenheit temperature, F. What
      is the Fahrenheit temperature equivalent to 72° C?

For problems 23 – 24, the graph below represents the number of fish present in an aquarium.

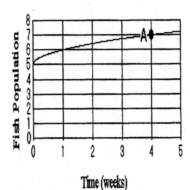

Time (weeks)

23.   Find the coordinates of point A and interpret the coordinates in   23. _____
      terms of the information given.

24.   How many fish were initially placed in the aquarium?   24. _____

25.   What is the difference in elevation between a plane traveling   25. _____
      21,625 feet above sea level and a submarine traveling 412 feet
      below sea level?

Chapter 1
Form B

For problems 1 – 8, perform the indicated operation or operations.

1. $(-2-3)+(-4-(-2))$ 1. _____

2. $-\dfrac{3}{4}+\dfrac{3}{5}$ 2. _____

3. $-8+8\div 4$ 3. _____

4. $\left(-\dfrac{6}{7}\right)\div\left(\dfrac{7}{8}\right)$ 4. _____

5. $-3-2(5^2-6^2)$ 5. _____

6. -3^2 6. _____

7. $(5-2)^3(4-6)^2$ 7. _____

8. $\dfrac{-4(12-2^4)}{(-1+2)(3+1)}$ 8. _____

For problems 9 – 10, simplify each algebraic expression.

9. $7(2x-1)-(4x-6)$ 9. _____

10. $-2[5a-3(a+1)]$ 10. _____

11.   List all the irrational numbers in this set: 11. _____
$\left\{-\sqrt{29},\ -4,\ -\dfrac{2}{3},\ 0,\ 1.46,\ \pi\right\}$

12. Give an example of a number that is a rational number but not an integer.

12. _____

13. Insert either < or > in the boxed area to make a true statement:
$-5 \; \square \; -2$

13. _____

14. Find the absolute value: $\left| -\dfrac{2}{3} \right|$

14. _____

15. For problems 15 – 16, plot and label the given point in the rectangular coordinate system below. Indicate in which quadrant each point lies.

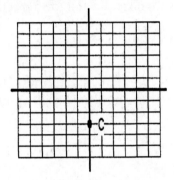

15. $\left(4, \, -3\right)$

15. _____

16. $\left(-3, \, \dfrac{4}{5}\right)$

16. _____

17. Find the coordinates of point C on the above graph.

17. _____

For problems 18 – 19, evaluate each algebraic expression for the given value of the variable.

18. $2(-x + 5); \; x = -3$

18. _____

19. $x - x^2; \; x = -1$

19. _____

Name _____   Date _____

20. Use the distributive property to rewrite without parentheses: 20. _____
     $-7(4x - 8y - 1)$

21. Use the associative property of multiplication to write an   21. _____
     equivalent algebraic expression. Then simplify the expression.
     $5(3x)$

22. The formula used to calculate the percentage of body fat for men   22. _____
     is % Body fat = $\dfrac{-98.42 + 4.15w - 0.082b}{b}$ where w is the waist
     measurement in inches and b is the total body weight in pounds.
     What is the percentage of body fat for a man weighing 175 pounds
     and a waist measurement of 38 inches. Round the percentage to the
     nearest integer.

For problems 23 – 24, the graph below represents the introduction of an endangered bird species
into a wildlife refuge. The population of the bird species is monitored and recorded each year.

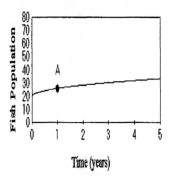

Time (years)

23. How many of the endangered birds were introduced into the   23. _____
     wildlife refuge?

24. Find the approximate coordinates of point A and interpret the   24. _____
     coordinates in terms of the information given.

25. What is the difference in elevation between a mountain climber   25. _____
     5186 feet above sea level and a scuba diver 25 feet below sea
     level?

Name _____   Date _____

Chapter 1
Form C

For problems 1 – 8, perform the indicated operation or operations.

1. $2(-47+15)-(32-40)$ 1. _____

2. $\dfrac{10}{11}-\left(-\dfrac{4}{33}\right)$ 2. _____

3. $15+9\div3$ 3. _____

4. $\left(\dfrac{48}{125}\right)\div\left(-\dfrac{4}{5}\right)$ 4. _____

5. $(8-10)^4(7-2)^3$ 5. _____

6. -8^2 6. _____

7. $(8-10)^4(7-2)^3$ 7. _____

8. $\dfrac{(-3)^2(5-3^2)}{4-2\cdot3}$ 8. _____

For problems 9 – 10, simplify each algebraic expression.

9. $5+4(3x-1)$ 9. _____

10. $-3x+[5-2(x+1)]$ 10. _____

11. List all the irrational numbers in this set: 11. _____

$\left\{-5,\ -\sqrt{3},\ 0,\ 0.333...,\ \pi,\ \dfrac{9}{2}\right\}$

12. Give an example of a number that is a whole number but not   12. _____
     a natural number.

13. Insert either < or > in the boxed area to make a true statement: 13. _____
     –86 ☐ –100

14. Find the absolute value: $\left|-1.24\right|$ 14. _____

15. For problems 15 – 16, plot and label the given point in the rectangular coordinate system
     below. Indicate in which quadrant each point lies.

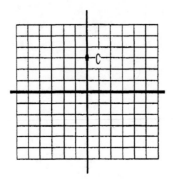

15. $A\left(-\dfrac{3}{4},\ 5\right)$ 15. _____

16. $B\left(4,\ 2\right)$ 16. _____

17. Find the coordinates of point C on the above graph.   17. _____

For problems 18 – 19, evaluate each algebraic expression for the given value of the variable.

18. $(x+2)(x-3);\ \ x=-1$ 18. _____

19. $x^{4}-x-x;\ \ x=-3$ 19. _____

20. Use the commutative property of addition to write an equivalent   20. _____
     algebraic expression. Then simplify the expression.
     $-7(4x-8y-1)$

21. Use the associative property of multiplication to write an   21. _____
     equivalent algebraic expression. Then simplify the expression.
     $4+x-3$

22. The formula for converting degrees Fahrenheit (F) to degrees   22. _____
     Celsius (C) is $C=\dfrac{5}{9}(F)-32)$. Find C when F is 86°.

For problems 23 – 24, use the circle graph shown in the chart below. The circle graph shows the
percentage of 7th, 8th, and 9th graders in a local junior high school with a total enrollment of 840
students.

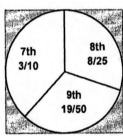

23. How many students are 7th graders?   23. _____

24. How many students are not 7th graders?   24. _____
     coordinates in terms of the information given.

25. What is the difference in elevation between a hang glider at   25. _____
     130 feet above sea level and a submarine 716 feet below sea
     level?

Chapter 1
Form D

Choose the correct answer to each problem.

1. Find $698 - [77 - (64 - 34)] - 24$
   a. 615   b. 627   c. 499   d. 675

2. Find $\dfrac{2}{5} + \left(-\dfrac{1}{6}\right)$
   a. $\dfrac{7}{30}$ b. $-\dfrac{17}{30}$ c. $-\dfrac{7}{30}$ d. $\dfrac{17}{30}$

3. Find $8 - 6 \div 2$
   a. 1   b. -24 c. -1 d. 5

4. Find $\left(-\dfrac{7}{25}\right) \div \left(\dfrac{42}{50}\right)$
   a. $-\dfrac{1}{3}$ b. $\dfrac{35}{50}$ c. $-\dfrac{2}{6}$ d. $\dfrac{7}{10}$

5. Find $\left(2^2 - 3^2\right) - (7 + 2)^2$
   a. -68 b. -86 c. 405   d. -405

6. Find -12^2
   a. -24 b. 24   c. -144 d. 144

7. Find $6 - 5(11 - 13)^2 + 3(4)$
   a. 28   b. 16   c. -2 d. 38

8. Find $\dfrac{-8(12-3)^2}{8^2 - 3 \cdot 2}$
   a. $-\dfrac{324}{29}$ b. 81   c. $\dfrac{725}{5}$ d. -16.125

Name _____   Date _____

9. Find $\left| -\dfrac{17}{19} \right|$

a. $\dfrac{17}{19}$ b. $1\dfrac{2}{17}$ c. $-\dfrac{17}{19}$ d. $-1\dfrac{2}{17}$

10. Simplify $5x - (x + 2) - 3(x - 4)$
 a. $x + 14$ b. $9x - 14$ c. $x - 14$ d. $x + 10$

11. Simplify $-3[4 - 2(y + 3)]$
 a. $6y + 6$ b. $6y - 30$ c. $-6y - 18$ d. $-2y - 18$

12. Evaluate $-x^2 + 2x - 4$ for $x = -2$
 a. -4 b. -64 c. -12 d. -8

13. What is the best classification for -7?
 a. Integer, rational number, real number   b. Irrational number, real number
 c. Rational number, real number   d. Whole number, integer, real number

For problem 14, the circle graph below shows the level of education of teachers in the local school district.

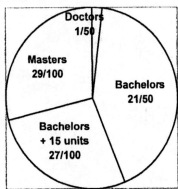

14. If there are 1400 teachers in the district, how many have a Bachelor's degree only?
 a. 378   b. 588   c. 406   d. 280

15. Identify the property or operation that is illustrated by $(x \cdot 2) \cdot 3 = x \cdot (2 \cdot 3)$.
 a. Associative property of addition   b. Associative property of multiplication
 c. Commutative property of addition   d. Commutative property of multiplication

16.   Identify the property or operation that is illustrated by $2b(a-2) = 2ab - 4b$
       a. Associative property of addition   b. Commutative property of multiplication
       c. Distributive property   d. Commutative property of addition

17.   The formula for the area of a circle is $A = \pi\, r^2$, where r is the radius and π is
       approximately 3.14. Find the area of a circle with the radius of 4m.
       a. $12.56\,\text{m}^2$ b. $16\,\text{m}^2$ c. $157.75\,\text{m}^2$ d. $50.24\,\text{m}^2$

Use the graph below for problems 18 – 20.

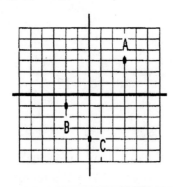

18.   What are the coordinates of point A and what quadrant is it located in?
       a. $(-3, 3)$ Quadrant IV   b. $(3, 3)$ Quadrant I
       c. $(3, -3)$ Quadrant III   d. $(-3, -3)$ Quadrant II

19.   What are the coordinates of point B and what quadrant is it located in?
       a. $(2, -1)$ Quadrant I   b. $(1, -2)$ Quadrant I
       c. $(-2, -1)$ Quadrant IV   d. $(1, -2)$ Quadrant IV

20.   What are the coordinates of point C?
       a. $(0, -4)$ b. $(4, 0)$ c. $(-4, 0)$ d. $(0, 4)$

Name _____   Date _____

Chapter 1
Form E

Choose the correct answer to each problem.

1.   Find $296 - [49 - (17 - 51)]$
       a. 213   b. 281   c. 379   d. 311

2.   Find $17 - 6 \cdot 3 + 4 \div 2$
       a. $\dfrac{37}{2}$ b. 35   c. $\dfrac{3}{2}$ d. 1

3.   Add $\left(-\dfrac{7}{12}\right) + \left(-\dfrac{5}{8}\right)$
       a. $\dfrac{29}{24}$ b. $-\dfrac{29}{24}$ c. $\dfrac{35}{96}$ d. $\dfrac{14}{15}$

4.   Divide $\left(\dfrac{15}{44}\right) \div \left(-\dfrac{20}{3}\right)$
       a. $\dfrac{9}{176}$ b. $-\dfrac{1}{11}$ c. $-\dfrac{25}{11}$ d. $-\dfrac{9}{176}$

5.   Find $(11 - 19)^2 (3^2 - 2^2)$
       a. 320   b. –320   c. 64   d. –64

6.   Find -14^2
       a. –28   b. 28   c. 196   d. –196

7.   Find $\left| -\dfrac{18}{19} \right|$
       a. $-\dfrac{18}{19}$ b. $-1\dfrac{1}{18}$ c. $\dfrac{18}{19}$ d. $1\dfrac{1}{18}$

8.   Find $\dfrac{5 - 4(12 - 5)^2}{4 \cdot 2 - 5 \cdot 2}$
       a. 49   b. $\dfrac{49}{2}$ c. $\dfrac{191}{2}$ d. $\dfrac{49}{0}$

Name _____   Date _____

9. Simplify $12 - 10(x + 3y)$
   a. $12 - 10x + 30y$ b. $12 - 10x - 30y$
   c. $2x + 6y$ d. $-120x - 360y$

10. Simplify $3[x + 4 - (x - 4)]$
    a. 24   b. 0   c. $2x + 16$ d. $2x + 8$

11. Simplify $4x^3 - 3x^2 + 6x^3 + x^2$
    a. $10x^6 - 2x^4$ b. $x + 7x^5$ c. $10x^3 - 2x^2$ d. $8x^6$

12. Evaluate $x^4 - x^3$ for $x = -4$
    a. -192 b. 192   c. -4 d. 320

13. What is the best classification for $\sqrt{11}$?
    a. Irrational number, real number   b. Integer, rational number, real number
    c. Whole number, integer, rational   d. Real Number
       number, real number

For problem 14, the circle graph below shows the television ownership status for a certain community.

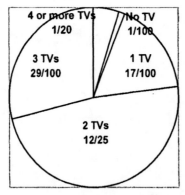

14. If there are 144,000 people in the community, how many people own 2 televisions?
    a. 42,340   b. 70,080   c. 7300   d. 24,820

15. Identify the property or operation that is illustrated by $(x \cdot 3) \cdot 4 = x \cdot (3 \cdot 4)$.
    a. Commutative property of addition   b. Associative property of multiplication
    c. Commutative property of multiplication d. Associative property of addition

16.   Identify the property or operation that is illustrated by $2 + 4 = 4 + 2$
        a. Commutative property of addition   b. Associative property of multiplication
        c. Commutative property of multiplication   d. Associative property of addition

17.   The formula for the perimeter, P, of a rectangle is $P = 2L + 2W$ where L is the length and
        W is the width. What is the perimeter of a rectangle with the length of 4 feet and the
        width of $\dfrac{5}{2}$ feet?

        a. 13 feet   b. 18 feet   c. 21 feet   d. $\dfrac{13}{2}$ feet

18.   What is the difference in elevation between a hang glider at 212 feet above sea level and
        a scuba diver at 32 feet below sea level?
        a. 180 feet   b. 488 feet   c. 360 feet   d. 244 feet

Use the graph below for problems 19 – 20.

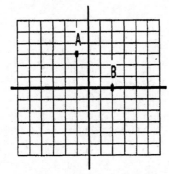

19.   Where are the coordinates of point A and what quadrant is it located in?
        a. (3, –1) Quadrant II   b. (3, –1) Quadrant IV
        c. (–1, 3) Quadrant II   d. (–1, 3) Quadrant IV

20.   What are the coordinates of point B?
        a. (–2, 0)   b. (0, –2)   c. (2, 0)   d. (0, 2)

Chapter 1
Form F

Choose the correct answer to each problem.

1. Find $838 - [71 - (54 - 46) - 21$
   a. 796   b. 646   c. 754   d. 780

2. Find $72 - 10 \div 2 + 8$
   a. 71   b. 75   c. $-\dfrac{11}{40}$ d. $-\dfrac{7}{32}$

3. Find $-\dfrac{5}{8} + 20$
   a. $\dfrac{1}{6}$ b. $\dfrac{2}{12}$ c. $-\dfrac{8}{15}$ d. $\dfrac{8}{15}$

4. Divide $\left(-\dfrac{12}{35}\right) \div \left(-\dfrac{9}{14}\right)$
   a. $-\dfrac{2}{15}$ b. $\dfrac{2}{15}$ c. $-\dfrac{8}{15}$ d. $\dfrac{8}{15}$

5. Find $(7-4)^3\left(4^2 - 3^2\right)$
   a. 63   b. 1890   c. 27   d. 675

6. Find $-15^2 + 5^2$
   a. −100   b. −200   c. 100   d. −20

7. Find $\left| -\dfrac{11}{13} \right|$
   a. $\dfrac{11}{13}$ b. $-\dfrac{11}{13}$ c. $1\dfrac{2}{11}$ d. $-1\dfrac{2}{11}$

8. Find $\dfrac{6 - 3(9-13)^2}{12^2 - 27}$
   a. $-\dfrac{48}{117}$ b. $\dfrac{169}{4}$ c. $\dfrac{48}{117}$ d. $-\dfrac{14}{39}$

9. Simplify $7 - 2(14x - 2y) + 4(x - 4y)$
   a. $74x - 26y$ b. $-24x - 20y + 7$ c. $-24x - 12y + 7$ d. $74x - 6y$

10. Simplify $2\,[x - y + 2 + (3x + 6)]$
    a. $5x - 2y + 10$ b. $8x - 2y + 16$ c. $3xy + 10$ d. $6xy + 16$

11. Simplify $4x^3 + 6x^2 - 3x^3 + 6x^3$
    a. $1^6 + 12x^5$ b. x^3 c. $7x^3 + 6x^2$ d. x^{11}

12. Evaluate $-2x^2 - x + 4$ for $x = -3$
    a. -11 b. 43 c. -17 d. 17

13. What is the best classification for 0.777...?
    a. Irrational number, real number   b. Rational number, real number
    c. Real number   d. Integer, rational number, real number

For problem 14, the circle graph below shows the family status of teachers in the local school district.

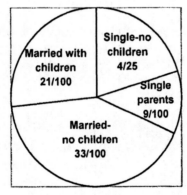

14. If there are 1600 teachers in the district, how many are married with no children?
    a. 528   b. 256   c. 144   d. 672

15. Identify the property or operation that is illustrated by $(2 + 9) + 7 = 2 + (9 + 7)$.
    a. Commutative property of multiplication   b. Distributive property
    c. Associative property of addition   d. Commutative property of addition

16.   Identify the property or operation that is illustrated by $(7 \cdot x) \cdot 3 = (x \cdot 7) \cdot 3$
      a. Commutative property of multiplication   b. Commutative property of addition
      c. Associative property of multiplication   d. Associative property of addition

17.   The formula for the surface area, S, of a closed cylinder is $S = 2\pi r^2 + 2\pi rh$ where π is
      approximately 3.14, h is the height and r is the radius. If the height of a cylinder is
      4 inches and the radius is 6 inches, what is the approximate surface area of the cylinder?
      a. 226.08 square inches   b. 114.04 square inches
      c. 188.4 square inches   d. 376.8 square inches

Use the graph below for problems 18 – 20.

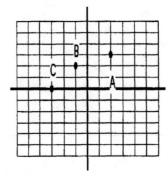

18.   Where are the coordinates of point A and what quadrant is it located in?
      a. (2, –3) Quadrant IV   b. (–3, –2) Quadrant III
      c. (–3, –2) Quadrant IV   d. (–2, –3) Quadrant III

19.   What are the coordinates of point B and what quadrant is it located in?
      a. (2, –1) Quadrant II   b. (–1, 2) Quadrant IV
      c. (–1, 2) Quadrant II   d. (2, –1) Quadrant IV

20.   What are the coordinates of point C?
      a. (0, 3)   b. (3, 0)   c. (–3, 0)   d. (0, –3)

Chapter 2
Form A

For problems 1 – 6, solve the equation.

1. $-3 = -5y + 12$ 1. _____

2. $7x - 5 = 3x - 4 + x + 5$ 2. _____

3. $4 - \dfrac{2x}{3} = -\dfrac{1}{6} + x$ 3. _____

4. $5(y + 3) = -2(y - 4)$ 4. _____

5. $-14(3 - 2x) = 7x + 3(7x - 12)$ 5. _____

6. $2z - 5(4 - z) = 3(2z - 6) + z - 2$ 6. _____

For problems 7 – 10, solve each inequality.

   a. Express the solution set in set-builder notation.
   b. Graph the set on a number line.
   If the inequality has no solution or is true for all real numbers, so state.

7. $-2x - 6 > 0$ 7a. _____

                                                       b.

8. $2x + 8 \le -16 + 8x$

                                                       8a. _____

                                                       b.

Name _____   Date _____

9. $18x - 6(3x - 4) > 0$ 9a. _____

b.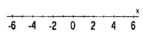

10. $7x - 6(3 - 5x) > x + 18$ 10a. _____

b.

11.   Use set builder notation to describe the following graph.   11. _____

12.   Solve $P = a + b + c$ for c.   12. _____

13.   Solve $A = \dfrac{1}{2} bh$ for b.   13. _____

14.   What is 1.5% of 750?   14. _____

15.   1250 is what percent of 800?   15. _____

16.   28 is 35% of what number?   16. _____

17.   The sum of 2 consecutive odd integers is 1344. Find the   17. _____
       two integers.

18.   The quotient of a number and 6 decreased by 5 is 4. Find   18. _____
       the number.

19.   Two angles of a triangle have the same measure and the third   19. _____

   angle is $\dfrac{1}{4}$ the size of each of the other two. Find the measure

   of each angle.

20.   Jason wants to host a catered dinner for his friends. If the   20. _____
   caterer charges a set up fee of 40 dollars and 15 dollars per
   person, how many people, including Jason, can attend the
   dinner and keep the cost at $145 or less?

Name _____   Date _____

For problems 1 – 6, solve the equation.

1. $6x - 9 = 21$ 1. _____

2. $-8 + 3x = 4x - 5 + 2x - 2$ 2. _____

3. $3y - 7(y + 4) = -y + 6 - 3y$ 3. _____

4. $\dfrac{1}{2}(4x - 6) = -3x + 2$ 4. _____

5. $-(3z + 8) - 9 = 17 + 3z$ 5. _____

6. $15 - \dfrac{2x}{3} = \left(-\dfrac{4x}{6} + 8\right) + 7$ 6. _____

For problems 7 – 10, solve each inequality.

   a. Express the solution set in set-builder notation.
   b. Graph the set on a number line.
   If the inequality has no solution or is true for all real numbers, so state.

7. $7x - 4 \geq 3x$ 7a. _____

                                                   b.
                                          -6   -4   -2   0   2   4   6

8. $2x + 8 \leq 4x - 2(x + 5)$

                                               8a. _____

                                                   b.
                                           -6   -4   -2   0   2   4   6

9. $13 - (2x + 4) < -1 + 3x$

9a. _____

b.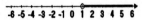
    -6 -4 -2 0 2 4 6

10. $4 - x + 3(5 + x) < 25$

10a. _____

b.
    -6 -4 -2 0 2 4 6

11.   Use set builder notation to describe the following graph.

11. _____

-6 -5 -4 -3 -2 -1 0 1 2 3 4 5 6

12.   Solve $x + 2y = 6$ for y.

12. _____

13.   Solve $A = P + Prt$ for r.

13. _____

14.   What is 125% of 800?

14. _____

15.   260 is 65% of what number?

15. _____

16.   42 is what percent of 672?

16. _____

17.   The sum of a number and 17 is equal to twice the number.
Find the number.

17. _____

18.   The sales tax is 6%. If the total cost of a book (including tax)
is $33.92, what is the price of the book before tax?

18. _____

19.   The angle's measure is four times that of its complement. Find   19. _____
      the measure of the angle described.

20.   A student has made an 89, 72, 91, and 72 on four major exams.   20. _____
      Determine the possible score on the fifth exam that will
      result in a 75 or higher average.

Chapter 2
Form C

For problems 1 – 8, solve the equation.

1. $4x = 2x + 13$ 1. _____

2. $17y - 4 - 6y + 8 = 2(4y - 1)$ 2. _____

3. $1 - \dfrac{z}{2} = 2 + \dfrac{z}{3}$ 3. _____

4. $2 - (x + 3) = 3(2x + 6) + 2$ 4. _____

5. $2(5x - 4) = 5(2x + 3)$ 5. _____

6. $\dfrac{3z}{2} = \dfrac{z}{6} + 4$ 6. _____

7. $2 - 2(y + 4) = (-3 - 2y) - 3$ 7. _____

8. $4(2 - 6y) + 7 = 3(5 - 7y)$ 8. _____

For problems 9 – 11, solve each inequality. Express the solution set in set-builder notation. If the inequality has no solution or is true for all real numbers, so state.

9. $3x - 28 > -13$ 9. _____

10. $4 - 3(x - 4) < 4 - 3x$ 10. _____

11. $7(x - 2) + 16 \le 3(2 + 3x)$ 11. _____

For problems 12 – 13, solve each inequality. Graph the set on a number line. If the inequality has no solution or is true for all real numbers, so state.

12. $8x + 9 \le 5x + 15$

12.

13. $2(x - 5) - (3x + 3) < x - 7$

13.

14.   Use set-builder notation to describe the following graph.   14. _____

$$\overset{\bullet}{\underset{-6\ -5\ -4\ -3\ -2\ -1\ 0\ 1\ 2\ 3\ 4\ 5\ 6}{\longrightarrow}}$$

15.   Solve $A = \dfrac{1}{2}bh$ for h.   15. _____

16.   Solve $2x + 3y = 6$ for x.   16. _____

17.   300 is 15% of what number?   17. _____

18.   27 is what percent of 1350?   18. _____

19.   What is 52% of 27,000?   19. _____

20.   One credit card balance exceeds the other credit card balance by $547. The total of the two credit card balances is $2113. What is the balance on each credit card?   20. _____

21   The product of 7 and a number, increased by 23, is 1710. Find the number.   21. _____

22.   The sum of two consecutive even integers is 6426. Find the two integers.   22. _____

23   Including a 7% sales tax, a car sold for $23,005. What was the price of the car, to the nearest cent, before the tax was added?   23. _____

24.   Find the supplement of an angle which measures 32°.   24. _____

25.   A college student has budgeted $25 a month for phone service. If the telephone company charges $18 a month for basic service and $.05 a minute for each long distance call, how many minutes can be spent on long distance calls each month?   25. _____

Name _____   Date _____

Chapter 2
Form D

Choose the correct answer to each problem.

1. $2x + 4 = 10$
    a. 3   b. 7   c. 6   d. 14

2. $6x - 4 + 2x = 7x - 4$
    a. No Solution   b. −8   c. 8   d. 0

3. $-9(x + 3) = -27 - 9x$
    a. No Solution   b. All real numbers   c. 0   d. −2

4. $1 - (y + 2) = 4(y + 3)$
    a. $-\dfrac{2}{5}$ b. $-\dfrac{4}{5}$ c. $-\dfrac{13}{5}$ d. $-\dfrac{9}{5}$

5. $\dfrac{4x}{5} - 2 = -\dfrac{7}{20} + \dfrac{x}{4}$

    a. 3   · b. −3   c. No solution   d. $\dfrac{11}{7}$

6. $3z - 2(1 - z) = 3(z + 1) + 2z$

    a. No solution   b. All real numbers   c. $-\dfrac{5}{4}$ d. $\dfrac{1}{2}$

For problems 7 − 10, choose the correct expression of the solution set.

7. $2x + 6 \geq 4$
    a. $\{x \mid x \geq -1\}$ b. $\{x \mid x \leq -1\}$ c. $\{x \mid x \geq -5\}$ d. $\{x \mid x \leq -5\}$

8. $14x - 24 < 8x + 20 + 6x - 2$
    a. $\left\{x \mid x < \dfrac{7}{4}\right\}$ b. $\left\{x \mid x < -\dfrac{7}{4}\right\}$
    c. $\{x \mid x \text{ is a real number}\}$ d. No solution

T-27

9. $5x + 2(1-x) \geq 14 - x$

    a.
      -8 -5 -4 -3 -2 -1 0 1 2 3 4 5 6

    b.
      -8 -5 -4 -3 -2 -1 0 1 2 3 4 5 6

    c.
      -8 -5 -4 -3 -2 -1 0 1 2 3 4 5 6

    d.
      -8 -5 -4 -3 -2 -1 0 1 2 3 4 5 6

10. $10 - 2(x-4) > -4(3-x)$

    a.
      -8 -5 -4 -3 -2 -1 0 1 2 3 4 5 6

    b.
      -8 -5 -4 -3 -2 -1 0 1 2 3 4 5 6

    c.
      -8 -5 -4 -3 -2 -1 0 1 2 3 4 5 6

    d.
      -8 -5 -4 -3 -2 -1 0 1 2 3 4 5 6

11.   Use set-builder notation to describe the following graph.

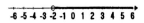

    -8 -5 -4 -3 -2 -1 0 1 2 3 4 5 6

    a. $\{x \mid x \geq -2\}$ b. $\{x \mid x \leq -2\}$ c. $\{x \mid x > -2\}$ d. $\{x \mid x < -2\}$

12.   Solve $t = 2S + d$ for S.

    a. $\dfrac{t+d}{2} = S$ b. $t - d - 2 = S$ c. $t - d + 2 = S$ d. $\dfrac{t-d}{2} = S$

13.   Solve $A = \dfrac{1}{3}\pi r^2 h$ for h.

    a. $\dfrac{3V}{\pi r^2} = h$ b. $3\pi r^2 V = h$ c. $\dfrac{1}{3}V - \pi r^2 = h$ d. $\dfrac{1}{3}V + \pi r^2 = h$

14.   What is 6% of 124?
       a. 744   b. 7.44   c. 2066.7   d. 20.7

15.   90 is 12% of what number?
       a. 1080   b. 10.8 .   c. 7.5   d. 750

16.   500 is what percent of 250?
       a. 200%   b. 20%   c. 2%   d. 50%

17.   The quotient of a number and 5 increased by 27 is 51. Find the number.
       a. 24   b. 228   c. 120   d. $\dfrac{24}{5}$

18.   A rectangle is three times as long as it is wide. If the perimeter is 104 feet, what are the
       length and the width?
       a. Length 13 feet, width 39 feet   b. Width 13 feet, length 39 feet
       c. Length 26 feet, width 78 feet   d. Width 26 feet, length 78 feet

19.   After a 30% price reduction, a sofa sells for $280. What was the original price of the
       sofa?
       a. $400   b. $840   c. $467.60   d. $420

20.   There are 4 major exams in an Introductory Algebra class and Jesse has scored a 97, 82,
       and 86 on the first 3 exams. What does Jesse need to receive on the last exam to make at
       least a 90 average?
       a. At least a 90   b. At least a 92   c. At least a 95   d. At least a 96

Name _____   Date _____

Choose the correct answer to each problem.

1. $-9x - 15 = -30$

     a. −5   b. 5   c. $-\dfrac{15}{9}$ d. $\dfrac{15}{9}$

2. $6x + 2 - 4x + 3 = 3x - 10$

     a. 5   b. −15   c. 15   d. −5

3. $4 - (7z + 3) = 7z + 1$

     a. $\dfrac{1}{2}$ b. 0   c. No solution   d. All real numbers

4. $2(x + 4) = 8 + 2x$

     a. 2   b. −2   c. No solution   d. All real numbers

5. $\dfrac{x}{4} + 3 = 2 + \dfrac{x}{3}$

     a. −12   b. 60   c. 12   d. −60

6. $2y + 3 - 7y = -4(y - 2) - y$

     a. 5   b. 11   c. No solution   d. All real numbers

For problems 7 – 10, choose the correct expression of the solution set.

7. $6x - 7 < -1$

     a. $\{x \mid x < -1\}$ b. $\{x \mid x > -1\}$ c. $\{x \mid x > 1\}$ d. $\{x \mid x < 1\}$

8. $36 + 7x < 2(3x + 6) + 24$

     a.   b.

     c.   No solution   d. $\{x \mid x$ is a real number$\}$

9. $2x - (x + 1) \geq -3x + (7 + 4x)$
    a. $\{x \mid x > 8\}$ b. $\{x \mid x < -8\}$
    c. No solution   d. $\{x \mid x \text{ is a real number}\}$

10. $4 - 6(3 - x) > 4(2 - x) + 8$

    a.   b.

    c.   d.

11. Use set-builder notation to describe the following graph.

    a. $\{x \mid x > 1\}$ b. $\{x \mid x \geq 1\}$ c. $\{x \mid x < 1\}$ d. $\{x \mid x \leq 1\}$

12. Solve $I = Prt$ for r.

    a. $r = I - P - t$ b. $r = IPt$ c. $r = \dfrac{I}{Pt}$ d. $r = I + P + t$

13. Solve $P = 2l + 2w$ for w.

    a. $w = \dfrac{P - 2l}{2}$ b. $w = P - l$ c. $w = P - \dfrac{l}{2}$ d. $w = P - 2l - 2$

14. 27 is 12% of what number?
    a. 225   b. 2.25   c. 3.24   d. 324

15. What is 87% of 1200?
    a. 104,400   b. 1044   c. 13.8   d. 1379.3

16. 120 is what percent of 600?
 a. 5%   b. 0.2%   c. 20%   d. 50%

17. The product of –9 and a number, increased by 15 is –7. Find the number.
 a. –13   b. $\dfrac{22}{9}$ c. $-\dfrac{22}{9}$ d. $-\dfrac{8}{9}$

18. Two business addresses are consecutive even integers. If the sum of the addresses is 10,226, what is the smaller integer?
 a. 5112   b. 5110   c. 5116   d. 5114

19. The circumference of a circle is 20π inches. Find the circle's radius and diameter.
 a. $r = 20$ in.   b. $r = 10$ in.   c. $r = 40$ in.   d. $r = 20$ in.
  $d = 40$ in. $d = 20$ in. $d = 20$ in. $d = 10$ in

20. A long distance telephone service charges $.08 for the first minute and $.04 for each minute thereafter. The cost, C, in cents, for a call lasting x minutes can be computed using the formula $C = 8 + 4(x - 1)$. How many minutes can you talk on the phone if you do not want the cost to exceed 100 cents, or $1?
 a. 24   b. 240   c. 0.75   d. 75

Name _____   Date _____

Choose the correct answer to each problem.

For problems 1 – 6, solve the equation.

1. $14x - 21 = 7$
    a. -1 b. 1 c. -2 d. 2

2. $15x - 8 + 7x - 6 = 22x - 14$
    a. -28 b. 28 c. No Solution d. All real numbers

3. $7(z - 2) = -3(4 - z)$
    a. 2 b. $\dfrac{1}{2}$ c. $\dfrac{13}{5}$ d. $-\dfrac{13}{5}$

4. $18 - 8(y + 2) = 2(y - 9)$
    a. 2 b. $-\dfrac{5}{2}$ c. No solution d. All real numbers

5. $\dfrac{x}{12} + \dfrac{x}{4} = \dfrac{7}{24} + x$
    a. $\dfrac{7}{16}$ b. $-\dfrac{5}{16}$ c. $-\dfrac{7}{16}$ d. $\dfrac{5}{16}$

6. $4t - (1 - t) = 2(3t - 4) - t$
    a. 1 b. -1 c. No solution d. All real numbers

For problems 7 – 10, choose the correct expression of the solution set.

7. $-7x + 11 \le -3$
    a. $\{x \mid x \ge 2\}$ b. $\{x \mid x \le 2\}$ c. $\left\{x \mid x \ge -\dfrac{8}{7}\right\}$ d. $\left\{x \mid x \le -\dfrac{8}{7}\right\}$

8. $2(x + 4) < 6 + 2x$
    a. $\{x \mid x > 2\}$ b. $\{x \mid x < 2\}$
    c. $\{x \mid x \text{ is a real number}\}$ d. No solution

9. $6 - 5(x - 1) < x - 1$

   a.   b.

      -6 -5 -4 -3 -2 -1 0 1 2 3 4 5 6   -6 -5 -4 -3 -2 -1 0 1 2 3 4 5 6

   c. $\{x \mid x \text{ is a real number}\}$ d.

                                                 -6 -5 -4 -3 -2 -1 0 1 2 3 4 5 6

10. $9x - 2(3 - x) > 10x - (8 - x)$

   a.   b.

      -6 -5 -4 -3 -2 -1 0 1 2 3 4 5 6   -6 -5 -4 -3 -2 -1 0 1 2 3 4 5 6

   c. $\{x \mid x \text{ is a real number}\}$ d. No solution

11.   Use set-builder notation to describe the following graph.

      -6 -5 -4 -3 -2 -1 0 1 2 3 4 5 6

a. $\{x \mid x \geq 2\}$ b. $\{x \mid x \leq 2\}$ c. $\{x \mid x \geq -2\}$ d. $\{x \mid x \leq -2\}$

12.   Solve $B = 7a^2 b$ for b.

   a. $b = B - 7a^2$ b. $b = 7\dfrac{B}{a^2}$ c. $b = B + 7a^2$ d. $b = \dfrac{B}{7a^2}$

13.   Solve $C = \dfrac{5}{9}(F - 32)$ for F.

   a. $F = \dfrac{5}{9}C - 32$ b. $F = \dfrac{5}{9}C + 32$ c. $F = \dfrac{9}{5}C + 32$ d. $F = \dfrac{9}{5}C - 32$

14. 60% of 500 is what number?

    a. $\dfrac{6}{5}$ b. 30   c. 3000   d. 300

15. 70 is what percent of 200?
    a. 28.6%   b. 35%   c. 0.286%   d. 350%

16. 21 is 30% of what number?
    a. 70   b. 700   c. 63   d. 630

17. A cylinder with radius of 2 inches and height of 3 inches has its radius tripled. How many times greater is the volume of the larger cylinder than the smaller cylinder?
    a. 3 times   b. 6 times   c. 9 times   d. same

18. You pay $56 for each of 2 tires which are marked 30% off. After the sale is over, you realize you need 2 more tires. How much will each of the two tires cost at regular price?
    a. $84   b. $186.67   c. $39.20   d. $80

19. The sum of two consecutive odd integers is 0. Find the two integers.
    a. −13 and 13   b. −3 and 3   c. 0 and 1   d. −1 and 1

20. The width of a rectangle is 29 centimeters. Find all possible values for the length of the rectangle if the perimeter is at least 752 centimeters. Let x represent the length.
    a. $x \geq 188$ cm   b. $x \geq 405$ cm   c. $x \geq 347$ cm   d. $x > 723$ cm

Name _____   Date _____

Cumulative Review 1 – 2
Form A

For problems 1 – 7, perform the indicated operation.

1. $42 - 3[6 - (4 - 15)]$ 1. _____

2. $19 - 16 \div 2 - 4^2$ 2. _____

3. $(7 - 3)^3 (6^2 - 2^5)$ 3. _____

4. $\left| \dfrac{2}{7} \right|$ 4. _____

5. $\dfrac{7 - 2(15 - 2^3)}{3^2 - 5 \cdot 3}$ 5. _____

6. $14[x - (3 - x)] - (2x - 4)$ 6. _____

7. $6x^3 + 2x^2 - 4 - 2x^3 + 5x^2$ 7. _____

8.   (a) Plot $(-2, -1)$ in the rectangular coordinate system below.   8.
      (b) In what quadrant does it lie?

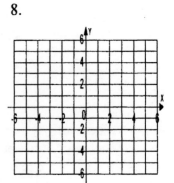

Quadrant _____

Name _____   Date _____

9. List all the whole numbers in the set: $\left\{-\dfrac{17}{3},\ -2,\ 0,\ 1,\ \sqrt{3},\ \pi\right\}$ 9. _____

10. What property is illustrated by: 10. _____

$(x + 3 + 4) = x + (3 + 4)$

For problems 11 – 13, solve the equation.

11. $2 - 4(x - 3) = 2x - 3$ 11. _____

12. $\dfrac{2x}{3} - 1 = 4 - \dfrac{x}{4}$ 12. _____

13. $7(x + 2) = 3x - 5 + 4(x - 1)$ 13. _____

For problems 14 – 16, solve the inequality and (a) express the solution in set-builder notation, and (b) graph the set on a number line.

14. $-6(x - 4) \geq 2x + 8$ 14a. _____

b.

-6 -5 -4 -3 -2 -1 0 1 2 3 4 5 6

15. $7x - (-4 - x) > 3(x - 2)$ 15a. _____

b.

-6 -5 -4 -3 -2 -1 0 1 2 3 4 5 6

16. $9 - 5(x - 3) < 7 - 4x - (x + 2)$ 16a. _____

b.

-6 -5 -4 -3 -2 -1 0 1 2 3 4 5 6

17.   Solve $2x + y = 6$ for y.   17. _____

18.   Solve $A = \dfrac{1}{2}(b + c)$ for b.   18. _____

19.   36 is 12% of what number?   19. _____

20.   A rectangular swimming pool has a width of 27 feet and an   20. _____
       area of 1215 square feet. What is the pool's length?

21.   A rectangular swimming pool has a width of 27 feet and an   21. _____
       area of 1215 square feet. What is the pool's length?

22.   An author earns $1.15 for every book sold. How many   22. _____
       books must be sold if the author wants to earn at least
       $46,000?

23.   The sum of two consecutive integers is 431. Find the integers.   23. _____

24.   Four times a number decreased by 25 is 307.   24. _____
       Find the number.

25.   The circle chart shows the percentage of freshmen and   25. _____
       sophomores at a local community college. If there are a
       total of 3900 students enrolled, how many are sophomores?

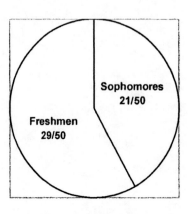

Name _____   Date _____

Cumulative Review 1 – 2
Form B

Choose the correct answer to each problem.

For problems 1 – 7, perform the indicated operation.

1. $79 - 16(3 - 5) + 2 \cdot 3$

   a. 339   b. 117   c. 126   d. –120

2. $2(3 - 4)^3 - (-3 - 2^2)$

   a. 9   b. 5   c. 27   d. –38

3. $7 - 4 \div 2 + 2$

   a. 3   b. $\dfrac{7}{2}$ c. $\dfrac{3}{4}$ d. 7

4. $|-2.9|$

   a. $\dfrac{1}{2.9}$ b. –2.9   c. 2.3   d. No solution

5. $\dfrac{9 - 3(2^3 - 4)}{3 \cdot 4 - 2^2}$

   a. $-\dfrac{3}{8}$ b. 3   c. $\dfrac{12}{5}$ d. $\dfrac{13}{4}$

6. $2[x - (y + 1)] - 4[x + 2(y - 3)]$

   a. $-2x - 10y - 4$ b. $-2x + 6y - 4$

   c. $-2x - 6y - 4$ d. $-2x - 10y + 22$

7. $4x^3 + 3x - 3x^3 + 4x$

   a. $-12x^3 + 12x$ b. $x^3 + 7x$ c. $8x^3$ d. $8x^8$

Name _____   Date _____

8.   List all the integers in the set $\left\{-20,\ -\dfrac{8}{3},\ 0,\ \dfrac{5}{2},\ \pi,\ 6\right\}$

   a. $\{0, 6\}$ b. $\{6\}$

   c. $\{-20, 0, 6\}$ d. $\left\{-20,\ -\dfrac{8}{3},\ 0,\ \dfrac{5}{2},\ 6\right\}$

9.   What property is illustrated by $2(3 + x) = 6 + 2x$?
   a. Distributive property   b. Commutative property of multiplication
   c. Associative property of multiplication   d. Associative property of addition

10. Plot (–2, 4) in the rectangular coordinate system. In which quadrant does it lie?

   a.   b.

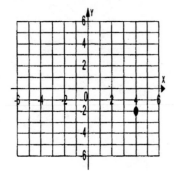   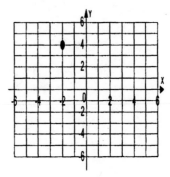

          Quadrant II   Quadrant IV

   c.   d.

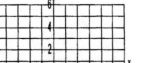   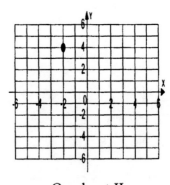

          Quadrant IV   Quadrant II

For problems 11 – 13, solve the equation.

11. $8 - 2(3 - 2x) = 3(x - 1)$

   a. $\dfrac{7}{5}$ b. –3   c. $\dfrac{19}{15}$ d. –5

12. $8(1-2x) = -6(2x-1) - (4x-2)$
     a. 5   b. 0   c. All real numbers   d. No solutions

13. $2 - \dfrac{2x}{5} = \dfrac{\pi}{3} - 4$

     a. $\dfrac{90}{11}$ b. $\dfrac{90}{17}$ c. $-\dfrac{90}{17}$ d. $\dfrac{30}{7}$

For problems 14 – 17, solve the inequality and select the correct expression of the solution set.

14. $-7x + 16 \le -5$
     a. $\{x \mid x \ge -3\}$ b. $\{x \mid x \ge 3\}$ c. $\{x \mid x \le -3\}$ d. $\{x \mid x \le 3\}$

15. $-(3x-4) \ge 1 - 2x + 4 - x$

     a.   b.

     c. All real numbers   d. No solution

16. $-8x + 6 \ge -2x + 6$

     a.   b.

     c. All real numbers   d. No solution

17. $12 + 3(x-2) < -3(x-2)$
     a. $\{x \mid x < 2\}$ b. $\{x \mid x < 0\}$
     c. $\{x \mid x \text{ is a real number}\}$ d. No solution

18.   Solve $t = 2s - v$ for s.
     a. $s = \dfrac{t-v}{2}$ b. $s = \dfrac{1}{2}t + v$ c. $s = \dfrac{1}{2}t - v$ d. $s = \dfrac{t+v}{2}$

19. Solve $A = \dfrac{bh}{2}$ for h.

a. $h = \dfrac{Ab}{2}$ b. $h = \dfrac{2A}{b}$ c. $h = \dfrac{2b}{A}$ d. $h = 2A - b$

20. What number is 41% of 1200?
a. 492,000   b. 4920   c. 492   d. 292.68

21. 295 is what percent of 59?
a. .05%   b. 5%   c. 500%   d. 50%

22. A rectangle has a length that is 4 less than 2 times its width. If the perimeter is 82 centimeters, what is the length?

a. $\dfrac{37}{3}$ cm   b. $\dfrac{62}{3}$ cm   c. 15 cm   d. 26 cm

23. The quotient of a number and 6, increased by 3, is 39. Find the number.
a. 216   b. 36   c. 6   d. 7

24. A sales job pays $500 a month plus a 10% commission of all sales. If you need at least $1200 a month to pay the bills, what value of sales must you sell?
a. ≥$70,000   b. ≥$7000   c. ≥$12,000   d. ≥$120,000

25. The circle chart shows the percentage of freshmen and sophomores at a local community college. If there are 1566 freshman, what is the total enrollment of freshmen and sophomores?

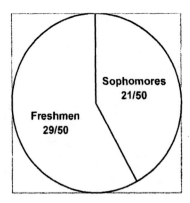

a. 1134   b. 908   c. 2700   d. 27

Name _____   Date _____

Chapter 3
Form A

1. Determine if the ordered pair $(0, -2)$ is a solution of $-3x + y = -2$.

1. _____

2. Complete the table of values for $y = \dfrac{1}{3}x - 2$.

2.

x	$y = \dfrac{1}{3}x - 2$	(x, y)
0		
3		
6		

3. Graph the equation $y = \dfrac{1}{3}x - 2$ using the ordered pairs from problem 2.

3.

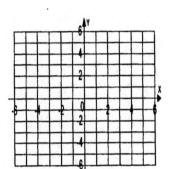

4. Graph $y = -x - 1$.

4.

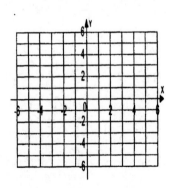

5. For the graph shown, identify the:
   (a) x–intercept
   (b) y–intercept.

5a. _____

b. _____

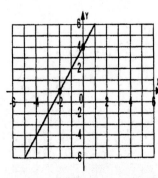

Name _____   Date _____

6.   For the graph shown, identify the: 6a. _____
       (a) *x*–intercept
       (b) *y*–intercept.   b. _____

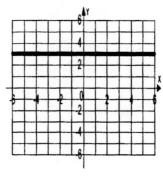

7.   For the equation $6x - 3y = 12$, identify the: 7a. _____
       (a) *x*–intercept
       (b) *y*–intercept.   b. _____

8.   Graph the equation $6x - 3y = 12$ using the   8.
       x and *y*–intercepts found in problem 7.

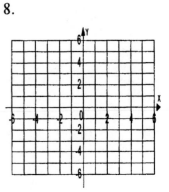

9.   Graph the equation $2x + 4y = 8$.   9.

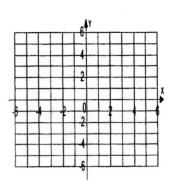

10.   Graph the equation $x = -3$.   10.

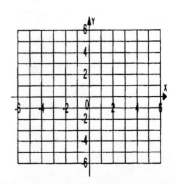

Name _____   Date _____

The graph shows the height *y* of a balloon, *x* minutes after its release.

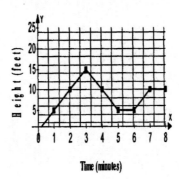

Use the graph for problems 11 – 12.

11.   (a) At what time did the maximum height occur?   11a. _____

      (b) What was the maximum height?   b. _____

12.   (a) What is the *y* – intercept?   12a. _____

      (b) In terms of time and height, interpret the meaning b. _____
          of this intercept.

For problems 13 – 14, calculate the slope of the line passing through the given points.

13.   (–4, 1) and (3, –4)   13. _____

14.   (0, 3) and (2, 3)   14. _____

15.   Determine whether the lines through each pair of points are   15. _____
      parallel.

      (0, 1) and (3, 7)
      (1, 1) and (2, 3)

T-45

16. For the equation $4x - 2y = 6$, find the   16a. _____
     (a) slope
     (b) y –intercept.   b. _____

17. Use the slope and y –intercept found in problem 16 to graph   17.
     $4x - 2y = 6$.

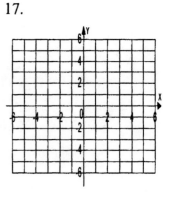

18. For the line with slope –3 and passing through (–2, 3) write   18a. _____
     the equation of the line in:
     (a) point-slope form
     (b) slope-intercept form.   b. _____

19. The equation of a line is given as $y = \dfrac{1}{2}x - 4$. Find the slope   19a. _____

     that is (a) parallel to the line with the given equation and
     (b) perpendicular to the line with the given equation.   b. _____

20. Find the equation of the line in (a) point-slope form and   20a. _____
     (b) slope-intercept form that passes through (1, 4) and is
     parallel to $2x - y = 6$.   b. _____

Name _____ Date _____

Chapter 3
Form B

1. Determine if the ordered pair $(-2, 1)$ is a solution   1. _____
    of $2x - y = -3$.

2. Complete the table of values for $y = \dfrac{1}{2}x + 4$.   2.

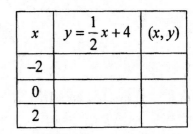

x	$y = \dfrac{1}{2}x + 4$	(x, y)
-2		
0		
2		

3. Graph the equation $y = \dfrac{1}{2}x + 4$ using the ordered pairs   3.
    from problem 2.

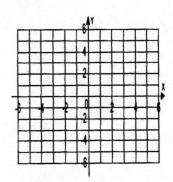

4. Graph $y = -x + 2$.   4.

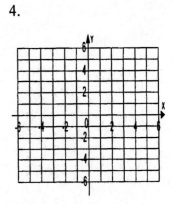

5. For the graph shown, identify the: 5a. _____

    (a) x–intercept
    (b) y–intercept.   b. _____

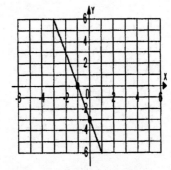

6.   For the graph shown, identify the: 6a. _____
(a) x–intercept
(b) y–intercept.   b. _____

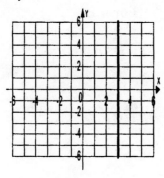

7.   For the equation $2x + 4y = 8$, identify the: 7a. _____
(a) x–intercept
(b) y–intercept.   b. _____

8.   Graph the equation $4x + 2y = 8$ using the   8.
x and y – intercepts found in problem 7.

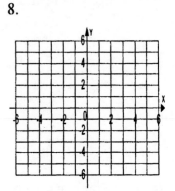

9.   Graph the equation $2x - 3y = 6$.   9.

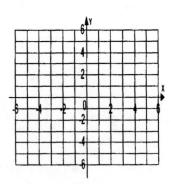

10.   Graph the equation $y = 3$.   10.

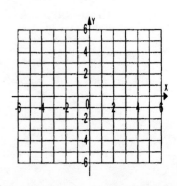

Name _____   Date _____

The following graph shows the number of cars, *y*, in a small parking lot *x* hours after noon.

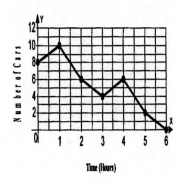

Time (Hours)

Use the graph for problems 11 – 12.

11.   (a) At what time were the maximum number of cars in the lot?   11a. _____

        (b) What was the maximum number of cars?   b. _____

12.   (a) What is the *x* – intercept?   12a. _____

        (b) In terms of time and number of cars, interpret the meaning
            of this intercept.   b. _____

For problems 13 – 14, calculate the slope of the line passing through the given points.

13.   (7, – 1) and (–4, –2)   13. _____

14.   (–4, 3) and (–4, 2)   14. _____

15.   Determine whether the lines through each pair of points are   15. _____
        parallel.
        (0, –1) and (1, 2)
        (2, –1) and (1, 1)

16. For the equation $8x - 3y = 6$, find the   16a. _____
     (a) slope
     (b) y–intercept.   b. _____

17. Use the slope and y–intercept found in problem 16 and   17.
     graph $8x - 3y = 6$.

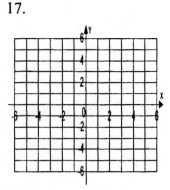

18. For the line with slope –2 and passing through (1, –2) write   18a. _____
     the equation of the line in:
     (a) point-slope form.
     (b) slope-intercept form.   b. _____

19. The equation of a line is given as $y = -\dfrac{2}{3}x + 5$. Find the slope   19a. _____

     that is (a) parallel to the line with the given equation and
     (b) perpendicular to the line with the given equation.   b. _____

20. Find the equation of the line in (a) point-slope form and   20a. _____
     (b) slope-intercept form that passes through (2, 6) and is
     parallel to $3x + 2y = 8$ b. _____

Name _____   Date _____

Chapter 3
Form C

1. Determine if the ordered pair $\left(2, \dfrac{1}{4}\right)$ is a solution of   1. _____

   $\dfrac{1}{8}x + 3y = 1$.

2. Complete the table of values for $y = \dfrac{2}{3}x + 1$.   2.

x	$y = \dfrac{2}{3}x + 1$	(x, y)
0		
−2		
−6		

3. Graph the equation $y = \dfrac{2}{3}x + 1$ using the ordered pairs   3.

   from problem 2.

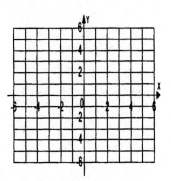

4. Graph $y = x + 3$.   4.

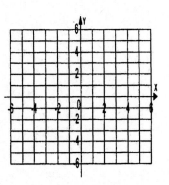

5. For the graph shown, identify the: 5a. _____

   (a) x–intercept
   (b) y–intercept.   b. _____

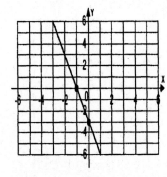

Name _____   Date _____

6.   For the graph shown, identify the: 6a. _____
      (a) *x*–intercept
      (b) *y*–intercept.   b. _____

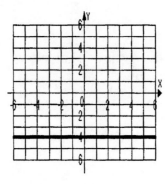

7.   For the equation $6x - 4y = 10$, identify the: 7a. _____
      (a) *x*–intercept
      (b) *y*–intercept.   b. _____

8.   Graph the equation $6x - 4y = 10$ using the   8.
      x and *y* – intercepts found in problem 7.

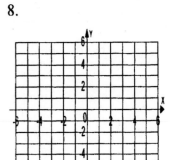

9.   Graph the equation $-3x - y = 2$.   9.

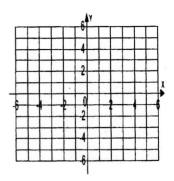

10.   Graph the equation $y = 2x$.   10.

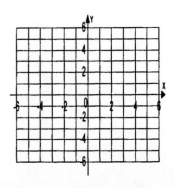

11.   Graph the equation $x = 3$.   11.

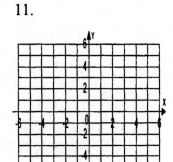

12.   Graph the equation $y = -4$.   12.

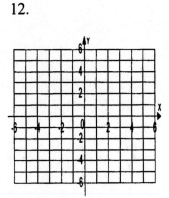

For problems 13 – 14, calculate the slope of the line passing through the given points.

13.   (–4, 1)(3, –5)   13. _____

14. $\left(4, \dfrac{2}{3}\right)\left(1, \dfrac{2}{3}\right)$ 14. _____

15.   For the equation $5x - 4y = 8$, find the: 15a. _____
       a. slope
       b. y-intercept   b. _____

16.   Use the slope and y-intercept found in problem 15 to graph   16.
       $5x - 4y = 8$.

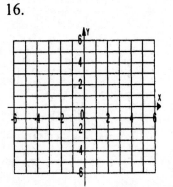

17.   Are the lines $2x - 4y = 6$ and $4x - 8y = 6$ parallel?   17. _____

18.   For the line passing through (2, 0) and (5, 3) write the   18a. _____
       equation of the line in:
       (a) point-slope form.   b. _____
       (b) slope-intercept form.

19.   A plain cheese pizza costs $8. Each additional topping costs   19. _____
       $0.75. Write the equation of the line that models the cost, y, in
       dollars, of a pizza with x toppings.

20.   For the equation you found in problem 18, what does the   20. _____
       ordered pair (2, 9.50) represent?

The following graph shows the height y of a canary, x minutes after its escape from its cage. Use
the graph for problems 21 –22.

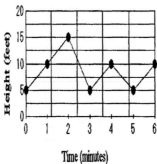

Time (minutes)

21.   a. What is the y-intercept?   21. _____
       b. In terms of time and height, interpret the meaning of
          this intercept.

22.   a. At what time did the maximum height occur?   22. _____
       b. What was the maximum height?

23.   The equation of a line is given as $y = \dfrac{2}{5}x + 9$. Find the slope   23a. _____

       that is (a) parallel to the line with the given equation and
       (b) perpendicular to the line with the given equation.   b. _____

24. Find the equation of the line in (a) point-slope form and (b) slope-intercept form that passes through (2, 5) and is parallel to $6x - 4 = 8$.

24a. _____

b. _____

25. Find the equation of the line in (a) point-slope form and (b) slope-intercept form that passes through (1, 1) and is perpendicular to $\frac{1}{9}x + 11$.

20a. _____

b. _____

Name _____   Date _____

Chapter 3
Form D

1. Which of the following ordered pairs is a solution of $2x - y = 7$?
   a. $(3, 1)$ b. $(4, -1)$ c. $(3, -1)$ d. $(5, 2)$

2. Which of the following ordered pairs is a solution of $y = -2x - 1$?
   a. $(1, -3)$ b. $\left(0, -\dfrac{1}{2}\right)$ c. $(2, -3)$ d. $(-1, -3)$

Use the graph shown below for problems 3 – 5.

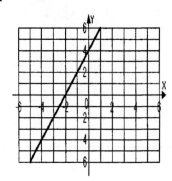

3. Identify the x-intercept and the y-intercept of the graph above.
   a. x-intercept $(2, 0)$ b. x-intercept $(-2, 0)$
        y-intercept $(0, 4)$ y-intercept $(0, 4)$

   c. x-intercept $(0, 2)$ d. x-intercept $(0, -2)$
        y-intercept $(4, 0)$ y-intercept $(4, 0)$

4. Calculate the slope of the line in the graph above.
   a. -2 b. $\dfrac{1}{2}$ c. 2 d. $-\dfrac{1}{2}$

5. Write the equation of the line shown in the graph above in slope-intercept form.
   a. $y = -2x + 2$ b. $y = -2x + 4$ c. $y = 2x + 4$ d. $y = -\dfrac{1}{2}x + 2$

6.   Graph the equation $x + 3y = 9$.

a.

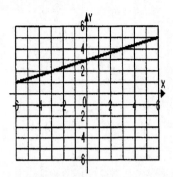

b.

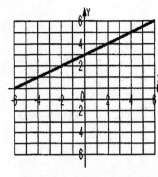

c.

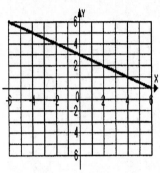

d.

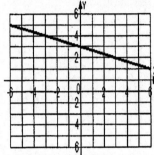

7.   Graph the equation $y = x^2 - 1$.

a.

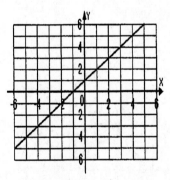

b.

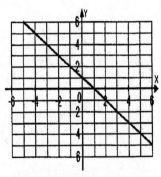

c.

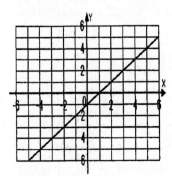

d.

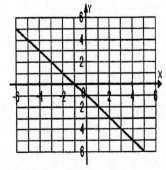

Name _____   Date _____

Use the graph shown below for problems 8 – 9.

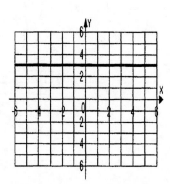

8.   Identify the *x*-intercept and the *y*-intercept of the above graph.
      a. *x*-intercept none   b. *x*-intercept (0, 3)
         y-intercept (0, 3)   *y*-intercept none

      c. *x*-intercept (3, 0)   b. *x*-intercept none
         y-intercept none   *y*-intercept (3, 0)

9.   Calculate the slope of the line in the above graph.
      a. Undefined   b. 3   c. 0   d. 1

10.   For the equation $4x - 8y = 16$, find the *x* and *y*-intercepts.
      a. *x*-intercept (0, 4)   b. *x*-intercept (–4, 0)
         y-intercept (2, 0)   *y*-intercept (0, 2)

      c. *x*-intercept (0, 4)   b. *x*-intercept (4, 0)
         y-intercept (–2, 0)   *y*-intercept (0, –2)

11.   Graph the equation $3x - 2y = 6$.
      a.   b.

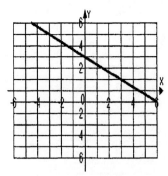

      c.   d.

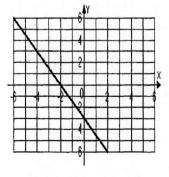

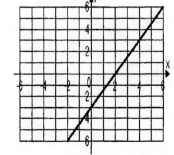

T-58

12.   Graph the equation $y = -x + 3$.

a.

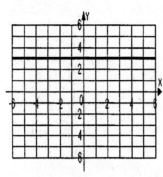

b.

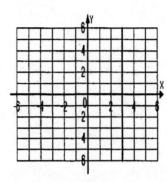

c.

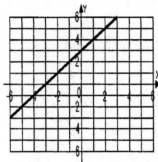

d.

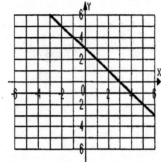

For problems 13 – 14, calculate the slope of the line passing through the given points.

13.   (–1, 3) and (–2, –5)

a. 8   b. $\dfrac{3}{8}$ c. $\dfrac{8}{3}$ d. $\dfrac{1}{8}$

14.   (4, 2) and (4, 8)

a. –6   b. 6   c. 0   d. Undefined

15.   For the equation $6x - 4y = 8$, find the slope and y-intercept.

a. slope $\dfrac{3}{2}$; y-intercept (0, 2)   b. slope $\dfrac{3}{2}$; y-intercept (0, –2)

c. slope $-\dfrac{3}{2}$; y-intercept (0, 2)   d. slope $-\dfrac{3}{2}$; y-intercept (0, –2)

16.   Write the point-slope form of the equation of the line passing through the point (–3, –4) and with slope of –3.

a. $y + 4 = -3(x + 3)$ b. $y - 4 = -3(x - 3)$

c. $y + 4 = 3(x + 3)$ d. $y - 4 = 3(x - 3)$

17. Give the equation of the line that passes through the points (5, –5) and (5, –7).

   a. $y = -\dfrac{1}{5}x - 4$ b. $x = 5$ c. $y = -5$ d. $y = -5x - \dfrac{55}{6}$

18. Write the slope-intercept form of the line passing through the points (5, –5) and (–5, –1).

   a. $y = -\dfrac{5}{2}x - 3$ b. $y = -\dfrac{5}{2}x - \dfrac{27}{2}$ c. $y = -\dfrac{2}{5}x - 3$ d. $y = \dfrac{2}{5}x + 3$

19. Find the slope of a line that is parallel to the line with the equation $y = \dfrac{1}{2}x + 4$.

   a. $m = 2$ b. $m = 4$ c. $m = \dfrac{1}{2}$ d. $m = -\dfrac{1}{2}$

20. Find the slope of a line that is perpendicular to the line with the equation $2x - 4y = 7$.

   a. $m = 2$ b. $m = -4$ c. $m = \dfrac{1}{2}$ d. $m = -2$

Name _____   Date _____

Chapter 3
Form E

1. Which of the following ordered pairs is a solution of $y = -x - 5$?

    a. $(-2, -7)$ b. $(-2, -3)$ c. $(3, -2)$ d. $(-3, -8)$

2. Which of the following ordered pairs is the solution of $3x - y \geq 4$?

    a. $(-2, 1)$ b. $(1, 2)$ c. $(0, -2)$ d. $(2, -1)$

Use the graph shown in Figure 1 for problems 3 – 5.

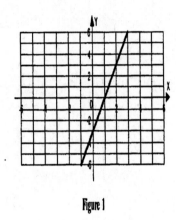

Figure 1

3. Identify the x- intercept and the y- intercept of Figure 1.

    a. x-intercept $(1, 0)$ b. x-intercept $(-3, 0)$
       y-intercept $(0, -3)$ y-intercept $(0, -1)$

    c. x-intercept $(0, -3)$ d. x-intercept $(0, -1)$
       y-intercept $(1, 0)$ y-intercept $(-3, 0)$

4. Calculate the slope of the line in Figure 1.

    a. -3 b. $\dfrac{1}{3}$ c. $-\dfrac{1}{3}$ d. 3

5. Write the equation of the line shown in Figure 1 in slope-intercept form.

    a. $y = 3x - 3$ b. $y = -\dfrac{1}{3}x - 1$ c. $y = -3x - 3$ d. $y = -\dfrac{1}{3}x - 3$

6.   Graph the equation $4x + 3y = 12$.

a.

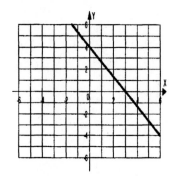

b.

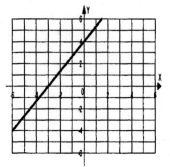

c.

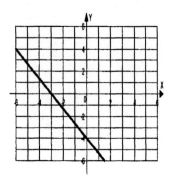

d.

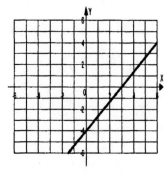

7.   Graph the equation $y = x + 2$

a.

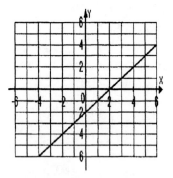

b.

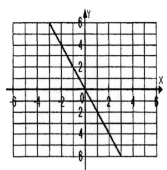

c.

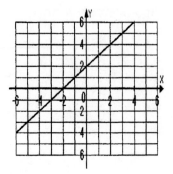

d.

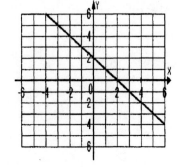

Use the graph shown in Figure 2 for problems 8 – 9.

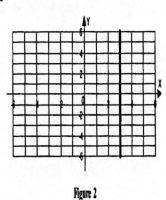

Figure 2

8.   Identify the x-intercept and the y-intercept of Figure 2.

   a. x-intercept none   b. x-intercept none
      y-intercept (3, 0)   y-intercept (0, 3)

   c. x-intercept (3, 0)   d. x-intercept (0, 3)
      y-intercept none   y-intercept none

9.   Calculate the slope of the line in Figure 2.

   a. 3   b. 1   c. 0   d. Undefined

10.   For the equation $7x - 14y = 7$, find the x and y-intercepts.

   a. x-intercept (1, 0)   b. x-intercept $\left(0, \dfrac{-1}{2}\right)$

      y-intercept $\left(0, -\dfrac{1}{2}\right)$ y-intercept (–1, 0)

   c. x-intercept $\left(0, \dfrac{1}{2}\right)$ d. x-intercept $\left(-\dfrac{1}{2}, 0\right)$

      y-intercept $\left(-1, 0\right)$ y-intercept (0, 1)

11.   Graph the equation $5x - 10y = 15$.

a.

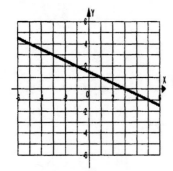

b.

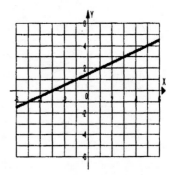

c.

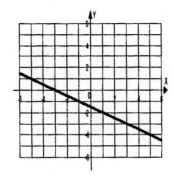

d.

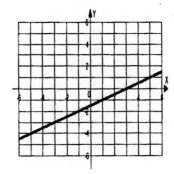

12.   Graph the equation $y = 2$.

a.

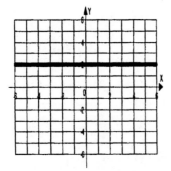

b.

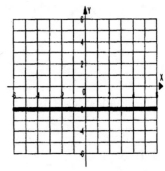

c.

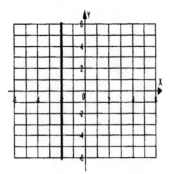

d.

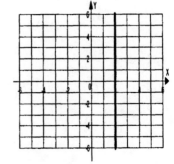

For problems 13 – 14, calculate the slope of the line passing through the given points.

13.   (–2, –4) and (3, –2)

a. $\dfrac{2}{5}$ b. $-\dfrac{2}{5}$ c. –6   d. $-\dfrac{1}{6}$

14.   (–3, 0) and (–3, 5)

a. $-\dfrac{5}{6}$ b. $-\dfrac{6}{5}$ c. 0   d. Undefined

15.   For the equation $5x + 3y = 7$, find the slope and y-intercept.

a. slope $-\dfrac{5}{3}$; y-intercept $\left(0, -\dfrac{7}{3}\right)$ b. slope $-\dfrac{5}{3}$; y-intercept $\left(0, \dfrac{7}{3}\right)$

c. slope $\dfrac{5}{3}$; y-intercept $\left(0, \dfrac{7}{3}\right)$ d. slope $\dfrac{5}{3}$; y-intercept $\left(0, -\dfrac{7}{3}\right)$

16.   Write the point-slope form of the equation of the line passing through the point (6, –2) and with slope of 8.
a. $y - 2 = 8(x - 6)$ b. $y + 2 = 8(x + 6)$
c. $y - 2 = 8(x + 6)$ d. $y + 2 = 8(x - 6)$

17.   Give the equation of the line that passes through the points (0, 3) and (–4, 5).

a. $y = -\dfrac{1}{2}x + 3$ b. $y = -\dfrac{1}{2}x - 3$

c. $y = -2x + 3$ d. $y = -2x - 3$

18.   Find the slope of a line that is parallel to the line with the equation $y = 3x - 5$.

a. $m = 3$ b. $m = -5$ c. $m = \dfrac{1}{3}$ d. $m = -3$

19.   Find the slope of a line that is perpendicular to the line with the equation $y = -\dfrac{5}{4}x + 1$.

a. $m = 1$ b. $m = \dfrac{4}{5}$ c. $m = -\dfrac{4}{5}$ d. $m = -1$

20.   Find the slope of a line that is perpendicular to the line with the equation $5x + 3y = 8$.

a. $m = 5$ b. $m = 3$ c. $m = -\dfrac{5}{3}$ d. $m = \dfrac{3}{5}$

Chapter 3
Form F

1.   Which of the following ordered pairs is a solution of $3x - y \geq 4$?

    a. $(2, -6)$ b. $(1, 1)$ c. $(4, 1)$ d. $(5, -1)$

Use the graph below for problems 2 – 4.

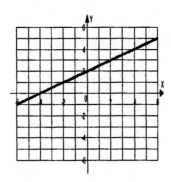

2.   Identify the x- intercept and the y- intercept of the above graph.

    a. x-intercept $(2, 0)$ b. x-intercept $(-2, 0)$
       y-intercept $(0, 4)$ y-intercept $(0, -4)$

    c. x-intercept $(0, 2)$ d. x-intercept $(0, 2)$
       y-intercept $(4, 0)$ y-intercept $(-4, 0)$

3.   Calculate the slope of the line of the above graph.

    a. 2   b. -2 c. $-\dfrac{1}{2}$ d. $\dfrac{1}{2}$

4.   Write the equation of the line shown in the above graph in slope-intercept form.

    a. $y = -\dfrac{1}{2}x + 2$ b. $y = \dfrac{1}{2}x + 2$ c. $y = 2x + 2$ d. $y = -2x + 2$

5. Graph the equation $4x + 3y = 12$.

a.

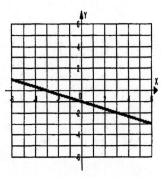

b.

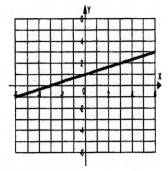

c.

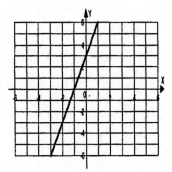

d.

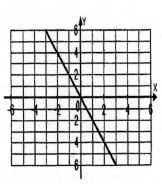

6. Graph the equation $y = x - 2$

a.

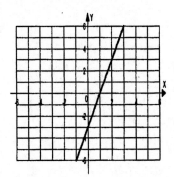

b.

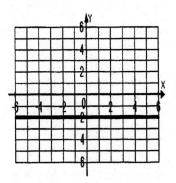

c.

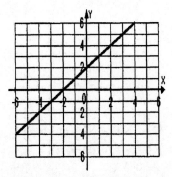

d.

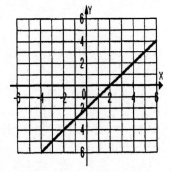

Name _____   Date _____

Use the graph shown below for problems 7 – 8.

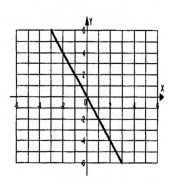

7.   Identify the x- intercept and the y- intercept of the above graph.

    a. x- intercept (0, 0)   b. x- intercept (0, 0)
       y- intercept none   y- intercept (0, 0)

    c. x- intercept none   d. x- intercept none
       y- intercept (0, 0)   y- intercept none

8.   Calculate the slope of the line in the above graph.

    a. –2   b. $-\dfrac{1}{2}$ c. 2   d. Undefined

The following graph shows the balance in a bank account (y, in dollars) x days after the account
was opened.

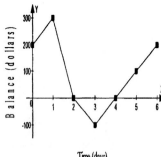

Use the graph for problems 9 –10.

9.   What is the meaning of the y –intercept?

    a. On day 2 and 4, the balance was $0.   b. The initial deposit was $200.
    c. The initial withdrawal was $200.   d. The initial deposit was $0.

10.   Where is the minimum and what does it represent?
        a. (0, 300) On day 1, the balance was $300.
        b. (2, 0) and (4, 0) On day 2 and 4, the balance was $0.
        c. (3, –100) On day 3, the account was $100 overdrawn.
        d. (6, 200) On day 6, the balance was $200

11.   For the equation $2x - 5y = 7$, find the x and y- intercept.

        a. x-intercept $\left(\dfrac{7}{2}, 0\right)$

            y-intercept $\left(0, -\dfrac{7}{5}\right)$

        b. x-intercept $\left(\dfrac{7}{5}, 0\right)$

            y intercept $\left(0, \dfrac{7}{2}\right)$

        c. x- intercept $\left(0, \dfrac{5}{7}\right)$

            y intercept $\left(\dfrac{2}{7}, 0\right)$

        d. x-intercept $\left(\dfrac{5}{7}, 0\right)$

            y intercept $\left(0, \dfrac{2}{7}\right)$

12.   Graph the equation $3x - 4y = 6$.

        a.

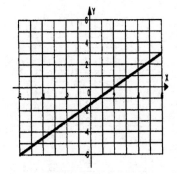

        b.

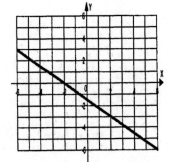

        c.

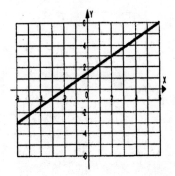

        d.

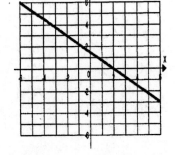

13.   Graph the equation $y = 2$.

a.

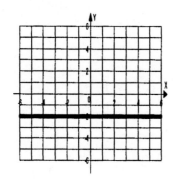

b.

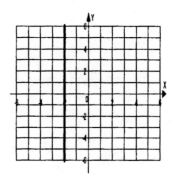

c.

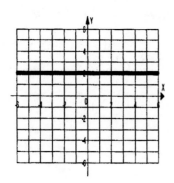

d.

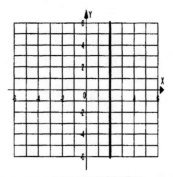

14.   Graph the equation $x = -\dfrac{1}{2}$.

a.

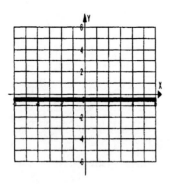

b.

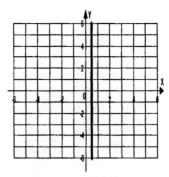

c.

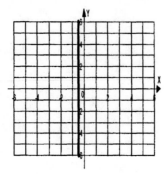

d.

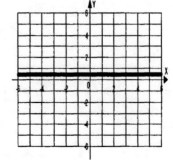

15. Calculate the slope of the line passing through $\left(2, \dfrac{1}{3}\right)$ and $\left(-5, \dfrac{1}{3}\right)$.

    a. 0   b. −7   c. −3   d. Undefined

16. Are the lines $4x - 2y = 6$ and $-6x + 3y = 8$ parallel?

    a. yes   b. no

    c. Not enough information   d. They are the same line.

17. For the equation $8x - 12y = 24$, find the slope and y-intercept.

    a. slope $\dfrac{2}{3}$; y- intercept $(0, 2)$ b. slope $-\dfrac{2}{3}$; y-intercept $(0, 2)$

    c. slope $\dfrac{2}{3}$; y- intercept $(0, -2)$ d. slope $-\dfrac{2}{3}$; y- intercept $(0, -2)$

18. Write the point –slope form of the equation of the line passing through $(-7, 3)$ and $(4, -2)$.

    a. $y - 3 = -\dfrac{5}{11}(x - 7)$ b. $y - 3 = -\dfrac{5}{11}(x + 7)$

    c. $y + 3 = -\dfrac{1}{3}(x - 7)$ d. $y - 3 = -\dfrac{1}{3}(x + 7)$

19. Find the slope of a line that is parallel to the line with the equation $y = \dfrac{3}{5}x - 6$.

    a. $m = -6$ b. $m = -\dfrac{3}{5}$ c. $m = \dfrac{3}{5}$ d. $m = -\dfrac{5}{3}$

20. Find the slope of a line that is perpendicular to the line with the equation $5x + 7y = 11$.

    a. $m = -\dfrac{5}{7}$ b. $m = \dfrac{5}{7}$ c. $m = \dfrac{7}{5}$ d. $m = -\dfrac{7}{5}$

Name _____ Date _____

Chapter 4
Form A

1. Is the ordered pair (2, 1) a solution to the system?   1. _____
    $2x + y = 5$
    $x - y = 1$

For problems 2 – 5, solve each system by graphing. If there is no solution or an infinite number of solutions, so state.

2. $x - y = 4$ 2.
    $x + y = 2$

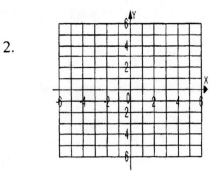

Solution: _____

3. $2x - y = 4$ 3.
    $y = -x - 1$

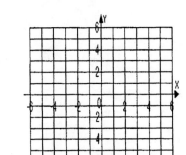

Solution: _____

4. $-4x + 4y = 4$ 4.
    $y = x + 1$

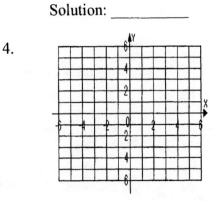

Solution: _____

5. $x = -2$
        $y = 1$

5.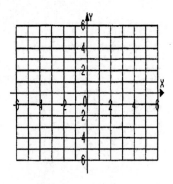

Solution: _____

For problems 6 – 9, solve each system by the substitution method. If there is no solution or an infinite number of solutions, so state.

6. $7x - 4y = 26$ 6. _____
        $y = x - 5$

7. $8x + 3y = -14$ 7. _____
        $-x + 2y = -3$

8. $y = 2x - 6$ 8. _____
        $y = x - 5$

9. $-3x + 2y = 8$ 9. _____
        $y = \dfrac{3}{2}x + 3$

For problems 10 – 13, solve each system by the addition method. If there is no solution or an infinite number of solutions, so state.

10. $4x + y = 7$ 10. _____
        $3x - y = 0$

11. $6x + 2y = 8$ 11. _____
        $2x - y = 6$

12. $4x - 10y = -24$ 12. _____
        $-2x + 5y = 12$

13. $3x + 5y = 4$ 13. _____
        $-4x + 2y = -1$

For problems 14 – 15, solve each system by the method of your choice. If there is no solution or an infinite number of solutions, so state.

14. $5x + 3y = 7$ 14. _____

        $2x - 3y = 14$

15. $x - 4 = 0$ 15. _____

        $8x - 5y = 2$

16.   A corporation allows each of its traveling employees an amount   16. _____
        of money per day for a hotel room and food expenses. One
        employee travels for 4 days and 4 nights and is allotted
        480 dollars while another employee travels for 3 days and 2 nights
        and is allotted 270 dollars. Find the amount allowed for a hotel
        room and daily food expenses.

17.   A charity sells tickets for a fundraising dinner. Each adult's   17. _____
        ticket costs 10 dollars and each child's ticket costs 5 dollars.
        A total of $1050 was raised by selling 130 tickets. How many
        adult and child tickets were sold?

18.   The weekly demand model for a new toy is given by   18. _____
        $N = -5p + 80$. The weekly supply model for the same toy is
        $N = 3p + 40$. For these models, p is the price of the toy and N
        is the number of toys sold or supplied each week to the toy store.
        Find the price at which supply and demand are equal.

Solve each system in Exercises 19 – 20. If there is no solution or if there are infinitely may solutions and a system's equations are dependent, so state.

19. $2x - y - z = 7$ 19. _____

        $3x + 5y + z = -10$

        $4x - 3y + 2z = 4$

20. $2x + 2y + 3z = -1$ 20. _____

        $3x - 5y - 2z = 21$

        $7x + 3y + 5z = 10$

Name _____   Date _____

Chapter 4
Form B

1. Is the ordered pair $(-1, -2)$ a solution to the system?   1. _____
    $4x - y = -2$
    $3x + y = -5$

For problems 2 – 5, solve each system by graphing. If there is no solution or an infinite number of solutions, so state.

2. $2x - y = 8$ 2.
    $y = x + 4$

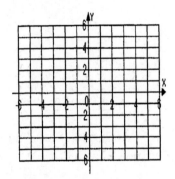

Solution: _____

3. $-3x + 3y = 9$ 3.
    $y = x + 4$

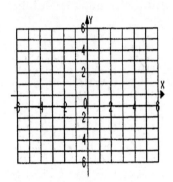

Solution: _____

4. $x - 2y = -6$ 4.
    $y = -\dfrac{3}{2}x - 1$

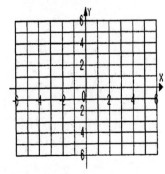

Solution: _____

Name _____   Date _____

5. $x = -1$
         $y = -3$

5.

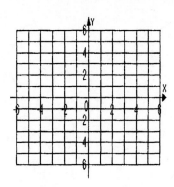

Solution: _____

For problems 6 – 9, solve each system by the substitution method. If there is no solution or an infinite number of solutions, so state.

6. $2x - y = 14$
        $y = 5x - 29$

6. _____

7. $-7x + 2y = -17$
        $x - 3y = -3$

7. _____

8. $x = 2y + 5$
        $x = -y + 8$

8. _____

9. $4x - 5y = 20$
        $y = \dfrac{4}{5}x - 4$

9. _____

For problems 10 – 13, solve each system by the addition method. If there is no solution or an infinite number of solutions, so state.

10. $x + 3y = 5$
         $-x + 2y = -5$

10. _____

11. $4x + 3y = 14$
         $3x - y = 4$

11. _____

12. $-14x + 4y = 8$
         $7x - 2y = 8$

12. _____

13. $9x - 6y = 36$
         $2x + 4y = 0$

13. _____

For problems 14 – 15, solve each system by the method of your choice. If there is no solution or an infinite number of solutions, so state.

14. $3x - 4y = 6$
       $2x + y = -7$ 14. _____

15. $y + 2 = 0$
       $5x - 2y = 9$ 15. _____

16.   A company budgets 30,000 dollars for advertisement costs   16. _____
promoting a new product. Television ads cost 500 dollars
each and radio ads cost 100 dollars each. If the company
wants to buy a total of 220 ads, how many television ads and
radio ads should the company buy?

17.   The sum of a first and second number is 130. If the second   17. _____
number is 20 less than four times the first number, find the two
numbers.

18.   The weekly demand model for a new video game is given by   18. _____
$N = -p + 520$. The weekly supply model for the same video
game is $N = 3p + 400$. For these models, p is the price of the
video game and N is the number of video games sold or supplied
each week. Find the price at which supply and demand are equal.

F Solve each system in Exercises 19 – 20. If there is no solution or if there are infinitely may solutions and a system's equations are dependent, so state.

19. $3x - y - 6z = 5$
       $2x + 3y - z = -1$
       $-x + 5y + 3z + -10$ 19. _____

20. $3x + 2y - z = 10$
       $x + 4y + 2z = 3$
       $2x + 3y - 5z = 23$ 20. _____

Name _____   Date _____

Chapter 4
Form C

1. Is the ordered pair (4, 3) a solution to the system?   1. _____
    $y = 2x - 5$
    $3x - y = 9$

For problems 2 – 5, solve each system by graphing. If there is no solution or an infinite number of solutions, so state.

2. $x + 2y = -4$ 2.
    $x - y = -1$

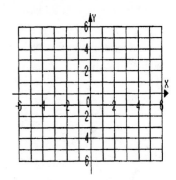

Solution: _____

3. $8x - 2y = 8$ 3.
    $y = -3x + 3$

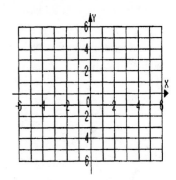

Solution: _____

4. $-2y - x = 2$ 4.
    $y = -\dfrac{1}{2}x - 1$

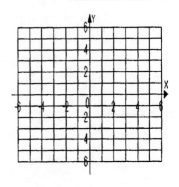

Solution: _____

5. $x = 2$
        $y = -3$

5.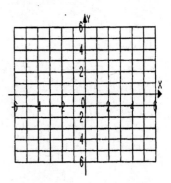

Solution: _____

For problems 6 – 9, solve each system by the substitution method. If there is no solution or an infinite number of solutions, so state.

6. $17x - 3y = 26$ 6. _____
        $x = -y - 2$

7. $8x + 3y = -16$ 7. _____
        $6x - y = 40$

8. $y = \dfrac{2}{3}x - 5$ 8. _____
        $4x - 6y = 30$

9. $x = 2y - 4$ 9. _____
        $x = 5y - 16$

For problems 10 – 13, solve each system by the addition method. If there is no solution or an infinite number of solutions, so state.

10. $x + 3y = 20$ 10. _____
        $-x - 4y = -10$

11. $4x + 3y = 12$ 11. _____
        $2x - 4y = 6$

12. $5x + 3y = 15$ 12. _____
        $2x - y = 6$

13. $3x + 4y = 0$ 13. _____
        $3x - y = 15$

For problems 14 – 15, solve each system by the method of your choice. If there is no solution or an infinite number of solutions, so state.

14. $x - 4y = 8$ 14. _____
     $2x - 8y = 6$

15. $y + 3 = 0$ 15. _____
     $4x + 3y = 23$

16. The daily demand model for a newly released CD is given by   16. _____
     $N = -10p + 300$. The daily supply model for the same CD
     is $N = 5p + 60$. For these models, p is the price of the CD and
     N is the number of CDs sold or supplied each day by the store.
     Find the price at which supply and demand are equal

17. The total cost of 2 jackets and 3 shirts is $225. The cost of a   17. _____
     jacket is three times the cost of a shirt. Find the cost of a jacket
     and a shirt.

18. The sum of a first and second number is 184. Three times the   18. _____
     first number decreased by 212 is equal to the second number.
     Find the two numbers.

Solve each system in Exercises 19 – 20. If there is no solution or if there are infinitely may solutions and a system's equations are dependent, so state.

19. $3x - y - 3z = -22$ 19. _____
     $2x + y + 5z = 8$
     $x - 2y + 3z = 3$

20. $3x - 2y + 5z = -17$ 20. _____
     $2x + 4y - 3z = 29$
     $5x - 6y - 7z = 7$

Name _____   Date _____

Chapter 4
Form D

Choose the correct answer to each problem.

1. Which of the ordered pairs is a solution to the system?
    $$3x - 7y = 20$$
    $$4x + 5y = -2$$
    a. (−8, 6)   b. (2, −2)   c. (9, 1)   d. (16, 4)

2. Which of the ordered pairs is not a solution to the system?
    $$x - y \geq 1$$
    $$y < x + 2$$
    a. (1, 1)   b. (2, −2)   c. (3, 2)   d. (16, 4)

For problems 3 − 6, solve each system by graphing.

3. $$x + y = 4$$
    $$-x + y = 2$$
    a. (1, 3)   b. No solution

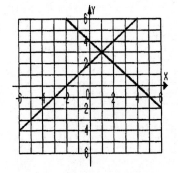   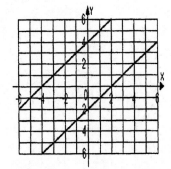

    c. No solution   d. (3, 1)

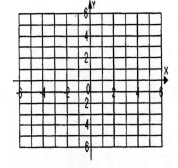   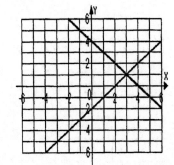

4. $3x - 5y = 7$
    $y = x - 1$

a. $\left(-\dfrac{1}{4},\ -\dfrac{1}{4}\right)$

b. $\left(\dfrac{3}{2},\ \dfrac{1}{2}\right)$

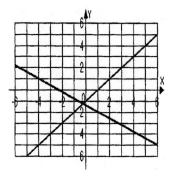

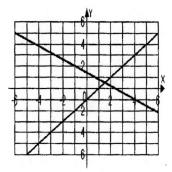

c. $(-1, -2)$

d. $(6, 5)$

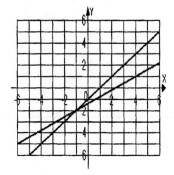

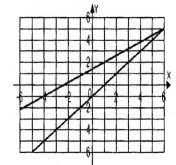

5. $-8x + 4y = 16$
    $y = 2x + 4$

a. $(0, -4)$

b. No solution

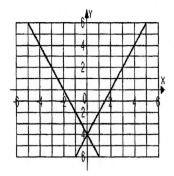

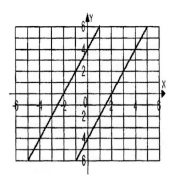

c. Infinite solutions

d. $(0, 4)$

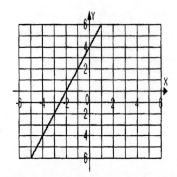

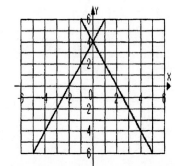

6. $y - 4 = 0$
    $x + 3 = 0$

a. $(4, -3)$ b. $(-3, 4)$

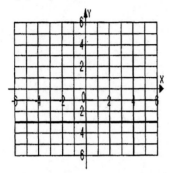   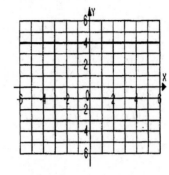

c. $(-4, 3)$ d. $(3, -4)$

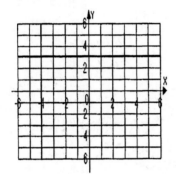   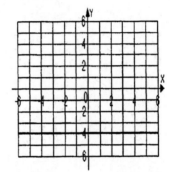

7. In order to solve the system with the substitution method, which of the following might be the result of the first step?
    $x - 4y = -5$
    $-2x + 3y = 5$

a. $2x - 8y = -5$ b. $2x - 8y = -10$
    $-2x + 3y = 5$ $-2x + 3y = 5$

c. $x = 4y - 5$ b. $x = -4y - 5$
    $-2x + 3y = 5$ $-2x + 3y = 5$

8. Solve the system by the substitution method.

    $x - 4y = -5$
    $-2x + 3y = 5$

a. $(0, 0)$ b. $(-1, 1)$ c. $(1, -1)$ d. No solution

9. In order to solve the system with the elimination method, which of the following might be the result of the first step?

$$4x - 2y = -6$$
$$3x + y = -7$$

a. $4x - 2y = -6$
    $6x + 2y = -14$

b. $4x - 2y = -6$
    $6x + 2y = -7$

c. $4x - 2y = -6$
    $y = -3x - 7$

d. $4x - 2y = -6$
    $y = 3x - 7$

10. Solve the system by the elimination method.

$$4x - 2y = -6$$
$$3x + y = -7$$

a. $(2, 1)$ b. $(-2, 1)$ c. $(-2, -1)$ d. $(-1, -3)$

11. Which system of equations has no solution?

a. $x - 2y = 0$
    $x + 2y = 0$

b. $x - 2y = 0$
    $5x + 2y = 4$

c. $x - 2y = 0$
    $x - 2y = 4$

b. $x - 2y = 0$
    $4x - 8y = 0$

12. Which system of equations has an infinite number of solutions?

a. $x - 2y = 0$
    $x + 2y = 0$

b. $x - 2y = 0$
    $5x + 2y = 4$

c. $x - 2y = 0$
    $x - 2y = 4$

b. $x - 2y = 0$
    $4x - 8y = 0$

For problems 13 – 14, solve each system by the substitution method.

13. $5x - y = 1$
    $-2x + 3y = 10$

a. $(1, 4)$ b. $(-1, -6)$ c. $\left(\dfrac{7}{15}, \dfrac{10}{3}\right)$ d. $\left(\dfrac{11}{13}, \dfrac{42}{13}\right)$

14. $8x - 6y = 4$
    $x = \dfrac{3}{4}y + \dfrac{1}{2}$

a. $(0, 0)$ b. $\left(\dfrac{1}{2}, 0\right)$ c. Infinite solutions   d. No solution

For problems 15 – 16, solve each system by the elimination method.

15. $x + y = 6$
     $2x - y = 6$
     a. $(4, 2)$ b. $(2, 4)$ c. Infinite solutions   d. No solution

16. $-3x + 6y = 18$
     $x - 2y = -6$
     a. $(0, 3)$ b. $(2, 4)$ c. Infinite solutions   d. No solution

17. Solve the system by the method of your choice.
     $5x + 3y = 15$
     $2x - 4y = 6$
     a. $(-3, 0)$ b. $(0, 3)$ c. $(0, -3)$ d. $(3, 0)$

18. You want to buy T-shirts and shorts. T-shirts cost 10 dollars each and shorts cost 15 dollars each. If you have 90 dollars to buy a total of 8 T-shirts and shorts, how many of each can you buy?
     a. 3 T-shirts, 5 shorts   b. 6 T-shirts, 2 shorts
     c. 5 T-shirts, 3 shorts   d. 2 T-shirts, 6 shorts

19. Determine which ordered triple is a solution of the given system:

     $x + 2y + z = 9$
     $2x + y + 2z = 15$
     $3x - y - 2z = 0$

     a. $(3, 1, 4)$ b. $(-3, 1, 4)$ c. $(3, 1, -4)$ d. $(3, -1, 4)$

20. Solve the following system:

     $3x + 2y - z = 9$
     $x + y + z = 7$
     $x - y + 4z = 5$

     a, $(1, 2, 4)$ b. $(1, 4, 2)$ c. $(4, 2, 1)$ d. $(2, 1, 4)$

Name _____   Date _____

Chapter 4
Form E

Choose the correct answer to each problem.

1. Which of the ordered pairs is a solution to the system?
    $2x - 6y = -2$
    $5x + y = 27$
    a. $(-4, -1)$ b. $(8, 3)$ c. $(5, 2)$ d. $(4, 7)$

2. Which of the ordered pairs is a solution to the system?
    $3x + y > 4$
    $y < x - 4$
    a. $(1, 1)$ b. $(6, 1)$ c. $(0, 5)$ d. $(1, 8)$

For problems 3 – 6, solve each system by graphing.

3. $-2x + y = 6$
    $-x + y = 3$

    a. $(-3, 0)$ b. No solution

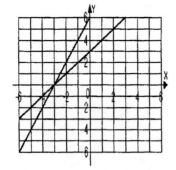 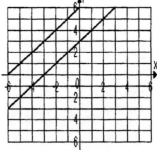

    c. $(1, 4)$ d. Infinite solutions

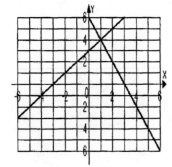 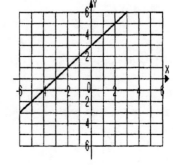

4. $-4x + 5y = 20$
    $y = -x + 4$

a. $(0, 4)$

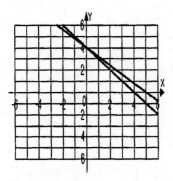

b. $(0, 4)$

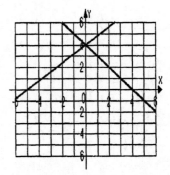

c. $(0, -4)$

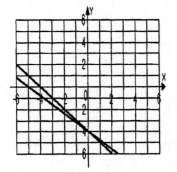

d. $(0, -4)$

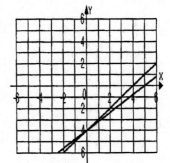

5. $-3x + y = 3$
    $y = 3x - 3$

a. $(0, -3)$

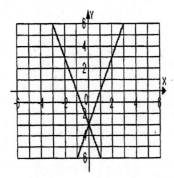

b. No solution

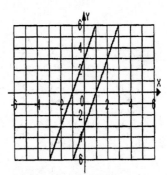

c. $(0, 3)$

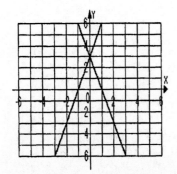

d. Infinite solutions

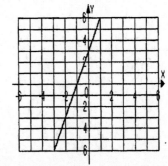

6. $y - 2 = 0$
       $x + 4 = 0$

   a. (4, –2)   b. (–2, 4)

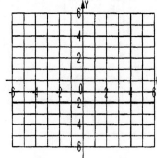   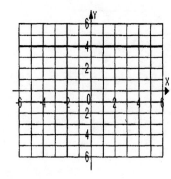

   c. (–4, 2)   d. (2, –4)

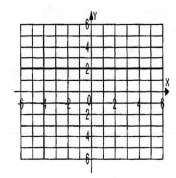   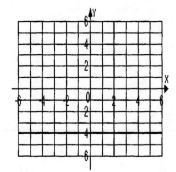

7.   In order to solve the system with the substitution method, which of the following might
       be the result of the first step?
       $4x + y = 8$
       $-2x + 2y = 4$

   a. $4x + y = 8$ b. $-8x - 2y = -16$
       $-4x + 4y = 8$ $-2x + 2y = 4$

   c. $y = 4x + 8$ b. $y = -4x + 8$
       $-2x + 2y = 4$ $-2x + 2y = 4$

8.   Solve the system by the substitution method.

       $4x + y = 8$
       $-2x + 2y = 4$

   a. $\left(\dfrac{6}{5}, \dfrac{16}{5} \right)$ b. (–2, 0)   c. (2, 0)   d. (0, 8)

9. In order to solve the system with the elimination method, which of the following might be the result of the first step?

$11x - 4y = 11$

$5x + y = 5$

a. $11x - 4y = 11$
   $20x + 4y = 20$

b. $11x - 4y = 11$
   $20x + 4y = 5$

c. $11x - 4y = 11$
   $y = -5x + 5$

d. $11x - 4y = 11$
   $y = 5x + 5$

10. Solve the system by the elimination method.

$11x - 4y = 11$

$5x + y = 5$

a. $\left(\dfrac{16}{31}, \dfrac{75}{31}\right)$ b. $(0, 1)$ c. $(1, 0)$ d. $\left(-\dfrac{31}{9}, -\dfrac{110}{9}\right)$

11. Which system of equations has an infinite number of solutions?

a. $3x + 4y = 5$
   $3x + 4y = -5$

b. $3x + 4y = 5$
   $12x + 16y = 20$

c. $3x + 4y = 5$
   $3x - 4y = 5$

b. $3x + 4y = 5$
   $5x - 2y = -5$

For problems 12 – 13, solve each system by the substitution method.

12. $x + y = -5$
    $2x - y = -7$

a. $(-12, -17)$ b. $(4, -1)$ c. $(12, -17)$ d. $(-4, -1)$

13. $5x - 10y = 10$
    $x = 2y - 4$

a. $(0, 2)$ b. $(2, 0)$ c, Infinite solutions   d. No solution

For problems 14 – 15, solve each system by the elimination method.

14. $2x + y = 6$
    $-4x - y = 12$

a. $(3, 0)$ b. $(-9, 24)$ c. Infinite solutions   d. No solution

15. $-3x + 6y = 18$
    $x - 2y = -6$

a. $(6, 0)$ b. $(0, 0)$ c. $(2, 2)$ d. $(-4, 2)$

16. Solve the system by the method of your choice.
$$2x + 3y = 5$$
$$3x + 2y = -5$$

    a. $(-5, 5)$ b. $(5, -5)$ c. $(1, 1)$ d. $(-1, -1)$

For problems 17 – 18, use the following information.
    The sum of twice a number and a second number is 124. The difference of the first and second number is 32.

17. What equation correctly represents this information.

    a. $2x + y = 124$ b. $2x + y = 124$
        $y - x = 32$ $x - y = 32$

    c. $x + 2y = 124$ b. $x + 2y = 32$
        $x - y = 32$ $x - y = 124$

18. Find the two numbers.

    a. $\dfrac{92}{3}$ and $\dfrac{188}{3}$ b. 52 and 20   c. 50 and 24   d. $-\dfrac{188}{3}$ and $-\dfrac{92}{3}$

19. Determine which ordered triple is a solution of the given system:

$$3x + 2y + z + 4$$
$$4x - y + 2z = 8$$
$$x - y - z = -4$$

    a. $(1, -2, 3)$ b. $(1, 2, 3)$ c. $(1, 2, -3)$ d. $(-1, 2, 3)$

20. Solve the following system:

$$2y - 3z = -5$$
$$x + y + z = 5$$
$$4x - y - z = -5$$

    a, $(0, 2, 3)$ b. $(1, 1, 3)$ c. $(1, 2, 2)$ d. $(0, 1, 2)$

Name _____   Date _____

Chapter 4
Form F

Choose the correct answer to each problem.

1.   Which of the ordered pairs is a solution to the system?
     $-2x - y = -23$
     $3x + 2y = 1$
     a. $(5, -7)$ b. $(-2, 7)$ c. $(1, -1)$ d. $(1, 1)$

2.   Which of the ordered pairs is a solution to the system?
     $x - 2y \le 4$
     $x - y \ge 6$
     a. $(0, 2)$ b. $(3, 0)$ c. $(20, 8)$ d. $(15, -20)$

For problems 3 – 6, solve each system by graphing.

3. $2x - 4y = 0$
     $x + 3y = 0$
     a. $(0, 0)$ b. $(0, 0)$

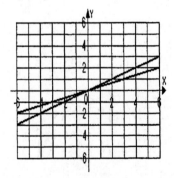   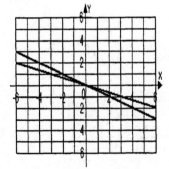

     c. $(0, 0)$ d. No Solution

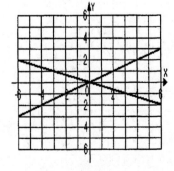   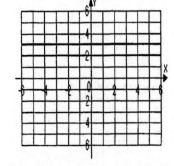

4. $-6x - 3y = -12$
        $-x + y = 4$

a. $(0, \; -4)$ b. $(0, \; 4)$

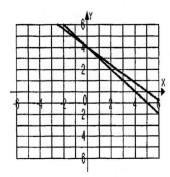   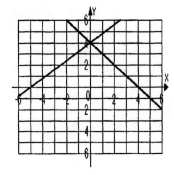

c. $\left(\dfrac{8}{3}, \; -\dfrac{4}{3} \right)$ d. $(0, 4)$

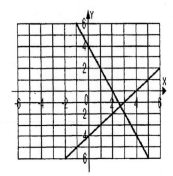   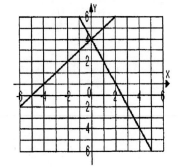

5.

        $8x - 2y = 4$
        $4x - y = 2$

a. No solution   b. No solution

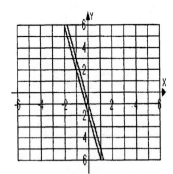   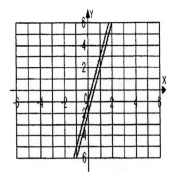

c. Infinite solutions   d. Infinite solutions

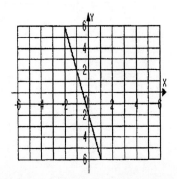   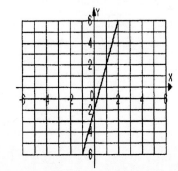

6. $y - 2 = 3$
       $x - 4 = -6$

   a. $(1, -2)$ b. $(-2, 5)$

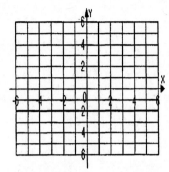   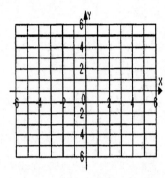

   c. $(5, -2)$ d. $(-2, 1)$

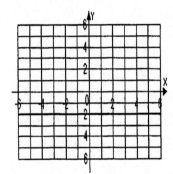   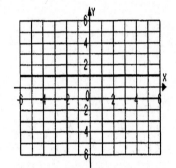

7.   In order to solve the system with the substitution method, which of the following might
       be the result of the first step? $3x + 3y = 9$
                                                  $-2x + y = -12$

   a. $3x + 3y = 9$ b. $x + y = 3$
       $6x - 3y = 36$ $-2x + y = -12$

   c. $3x + 3y = 9$ b. $3x + 3y = -9$
       $y = -2x - 12$ $y = 2x - 12$

8.   Solve the system by the substitution method.

       $3x + 3y = 9$
       $-2x + y = -12$

   a. $(9, -6)$ b. $(-15, 18)$ c. $(5, -2)$ d. $(3, 6)$

9. In order to solve the system with the elimination method, which of the following might be the result of the first step? $-2x + 5y = -24$
    $$3x + y = 2$$

    a. $-2x + 5y = -24$
        $-15x - 5y = -10$

    b. $-2x + 5y = -24$
        $-15x - 5y = 2$

    c. $-2x + 5y = -24$
        $y = -3x + 2$

    d. $-2x + 5y = -24$
        $y = 3x + 2$

10. Solve the system by the elimination method.
     $-2x + 5y = -24$
     $3x + y = 2$
     a. $(2, -4)$ b. $(-4, 2)$ c. $(1, -1)$ d. $(7, 2)$

For problems 11 – 12, solve each system by the substitution method.

11. $y = -x - 3$
     $y = 3x + 1$
     a. $(2, -5)$ b. $(1, -2)$ c. $(-2, -5)$ d. $(-1, -2)$

12. $6x + 3y = 6$
     $x - 2y = -4$
     a. $(1, 0)$ b. $(0, 2)$ c. $(-4, 0)$ d. $(-2, 2)$

For problems 13 – 14, solve each system by the elimination method.

13. $x + y = -1$
     $-2x - 2y = 2$
     a. $(0, -1)$ b. $(3, -4)$ c. Infinite solutions   d. No solution

14. $12x - 10y = 0$
     $3x - 2y = 0$
     a. $(0, 0)$ b. $(2, 3)$ c. Infinite solutions   d. No solution

15. Solve the system by the method of your choice
     $8x + 3y = -4$
     $3x + 4y = 10$
     a. $(4, -2)$ b. $(2, 4)$ c. $(4, 2)$ d. $(-2, 4)$

16.   The perimeter of a rectangular room is 120 feet. The sum of four times the width and three times the length is 204 feet. Find the length and the width.

     a. 104 feet and 16 feet   b. 51 feet and 9 feet
     c. 18 feet and 15 feet   d. 36 feet and 24 feet

17.   The nationwide weekly demand model for a new economy car is given by
$N = -12p + 388,000$. The weekly supply model for the new economy car is
$N = 8p + 20,000$. For these models, p is the price of the car and N is the number of cars sold or supplied each week. Find the price at which supply and demand are equal. At this price, how many cars can be supplied and sold each week?

     a. $92,000   b. $18,400   c. $20,400   d. $19,000
        756,000 cars   167,200 cars   183,200 cars   172,000 cars

18.   The sum of a first number and a second number is 281. The second number is equal to 400 decreased by three times the first number. Find the numbers.
     a. 119 and 162   b. 227 and 54   c. 40 and 241   d. 61 and 220

19.   Determine which ordered triple is a solution of the given system:

$3x - 2y + 5z = -17$
$2x + 4y - 3z = 29$
$5x - 6y - 7z = 7$

     a. (2, 4, 3)   b. (–2, 4, 3)   c. (–2, –4, 3)   d. (2, 4, –3)

20.   Solve the following system:

$3x - 2y + 5z = -1$
$4x + 3y - 2z = -13$
$2x + 5y - 4z = -9$

     a, (3, –1, 2)   b. (3, –1, –2)   c. (–3, 1, 2)   d. (–3, –1, –2)

Name _____   Date _____

Cumulative Review 1 – 4
Form A

For problems 1 – 3, perform the indicated operations.

1. $15 - |3 - 6| - 2^3$

1. _____

2. $\dfrac{9 - 2(10 - 3^3)}{(4 - 6)^2}$

2. _____

3. $5[2x - (x + 3)] - (4 - x)$

3. _____

4. List all the integers in the set $\left\{ -\dfrac{5}{3},\ -1,\ 0,\ \sqrt{5},\ 6 \right\}$

4. _____

For problems 5 – 7, solve the equation.

5. $7 - 4(x + 3) = -2(x - 2)$

5. _____

6. $2 - \dfrac{3x}{4} = -\dfrac{1}{8}x - 3$

6. _____

7. $\dfrac{x + 1}{5} = \dfrac{x - 3}{15}$

7. _____

8. Solve $2x - 3y = 6$ for y.

8. _____

9. What number is 42% of 2100?

9. _____

For problems 10 – 11, solve each inequality and (a) express the solution in set-builder notation and (b) graph the set on a number line.

10. $4x - 5 < 5x - 8$

10a. _____

b.
-6 -5 -4 -3 -2 -1 0 1 2 3 4 5 6

Name _____   Date _____

11     $2(3x + 4) \geq -4 - 2(x + 2)$ 11a. _____

                                         b.

12.   A carpenter presents you with a bill for $423 including   12. _____
        labor and supplies. If the carpenter charges $40 per hour
        for labor and $163 for supplies, how many hours did he work?

13.   You deposit a total of $4000 in two accounts. One account   13. _____
        pays 5% interest and the other pays 6% interest. At the end
        of the first year, the interest paid is $223.60. How much was
        invested in each account?

14.   A cylinder has a diameter of 8 inches and a height of 12   14. _____
        inches. Find the volume in terms of π.

15.   The measure of an angle is 20° more then its supplement.   15. _____
        Find the measure of the angle.

16.   Calculate the slope of the line passing through the given   16. _____
        points: (−1, 4) and (3, −6).

17.   For the equation $3x - 6y = 12$, find the: (a) slope   17a. _____
        (b) y – intercept.   b. _____

18.   For the line with slope −4 and passing through (1, −2)   18. _____
        write the equation of the line in slope – intercept form.

For problems 19 – 20, graph each equation in the rectangular coordinate system.

19. $y = 4x - 1$ 19.

T-97

20      $-2x + 4y = 4$

20.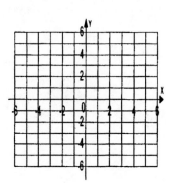

Solve the system graphically.

21. $x + 3y = 12$
       $2x - 4y = 4$

21.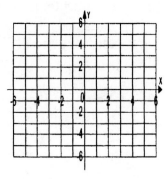

Solve the system by the addition method.

22. $x + y - 4$
       $2x - y = 5$

22. _____

23.   Solve the system by the substitution method.

23. _____

       $3x + y = 1$
       $x = 2y + 5$

24.   Solve the system by the method of your choice.

24. _____

       $5x - 2y = 2$
       $3x - 7y = 36$

25.   Solve the following system with three variables.

25. _____

       $3x + 2y + z = 10$
       $2x - y - 2z = -6$
       $x - 3y - z = -8$

Name _____   Date _____

Cumulative Review 1 – 4
Form B

Choose the correct answer to each problem.

For problems 1 – 3, perform the indicated operations.

1. $10 + 6 \div 2 - 2^4$
    a. –8   b. 16   c. –3   d. 2

2. $\dfrac{7 - 4(3 - 5)}{10 - 5^2}$
    a. $\dfrac{9}{10}$ b. –1   c. $-\dfrac{6}{35}$ d. $\dfrac{2}{5}$

3. $5x + [3(x - 3) - (6 - x)]$
    a. $7x + 15$ b. $7x - 15$ c. $9x + 15$ d. $9x - 15$

4. List all the natural numbers in the set $\left\{ -\dfrac{15}{4},\ -3,\ 0,\ \dfrac{1}{2},\ 2,\ \pi \right\}$

    a. $\{2\}$ b. $(0, 2\}$ c. $\{-3, 0, 2\}$ d. $\left\{ \dfrac{1}{2},\ 2 \right\}$

For problems 5 – 7, solve the equation.

5. $4x - (2x + 3) = 5 - 3(x + 2)$
    a. $\dfrac{8}{5}$ b. $-\dfrac{4}{5}$ c. No solution   d. $\dfrac{2}{5}$

6. $\dfrac{3}{5} = -\dfrac{20}{x}$
    a. $-\dfrac{100}{3}$ b. 4   c. $\dfrac{100}{3}$ d. -4

7. $\dfrac{5x}{6} - 2 = \dfrac{2x}{3} + 6$
    a. 12   b. 13   c. 48   d. 16

8. Solve $c = \dfrac{2a}{b}$ for a.
    a. $a = \dfrac{2c}{b}$ b. $a = \dfrac{bc}{2}$ c. $a = 2bc$ d. $a = \dfrac{2}{bc}$

9. 175 is what percent of 50?

   a. 3.5%   b. 28.6%   c. 350%   d. $\frac{2}{7}$%

10. A local library decides they should employ two librarians for every 75 daily visitors. How many librarians should be employed if the library averages 1020 daily visitors? Round your answer to the nearest integer.

    a. 27   b. 38,250   c. 20   d. 38

11. Solve the inequality and express the solution set in set-builder notation.
    $$7x - 19 < 9x + 19$$
    a. $\{x \mid x < -19\}$ b. $\{x \mid x > -19\}$ c. $\{x \mid x > 0\}$ d. $\{x \mid x < 0\}$

12. Solve the inequality and express the solution set on a number line.
    $$3(x - 4) \geq -12 + 6(x + 2)$$

    a.   b.

    c.   d.

13. Solve the inequality and select the correct expression of the solution set.
    $$2(x - 5) > 4x - 2(x - 2)$$

    a. $\{x \mid x \text{ is a real number}\}$ b.

    c.   d. No solution

14. A motorcycle and a car leave a store at the same time traveling in opposite directions. If the motorcycle averages 45 mph and a car averages 40 mph, how long will it take them to be 106.25 miles apart?

    a. 1 hr   b. $\frac{5}{4}$ hrs   c. $\frac{85}{8}$ hrs   d. $\frac{3}{2}$ hrs

15. At the end of the first year, an account earns 3% interest earns $126 in interest.
     How much money was deposited in the account at the start of the year?
     a. $378   b. $3780   c. $4200   d. $420

16. The outside dimensions of a picture frame are 48 inches by 31 inches. The inside
     dimensions are 33 inches by 24 inches. Find the area of the frame.
     a. 1488 in^2 b. 696 in^2 c. 105 in^2 d. 792 in^2

17. Find the volume of a sphere with a radius of 6 centimeters. Round the answer to
     the nearest integer.
     a. 151 cm^3 b. 113 cm^3 c. 288 cm^3 d. 905 cm^3

18. One angle of a triangle is 30° less than another. The third angle is 60°. Find the
     measure of the smallest angle.
     a. 45°   b. 30°   c. 60°   d. 75°

19. Calculate the slope of the line passing through the given points: (–2, 6) and (–2, 2).
     a. 0   b. Undefined   c. 1   d. –2

20. For the equation $7x + 2y = 14$, find the slope.
     a. $-\dfrac{7}{2}$ b. $\dfrac{2}{7}$ c. $\dfrac{7}{2}$ d. $-\dfrac{2}{7}$

21. For the equation $-12x - 6y = 36$, find the y-intercept.
     a. (0, –3)   b. (0, –6)   c. (–3, 0)   d. (6, 0)

Name _____   Date _____

22.   For the line with slope 5 and passing through (−2, 4) write the equation of the line in slope-intercept form.

  a. $y = 5x - 14$ b. $y = 5x - 6$ c. $y = 5x + 6$ d. $y = 5x + 14$

23.   Solve the following system by graphing.

$$2x + y = 1$$
$$x = 2y + 8$$

a.
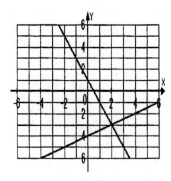

b.
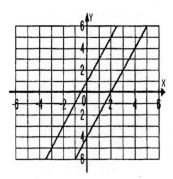

c.
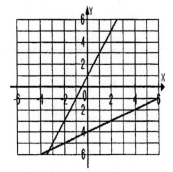

d.
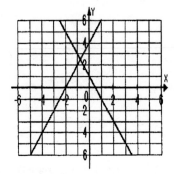

24.   Solve the following system by the addition method.

$$2x + y = 1$$
$$x - 2y = 8$$

  a. (3, −5)   b. (0, 1)   c. (1, −1)   d. (2, −3)

25.   Solve the following system by the substitution method.

$$x + 3y = 1$$
$$2x - y = -5$$

  a. (1, 0)   b. (−2, 1)   c. (−5, 2)   d. (4, −1)

Chapter 5
Form A

For problems 1 – 2, identify each polynomial as a monomial, binomial, or trinomial. Give the degree of the polynomial.

1. $7x^4 - 4x^2$

    1. _____

2. $8x^3y^2 - 5x^2y + 3x$

    2. _____

For problems 3 – 6, add or subtract as indicated.

3. $(7x^5 - 4x^3 + 3x^2 - 4x) + (6x^3 - 2x^2 + 2x)$

    3. _____

4. $(5x^2 - 4xy + 2y) - (-x^2 + xy - 2y)$

    4. _____

5. Subtract $11x^3 - 8x + 3$ from $9x^3 + 3x^2 - 2$

    5. _____

6. Add $14y^4 - 5y^3 + 18y^2 - 4y + 2$
        $+\qquad y^3 - 4y^2 + 5y - 5$

    6. _____

For problems 7 – 14, simplify each expression.

7. $y^7 \cdot y^4$

    7. _____

8. $\left(-9y^3\right)^4$

    8. _____

9. $55x^0$

    9. _____

10. $(3x^{-3})^2(7x^4)$

    10. _____

11. $(3x^2y^{-3})(-5x^{-1}y^4)^2$

    11. _____

12. $\left(\dfrac{5x^2y^4}{2xy^6}\right)^2$

    12. _____

13. $3^{-2} + 2^{-1}$

    13. _____

14. $\dfrac{x^6 \cdot x^{-2}}{x^{-4}}$

    14. _____

For problems 15 – 19, find each product.

15. $-3x^2y(6x^4y^3 - 5x^3y + 4y)$

15. _____

16. $(2x + 3)(5x - 4)$

16. _____

17. $(3t - 5)^2$

17. _____

18. $(3a - 4b)(3a + 4b)$

18. _____

19. $(5y - 2)(y^2 - 4y + 3)$

19. _____

For problems 20 – 21, divide.

20. $\dfrac{12x^4 - 16x^3 + 8x}{4x}$

20. _____

21. $\dfrac{3x^3 + 5x^2 - 5x + 8}{3x - 1}$

21. _____

22. Write 2.14×10^{-4} in decimal notation.

22. _____

23. Write 1,457,000 in scientific notation.

23. _____

24. Simplify $\dfrac{4.2 \times 10^5}{8.4 \times 10^{-3}}$

24. _____

25. Write a polynomial in descending powers of x that represents the area of the figure below.

25. _____

Chapter 5
Form B

For problems 1 – 2, identify each polynomial as a monomial, binomial, or trinomial. Give the degree of the polynomial.

1. $14xy^7$

1. _____

2. $-x^7 + 3x^2 - 4$

2. _____

For problems 3 – 6, add or subtract as indicated.

3. $(-4x^6 + 3x^5 - 2x^2 + 3x) + (-3x^6 + 2x^2 - 4x + 5)$

3. _____

4. $(2x^5 - 4xy^3 + 3y^2) - (-4x^5 + 3xy^3 - y^2)$

4. _____

5. Subtract $7x^2 - 5x + 2$ from $x^2 - 4x + 3$

5. _____

6. Evaluate $6x^2 y - xy + 7$ for $x = 2, y = -3$

6. _____

For problems 7 – 14, simplify each expression.

7. $5y^{10} \cdot 2y^{-4}$

7. _____

8. $\left(-4y^5\right)^3$

8. _____

9. $9^0 - 6^1$

9. _____

10. $(-2x^4)^3 (3x^{-2})^2$

10. _____

11. $\dfrac{(3y^{-2})^4}{y^{12}}$

11. _____

12. $\left(\dfrac{y^{-3}}{y^4}\right)^{-4}$

12. _____

13. $\dfrac{(5x^3)(2x^{-2})^4}{4x^{-4}}$ 13. _____

For problems 14 – 18, find each product.

14. $-2x^2y^3(4x^3y^2 - 7x^2y - 3x)$ 14. _____

15. $(2x - 5)(3x + 4)$ 15. _____

16. $(3y - 8)^2$ 16. _____

17. $(2a - 3b)(2a + 3b)$ 17. _____

18. $(5t - 1)(25t^2 + 5t + 1)$ 18. _____

For problems 19 – 20, divide.

19. $\dfrac{20x^3y^2 - 12x^2y + 16xy}{4xy}$ 19. _____

20. $\dfrac{8x^3 - 2x^2 - 7x - 5}{4x - 3}$ 20. _____

21.   Write 1.78×10^{-3} in decimal notation.   21. _____

22.   Write 42,500 in scientific notation.   22. _____

23.   Simplify $(5.4 \times 10^{-7})(3.2 \times 10^{-4})$ 23. _____

24.   Simplify $\dfrac{6.6 \times 10^9}{1.1 \times 10^{-5}}$ 24. _____

25.   The mass of a proton is approximately 1.7×10^{-24} gram. Find   25. _____
      the mass of 5 billion protons. Express your answer in
      scientific notation.

Chapter 5
Form C

For problems 1 – 2, identify each polynomial as a monomial, binomial, or trinomial. Give the degree of the polynomial.

1. $-15x^7y^2 - 8x^5y^4 + 7x^6y^5$ 1. _____

2. $7x^5 - 2x^2$ 2. _____

For problems 3 – 6, add or subtract as indicated.

3. $\left(\dfrac{4}{5}x^4 - \dfrac{1}{2}x^3 - 1\right) + \left(\dfrac{1}{2}x^4 + \dfrac{3}{5}x^2 + \dfrac{1}{3}\right)$ 3. _____

4. $(6x^4y^3 - 7x^3y^3 + 3x^2y^2) - (3x^4y^3 + 3x^3y^3 - 3x^2y^2)$ 4. _____

5.   Subtract $-7x^3 - 3x^2 + 4x - 5$ from $-x^3 + 3x - 6$.   5. _____

6.   Evaluate $-xy^2 + 3xy - 4y$ for $x = -1, y = -3$.   6. _____

For problems 7 – 13, simplify each expression.

7. $4y^2 \cdot 4^{-4}x^5 \cdot x^{-2}$ 7. _____

8. $\left(-3x^4y^5\right)^4$ 8. _____

9. $2x^0 + 3^1$ 9. _____

10. $(3xy^4)^3(-2x^{-2}y^3)^2$ 10. _____

11. $\dfrac{(5x^{-2}y)^4}{(5x^2y^{-3})^2}$ 11. _____

12. $\left(\dfrac{4x^{-1}y^{-2}}{x^4}\right)^{-1}$ 12. _____

13. $\dfrac{(8x)^2(2x^{-4})^{-2}}{2x^{-4}}$ 13. _____

For problems 14 – 18, find each product.

14. $-2x^2y^3(5x^3y^2 - 4x^2y^3 + 3x^2y^2)$ 14. _____

15. $(8x - 3)(5x + 3)$ 15. _____

16. $(5x + 2y)^2$ 16. _____

17. $(t^2 + 5)(t^2 - 5)$ 17. _____

18. $(4y - 3)(16y^2 + 12y + 9)$ 18. _____

For problems 19 – 20, divide.

19. $\dfrac{40x^2y - 25xy^2 + 50xy}{-5xy}$ 19. _____

20. $\dfrac{x^3 - 8}{x - 2}$ 20. _____

21. Write 1.43×10^7 in decimal notation.   21. _____

22. Write 0.0000159 in scientific notation.   22. _____

23. Simplify $(4.8 \times 10^5)(3.2 \times 10^6)$ 23. _____

24. Simplify $\dfrac{17.6 \times 10^{-4}}{4.4 \times 10^{-8}}$ 24. _____

25. Write a polynomial in descending powers of x that represents   25. _____
     the area of the figure below.

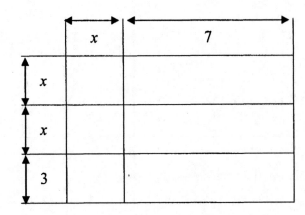

Chapter 5
Form D

Choose the correct answer to each problem.

1.   Classify as a monomial, binomial or trinomial: $3x^2 - 4x$.
      a. monomial   b. binomial   c. trinomial   d. none of these

2.   Determine the degree of the polynomial: $14x^2 y^7 - 6x^5 y^3$.
      a. 14   b. 9   c. 8   d. 15

For problems 3 – 5, add or subtract as indicated.

3. $(-2x^3 + 5x^2 - 6x) + (-2x^2 + 3x - 5)$
      a. $-2x^3 + 3x^2 - 3x - 5$ b. $-4x^5 + 8x^3 - 11x$
      c. $-2x^3 + 7x^2 - 3x - 5$ d. $4x^5 + 15x^3 + 30x$

4. $(15x^3 y^2 - 8x^2 y + 7xy^2) - (3x^3 y^2 + 3x^2 y - 4xy^2)$
      a. $12x^3 y^2$ b. $12x^3 y^2 - 11x^2 y + 11xy^2$
      c. $45x^6 y^4 - 24x^4 y^2 - 28x^2 y^4$ d. $12x^3 y^2 - 5x^2 y + 3xy^2$

5.   Subtract $12x^3 - 5x^2 - 6x + 3$ from $20x^3 + 7x^2 + 3x - 5$.
      a. $-8x^3 - 12x^2 - 9x + 8$ b. $32x^3 + 2x^2 - 3x - 2$
      c. $-8x^3 + 2x^2 - 2x - 8$ d. $8x^3 + 12x^2 + 9x - 8$

6.   Evaluate $-x^2 y^2 + 3xy - y^2$ for $x = -1, y = -4$.
      a. 28   b. 12   c. 42   d. –20

For problems 7 – 13, simplify each expression.

7. $2x^5 \cdot 2^3 x^{12}$
      a. $64x^{60}$ b. $16x^{60}$ c. $16x^{17}$ d. $4x^{20}$

8. $(-4x^4y^5)^2$

    a. $64x^8y^{10}$ b. $16x^8y^{10}$ c. $64x^{16}y^{25}$ d. $-64x^{16}y^{25}$

9. $2^0 - 3^{-1}$

    a. $\dfrac{1}{3}$ b. $\dfrac{1}{5}$ c. $\dfrac{4}{3}$ d. $\dfrac{2}{3}$

10. $(2ab^3)^3(ab)^4$

    a. $8a^7b^{13}$ b. $8a^7b^7$ c. $2a^7b^{13}$ d. $2a^4b^{13}$

11. $\dfrac{(7a^{-4}b^{-2})^3}{49a^{-15}b^3}$

    a. $\dfrac{3}{7a^{27}b^3}$ b. $\dfrac{7}{a^3b^3}$ c. $\dfrac{1}{7b^3}$ d. $\dfrac{7a^3}{b^9}$

12. $\left(\dfrac{12x^{-3}y^5}{x^{-4}}\right)^{-1}$

    a. $\dfrac{1}{12xy^5}$ b. $\dfrac{-12x^7}{y^5}$ c. $\dfrac{12}{x^7y^5}$ d. $\dfrac{x}{12y^5}$

13. $\dfrac{(3y^5)^2(4y^{-3})^{-2}}{18y^{-5}}$

    a. $\dfrac{2y^2}{3}$ b. $\dfrac{y^{21}}{32}$ c. $\dfrac{2y^{55}}{3}$ d. $\dfrac{-8y^{16}}{3}$

14. $-4x^2y^3(15x^2y^3 - 9x^2y^2 + 8xy)$

    a. $-60x^2y^3 + 36x^2y^5 - 32x^2y^3$ b. $-60x^4y^6 - 36x^4y^5 + 32x^3y^4$

    c. $-60x^4y^9 + 36x^4y^6 - 32x^2y^3$ d. $-60x^4y^6 + 36x^4y^5 - 32x^3y^4$

15. $(7x - 4)(3x + 2)$

    a. $21x^2 - 8$ b. $21x^2 + 2x - 8$

    c. $21x^2 - 2x - 8$ d. $21x^2 - 26x - 8$

16. $(8t+9)(8t-9)$
   a. $64t^2-81$ b. $64t^2+81$
   c. $16t-18$ d. $64t^2-144t+81$

17. $(z^2-5)^2$
   a. z^2-25 b. z^4-10z^2+25 c. z^4-25 d. z^4+10z^2-25

18. $(2x-3)(x^2+4x-6)$
   a. $2x^3+11x^2+18$ b. $2x^3+5x^2-24x-18$
   c. $2x^3+5x^2-24x+18$ d. $2x^3+11x^2-24x+18$

For problems 19 – 20, divide.

19. $\dfrac{30x^3y^2-20x^2y^2+15xy}{-5xy}$
   a. $-6x^2y+4xy-3$ b. $-5x$
   c. $30x^3y^2-20x^2y-3$ d. $6x^2y+4xy+3$

20. $\dfrac{6x^3+3x^2-5x-6}{2x-1}$
   a. $3x^2-2+\dfrac{1}{2x-1}$ b. $3x^2+3x-1-\dfrac{7}{2x-1}$
   c. $3x^2+3x-1-\dfrac{5}{2x-1}$ d. $3x^2+3x-4-\dfrac{10}{2x-1}$

21. Write 6.29×10^{-3} in decimal notation.
   a. 62900   b. 0.00629   c. 629000   d. 0.0000629

22. Write 270,600,000 in scientific notation.
   a. 2.706×10^8 b. 2.76×10^9 c. 2.706×10^{-8} d. 2.76×10^{-9}

23. Simplify $(4.9\times10^{-3})(5.2\times10^{-8})$.
   a. 25.48×10^{24} b. 25.48×10^{-11} c. 2.548×10^{-10} d. 2.548×10^{30}

Name _____   Date _____

24.   Simplify $\dfrac{28.6 \times 10^{-12}}{14.3 \times 10^{-4}}$.

    a. 2×10^{-16} b. 2×10^{3} c. 2×10^{-3} d. 2×10^{-8}

25.   Write a polynomial in descending powers of x that represents the area of the figure below.

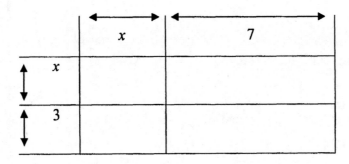

    a. $21x^2$ b. $x^2 + 21$ c. $x^2 + 10x + 21$ d. $2x + 10$

Chapter 5
Form E

Choose the correct answer to each problem.

1. Classify as a monomial, binomial or trinomial: $6x^4y^3 - 8x^3y^2$,
   a. monomial   b. binomial   c. trinomial   d. none of these

2. Determine the degree of the polynomial: $6x^4y^2 - 8x^3y^2$.
   a. 4   b. 6   c. 7   d. 12

For problems 3 – 5, add or subtract as indicated.

3. $(9x^3 + 4x^2 - 6x) + (-5x^3 - 5x^2 + 2x)$
   a. $4x^3 + 4x^2 - 11x + 2$ b. $4x^3 - x^2 - 4x$
   c. $-45x^6 - 20x^3 - 12x$ d. $-45x^3 - 20x^3 - 12x$

4. $(4x^2y^2 - 2xy + 8y^2) - (-2x^2y^2 + 3xy - 8y^2)$
   a. $2x^2y^2 + xy$ b. $6x^2y^2 + 5xy$
   c. $6x^2y^2 - 5xy + 16y^2$ d. $8x^4y^2 + 6x^2y^2 + 64y^2$

5. Subtract $5x^3 - 4x^2 - 3x + 2$ from $5x^3 + 4x^2 + 3x - 2$.
   a. 0   b. $10x^3$ c. $-8x^2$ d. $8x^2 + 6x - 4$

6. Evaluate $x^3y + x^2y^2 - y^2$ for $x = -2$, $y = -3$.
   a. 45   b. 51   c. –21   d. 21

For problems 7 – 13, simplify each expression.

7. $(-3x^4y^2)^3$
   a. $-9x^{12}y^6$ b. $-27x^{12}y^6$ c. $-9x^7y^5$ d. $-27x^7y^5$

8. $5x^2 y(2x^4 y)^4$

   a. $10x^6 y^4$ b. $40x^{10}y^5$ c. $10x^{10}y^5$ d. $80x^{18}y^5$

9. $2x^0 + 4^1$

   a. 3   b. 4   c. 5   d. 6

10. $(-2a^3 b)^2 (3a^2 b)^3$

    a. $-776a^{25}b^{10}$ b. $-6a^{12}b^5$ c. $-108a^6 b^5$ d. $108a^{12}b^5$

11. $\dfrac{(5a^{-3}b^{-4})^2}{15a^{-3}b^4}$

    a. $\dfrac{1}{3b^{12}}$ b. $\dfrac{5}{3a^3 b^{12}}$ c. $\dfrac{5b^4}{3a^3}$ d. $\dfrac{5}{3a^9 b^4}$

12. $\left(\dfrac{-7x^{-4}y^6}{y^{-12}}\right)^{-1}$

    a. $\dfrac{7x^4}{y^{18}}$ b. $-\dfrac{x^4}{7y^6}$ c. $-\dfrac{7x^4}{y^6}$ d. $-\dfrac{x^4}{7y^{18}}$

13. $\dfrac{(2y^4)^3 (4y^{-4})^{-2}}{(4y^6)^{-1}}$

    a. $2y^{26}$ b. $\dfrac{y^{14}}{8}$ c. $\dfrac{y^{14}}{32}$ d. $16y^{14}$

14. $-2a^3 b(13a^4 b^5 - 4a^2 b^2 - 3ab)$

    a. $-12a^4 b^3$ b. $-26a^7 b^6 + 8a^5 b^3 + 6a^4 b^2$

    c. $-26a^7 b^6 - 8a^4 b^3 - 6a^4 b^2$ d. $-26a^{12}b^5 + 8a^6 b + 6a^3 b$

15. $(3x - 4)(2x + 5)$

    a. $6x^2 - 7x - 20$ b. $6x^2 - 20$

    c. $6x^2 + 7x - 20$ d. $6x^2 + 23x - 20$

16. $(4z + 7)(4z - 7)$

    a. $16z^2 - 49$ b. $16z^2 + 49$

    c. $16z^2 - 56z + 49$ d. $8z - 14$

17. $(3t^2 - 5)^2$

    a. $9t^4 - 30t^2 + 25$ b. $9t^4 + 30t^2 - 25$

    c. $9t^4 - 25$ d. $9t^2 - 25$

18. $(7x - 3)(2x^2 - 5x - 3)$

    a. $14x^3 - 29x^2 - 6x + 9$ b. $14x^3 - 41x^2 - 6x + 9$

    c. $14x^3 - 29x^2 + 36x + 9$ d. $14x^3 - 41x^2 - 36x + 9$

For problems 19 – 20, divide.

19. $\dfrac{-50x^4y^3 + 45x^3y^2 - 20x^2y}{-5x^2y}$

    a. $5x^7y^5$ b. $-50x^4y^3 + 45x^3y^2 + 4$

    c. $10x^2y^2 + 45x^3y^2 - 20x^2y$ d. $10x^2y^2 - 9xy + 4$

20. $\dfrac{12x^3 + 5x^2 + 5x + 1}{4x + 3}$

    a. $3x^2 - x + 2 - \dfrac{5}{4x + 3}$ b. $3x^2 - x + 2 + \dfrac{7}{4x + 3}$

    c. $3x^2 + x - 3 + \dfrac{5}{4x + 3}$ d. $3x^2 - x + 2 + \dfrac{5}{4x + 3}$

21.   Write 4.56×10^5 in decimal notation.

    a. 0.00000456   b. 4,560,000   c. 456,000   d. 0.000456

22.   Write 0.0000056 in scientific notation.

    a. 5.6×10^{-7} b. 5.6×10^6 c. 5.6×10^{-6} d. 5.6×10^7

Name _____   Date _____

23. Simplify $(5.8 \times 10^{-5})(4.1 \times 10^{8})$.

   a. 23.78×10^{-40} b. 23.78×10^{3} c. 2.378×10^{3} d. 2.378×10^{4}

24. Simplify $\dfrac{4.2 \times 10^{-4}}{7 \times 10^{-6}}$.

   a. 0.6×10^{-10} b. 6×10^{1} c. 6×10^{-10} d. 0.6×10^{4}

25. Write a polynomial in descending powers of x that represents the area of the figure below.

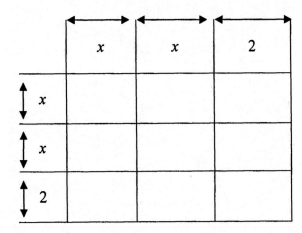

   a. $4x^{2} + 8x + 4$ b. $4x^{2} + 4$ c. $2x + 4$ d. $16x^{2}$

Name _____   Date _____

Chapter 5
Form F

Choose the correct answer to each problem.

1. Classify as a monomial, binomial or trinomial: $15x^4y^3 + 3x^3y^2 - 4xy^5$,
    a. monomial   b. binomial   c. trinomial   d. none of these

2. Determine the degree of the polynomial: $15x^4y^3 + 3x^3y^2 - 4xy^5$.
    a. 4   b. 6   c. 7   d. 12

For problems 3 – 5, add or subtract as indicated.

3. $\left(\dfrac{2}{3}x^5 + \dfrac{1}{4}x^2 - x + \dfrac{2}{5}\right) + \left(\dfrac{1}{2}x^5 + \dfrac{2}{3}x^3 + \dfrac{1}{2}x + \dfrac{3}{10}\right)$

    a. $\dfrac{3}{5}x^5 + \dfrac{2}{3}x^3 + \dfrac{1}{4}x^2 - \dfrac{1}{2}x + \dfrac{1}{3}$ b. $\dfrac{7}{6}x^5 + \dfrac{2}{3}x^3 + \dfrac{1}{4}x^2 - \dfrac{1}{2}x + \dfrac{7}{10}$

    c. $\dfrac{2}{6}x^{10} + \dfrac{2}{12}x^5 - \dfrac{1}{2}x^2 + \dfrac{6}{50}$ d. $\dfrac{7}{6}x^{10} + \dfrac{11}{12}x^5 - \dfrac{1}{2}x^2 + \dfrac{7}{10}$

4. $(7x^3y^2 + 4x^2y^2 - 5xy^2) - (2x^3y^2 + 3x^2y^2 - 3xy^2)$
    a. $5x^3y^2 + 7x^2y^2 - 8xy^2$ b. $5x^3y^2 + x^2y^2 - 2xy^2$
    c. $5x^3y^2 + 7x^2y^2 - 2xy^2$ d. $14x^3y^2 - 12x^2y^2 - 15xy^2$

5. Subtract $14x^3 - 5x^2 - 2x + 3$ from $7x^3 + 3x - 4$.
    a. $21x^3 - 5x + x - 1$ b. $7x^3 - 5x^2 - 5x + 7$
    c. $21x^3$ d. $-7x^3 + 5x^2 + 5x - 7$

6. Evaluate $x^3y^2 - xy^2 + xy$ for $x = -2$, $y = 3$.
    a. –87   b. –72   c. –60   d. –48

For problems 7 – 13, simplify each expression.

7. $6^3 \cdot 6^{-5} x^7 \cdot x^{-3}$

    a. $36^{-2} x^{-21}$ b. $\dfrac{1}{1296x^{21}}$ c. $-12x^4$ d. $\dfrac{x^4}{36}$

8. $\left(-\dfrac{2}{3}x^4y^2\right)^2$

    a. $\dfrac{4x^8y^4}{9}$ b. $\dfrac{3x^8y^4}{2}$ c. $\dfrac{9x^{16}y^4}{4}$ d. $-\dfrac{4x^8y^4}{3}$

T-118

9. $3x^0 - 4^{-1}$

     a. $\dfrac{3}{4}$ b. -1 c. $\dfrac{11}{4}$ d. $-\dfrac{11}{4}$

10. $(5x^2y^4)^2(-3x^{-4}y^{-1})^3$

     a. $-\dfrac{15y^5}{x^8}$ b. $\dfrac{y^5}{15x^8}$ c. $-\dfrac{675y^5}{x^8}$ d. $-\dfrac{270y^{15}}{x^{48}}$

11. $\dfrac{(6^{-2}x^3y^{-4})^2}{2^{-4}x^3y^{-4}}$

     a. $-\dfrac{12x^9}{y^{12}}$ b. $\dfrac{x^3}{81y^4}$ c. $\dfrac{x^9}{81y^{12}}$ d. $-\dfrac{12x^3}{y^4}$

12. $\left(\dfrac{-8a^{-1}b^{-3}}{2a^3b}\right)^{-2}$

     a. $\dfrac{8b^5}{a}$ b. $8a^5b^7$ c. $\dfrac{a^{16}b^{16}}{16}$ d. $\dfrac{a^8b^8}{16}$

13. $\dfrac{(3x^4)^2(4x^{-5})^{-1}}{12x^{-6}}$

     a. $\dfrac{3x^{19}}{16}$ b. x^7 c. $\dfrac{x^7}{16}$ d. $\dfrac{x^9}{16}$

14. $-5x^4y^2(3x^3y^5 - 2x^2y^4 - 6xy^3)$

     a. $-15x^7y^7 - 10x^6y^6 - 30x^5y^5$ b. $-15x^7y^7 + 10x^6y^6 + 30x^5y^5$

     c. $-15x^{12}y^{10} + 10x^8y^8 + 30x^4y^6$ d. $-15x^{12}y^{10} - 10x^8y^8 - 30x^4y^6$

15. $(7t + 5)(3t - 7)$

     a. $21t^2 + 64t + 35$ b. $21t^2 - 34t - 35$

     c. $21t^2 - 35$ d. $21t^2 + 34t - 35$

16. $(4u - 5v)(4u + 5v)$

     a. $16u^2 - 25v^2$ b. $16u^2 + 25v^2$

     c. $16u^2 - 40uv + 25v^2$ d. $16u^2 - 40uv - 25u^2$

17. $(8x^2 - 3)^2$

    a. $64x^4 - 9$ b. $64x^4 - 48x^2 + 9$

    c. $64x^2 - 9$ d. $64x^4 + 48x^2 - 9$

18. $\left(t - \dfrac{1}{2}\right)\left(t^2 + \dfrac{1}{2}t + \dfrac{1}{4}\right)$

    a. $t^3 + \dfrac{1}{2}t - \dfrac{1}{8}$ b. $t^3 + \dfrac{1}{4}t - \dfrac{1}{8}$

    c. $t^3 - t^2 - \dfrac{1}{2}t - \dfrac{1}{8}$ d. $t^3 - \dfrac{1}{8}$

For problems 19 – 20, divide.

19. $\dfrac{-24a^3b^5 + 36a^2b^2 - 12ab^2}{-4ab}$

    a. $6a^2b^4 + 9ab - 3b$ b. $6a^2b^4 - 9ab + 3b$

    c. $6a^2b^4 + 36a^3b^2 - 12ab^2$ d. $-12a^3b^5 - 9ab - 12ab^2$

20. $\dfrac{8a^3 - 27}{2a - 3}$

    a. $4a^2 + 9$ b. $4a^2 - 6a + 9$

    c. $4a^2 + 6a + 9$ d. $4a^2 - 6a - 9 - \dfrac{54}{2a + 3}$

21. Write 2.56×10^{-3} in decimal notation.

    a. 0.00256   b. 25,600   c. 0.0000256   d. 256,000

22. Write 3,250,000,000 in scientific notation.

    a. 3.25×10^9 b. 3.205×10^9 c. 3.205×10^{-9} d. 3.205×10^{-10}

23. Simplify $(7.3 \times 10^8)(4.9 \times 10^{-3})$.

    a. 3.577×10^6 b. 3.577×10^{-6} c. 35.77×10^{-24} d. 3.577×10^{-23}

24. Simplify $\dfrac{2 \times 10^7}{5 \times 10^{-2}}$.

    a. 0.4×10^5 b. 4×10^4 c. 0.4×10^9 d. 4×10^8

25. The mass of an electron is approximately 9.1×10^{-28} gram. The mass of a neutron is approximately 1840 times that of an electron. What is the mass of 2000 neutrons?

    a. 1.82×10^{-24} b. 1.6744×10^{-24} c. 3.3488×10^{-21} d. 9.89×10^{-28}

Name _____   Date _____

Chapter 6
Form A

For problems 1 – 13, factor completely or state that the polynomial is prime.

1. $x^2 - x - 12$

                1. _____

2. $x^3 - 64x$

                2. _____

3. $12x^2 - 12xy + 3y^2$

                3. _____

4. $24x^2 - 22x - 10$

                4. _____

5. $9x^2 + 25$

                5. _____

6. $8x^3 - 125$

                6. _____

7. $x^2y^3 + x^2y^2 - 6x^2y - 6x^2$

                7. _____

8. $12x^2 + 4x - 5$

                8. _____

9. $x^4 - 625$

                9. _____

10. $x^3y + 2x^2y + xy$

                10. _____

11. $4x^3 - 8x$ 11. _____

12. $x^2 + 5x - 6$ 12. _____

13. $y^3 - 4y^2 - 25y + 100$ 13. _____

For problems 14 – 18, solve each quadratic equation.

14. $x^2 + 13x + 36 = 0$ 14. _____

15. $12x^2 - 11x = 5$ 15. _____

16. $9x^2 = 25$ 16. _____

17. $x(x - 4) = 12$ 17. _____

18. $(2x - 7)(x - 2) = 5$ 18. _____

19.   A ball falls off the top of a roof 320 feet above the   19. _____
      ground. The formula $h = -16t^2 + 16t + 320$ describes
      the height of the ball above the ground, h, in feet,
      t seconds after the fall begins. How long will it take
      the ball to strike the ground?

20.   The length of a rectangular garden is 6 feet greater than   20. _____
      the width. The area of the rectangle is 135 square feet. Find
      the length and the width.

Name _____   Date _____

Chapter 6
Form B

For problems 1 – 13, factor completely or state that the polynomial is prime.

1. $x^2 + 4x + 3$

1. _____

2. $x^3 + 5x^2 - 4x - 20$

2. _____

3. $6x^2 y + 2xy^2$

3. _____

4. $16x^2 - 48xy + 36y^2$

4. _____

5. $64x^3 - 27$

5. _____

6. $4x^2 + 9$

6. _____

7. $16x^2 + 22x - 3$

7. _____

8. $x^4 - 5x^3 - 14x^2$

8. _____

9. $49y^2 + 14y + 1$

9. _____

10. $y^3 + 4y^2 - 8y - 32$

10. _____

11. $5x^2 - 25x - 120$ 11. _____

12. $81x^4 - 16$ 12. _____

13. $18y^4 - 6y^3 - 40y^2$ 13. _____

For problems 14 – 18, solve each quadratic equation.

14. $x^2 - 8x + 16 = 0$ 14. _____

15. $2x(x + 5) = 100$ 15. _____

16. $25x^2 = 16$ 16. _____

17. $(4x + 1)(3x - 2) = 91$ 17. _____

18. $x^2 + 4x + 3 = 0$ 18. _____

19.   The length of a rectangle is 2 more than three times   19. _____
       the width. If the area of the rectangle is 161 square
       feet, find the length and the width.

20.   A water balloon is released from a window 96 feet   20. _____
       above the ground. The formula $h = -16t^2 + 16t + 96$
       describes the height of the water balloon above the
       ground, h, in feet, t seconds after the release. How
       long will it take the water balloon to strike the ground?

Chapter 6
Form C

For problems 1 – 13, factor completely or state that the polynomial is prime.

1. $x^3 - 9x$ 1. _____

2. $x^2 - 3x - 108$ 2. _____

3. $50x^4y + 40x^3y^2 + 8x^2y^3$ 3. _____

4. $3x^2y^3 - 21x^3y^4$ 4. _____

5. $2y^3 + y^2 - 18y - 9$ 5. _____

6. $25x^2 - 4$ 6. _____

7. $128x^4 - 162$ 7. _____

8. $32x^2 - 52x - 45$ 8. _____

9. $8x^3 - 125$ 9. _____

10. $9x^2 - 72x + 144$ 10. _____

11. $x^2 - 6x - 7$ 11. _____

12. $y^3 + 4y^2 - 5y - 20$ 12. _____

13. $49x^2 + 25$ 13. _____

For problems 14 – 18, solve each quadratic equation.

14. $4x^2 = 16$ 14. _____

15. $x^2 - 8x = 20$ 15. _____

16. $4x(x + 3) = -9$ 16. _____

17. $6x^2 + x - 2 = 0$ 17. _____

18. $(x + 5)(x - 4) = 10$ 18. _____

19.   A rock is thrown from the top of a building. The   19. _____
        formula $h = -16t^2 - 6t + 27$ describes the height
        of the rock, h, in feet, t seconds after the rock is
        thrown. How long after the rock is thrown does
        it hit the ground?

20.   The length of a rectangular garden is 4 feet greater than 20. _____
        the width. The area of the rectangle is 96 square feet. Find
        the length and width.

Name _____   Date _____

Chapter 6
Form D

Choose the correct answer to each problem.

For problems 1 – 13, factor completely or state that the polynomial is prime.

1. $x^2 - 2x - 35$
    a. $(x-7)(x+5)$ b. $(x+7)(x+5)$ c. $(x-7)(x-5)$ d. Prime

2. $2x^2 - 98$
    a. $2(x^2 - 49)$ b. $2(x+7)(x-7)$ c. $2(x-7)^2$ d. Prime

3. $27x^3 + 125$
    a. $(3x+5)^3$ b. $(3x+5)(9x^2 - 15x + 25)$
    c. $(3x+5)(9x^2 + 15x + 25)$ d. $(3x+5)(9x^2 - 30x + 25)$

4. $81x^2 - 72xy + 16y^2$
    a. $(9x-4y)^2$ b. $(9x-4y)(9x+4y)$ c. $(9x+4y)^2$ d. Prime

5. $18x^2 + 9x$
    a. $9(2x^2 + x)$ b. $x(18x+9)$ c. $9x(2x+1)$ d. $9x(2x)$

6. $6x^2 + 7x - 20$
    a. $(2x-10)(3x+2)$ b. $(2x+5)(3x-4)$ c. $(6x-4)(x+5)$ d. Prime

7. $4x^2 + 25$
    a. $(2x+5)^2$ b. $(2x+5)(2x-5)$ c. $(2x-5)^2$ d. Prime

8. $4x^2 y - 4xy - 120y$
    a. $4y(x^2 - x - 30)$ b. $4y(x+6)(x-5)$
    c. $4y(x-6)(x+5)$ d. Prime

9. $5x^2 + 3x - 2$
    a. $(5x-1)(x+2)$ b. $(5x+1)(x-2)$ c. $(5x-2)(x+1)$ d. Prime

10. $81x^4 - 16$
    a. $(9x^2 - 4)(9x^2 + 4)$ b. $(3x-2)^4$
    c. $(9x^2 + 4)(3x+2)(3x-2)$ d. $(3x+2)^2(3x-2)^2$

11. $y^3 + 3y^2 - 8y - 24$

    a. $y^2(y+3) - 8(y+3)$ b. $(y^2 - 8)(y+3)$

    c. $(y^2 - 8)(y+3)(y+3)$ d, $(y-4)(y-2)(y+3)$

12. $x^2 + 16x + 64$

    a. $(x+8)^2$ b. $(x-16)^2$ c. $(x-8)^2$ d. $(x+8)(x-8)$

13. $5x^4 - 35x^3 - 90x^2$

    a. $5x^2(x^2 - 7x - 18)$ b. $5x^2(x-6)(x-3)$

    c. $5x^2(x-9)(x+2)$ d. Prime

For problems 14 – 18, solve each quadratic equation.

14. $x^2 - 2x = 0$

    a. $\{0, -2\}$ b. $\{-2, 2\}$ c. $\{0, 2\}$ d. $\{-2, 1\}$

15. $x^2 - 3x - 10 = 0$

    a. $\{5, 2\}$ b. $\{5, -2\}$ c. $\{-5, 2\}$ d. $\{-5, -2\}$

16. $3x(3x + 4) = -4$

    a. $\left\{-\dfrac{3}{2}\right\}$ b. $\left\{-\dfrac{2}{3}\right\}$ c. $\left\{-\dfrac{4}{3}, -\dfrac{8}{3}\right\}$ d. $\left\{-\dfrac{4}{3}, 0\right\}$

17. $25x^2 = 16$

    a. $\left\{\dfrac{4}{5}\right\}$ b. $\left\{-\dfrac{4}{5}\right\}$ c. $\left\{-\dfrac{4}{5}, \dfrac{4}{5}\right\}$ d. $\left\{-\dfrac{16}{25}, \dfrac{16}{25}\right\}$

18. $2x^2 - x = 15$

    a. $\{15, 8\}$ b. $\{3, 5\}$ c. $\left\{-3, \dfrac{5}{2}\right\}$ d. $\left\{-\dfrac{5}{2}, 3\right\}$

19.   A rock is thrown from the top of a tall building. The vormula $h = -16t + 234$ describes the height of the rock, h, in feet, t seconds after the rock is thrown. How long after the rock is thrown does it hit the ground?

    a. $\dfrac{9}{4}$ sec   b. $\dfrac{13}{2}$ sec   c. $\dfrac{9}{2}$ sec   d. $\dfrac{3}{4}$ sec

20.   A rectangular parking lot has a length that is 4 yards greater than the width. The area of the parking lot is 140 square yards. Find the length and the width of the parking lot.

    a. width 10 yards; length 14 yards   b. width 8 yards; length 12 yards

    c. width 14 yards; length 18 yards   d. width 6 yards; length 10 yards

Name _____   Date _____

Chapter 6
Form E

Choose the correct answer to each problem.

For problems 1 – 13, factor completely or state that the polynomial is prime.

1. $x^2 + 24x + 144$
   a. $(x-12)^2$
   b. $(x-12)(x+12)$
   c. $(x+12)^2$
   d. Prime

2. $x^2 - 3x - 28$
   a. $(x-14)(x+2)$
   b. $(x+4)(x-7)$
   c. $(x-4)(x+7)$
   d. Prime

3. $8x^3 - 27$
   a. $(2x-3)^3$
   b. $(2x+3)(2x^2-9)$
   c. $(2x-3)(4x^2+6x+9)$
   d. $(2x-3)(4x^2-6x+9)$

4. $10x^2 - 2x - 12$
   a. $(5x-6)(x+1)$
   b. $(2x+3)(5x+4))$
   c. $(2x-3)(5x+4)$
   d. Prime

5. $36x^2 + 12xy + y^2$
   a. $(6x-y)^2$
   b. $(6x+y)^2$
   c. $(36x+y)(x+y)$
   d. $(18x+y)(2x+y)$

6. $x^2 - 9$
   a. $(x+3)^2$
   b. $(x-3)^2$
   c. $(x+3)(x-3)$
   d. Prime

7. $2x^3y - 30x^2y + 108xy$
   a. $2xy(x-9)(x-6)$
   b. $2x(x-9y)(x-6y)$
   c. $2xy(x+9)(x+6)$
   d. $2(x^2-9y)(x-6y)$

8. $8x^2y^2 - 24xy^3 + 18y^4$
   a. $2y^2(2x-3y)^2$
   b. $2y^2(2x-3y)(2x+3y)$
   c. $2xy(4x^2-12y+9y^2)$
   d. $2xy^2(4x-12y+9y^2)$

9. $y^3 + 4y^2 - 25y - 100$
   a. $y^2(y+4)-5(5y+20)$
   b. $(y+5)^2(y+4)$
   c. $(y+5)(y-5)(y+4)$
   d. $(y+4)^2(y-5)$

10. $64x^2y^2 - 16xy$
    a. $(8xy-4x)(8xy+4y)$
    b. $16xy(4xy-1)$
    c. $16xy(-4xy)$
    d. $(8xy-4x)^2$

T-129

11. $72x^2y - 150xy - 27y$
  a. $y(12x - 27)(6x + 1)$ b. $3y(6x - 1)(4x + 9)$
  c. $y(4x - 9)(18x + 3)$ d. $3y(6x + 1)(4x - 9)$

12. $81x^4 - 1$
  a. $(9x^2 + 1)(9x^2 - 1)$ b. $(3x - 1)^4$
  c. $(9x^2 + 1)(3x + 1)(3x - 1)$ d. Prime

13. $2y^3 + 3y^2 - 16y - 24$
  a. $(y^2 - 8)(2y + 3)$ b. $(y - 4)^2(2y + 3)$
  c. $y(2y^2 + 3y - 16) - 24$ d. Prime

For problems 14 – 18, solve each quadratic equation.

14. $x^2 + 4x - 21 = 0$
  a. $\{1, 121\}$ b. $\{1, -21\}$ c. $\{3, -7\}$ d. $\{7, -3\}$

15. $16x^2 = 81$
  a. $\left\{\dfrac{9}{4}\right\}$ b. $\left\{-\dfrac{9}{4}\right\}$ c. $\left\{-\dfrac{9}{4}, \dfrac{9}{4}\right\}$ d. $\left\{-\dfrac{4}{9}, \dfrac{4}{9}\right\}$

16. $4x^2 + 8x = 0$
  a. $\{-4, 2\}$ b. $\{0, -2\}$ c. $\left\{\dfrac{1}{4}, 2\right\}$ d. $\{0, 2\}$

17. $3x(x - 1) = 36$
  a. $\{4, 13\}$ b. $\{4, -3\}$ c. $\{4, 11\}$ d. $\{-4, 3\}$

18. $6x^2 + 13x = 28$
  a. $\left\{-\dfrac{7}{2}, \dfrac{4}{3}\right\}$ b. $\left\{\dfrac{5}{2}, 28\right\}$ c. $\left\{\dfrac{7}{2}, -\dfrac{4}{3}\right\}$ d. $\left\{-\dfrac{5}{2}, -28\right\}$

19. The product of two consecutive even integers is 224. Find the two integers.
  a. 14 and 16   b. 7 and 32   c. 8 and 28   d. 14 and 16
                                                                                                                   −16 and −14

20. The length of a rectangle is 5 less than 3 times the width. The area of the rectangle is 78 square inches. Find the length and the width.
  a. length 26 in; width 3 in   b. length 6 in; width 13 in
  c. length 13 in; width 6 in   d. length 3 in; width 26 in

Name _____ Date _____

Choose the correct answer to each problem.

For problems 1 – 13, factor completely or state that the polynomial is prime.

1. $x^2 - 7x - 30$
    a. $(x+10)(x-3)$ b. $(x-10)(x+3)$ c. $(x+6)(x-5)$ d. Prime

2. $16x^2 + 25$
    a. $(4x-5)^2$ b. $(4x-5)(4x+5)$ c. $(4x+5)^2$ d. Prime

3. $98x^2 - 224x + 128$
    a. $2(49x^2 - 112x + 64)$ b. $2(7x-8)^2$
    c. $2(7x+8)(7x-8)$ d. Prime

4. $15x^6 - 9x^5 + 12x^4 + 9x^3$
    a. $3x^5(5x-3)(4x+3)$ b. $3x^3(5x^3 - 3x^2 + 4x + 3)$
    c. $3x^3(5x^4 - 3x^3 + 4x^2 + 3x)$ d. $3x^3(5x-3)(4x+3)$

5. $12x^2 - 25xy + 12y^2$
    a. $(4x-3y)(3x-4y)$ b. $(4x+3y)(3x+4y)$
    c. $(4x-3y)^2$ d. Prime

6. $x^2 + 7x + 6$
    a. $(x+1)(x+6)$ b. $(x+1)(x+1)$ c. $(x+1)(7x+1)$ d. Prime

7. $8x^2y^2 - 18y^4$
    a. $2y^2(2x-3y)^2$ b. $2y^2(2x-3y)(2x+3y)$
    c. $2y^2(4x^2 - 12y + 9y^2)$ d. $2xy^2(4x - 12y + 9y^2)$

8. $8x^3 + 64$
    a. $(2x+4)^3$ b. $8(x+2)^3$
    c. $(2x+4)(4x^2 - 8x + 16)$ d. $8(x+2)(x^2 - 2x + 4)$

9. $2y^3 - 5y^2 - 12y + 30$
    a. $(y+3)(y-2)(2y-5)$ b. $(y-3)(y+2)(2y-5)$
    c. $(y^2 - 6)(2y-5)$ d. Prime

10. $x^2y^2 + 11x^2y + 24x^2$
    a. $x^2(y+3)(y+8)$ b. $x^2(y+6)(y+4)$
    c. $x^2(y+12)(y-2)$ d. Prime

11. $7x^2 - 21y^2$
    a. $7(x-y)^2$
    b. $7(x+3y)(x-y)$
    c. $7(x^2 - 3y^2)$
    d. Prime

12. $15x^2 + x - 6$
    a. $(5x+3)(3x-2)$
    b. $(5x-3)(3x+2)$
    c. $(5x+2)(3x-3)$
    d. Prime

13. $3x^2 - 18x - 48$
    a. $3(x^2 - 6x - 16)$
    b. $(3x+6)(x-8)$
    c. $3(x+8)(x-2)$
    d. $3(x-8)(x+2)$

For problems 14 – 18, solve each quadratic equation.

14. $x^2 = -10x$
    a. $\{10, 0\}$
    b. $\{0, 10\}$
    c. $\{10\}$
    d. No solution

15. $x^2 + 10x - 24 = 0$
    a. $\{4, 6\}$
    b. $\{-6, -4\}$
    c. $\{-2, 12\}$
    d. $\{-12, 2\}$

16. $25x^2 = 64$
    a. $\left\{\dfrac{8}{5}\right\}$
    b. $\left\{-\dfrac{5}{8}, \dfrac{8}{5}\right\}$
    c. $\left\{-\dfrac{8}{5}, \dfrac{8}{5}\right\}$
    d. No solution

17. $2x(4+7) = 30$
    a. $\left\{-3, \dfrac{5}{4}\right\}$
    b. $\left\{15, \dfrac{23}{4}\right\}$
    c. $\left\{3, -\dfrac{5}{4}\right\}$
    d. $\left\{-15, -\dfrac{23}{4}\right\}$

18. $4x^2 + 20x + 25 = 0$
    a. $\left\{\dfrac{5}{2}, \dfrac{5}{2}\right\}$
    b. $\left\{\dfrac{5}{2}\right\}$
    c. $\left\{0, \dfrac{5}{2}\right\}$
    d. $\left\{-\dfrac{5}{2}\right\}$

19. A rock is thrown from the top of a tall building. The formula $h = -16t - 2t + 524$ describes the height of the rock, h, in feet, t seconds after the rock it thrown. How long after the rock is thrown is it 321 feet above the ground?
    a. $\dfrac{29}{8}$ sec
    b. $\dfrac{7}{2}$ sec
    c. $\dfrac{37}{8}$ sec
    d. $\dfrac{9}{2}$ sec

20. A rectangular parking lot has a length twice as long as the width. The area of the parking lot is 288 square yards. Find the length and the width of the parking lot.
    a. width 10 yards; length 24 yards
    b. width 11 yards; length 22 yards
    c. width 12 yards; length 24 yards
    d. width 13 yards; length 26 yards

Name _____   Date _____

Cumulative Review 1 – 6
Form A

For problems 1 – 8, perform the indicated operations.

1. $7[x - 2(4 + 3x)]$

    1. _____

2. $\dfrac{14 - 2(8 - 3^2)}{6}$

    2. _____

3. $\dfrac{(2x)^3 (3x^{-4})^2}{4x^3}$

    3. _____

4. $7x^3 - 2x^2 + 5x - (4x^3 - 3x^2 + 6x)$

    4. _____ .

5. $\dfrac{4x^6 - 8x^4 + 6x}{2x}$

    5. _____

6. $\dfrac{x^3 + 125}{x + 5}$

    6. _____

7. $2xy(6x^2 - 4x - 3y^2)$

    7. _____

8. $(7x + 2y)^2$

    8. _____

For problems 9 – 10, solve each equation.

9. $\dfrac{x + 3}{6} = \dfrac{x - 2}{12}$

    9. _____

10. $5(x - 4) = 9 - 5(x + 2)$

    10. _____

11. Solve $2(x - 4) < 3x + 8$ and express the solution
    in set-builder notation.

    11. _____

For problems 9 – 10, solve each system by the method of your choice.

12. $2x - 4y = 6$
    $4x + y = 21$

    12. _____

13. $6x + 3y = 9$
    $y = -2x + 2$

    13. _____

Name _____   Date _____

For problems 14 – 17, solve the system by graphing.

14. $5x + 10y = 15$
         $-x + 2y = 5$

14.

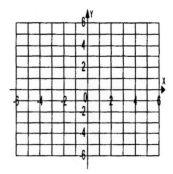

15. $3x + 6y = 6$
         $x + 2y = 2$

15.

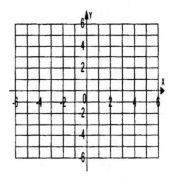

16. $7x + 14y = 28$
         $-x + y = -1$

16.

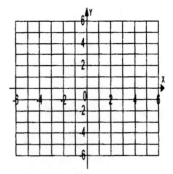

17. $x = 3$
       $y = -1$

17.

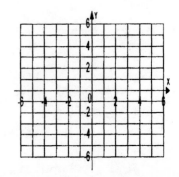

Name _____   Date _____

18.   Find the slope of $3x - 4y = 12$.   18. _____

19.   Find the y – intercept of $6x - 8y = 24$.   19. _____

20.   Find the slope of the line passing through the   20. _____
        points (3, 7) and (–5, 7).

21.   Find the equation of the line with the slope of –2   21. _____
        passing through the point (4, –1). Write the equation
        in point-slope form.

22.   Find the interest earned at the end of the first year   22. _____
        by depositing $4750 in an account that pays 5.2%
        interest.

23.   One bolt of material holds 20 yards of material   23. _____
        and makes 10 dresses. How many bolts are necessary
        to make 40 dresses?

24.   Find the volume of a cone with diameter 4 feet   24. _____
        and height 12 feet. Express the answer in terms
        of π.

25.   The sum of a first and second number is 42. The   25. _____
        difference between the first and second number
        is 24. Find the two numbers.

Name _____   Date _____

Cumulative Review 1 – 6
Form B

Choose the correct answer.

For problems 1 – 8, perform the indicated operations.

1. $12x - 4[2x - (4 + 3x)]$

    a. $16x + 16$ b. $12x - 4$ c. $4x + 28$ d. $16x - 16$

2. $\dfrac{18 - 5(5 - 2)^2}{3^2 - 10}$

    a. -117 b. $\dfrac{9}{2}$ c. 27 d. $-\dfrac{13}{10}$

3. $\dfrac{(5x^2)^3(2x)^4}{25x^{-4}}$

    a. $5x^{14}$ b. $5x^{10}$ c. $80x^{10}$ d. $80x^{14}$

4. $16x^5 - 4x^3 + 7x - (3x^5 + 7x^3 - 7x)$

    a. $13x^5 - 11x^3$ b. $13x^5 - 11x^3 + 14x$

    c. $13x^5 + 3x^3$ d. $19x^5 + 3x^3$

5. Divide $\dfrac{x^3 + 8}{x + 2}$

    a. $x^2 + 4$ b. $x^2 + 2x + 4$ c. $(x + 2)^2$ d. $x^2 - 2x + 4$

6. $4^{-1} + 5^{-1}$

    a. $\dfrac{9}{20}$ b. 9^{-1} c. $\dfrac{1}{9}$ d. $\dfrac{2}{9}$

7. $-4x^3(3x^3 + 5x^2 - 3x)$

    a. $-12x^9 - 20x^6 + 12x^3$ b. $-12x^6 - 20x^5 + 12x^4$

    c. $-12x^6 + 20x^5 - 12x^4$ d. $-12x^9 - 20x^6 - 12x^3$

8. $(6x + 2y)(6x - 2y)$

    a. $36x^2 - 4y^2$ b. $36x^2 - 24xy + 4y^2$

    c. $36x^2 + 4y^2$ d. $36x^2 + 24xy + 4y^2$

For problems 9 – 10, solve each equation.

9. $4x - 3(4 - x) = 6 - 3(x + 2)$

    a. $\dfrac{6}{5}$ b. -3 c. 3 d. 6

10. $\dfrac{2x+1}{5} - \dfrac{x}{10} = 5$

    a. 4   b. 49   c. 1   d. 16

11. Solve $5x + 6 < 7x + 4$ and express the solution in set-builder notation.

    a. $\{x \mid x < 1\}$ b. $\{x \mid x > 1\}$ c. $\{x \mid x > -1\}$ d. $\{x \mid x < -1\}$

For problems 12 – 13, solve each system by the method of your choice.

12. $5x + 10y = 20$
    $x + 2y = 4$

    a. $(2, 1)$ b. $(0, 2)$ c. Infinite solutions   d. No solution

13. $8x + 4y = 4$
    $y = -x - 4$

    a. $(5, -9)$ b. $(-3, 5)$ c. Infinite solutions   d. No solution

For problems 14 – 15, solve the system by graphing.

14. $-3x + 6y = 9$
    $-x - y = 1$

a.
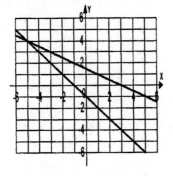

$(-5, 4)$

b.
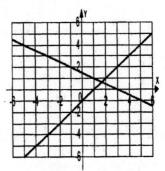

$\left(\dfrac{5}{3}, \dfrac{2}{3}\right)$

c.
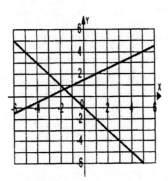

$\left(-\dfrac{5}{3}, \dfrac{2}{3}\right)$

d.
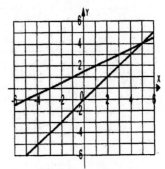

$(5, 4)$

15. $-2x + y = 3$
        $y = 2$

a.

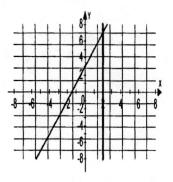

$(2, 7)$

b.

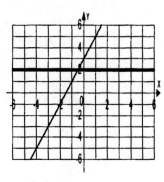

$\left(-\dfrac{1}{2},\ 2\right)$

c.

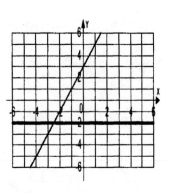

$\left(-\dfrac{5}{2},\ -2\right)$

d.

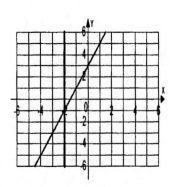

$(-2, -1)$

For problems 16 – 17, graph the solution for the system of linear inequalities.

16. $6x - 4y = -12$
        $x + y = 2$

a.

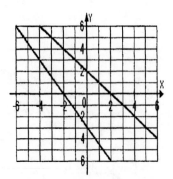

b.

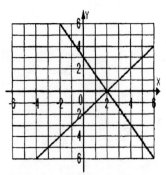

c.

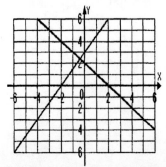

d.

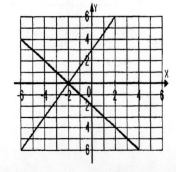

17. $x \geq -2$
     $y \leq 5$

a.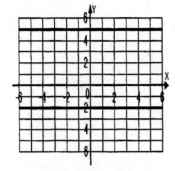

b.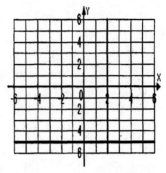

c.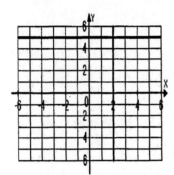

d.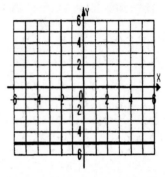

18. Find the slope and y- intercept of $4x - y = 12$.

   a. slope: 4
      y-intercept: $(0, -12)$

   b. slope: -4
      y-intercept: $(-12, 0)$

   c. slope: -4
      y-intercept: $(0, -12)$

   d. slope: 4
      y-intercept: $(-12, 0)$

19. Find the x- intercept and y-intercept of $3x + 9y = 18$.

   a. x–intercept: $(2, 0)$
      y–intercept: $(0, 6)$

   b. x–intercept: $(6, 0)$
      y–intercept: $(0, 2)$

   c. x–intercept: $(0, 6)$
      y–intercept: $(2, 0)$

   b. x–intercept: $(0, 2)$
      y–intercept: $(6, 0)$

20. Find the slope of the line passing through $(-7, 4)$ and $(4, -2)$.

   a. $-\dfrac{2}{3}$ b. $-\dfrac{6}{11}$ c. 0   d. Undefined

21. Find the equation of the line passing through (–1, –4) and (0, –6). Write the equation in slope-intercept form.

   a. $y = 10x + 6$ b. $y = 10x - 6$ c. $y = -2x - 6$ d. $y = -2x + 6$

22. Train A leaves a station traveling at 50 mph. Four hours later, train B leaves the same station traveling at 60 mph in the same direction as train A. How long does it take for train B to catch up to train A?

   a. 24 hours   b. 20 hours   c. 30 hours   d. 22 hours

23. The outside dimensions of a picture frame are 39 inches by 29 inches. If its inside dimensions are 32 inches by 20 inches, find the area of the frame.

   a. 640 in^2 b. 491 in^2 c. 120.67 in^2 d. 416 in^2

24. If you pay 32% of your income in taxes and your income after taxes is $23,256. What is your gross (before taxes) income?

   a. $10,944   b. $7441.92   c. $15,814.08   d. $34,200

25. A person invests $7500, part at 5% and the remainder at 4% simple interest. If the total interest at the end of the first year was $346.50, find the amount invested at 4%.

   a. $2850   b. $4650   c. $114   d. $232.50

Chapter 7
Form A

For problems 1 – 2, find all numbers for which each rational expression in undefined. If the rational expression is defined for all real numbers, so state.

1. $\dfrac{x+1}{x+5}$

1. _____

2. $\dfrac{3x}{x^2+6x+5}$

2. _____

For problems 3 – 5, simplify each rational expression. If the rational expression cannot be simplified, so state.

3. $\dfrac{40x^5}{15x^2}$

3. _____

4. $\dfrac{x^2-1}{x^2-4x-5}$

4. _____

5. $\dfrac{4x^2-y^2}{y-2x}$

5. _____

For problems 6 – 12, perform the indicated operations. Simplify the result, if possible.

6. $\dfrac{x+4}{2x} \cdot \dfrac{6x^2}{x^2-16}$

6. _____

7. $\dfrac{y^2-4y+3}{y^2-9} \cdot \dfrac{4y+12}{y^2-2y+1}$

7. _____

8. $\dfrac{x+2}{x^2-1} \div \dfrac{x^2+4x+4}{x^2-3x+2}$

8. _____

9. $\dfrac{x^2+x}{x^2-6x+8} \div \dfrac{x^2+3x+2}{2x^2-7x+6}$

9. _____

10. $\dfrac{7x+4}{2x-1} - \dfrac{5x+3}{2x-1}$

10. _____

11. $\dfrac{4}{y-5} + \dfrac{2}{y}$

11. _____

12. $\dfrac{3}{x^2 - 5x + 6} - \dfrac{2}{x^2 - 9}$ 12._____

For problems 13 – 14, simplify each complex rational expression.

13. $\dfrac{\dfrac{1}{x} - \dfrac{1}{y}}{\dfrac{1}{x}}$ 13._____

14. $\dfrac{2 + \dfrac{4}{x}}{1 - \dfrac{4}{x^2}}$ 14._____

For problems 15 – 16, solve each rational equation. If an equation has no solution, so state.

15. $\dfrac{2}{3x} + \dfrac{1}{x} = \dfrac{1}{6}$ 15._____

16. $\dfrac{1}{x + 4} - \dfrac{1}{x - 2} = \dfrac{x + 2}{x^2 + 2x - 8}$ 16._____

17. Solve for s: $R = \dfrac{as}{a + s}$ 17._____

18. The formula for the total resistance, R, in a parallel circuit   18._____
     is $\dfrac{1}{R} = \dfrac{1}{r_1} + \dfrac{1}{r_2}$ where r_1 is the resistance of the first resistor
     and r_2 is the resistance of the second resistor in ohms. If r_1
     is 5 ohms and r_2 is 10 ohms, what is the total resistance, R,
     of the parallel circuit?

19. A boat travels 30 miles upstream against the current in the   19._____
     same amount of time it takes to travel 42 miles downstream
     with the current. If the rate of the current is 4 mph, what is the
     rate of the boat in still water?

20. The intensity of a light source varies inversely with the square   20._____
     of the distance from the source. The intensity is 8 foot-candles
     at a distance of 2 feet. At what distance is the intensity 2 foot-
     candles?

Chapter 7
Form B

For problems 1 – 2, find all numbers for which each rational expression in undefined. If the rational expression is defined for all real numbers, so state.

1. $\dfrac{5}{x^2 + 9}$

1. _____

2. $\dfrac{x+2}{x^2 - 16}$

2. _____

For problems 3 – 5, simplify each rational expression. If the rational expression cannot be simplified, so state.

3. $\dfrac{9x^5}{3x^9}$

3. _____

4. $\dfrac{x-2}{x^3 - 8}$

4. _____

5. $\dfrac{6x - 3y}{y - 2x}$

5. _____

For problems 6 – 12, perform the indicated operations. Simplify the result, if possible.

6. $\dfrac{8x^3}{x+2} \cdot \dfrac{x^2 - 4x - 12}{16x^2}$

6. _____

7. $\dfrac{2y^2 + 9y + 10}{y^2 - 4} \cdot \dfrac{y+2}{y^2 + 4y + 4}$

7. _____

8. $\dfrac{9x^2 - 18x}{x^2 + 5x - 14} \div \dfrac{x^2}{3x + 21}$

8. _____

9. $\dfrac{x^2 + 4x - 5}{3x^2 + x - 4} \div \dfrac{2x^2 + 11x - 6}{6x^2 + 5x - 4}$

9. _____

10. $\dfrac{2x - 1}{4x - 5} - \dfrac{4 - 2x}{4x - 5}$

10. _____

11. $\dfrac{y-1}{y+4} + \dfrac{3 - 2y}{2y}$

11. _____

12. $\dfrac{2x-1}{x^2+x-6} - \dfrac{x+2}{x^2+5x+6}$ 12. _____

For problems 13 – 14, simplify each complex rational expression.

13. $\dfrac{\dfrac{3}{x^2} - \dfrac{2}{x}}{\dfrac{1}{4x}}$ 13. _____

14. $\dfrac{x - \dfrac{1}{y}}{y + \dfrac{1}{x}}$ 14. _____

For problems 15 – 16, solve each rational equation. If an equation has no solution, so state.

15. $\dfrac{2}{y} + \dfrac{1}{2y} = \dfrac{1}{4}$ 15. _____

16. $\dfrac{4}{x+3} + \dfrac{2}{x-3} - \dfrac{6}{x^2-9}$ 16. _____

17. Solve for p: $\dfrac{1}{p} + \dfrac{1}{q} = \dfrac{1}{f}$ 17. _____

18. Shara can mow a lawn in 4 hours while Megan can mow   18. _____
     the same lawn in 5 hours. How long will it take to mow the
     if they work together?

19. A train can travel 280 miles in the same time that it takes a car   19. _____
     to travel 140 miles. If the train's rate is 40 miles per hour
     faster than the car's, find the average rate for each.

20. The resistance in an electric circuit varies inversely with   20. _____
     the current. If the resistance is 12 ohms when the current
     is 5 amps, what is the resistance when the current is 8 amps?

Name _____   Date _____

Chapter 7
Form C

For problems 1 – 2, find all numbers for which each rational expression in undefined. If the rational expression is defined for all real numbers, so state.

1. $\dfrac{x+5}{x-6}$

1. _____

2. $\dfrac{2x}{x^2-4}$

2. _____

For problems 3 – 5, simplify each rational expression. If the rational expression cannot be simplified, so state.

3. $\dfrac{54x^4}{18x^7}$

3. _____

4. $\dfrac{x+1}{x^2+4x+3}$

4. _____

5. $\dfrac{x^2-y^2}{4y-4x}$

5. _____

For problems 6 – 12, perform the indicated operations. Simplify the result, if possible.

6. $\dfrac{2x}{x^3-2x^2}\cdot\dfrac{x^2-3x+2}{2x-2}$

6. _____

7. $\dfrac{x+5}{x^2-25}\div\dfrac{x^2+6x+9}{x^2-2x-15}$

7. _____

8. $\dfrac{x^2+6x+5}{x^2-3x-18}\div\dfrac{x^2+6x+5}{x^2-4x-21}$

8. _____

9. $\dfrac{4x-4y}{2x^2+xy-y^2}\cdot\dfrac{16x-8y}{x^2-y^2}$

9. _____

10. $\dfrac{2x+7}{x+4}-\dfrac{x+3}{x+4}$

10. _____

11. $\dfrac{x}{x-5}+\dfrac{3}{x}$

11. _____

12. $\dfrac{x}{2x^2+2x}+\dfrac{1}{x^2-1}$

12. _____

For problems 13 – 14, simplify each complex rational expression.

13. $\dfrac{\dfrac{1}{y}+\dfrac{1}{3}}{\dfrac{1}{2}-\dfrac{1}{3}}$

13. _____

14. $\dfrac{2-\dfrac{1}{x}}{8-\dfrac{2}{x^2}}$

14. _____

For problems 15 – 16, solve each rational equation. If an equation has no solution, so state.

15. $\dfrac{x}{5}=\dfrac{5}{x}$

15. _____

16. $\dfrac{2y}{y-4}-\dfrac{10}{3}=\dfrac{8}{y-4}$

16. _____

17. Solve for E: $I=\dfrac{E}{R+r}$

17. _____

18. Three young people are going door to door shoveling the snow off sidewalks. Jesse can clear your sidewalks in 4 hours, Kendra can clear your sidewalks in 6 hours and Joe can clear your sidewalks in 3 hours. If you hire all three to clear your sidewalks, how long will it take?

18. _____

19. A plane travels 600 miles with the wind, in the same amount of time it takes to travel 500 miles against the wind. If the wind is blowing at a rate of 40 miles per hour, find the rate of the airplane in still air.

19. _____

20. The volume of a gas in a container at a constant pressure varies directly as the temperature. If the volume is 30 cubic centimeters at a temperature of 80° F, find the volume when the temperature is 96° F.

20. _____

Chapter 7
Form D

Choose the correct answer for each problem.

For problems 1 – 2, find all numbers for which each rational expression in undefined. If the rational expression is defined for all real numbers, so state.

1. $\dfrac{x^2 - x - 20}{x^2 - 14x + 48}$

    a. $-4, 5$ b. $6, 8$
    c. $-5, 4$ d. Defined for all real numbers

2. $\dfrac{x}{x + 2}$

    a. 0 b. -2
    c. -4 d. Defined for all real numbers

For problems 3 – 5, simplify each rational expression. If the rational expression cannot be simplified, so state.

3. $\dfrac{4x^7 y^5}{8x^2}$

    a. $2xy^5$ b. $\dfrac{xy^5}{2}$

    c. $\dfrac{x^5 y^5}{2}$ d. Cannot be simplified

4. $\dfrac{x^2 + 2x - 15}{x^2 - 25}$

    a. $\dfrac{x + 3}{x + 5}$ b. $\dfrac{x - 3}{x - 5}$

    c. $\dfrac{3}{5}$ d. Cannot be simplified

5. $\dfrac{x^2 - y^2}{2y - 2x}$

    a. $-\dfrac{x + y}{2}$ b. $\dfrac{x + y}{2}$

    c. $\dfrac{x - y}{2}$ d. Cannot be simplified

Name _____   Date _____

For problems 6 – 12, perform the indicated operations. Simplify the result, if possible.

6. $\dfrac{15x}{5x+5} \cdot \dfrac{x^2+3x+2}{x^2+2x}$

    a. $\dfrac{3(3x+2)}{5(2x)}$ b. $\dfrac{3x(x+2)}{x^2+2x}$ c. $\dfrac{3(x+2)}{5}$ d. 3

7. $\dfrac{x^2-y^2}{2x+2y} \cdot \dfrac{2x+16y}{x^2+7xy-8y^2}$

    a. 4   b. –1   c. 1   d. 2

8. $\dfrac{y^2+12y+35}{y^2+9y+20} \div \dfrac{y^2-49}{y^2+7y+12}$

    a. $\dfrac{y+3}{y-7}$ b. $\dfrac{y-7}{y+3}$

    c. $\dfrac{(y+7)^2(y-7)}{(y+4)^2(y+3)}$ d. $\dfrac{(y+4)^2(y+3)}{(y+7)^2(y-7)}$

9. $\dfrac{x^2-13x+12}{x^2-4x-12} \div \dfrac{x^2-6x-72}{x^2-7x+6}$

    a. $\dfrac{13}{2}$ b. $\dfrac{(x+6)(x-1)}{x+2}$ c. $\dfrac{2}{13}$ d. $\dfrac{(x-1)^2}{(x+2)(x+6)}$

10. $\dfrac{y^2}{y-4} - \dfrac{8y-16}{y-4}$

    a. $y+4$ b. $\dfrac{y^2-8y-16}{y-4}$

    c. $y-4$ d. Cannot be simplified

11. $\dfrac{-4}{x^2-2x-15} - \dfrac{2}{x-5}$

    a. $\dfrac{-2(x-1)}{(x-5)(x+3)}$ b. $\dfrac{-6}{x-5}$

    c. $\dfrac{-2(x+5)}{(x-5)(x+3)}$ d. $\dfrac{-6x-18}{(x-5)(x+3)}$

12. $\dfrac{2}{x+4} + \dfrac{4}{x-4}$

    a. $\dfrac{6}{2x}$ b. $\dfrac{2(3x+4)}{(x+4)(x-4)}$ c. $\dfrac{3}{x}$ d. $\dfrac{6x}{x(x-4)}$

For problems 13 – 14, simplify each complex rational expression.

13. $\dfrac{\dfrac{1}{x} - \dfrac{1}{x^2}}{\dfrac{1}{x}}$

   a. $\dfrac{x-1}{x}$ b. 1   c. 2   d. $\dfrac{x^2-1}{x}$

14. $\dfrac{2 + \dfrac{1}{x}}{3 - \dfrac{1}{y}}$

   a. $\dfrac{2x+1}{3y-1}$ b. $\dfrac{y(2x+1)}{x(3y-1)}$

   c. $\dfrac{2x}{3y}$ d. Cannot be simplified

For problems 15 – 16, solve each rational equation. If an equation has no solution, so state.

15. $\dfrac{6}{x} = \dfrac{x}{6}$

   a. $\{6\}$ b. $\{1\}$ c. $\{-6, 6\}$ d. No solution

16. $\dfrac{1}{x} - \dfrac{1}{x-1} = \dfrac{x-5}{3x}$

   a. $\{2, 4\}$ b. $\{-4, -2\}$ c. $\{4\}$ d. No solution

17. Solve for z: $\dfrac{1}{x} + \dfrac{1}{y} = \dfrac{1}{z}$

   a. $z = xy - y - x$ b. $z = \dfrac{y+x}{xy}$ c. $z = \dfrac{xy}{yx}$ d. $z = xy$

18. A tank can be filled by one pipe in 8 hours and by a second pipe in 10 hours. How long will it take to fill the tank using both pipes?

   a. 18 hours   b. $\dfrac{40}{9}$ hours   c. 9 hours   d. 2 hours

19. In still water, a boat averages 35 miles per hour. It takes the boat the same amount of time to travel 42 miles downstream, with the current, as 14 miles upstream, against the current. What is the rate of the water's current?
   a. 21 mph   b. 70 mph   c. 14 mph   d. 17.5 mph

20. A building casts a shadow 10 feet long. At the same time, a person 6 feet tall casts a shadow of 1.5 feet long. How tall is the building?

   a. 40 ft.   b. $\dfrac{5}{2}$ feet   c. 60 ft.   d. 90 ft.

Name _____   Date _____

Chapter 7
Form E

Choose the correct answer for each problem.

For problems 1 – 2, find all numbers for which each rational expression in undefined. If the rational expression is defined for all real numbers, so state.

1. $\dfrac{x^2 - 4}{x^2 - 7x + 6}$

    a. $-6, -1$ b. $1, 6$

    c. $-2, 2$ d. Defined for all real numbers

2. $\dfrac{x + 5}{x + 9}$

    a. -5 b. -3

    c. -9 d. Defined for all real numbers

For problems 3 – 5, simplify each rational expression. If the rational expression cannot be simplified, so state.

3. $\dfrac{24x^2 y}{10x^3}$

    a. $\dfrac{14y}{x}$ b. $\dfrac{12y}{5x}$

    c. $\dfrac{12xy}{5}$ d. Cannot be simplified

4. $\dfrac{x^2 - 7x - 18}{x^2 + 12x + 20}$

    a. $\dfrac{x - 9}{x + 10}$ b. $\dfrac{x + 9}{x - 10}$

    c. $-\dfrac{9}{10}$ d. Cannot be simplified

5. $\dfrac{9y^2 - 9x^2}{x^2 - 3xy + 2y^2}$

    a. $\dfrac{9(x + y)}{x - 2y}$ b. $-\dfrac{9(x + y)}{x - 2y}$

    c. $-\dfrac{9(x - y)}{x - 2y}$ d. Cannot be simplified

Name _____   Date _____

For problems 6 – 12, perform the indicated operations. Simplify the result, if possible.

6. $\dfrac{18x-18}{x+2} \cdot \dfrac{x^2+3x+2}{x^2-1}$

    a. 18   b. 9   c. $18(x+1)$ d. $\dfrac{9}{x-1}$

7. $\dfrac{5x-5y}{x^2-y^2} \cdot \dfrac{x^2-xy-2y^2}{x^2+3xy-10y^2}$

    a. $\dfrac{5(x+2y)}{(x-2y)(x-5y)}$ b. $\dfrac{5(x-2y)}{(x+2y)(x+5y)}$ c. $\dfrac{1}{x+y}$ d. $\dfrac{5}{x+5y}$

8. $\dfrac{x^2+4}{x+2} \div \dfrac{x^4-16}{x^2+4x+4}$

    a. $\dfrac{x^3-8}{4x}$ b. $x-2$ c. $\dfrac{1}{x-2}$ d. x^3-8

9. $\dfrac{y^2-11y+24}{y^2+2y-35} \div \dfrac{y^2-6y-16}{y^2+9y+14}$

    a. $\dfrac{3(y-8)^2}{5(y+7)^2}$ b. $\dfrac{y-3}{y-5}$ c. $\dfrac{3}{5}$ d. $\dfrac{(y-8)^2(y-3)}{(y+7)^2(y-5)}$

10. $\dfrac{x^2}{x-5} - \dfrac{10x-25}{x-5}$

    a. $\dfrac{x^2-10x-25}{x-5}$ b. $x-5$

    c. $\dfrac{x^2-10x-25}{-10}$ d. Cannot be simplified

11. $\dfrac{4}{y-4} + \dfrac{10}{y}$

    a. $\dfrac{14y-40}{y(y-4)}$ b. $\dfrac{10}{y-4}$ c. $\dfrac{14}{2y-4}$ d. $\dfrac{7}{y-2}$

12. $\dfrac{x}{x-4} + \dfrac{3}{x-2}$

    a. $-\dfrac{3}{2}$ b. $\dfrac{x-3}{x-2}$ c. $\dfrac{(x+4)(x-3)}{(x-4)(x-2)}$ d. $\dfrac{3}{2}$

Name _____   Date _____

For problems 13 – 14, simplify each complex rational expression.

13. $\dfrac{\dfrac{1}{y^2} - 4}{\dfrac{1}{y} + 2}$

    a. $\dfrac{1 - 4y^2}{1 + 2y}$ b. $\dfrac{1 - 4y^2}{y(1 + 2y)}$ c. $-2y$ d. $\dfrac{1 - 2y}{y}$

14. $\dfrac{5 + \dfrac{1}{x-1}}{4 - \dfrac{1}{x-1}}$

    a. $\dfrac{5x - 4}{4x - 5}$ b. $\dfrac{5}{4}$ c. 1 d. $\dfrac{5x - 5}{4x - 4}$

For problems 15 – 16, solve each rational equation. If an equation has no solution, so state.

15. $\dfrac{4}{x} = \dfrac{x}{4}$

    a. $\{4\}$ b. $\{-4, 4\}$ c. $\{16\}$ d. $\{-16, 16\}$

16. $\dfrac{1}{x-1} - \dfrac{1}{x} = \dfrac{1}{6x}$

    a. $\{-7\}$ b. $\{7\}$ c. $\{-5\}$ d. No solution

17.   Solve for h: $A = \dfrac{(b_1 + b_2)h}{2}$

    a. $h = \dfrac{2A}{b_1 + b_2}$ b. $h = 2A - b_1 + b_2$ c. $h = 2A - b_1 - b_2$ d. $h = \dfrac{A}{b_1 + b_2}$

18.   Car A travels 90 miles in the same time that Car B, traveling 20 miles an hour slower, travels 60 miles. What is the rate of each car?
    a. Car A 60 mph; Car B 40 mph   b. Car A 40 mph; Car B 60 mph
    c. Car A 10 mph; Car B 30 mph   d. Car A 30 mph; Car B 10 mph

19.   A teacher can grade 4 sets of homework in 2 hours. Another teacher can grade the same four sets of homework in 3 hours. How many hours would it take them to grade homework if they worked together?

    a. 2.5 hours   b. $\dfrac{5}{6}$ hours   c. $\dfrac{6}{5}$ hours   d. 5 hours

20.   The waiting time for a doctor's appointment varies directly as the number of people in the waiting room. If you must wait 45 minutes when there are 5 people seated in the waiting room, how long will you wait when there are 7 people seated?

    a. 30 min.   b. 60 min.   c. $\dfrac{294}{5}$ min.   d. 63 min.

Name _____   Date _____

Chapter 7
Form F

Choose the correct answer for each problem.

For problems 1 – 2, find all numbers for which each rational expression in undefined. If the rational expression is defined for all real numbers, so state.

1. $\dfrac{x^2 - 10x + 24}{x^2 - 3x - 54}$

     a. –6, 9   b. 4, 6

     c. –6, –4   d. Defined for all real numbers

2. $\dfrac{x}{x^2 - 9}$

     a. –3, 3   b. –3

     c. 0   d. Defined for all real numbers

For problems 3 – 5, simplify each rational expression. If the rational expression cannot be simplified, so state.

3. $\dfrac{4x^2 y^3}{2xy^2}$

     a. $2xy$ b. $\dfrac{x^3 y^5}{2}$ c. $\dfrac{xy}{2}$ d. $2x^3 y^5$

4. $\dfrac{x^2 - 4x - 32}{x^2 - 64}$

     a. $2x$ b. $\dfrac{1}{2}$ c. $\dfrac{x+1}{x+2}$ d. $\dfrac{x+4}{x+8}$

5. $\dfrac{x+2}{x^3 + 8}$

     a. $\dfrac{1}{x^2 - 2x + 4}$ b. $\dfrac{1}{x^2 + 4}$

     c. $\dfrac{1}{4}$ d. Cannot be simplified

For problems 6 – 12, perform the indicated operations. Simplify the result, if possible.

6. $\dfrac{x^2 + 5x + 6}{2x^2 + 15x - 8} \cdot \dfrac{2x^2 + 3x - 2}{x^2 + 11x + 24}$

     a. 1   b. $\dfrac{1}{16}$ c. $\dfrac{1}{4}$ d. $\dfrac{(x+2)^2}{(x+8)^2}$

7. $\dfrac{x^2}{x+6} - \dfrac{2x+48}{x+6}$

     a. $x-5$ b. $x-8$ c. $\dfrac{x^2-2x+48}{x+6}$ d. $x+8$

8. $\dfrac{x^2+16}{x^2-16} \div \dfrac{x+4}{x^2+2x-8}$

     a. $-(x-2)$ b. $\dfrac{(x^2+16)(x-2)}{(x-4)(x+4)}$

     c. $x-2$ d. $\dfrac{x^2+16}{(x-4)(x+4)(x-2)}$

9. $2 + \dfrac{2}{x-2}$

     a. $\dfrac{2x-2}{x-2}$ b. 2 c. 3 d. 1

10. $\dfrac{8}{x+9} + \dfrac{5}{x-9}$

     a. $\dfrac{13}{(x+9)(x-9)}$ b. $\dfrac{13}{x+9}$

     c. $\dfrac{13x-27}{(x+9)(x-9)}$ d. $\dfrac{1}{x+3}$

11. $\dfrac{y^2-4y+3}{y^2+3y-18} \div \dfrac{y^2-1}{y^2+10y+24}$

     a. $\dfrac{(y+6)^2(y+4)}{(y-1)^2(y+1)}$ b. $\dfrac{(y-1)^2(y+1)}{(y+6)^2(y+4)}$ c. $\dfrac{y+1}{y+4}$ d. $\dfrac{y+4}{y+1}$

12. $\dfrac{3x^2+14x+15}{x^2-6x+9} \cdot \dfrac{x^2-3x}{25-9x^2}$

     a. $\dfrac{x}{(5-3x)(x-3)}$ b. $\dfrac{x(x-3)}{(5-3x)(x+3)}$

     c. $\dfrac{(x-3)(x+3)}{(5-3x)(x-3)}$ d. $\dfrac{x(x+3)}{(x-3)(5-3x)}$

For problems 13 – 14, simplify each complex rational expression.

13. $\dfrac{1-\dfrac{1}{x}}{1-\dfrac{1}{x^2}}$

     a. $x+1$ b. -1 c. $\dfrac{x}{x+1}$ d. $-\dfrac{1}{x}$

14.
$$\dfrac{\dfrac{1}{x} - \dfrac{1}{y}}{\dfrac{1}{x} + \dfrac{1}{y}}$$

   a. -1 b. $\dfrac{y + x}{y - x}$ c. $\dfrac{y - x}{y + x}$ d. 1

For problems 15 – 16, solve each rational equation. If an equation has no solution, so state.

15. $\dfrac{x}{x^2 - 36} - \dfrac{6}{x - 6} = \dfrac{1}{x + 6}$

   a. $\{6\}$ b. $\{-6\}$ c. $\{-5\}$ d. $\{5\}$

16. $\dfrac{4}{x - 2} = \dfrac{x}{12}$

   a. $\{-1, 3\}$ b. $\{-6, 8\}$ c. $\{2\}$ d. No solution

17.   Solve for h: $V = \pi r^2 h$

   a. $h = V - \pi r^2$ b. $h = \dfrac{V}{r^2}$ c. $h = V\pi r^2$ d. $h = \dfrac{V}{\pi r^2}$

18.   In still water, a boat averages 20 miles per hour. It takes the boat the same amount of time to travel 50 miles downstream, with the current, as 30 miles upstream, against the current. What is the rate of the water's current?

   a. 8 mph   b. 10 mph   c. 20 mph   d. 5 mph

19.   The hot water faucet can fill a tub in 10 minutes and the cold water faucet can fill the same tub in 8 minutes. If the tub is empty, how long will it take to fill it using both the hot and cold water faucets?

   a. 6 min.   b. 9 min.   c. $\dfrac{40}{9}$ min.   d. 18 min.

20.   The triangles in the figure are similar. Find the length of the side marked with an x.

   a. $\dfrac{25}{4}$ b. 3   c. 8   d. $\dfrac{25}{6}$

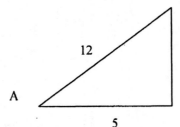

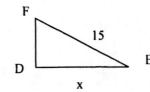

Name _____   Date _____

Chapter 8 Test
Form A

1. For the set {2, 1), (5, 7), and (7, 8)}   1a. _____
    (a) determine whether the relation is a   b. _____
    function and give the (b) domain and   c. _____
    (c) range of the relation.

For problems 2 – 3, find the indicated function values.

2. $f(x) = 3x + 1$
    a. $f(0)$ 2a. _____

    b. $f(-2)$ b. _____

    c. $f(5)$ c. _____

3. $g(x) = 2x^2 - 4x + 1$
    a. $g(0)$ 3a. _____

    b. $g(-2)$ b. _____

    c. $g(5)$ c. _____

4. Does the graph represent a function?   2. _____

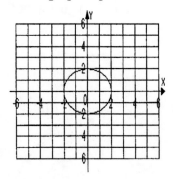

5. Does the graph represent a function: 5. _____

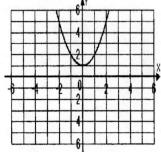

Name _____   Date _____

For problems 6 – 7, express each interval in (a) set-builder notation and (b) graph the interval on a number line.

6.   (–5, 2]

6a. _____

-6 -5 -4 -3 -2 -1 0 1 2 3 4 5 6

7.   (–∞, 8)

7a. _____

-6 -5 -4 -3 -2 -1 0 1 2 3 4 5 6

Use the graph below to solve problems 8 – 9.

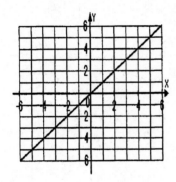

8.   Find $f(0)$

8. _____

9.   Find $f(4)$

9. _____

10.   Find the domain of $f(x) = 3x + 4$.

10. _____

11.   Find the domain of $g(x) = \dfrac{x-3}{x+5}$.

11. _____

Let $f(x) = x^2 + 4x - 2$ and $g(x) = 2x + 1$. Find:

12. $g(a + 4)$ 12. _____

13. $f(-3)$ 13. _____

14. $(f + g)(0)$ 14. _____

15. $(fg)(-2)$ 15. _____

16.   The domain of $\dfrac{f}{g}$.   16. _____

Find the composition.

17.   If $f(x) = x^2 - 1$ and $g(x) = x + 3$, find $(f \circ g)(2)$.   17. _____

18.   If $f(x) = 3x - 2$ and $g(x) = 2x + 4$, find $(g \circ f)(x)$.   18. _____

Determine whether the pair of f and g are inverses of each other.

19. $f(x) = 5x$ and $g(x) = \dfrac{x}{5}$.   19. _____

20. $f(x) = 2x - 4$ and $g(x) = \dfrac{x + 2}{4}$.   20. _____

Name _____   Date _____

Chapter 8 Test
Form B

1. For the set {(–2, –2), (3, 3), and (4, 4)}
    (a) determine whether the relation is a
    function and give the (b) domain and
    (c) range of the relation.

    1a. _____
    b. _____
    c. _____

For problems 2 – 3. find the indicated function values.

2. $f(x) = 2x - 5$
    a. $f(0)$

    2a. _____

    b. $f(-3)$

    b. _____

    c. $f(4)$

    c. _____

3. $g(x) = 3x^2 - 5x + 2$
    a. $g(0)$

    3a. _____

    b. $g(-2)$

    b. _____

    c. $g(5)$

    c. _____

4. Does the graph represent a function?

    4. _____

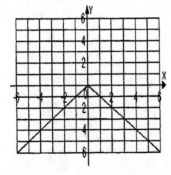

5. Does the graph represent a function?

    5. _____

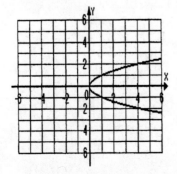

Name _____   Date _____

For problems 6 – 7, express each interval in (a) set-builder notation and (b) graph the interval on a number line.

6. $(4, \infty]$ 6a. _____

<number line marked -6 -5 -4 -3 -2 -1 0 1 2 3 4 5 6>

7. $[-3, 6)$ 7a. _____

<number line marked -6 -5 -4 -3 -2 -1 0 1 2 3 4 5 6>

Use the graph below to solve exercise 8 – 9.

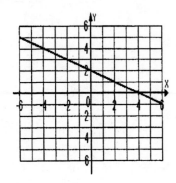

8.   Find $f(0)$.   8. _____

9.   Find $f(4)$.   9. _____

10.   Find the domain of $g(x) = \dfrac{3x - 6}{x + 4}$.   10. _____

11.   Find the domain of $y = x^2 - 9$.   11. _____

Let $f(x) = x^2 + 3x$ and $g(x) = 4 - x$. Find:

12. $f(-2)$ 12. _____

13. $g(a + 3)$ 13. _____

14. $(f - g)(3)$ 14. _____

15. $\left(\dfrac{f}{g}\right)(5)$ 15. _____

16.   The domain of $f + g$.   16. _____

Find the composition.

17.   If $f(x) = x^2 - 4$ and $g(x) = x + 5$, find $(f \circ g)(1)$.   17. _____

18.   If $f(x) = 4x + 2$ and $g(x) = 3x - 1$, find $(g \circ f)(x)$.   18. _____

Determine whether the pair of f and g are inverses of each other.

19. $f(x) = 2x + 5$ and $g(x) = \dfrac{x - 5}{2}$ 19. _____

20. $f(x) = 5x + 1$ and $g(x) = \dfrac{x + 5}{2}$ 20. _____

Name _____   Date _____

Chapter 8 Test
Form C

For problems 1 – 2, (a) determine whether each relation is a function. Give the (b) domain and (c) range of the relation.

1. $\{(-2, 3), (4, -2), (3, -6)\}$ 1a. _____
                                                                  b. _____
                                                                  c. _____

2. $\{(2, 6), (2, 7), (2, 8)\}$ 2a. _____
                                                                  b. _____
                                                                  c. _____

For problems 3 – 4, find the indicated function values.

3. $f(x) = 5x - 4$
      a. $f(0)$ 3a. _____

      b. $f(-1)$ b. _____

      c. $f(3)$ c. _____

4. $g(x) = 2x^2 + 3x - 6$
      a. $g(0)$ 4a. _____

      b. $g(-2)$ b. _____

      c. $g(3)$ c. _____

For problems 5 – 6, use the vertical line test to determine if the graph represents a function.

5.   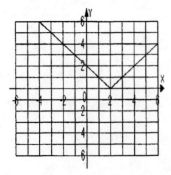   5. _____

6.

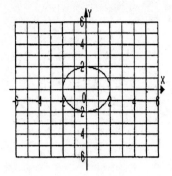

6. _____

For problems 7 – 9, express each interval in (a) set-builder notation and (b) graph the interval on a number line.

7.   (2, 5]

7a. _____

```
 -6 -5 -4 -3 -2 -1  0  1  2  3  4  5  6
```

8.   (−∞, −3)

8a. _____

```
 -6 -5 -4 -3 -2 -1  0  1  2  3  4  5  6
```

9.   (−∞, −3)

9a. _____

```
 -6 -5 -4 -3 -2 -1  0  1  2  3  4  5  6
```

Use the graph below to solve problems 10 – 12.

10.   Find $f(1)$

10. _____

11.   Find $f(0)$

11. _____

12.   Find $f(-1)$

12. _____

13.   Find the domain of $f(x) = 6x + 9$.   13._____

14.   Find the domain of $f(x) = \dfrac{x}{x+7}$ 14._____

For problems 15 – 19, let $f(x) = 3x^2 - x + 4$ and $g(x) = x + 1$. Find:

15. $f(-2)$ 15._____

16. $g(2a + 3)$ 16._____

17. $(f + g)(5)$ 17._____

18. $f(2) - g(4)$ 18._____

19.   The domain of $\dfrac{f}{g}$.   19._____

For problems 20 – 22, find the composition.

20.   If $f(x) = 3x + 1$ and $g(x) = x - 5$, find $(f \circ g)(x)$.   20._____

21.   If $f(x) = 2x$ and $g(x) = x + 4$, find $(f \circ g)(x)$.   21._____

22.   If $f(x) = \sqrt{x}$ and $g(x) = x + 5$, find $(g \circ f)(x)$. 22._____

For problems 23 – 25, determine whether the pair of f and g are inverses of each other.

23. $f(x) = 7x$ and $g(x) = \dfrac{x}{7}$.   23._____

24. $f(x) = 3x + 5$ and $g(x) = \dfrac{x-5}{3}$.   24._____

25. $f(x) = 5x + 2$ and $g(x) = \dfrac{x+5}{2}$.   25._____

Chapter 8 Test
Form D

Choose the correct answer.

1.   Which of the following is a function?

   a.   {(1, 2), (1, 3), (1, 4)}
   b.   {(4, 3), (−4, 5), (4, −6)}
   c.   {(4, 5), (5, 5), (6, 5)}
   d.   {(7, 9), (7, 8), (7, 6)}

2.   Give the domain and range for the relation {(−2, 0), (0, 4), (3,8)}.

   a.   Domain: {−2, 0, 3}; Range: {0, 4, 8}
   b.   Domain: {−2, 4, 8}; Range {−2, 0, 3}
   c.   Domain: {−2, 0, 3}; Range {0, 4}
   d.   Domain: {0, 4}; Range {−2, 0, 3}

3.   Which of the following graphs is not a function?

   a.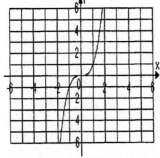

   b.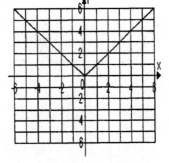

   c.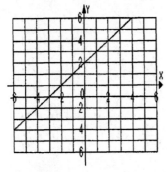

   d.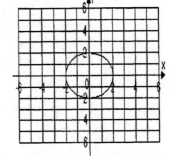

4.   Which of the following graphs is a function?

a.

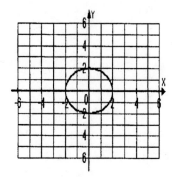

b.

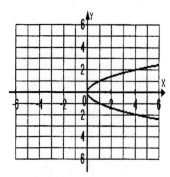

c.

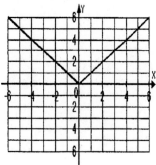

d.

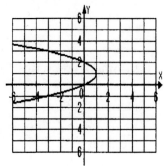

For problems 5 – 8, let $f(x) = 3x - 4$ and $g(x) = x^2 + 1$.

5.   Find $f(a - 4)$

a. $3a + 8$ b. $3a - 16$ c. $3a - 12$ d. $3a - 4$

6.   Find $(f + g)(2)$

a. $2x^2 + 6x - 6$ b. 5 c. 7 d. $6x^2 - 8$

7.   Find $g(6) - f(-3)$

a. 32   b. 24   c. 401   d. 50

8.   Find $(fg)(2)$

a. -10 b. 10   c. 7   d. 6

Name _____   Date _____

For problems 9 – 11, choose the interval that represents what is illustrated on the number line.

9.

        -6 -5 -4 -3 -2 -1 0 1 2 3 4 5 6

    a. $(3, \infty)$ b. $(-\infty, 3)$ c. $[3, \infty)$ d. $(-\infty, 3]$

10.

        -6 -5 -4 -3 -2 -1 0 1 2 3 4 5 6

    a. $[2, 5]$ b. $(2, 5]$ c. $(2, 5)$ d. $[2, 5)$

11.

        -6 -5 -4 -3 -2 -1 0 1 2 3 4 5 6

    a. $(-\infty, -1)$ b. $(1, \infty)$ c. $(-1, 1)$ d. $(-1, \infty)$

12.   Find the domain of $(x) = \dfrac{x-3}{x+5}$.

    a. $\{x \mid x \text{ is a real number and } x \neq 3\}$
    b. $\{x \mid x \text{ is a real number and } x \neq 5\}$
    c. $\{x \mid x \text{ is a real number and } x \neq 3\}$
    d. $\{x \mid x \text{ is a real number and } x \neq 5 \text{ and } x \neq -3\}$

13.   Find the domain of $f(x) = \dfrac{x}{x-7}$.

    a. $\{x \mid x \text{ is a real number and } x \neq 0\}$
    b. $\{x \mid x \text{ is a real number and } x \neq 7\}$
    c. $\{x \mid x \text{ is a real number and } x \neq 0 \text{ and } x \neq 7\}$
    d. $\{x \mid x \text{ is a real number and } x \neq -7\}$

14.   Find the domain of $f(x) = \dfrac{x-2}{x}$.

    a. $\{x \mid x \text{ is a real number and } x \neq 2\}$

    b. $\{x \mid x \text{ is a real number and } x \neq -2\}$

    c. $\{x \mid x \text{ is a real number and } x \neq 2 \text{ and } x \neq 0\}$

    d. $\{x \mid x \text{ is a real number and } x \neq 0\}$

In problems 15 – 16, $f(x) = 3x + 2$ and $g(x) = 2x - 4$.

15.   Find $(f + g)(x)$.

    a. $x - 2$ b. $5x - 6$ c. $5x + 2$ d. $5x - 2$

16.   Find $(f + g)(2)$.

    a. 8   b. 12   c. 4   d. 0

For problems 17 – 20, $f(x) = 3x - 4$ and $g(x) = 2x^2 + 3$.

17.   Find $(f \circ g)(-2)$

    a. –11   b. –22   c. 37   d. 58

18.   Find $(g \circ f)(2)$

    a. 28   b. 403   c. 110   d. 203

19.   Find $(g \circ f)(x)$

    a. $32x^2 - 183$ b. $32x^2 - 128x + 123$

    c. $32x^2 + 59$ d. $32x^2 - 64x + 59$

20.   Find $f^{-1}(x)$

    a. $f^{-1}(x) = x + 4$ b. $f^{-1}(x) = \dfrac{x+4}{3}$ c. $f^{-1}(x) = \dfrac{x-4}{3}$ d. $f^{-1}(x) = x - 4$

Name _____   Date _____

Chapter 8 Test
Form E

Choose the correct answer.

1.   Which of the following is not a function?

    a. $\{(0, 1), (1, 2), (2, 3)\}$
    b. $\{(1, 0), (2, 0), (5, 0)\}$
    c. $\{(4, 1), (1, 4), (4, 2)\}$
    d. $\{(0, 4), (1, 5), (2, 6)\}$

2.   Give the domain and range for the relation $\{(0, 4), (1, 4), (0, 3)\}$.

    a.   Domain: $\{0, 1, 3, 4\}$; Range: $\{0, 1, 3, 4\}$
    b.   Domain: $\{3, 4\}$; Range $\{0, 1\}$
    c.   Domain: $\{1, 4, 3\}$; Range $\{0, 4, 3\}$
    d.   Domain: $\{0, 1\}$; Range $\{4, 3\}$

3.   Which of the following graphs is a function?
    a.   b.

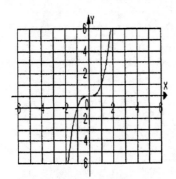   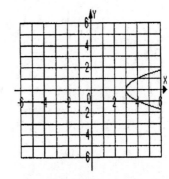

    c.   d.

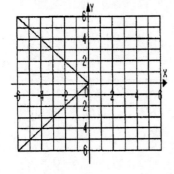   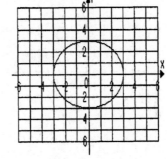

T-169

4.   Which of the following graphs is not a function?

a.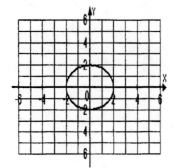

b.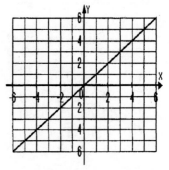

c.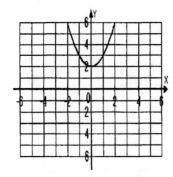

d.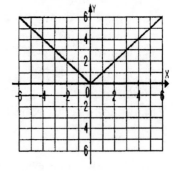

For problems 5 – 8, let $f(x) = x^2 + 2x + 1$ and $g(x) = 4 - 5x$.

5.   Find $g(5)$

    a. 29   b. 21   c. –21   d. 20

6.   Find $g(a-2)$

    a. –5a–14   b. $-5a + 24$ c. $-5a + 14$ d. $-5a + 6$

7.   Find $\left(\dfrac{f}{g}\right)(-1)$

    a. –2   b. 2   c. $-\dfrac{2}{9}$ d. 0

8.   Find $f(-2) - g(-6)$

    a. –33   b. –35   c. –41   d. 50

For problems 9 – 11, choose the interval that represents what is illustrated on the number line.

9.

    a. $[2, 4\}$ b. $(2, 4]$ c. $(2, 4)$ d. $[2, 4)$

10.

    a. $(1, \infty)$ b. $(-\infty, 1]$ c. $(-\infty, -1]$ d. $[1, \infty)$

11.

    a. $(-\infty, 0)$ b. $(0, \infty)$ c. $(-\infty, 0]$ d. $[1, \infty)$

12.   Find the domain of $f(x) = \dfrac{x+3}{3x+6}$

    a. $\{x \mid x$ is a real number and $x \neq -2\}$
    b. $\{x \mid x$ is a real number and $x \neq -3\}$
    c. $\{x \mid x$ is a real number and $x \neq 0\}$
    d. $\{x \mid x$ is a real number and $x \neq 2$ and $x \neq -3\}$

13.   Find the domain of $f(x) = \dfrac{3x}{2x+1}$

    a. $\{x \mid x$ is a real number and $x \neq -1\}$
    b. $\{x \mid x$ is a real number and $x \neq 0\}$
    c. $\{x \mid x$ is a real number and $x \neq \ x \neq -\dfrac{1}{2}\}$
    d. $\{x \mid x$ is a real number and $x \neq \dfrac{1}{2}\}$

14.   Find the domain of $f(x) = \dfrac{x+3}{x+5}$

     a. $\{x \mid x$ is a real number and $x \neq 5\}$
     b. $\{x \mid x$ is a real number and $x \neq 3\}$
     c. $\{x \mid x$ is a real number and $x \neq 3$ and $x \neq -5\}$
     d. $\{x \mid x$ is a real number and x $-5\}$

In problems 15 – 16, $f(x) = 4x - 7$ and $g(x) = 3x + 2$.

15.   Find $(f + g)(x)$.

    a. $7x + 5$ b. $7x - 5$ c. $7x - 9$ d. $7x + 9$

16.   Find $(f + g)(3)$.

    a. 26   b. 12   c. 16   d. 30

For problems 17 – 20, $f(x) = 3x - 4$ and $g(x) = 2x^2 + 3$.

17.   Find $(f \circ g)(-2)$
    a. -11 b. -22 c. 37   d. 58

18.   Find $(g \circ f)(2)$
    a. 28   b. 403   c. 110   d. 203

19.   Find $(g \circ f)(x)$
    a. $32x^2 - 183$ b. $32x^2 - 128x + 123$
    c. $32x^2 + 59$ d. $32x^2 - 64x + 59$

20.   Find $f^{-1}(x)$

    a. $f^{-1}(x) = x + 4$ b. $f^{-1}(x) = \dfrac{x+4}{3}$ c. $f^{-1}(x) = \dfrac{x-4}{3}$ d. $f^{-1}(x) = x - 4$

Chapter 8 Test
Form F

Choose the correct answer.

1. Which of the following is a function?

    a.   {(–4, 0), (0, 5), (0, 6)}
    b.   {(1, 4), (1, 5), (1, 6)}
    c.   {(3, –2), (4, –2), (3, 4)}
    d.   {(4, 1), (5, 1), (6, 1)}

2. Give the domain and range for the relation {(4, 2), (6, 4), (3, 2)}.

    a.   Domain: {4, 6, 3}; Range: {2, 4}
    b.   Domain: {4, 2, 6, 3}; Range {2, 4, 3}
    c.   Domain: {2, 4}; Range {4, 6, 3}
    d.   Domain: {2, 4, 3}; Range {4, 2, 6, 3}

3. Which of the following graphs is not a function?

a.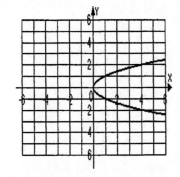

b.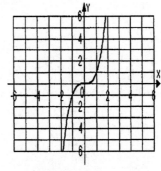

c.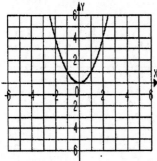

d.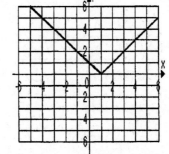

4.   Which of the following graph is a function?

a.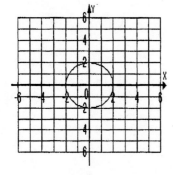

b.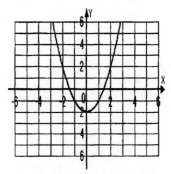

c.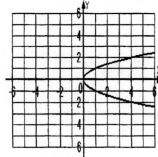

d.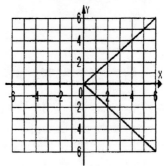

For problems 5–8, let $f(x) = x^2 + 2x - 3$ and $g(x) = 4x + 2$.

5.   Find $g(a - 2)$

   a. $4a$ b. $4a - 6$ c. $4a - 16$ d. $-16a$

6.   Find $g(-1) - f(-2)$
   a. 1   b. -13 c. -1 d. 13

7.   Find $(fg)(3)$
   a. -26 b. -7 c. -1 d. 168

8.   Find the domain $\dfrac{f}{g}$.

   a. $\{x \mid x \text{ is a real number and } x \neq 1 \text{ and } x \neq 3\}$

   b. $\{x \mid x \text{ is a real number and } x \neq -\dfrac{1}{2}\}$

   c. $\{x \mid x \text{ is a real number }\}$

   d. $\{x \mid x \text{ is a real number and } x \neq -\dfrac{1}{2} \text{ and } x \neq 1 \text{ and } x \neq 3\}$

Name _____   Date _____

For problems 9 – 11, choose the interval that represents what is illustrated on the number line.

9.

-6 -5 -4 -3 -2 -1 0 1 2 3 4 5 6

   a. $(-\infty, 4]$ b. $(-\infty, 4)$ c. $(4, \infty)$ d. $[4, \infty)$

10.

-6 -5 -4 -3 -2 -1 0 1 2 3 4 5 6

   a. $(-2, 3]$ b. $(-2, 3)$ c. $[-2, 3)$ d. $[-2, 3]$

11.

-6 -5 -4 -3 -2 -1 0 1 2 3 4 5 6

   a. $(1, \infty)$ b. $(-\infty, 1]$ c. $(-\infty, 1)$ d. $[1, \infty)$

12.   Find the domain of $f(x) = \dfrac{x+1}{x-8}$

   a. $\{x \mid x$ is a real number and $x \neq 8\}$
   b. $\{x \mid x$ is a real number and $x \neq -1\}$
   c. $\{x \mid x$ is a real number and $x \neq -8\}$
   d. $\{x \mid x$ is a real number and $x \neq 1$ and $x \neq 3\}$

13.   Find the domain of $f(x) = \dfrac{x+2}{3x-1}$

   a. $\{x \mid x$ is a real number and $x \neq -2\}$
   b. $\{x \mid x$ is a real number and $x \neq -2$ and $x \neq 1\}$
   c. $\{x \mid x$ is a real number and $x \neq \dfrac{1}{3}\}$
   d. $\{x \mid x$ is a real number and $x \neq -\dfrac{1}{3}\}$

14.   13.   Find the domain of $f(x) = \dfrac{2x - 3}{x + 5}$

    a. $\{x \mid x \text{ is a real number and } x \neq \dfrac{3}{2}\}$

    b. $\{x \mid x \text{ is a real number and } x \neq 5\}$

    c. $\{x \mid x \text{ is a real number and } x \neq -5\}$

    d. $\{x \mid x \text{ is a real number and } x \neq -\dfrac{3}{2}\}$

In problems 15 – 16, $f(x) = 3x - 6$ and $g(x) = 2x + 5$.

15.   Find $(f + g)(x)$.

    a. $x - 11$ b. $x - 1$ c. $5x - 11$ d. $5x - 1$

16.   Find $(f + g)(2)$.

    a. -10 b. 0 c. -6 d. 9

Choose the correct answer.

17.   If $f(x) = \sqrt{x + 2}$ and $g(x) = x^2 - 3$, find $(g \circ f)(7)$.
    a. 6 b. 46 c. 49 d. 12

18.   If $f(x) = \sqrt{x + 2}$ and $g(x) = x^2 + 10$, find $(f \circ g)(-2)$.
    a. 4 b. $2\sqrt{2}$ c. 10 d. 46

19.   If $f(x) = x^3$ and $g(x) = x - 6$, find $(g \circ f)(x)$.
    a. $x^3 - 216$ b. $x^3 - 18x^2 + 108x - 216$
    c. $x^3 + 216$ d. $x^3 - 6x^2 + 108x + 216$

20.   If $f(x) = 3x - 7$ find $f^{-1}(x)$.

    a. $f^{-1}(x) = x + 7$ b. $f^{-1}(x) = -3x + 7$ c. $f^{-1}(x) = \dfrac{x}{3} + 7$ d. $f^{-1}(x) = \dfrac{x + 7}{3}$

Name _____   Date _____

Cumulative Review 1 – 8
Form A

For problems 1 – 8, perform the indicated operations. If possible, simplify the answer.

1. $\dfrac{6-2(3-6)^2}{12-3\cdot 2}$

   1. _____

2. $\dfrac{x-1}{x}-\dfrac{3}{x-2}$

   2. _____

3. $\dfrac{16x^8-4x^5+12x^3}{-2x^3}$

   3. _____

4. $\dfrac{x^2+7x+4}{x-3}$

   4. _____

5. $\dfrac{(-3x)^2(-2x^3)}{3x^{-6}}$

   5. _____

6. $2x^4(x^2+3x-4)$

   6. _____

7. $(3x-4y)^2$

   7. _____

8. $\dfrac{x^2-5x-6}{x-2}\div\dfrac{x^2-1}{x^2-3x+2}$

   8. _____

For problems 9 – 11, factor completely.

9. x^4-81

   9. _____

10. $7x^2y-14x^3y^2$

    10. _____

11. $6x^2 - 11x - 10$ 11. _____

For problems 12 – 17, solve each equation, inequality or system of equations.

12. $7x - 4(2 - x) = 5(x + 2)$ 12. _____

13. $2(5 - x) \leq x - 5$ 13. _____

14. $\dfrac{x+3}{4} + \dfrac{3}{x+6} = 1$ 14. _____

15. $(x - 2)(3x - 5) = 52$ 15. _____

16. $2x + 3y = 4$ 16. _____
       $x + y = 6$

17. $12x - 14y = 28$ 17. _____
       $y = x - 4$

For problems 18 – 19, graph the equation or system of equations.

18. $4x + 2y = 8$ 18.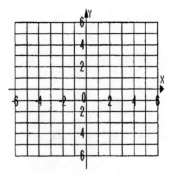

19. $y = 3x + 2$ 19.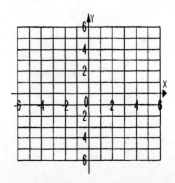
       $2x - y = -4$

20. One line passes through the points (1, –2) and (3, –1). A second line passes through the points (–3, 0) and (–4, 2). Are the lines parallel, perpendicular, or intersecting?

20. _____

21. If a school district decides that there must be 5 teachers for every 125 students, how many teachers must be hired if there are 1625 students?

21. _____

22. A sailboat has a triangular sail with an area of 65 square feet and a base that measures 10 feet. Find the height of the sail.

22. _____

23. 180 is what percent of 30?

23. _____

24. Solve $T = \dfrac{1}{2}(a+b)$ for a.

24. _____

25. Find the measure of the supplement of an angle measuring 58°.

25. _____

Name _____   Date _____

Cumulative Review 1 – 8
Form B

Choose the correct answer.

For problems 1 – 8, perform the indicated operations. If possible, simplify the answer.

1. $7 - 2\,[x - 4 + 3(x + 2)]$
    a. $-8x + 27$ b. $20x - 50$ c. $-8x - 3$ d. $20x - 10$

2. $-3xy^2(2x^2 - 5x - 4)$
    a. $-6xy^4 + 15x^2 y^2 + 12xy^2$ b. $-6xy^4 - 15x^2 y^2 - 12xy^2$
    c. $-6x^3 y^2 - 15x^2 y^2 - 12xy^2$ d. $-6x^3 y^2 + 15x^2 y^2 + 12xy^2$

3. $\dfrac{-5x^5 + 10x^3 + 25x}{-5x}$
    a. $x^4 + 10x^2 - 25$ b. $-5x^5 + 10x^3 + 5$
    c. $x^4 - 2x^2 + 5$ d. $x^4 - 2x^2 - 5$

4. $(5x + 3y)^2$
    a. $25x^2 - 9y^2$ b. $25x^2 - 30xy - 9y^2$
    c. $25x^2 + 30xy + 9y^2$ d. $25x^2 + 30xy - 9y^2$

5. $(6x + 2y)(6x - 2y)$
    a. $36x^2 + 4y^2$ b. $36x^2 - 24xy + 4y^2$
    c. $36x^2 - 4y^2$ d. $16xy^2$

6. $\dfrac{2x^{-4} \cdot (3x)^2}{6x^{-2}}$
    a. $\dfrac{3}{x^4}$ b. $3x^{-4}$ c. 3 d. $2x^{-4}$

7. $\dfrac{6}{x^2 - 1} + \dfrac{3}{x + 1}$
    a. $\dfrac{3x + 3}{x^2 - 1}$ b. $\dfrac{3}{x - 1}$ c. $\dfrac{3x + 6}{x^2 - 1}$ d. $\dfrac{3}{x}$

8. $\dfrac{x^2 + x - 2}{x^2 + 5x + 6} \div \dfrac{x - 1}{x}$
    a. $\dfrac{x}{x + 3}$ b. $\dfrac{1}{3}$ c. $\dfrac{x(x + 2)}{(x + 6)(x - 1)}$ d. $\dfrac{x(x - 2)}{(x + 6)(x - 1)}$

Name _____   Date _____

For problems 9 – 11, factor completely.

9. $xy + 4x - 7y - 28$
    a. $(x - 7)(y + 4)(y + 4)$ b. $(x - 7)(y + 4)(y - 4)$
    c. $(x - 7)(y + 4)$ d. $(x + 7)(y + 4)$

10. $y^3 - 8$
    a. $(y - 2)^3$ b. $(y - 2)(y + 2)^2$
    c. $(y - 2)(y^2 - 4y + 4)$ d. $(y - 2)(y^2 + 2y + 4)$

11. $20x^2 - 7x - 6$
    a. $(5x - 2)(4x + 3)$ b. $(5x + 2)(4x - 3)$
    c, $(5x - 3)(4x + 2)$ d. $(5x + 3)(4x - 2)$

For problems 12 – 17, solve each equation, inequality, or system of equations.

12. $5 - 2(x - 3) + 4x = 2x + 5$
    a. $\left\{\dfrac{14}{5}\right\}$ b. $\{-6\}$ c. Infinite solutions   d. No solution

13. $18(x - 2) \le 20(x - 4)$
    a. $\{x \mid x \le 3.05\}$ b. $\{x \mid x \le 22\}$ c. $\{x \mid x \ge 22\}$ d. $\{x \mid x \ge 56\}$

14. $2 + \dfrac{3}{x} = -\dfrac{1}{x^2}$
    a. $\left\{-1, \ -\dfrac{1}{2}\right\}$ b. $\{-1\}$ c. $\left\{\dfrac{1}{2}, 1\right\}$ d. $\left\{-\dfrac{1}{2}\right\}$

15. $\dfrac{x}{x - 5} + \dfrac{5}{2} = \dfrac{5}{x - 5}$
    a. $\{-5\}$ b. $\{5\}$ c. Infinite solutions   d. No solution

16. $3x - y = 7$
     $2x - y = 4$
    a. $(-3, 2)$ b. $(3, 10)$ c. $(3, 2)$ d. $(-3, 10)$

17. $y = 5x - 4$
     $y = -4x - 1$
    a. $(5, -21)$ b. $(5, 21)$ c. $\left(\dfrac{1}{3}, \dfrac{7}{3}\right)$ d. $\left(\dfrac{1}{3}, -\dfrac{7}{3}\right)$

Name _____ Date _____

For problems 18 – 19, graph the equation or inequalities in a rectangular coordinate system.

18. $x + 2y = 6$

a.

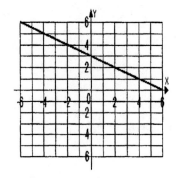

b.

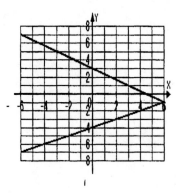

c.

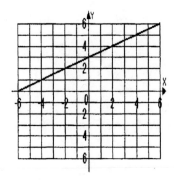

d.

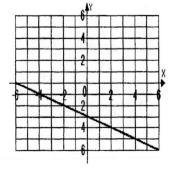

19. $7x + 14y > 7$

a.

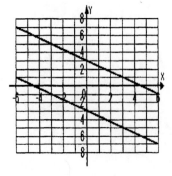

b.

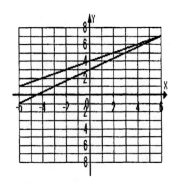

c.

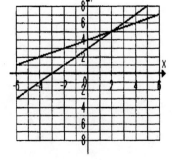

d.

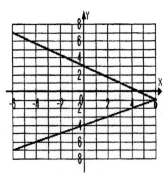

20.   Find the slope for the line $8x + 16y = 4$.

   a. $\dfrac{1}{2}$ b. $-\dfrac{1}{2}$ c. 2   d. –2

21.   9 is 20% of what number?
   a. 45   b. 1800   c. 450   d. 18

22.   In a triangle, the measure of the second angle is 40° less than the measure of the first angle. The measure of the third angle is three times the first. What is the measure of the smallest angle?
   a. 44°   b. 4°   c. 8°   d. 28°

23.   One pipe can empty a tank in 15 minutes and a second pipe can empty the same tank in 10 minutes. If the tank is full, how long will it take both pipes to empty it?
   a. 5 min   b. 25 min   c. 12.5 min   d. 6 min

24.   The length of rectangular yard is 20 feet more than twice the width. If the area is 238 square feet, find the length of the yard.
   a. 14 ft   b. 34 ft   c. 24 ft   d. 44 ft

25.   Find the volume, to the nearest tenth, of a cylinder with a diameter of 10 inches and a height of 15 inches.
   a. 1178.1 in^3 b. 314.2 in^3 c. 4712.4 in^3 d. 78.5 in^3

Name _____   Date _____

Chapter 9 Test
Form A

For problems 1 – 2, let A = {a, b, c, d, e} and B = {a, e i, o, u}.

1. $A \cap B$ 1. _____

2. $A \cup B$ 2. _____

For problems 3 – 7, solve each linear inequality. Express the solution in a) interval notation, and (b) graph the interval on a number line.

3. $4x + 7 > 3(x + 2)$ 3a. _____

                                                             b.

4. $4 - 2(x - 3) \geq 4(2x - 3) + 2$ 4a. _____

                                                             b.

5. $x + 3 \leq 4$ and $-7x < 14$ 5a. _____

                                                             b.

6. $9x - 4 \geq 14$ or $4(2x - 3) + 2$ 6a. _____

                                                             b.

Name _____   Date _____

7. $-8x + 12 \le 20$ and $-4(x-2) \ge 20$

7a. _____

b.

For problems 8 – 10, solve the absolute value inequality. Express the solution set in both (a) set-builder and (b) interval notation.

8. $|4x - 3| + 1 \le 6$

8a. _____

b. _____

9. $\left|\dfrac{2x+1}{3}\right| > 4$

9a. _____

b. _____

10. $|5x - 3| - 2 < -10$

10a. _____

b. _____

For problems 11 – 12, solve the absolute value equation.

11. $|2x - 1| + 4 = 7$

11a. _____

b. _____

12. $|x + 2| = |3x - 4|$

12a. _____

b. _____

For problems 13 – 14, graph each inequality in a rectangular coordinate system.

13. $4x - 37 \le 12$

13.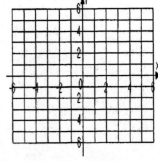

14. $y > -2x - 3$ 14.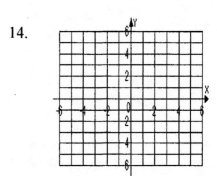

For problems 15 – 18, graph the solution set of each system on inequalities.

15. $2x - y < 0$ 15.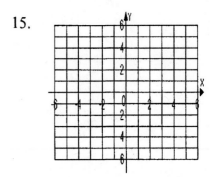
        $x + 3y > 0$

16. $y \geq -x + 4$ 16.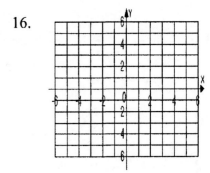
        $y \leq 5$

17. $5x - 10y \leq 15$ 17.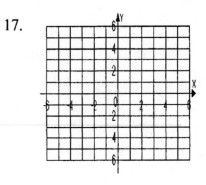
            $y \leq -2x + 2$

18. $x > 4$
      $y < 3$

18.

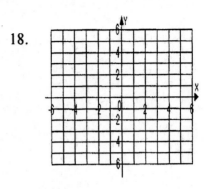

19.   Your first four exams in a class are 72, 85, 92, and 95.
      You want a B for the class and there is only one test
      left. To achieve an average of your five exams greater
      than or equal to 80 and less than 90, what range of
      grades on the fifth exam is necessary? Use interval
      notation to express the range.

19. _____

20.   A retired engineer wants to raise horses and cattle.
      Each horse costs an average of $1000 and each cow
      costs an average of $500. The retiree can afford to
      spend a maximum of $7000. On a monthly basis, it
      takes approximately 60 hours of labor per horse and
      10 hours of labor per cow to care for the livestock
      and she has a maximum of 180 hours of labor
      available. She can make a $2000 profit per horse and
      a $400 profit per cow. (a) How many horses and cows
      should she raise if she wants to maximize her profit?
      (b) What is the maximum profit?

20a. _____

  b. _____

Name _____   Date _____

Chapter 9 Test
Form B

For problems 1 – 2, let $A = \{2, 4, 6, 8, 10\}$ and $B = \{1, 2, 3, 4, 5, 6, 7, 8\}$.

1. $A \cap B$

1. _____

2. $A \cup B$

2. _____

b.

For problems 3 – 7, solve each linear inequality. Express the solution in a) interval notation, and (b) graph the interval on a number line.

3. $8x - 9 < 6(2x - 1) + 1$

3a. _____

b.

4. $7 - 5(x - 3) \geq 3(2x + 1) - (4x + 2)$

4a. _____

b.

5. $4x + 5 \leq -3$ and $-3x < 12$

5a. _____

b.
-6   -4   -2   0   2   4   6

6. $-3(4x - 12) < -12$ or $-2x > -4$

6a. _____

b.
-6   -4   -2   0   2   4   6

7. $-4(3-x) < -12$ or $2x+3 > -9$

7a. _____

b. _____

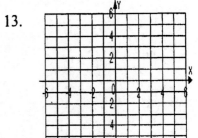

For problems 8 – 10, solve the absolute value inequality. Express the solution set in both (a) set-builder and (b) interval notation.

8. $|5x-1| \geq 4$

8a. _____

b. _____

9. $\left|\dfrac{3x+2}{4}\right| - 7 < 3$

9a. _____

b. _____

10. $|5x+1| < -3$

10a. _____

b. _____

For problems 11 – 12, solve the absolute value equation.

11. $|2x+5| - 3 = 4$

11a. _____

b. _____

12. $|4+x| = |2x-5|$

12a. _____

b. _____

For problems 13 – 14, graph each inequality in a rectangular coordinate system.

13. $6x - 12y < 24$

13.

14. $y \leq -x - 4$

14.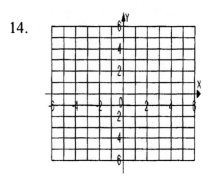

For problems 15 – 18, graph the solution set of each system on inequalities.

15. $3x - y \leq 6$
        $7x + 14y \geq 7$

15.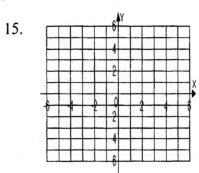

16. $y < -x - 2$
        $x > -3$

16.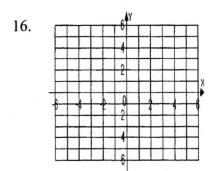

17. $4x + 2y \leq 8$
            $y \geq x - 1$

17.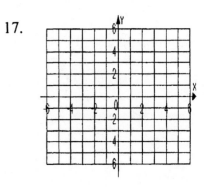

18    $x > -3$
    $y < 4$

18.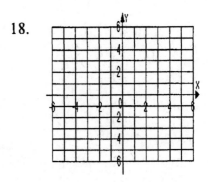

19.   The inequality $|T - 60| \leq 30$ describes the range of monthly average temperature, T, in degrees Fahrenheit, for Ocean City. Solve the inequality and interpret the solution.

19. _____

20.   A clothing manufacturer makes two types of T-shirts, plain and with a logo. The profit on the plain T-shirt is $4 and the profit on the logo T-shirt is $5. To meet demand the company must manufacture at least 40 plain and 60 logo T-shirts per week. The company cannot support making more than 240 shirts combined per week.
(a) How many of each type of shirt should be made?
(b) What is the maximum weekly profit?

20a. _____

b. _____

Name _____   Date _____

Chapter 9 Test
Form C

1. Find $\{4, 8, 10, 12\} \cup \{3, 4, 5, 6\}$ 1. _____

2. Find $\{2, 3, 4\} \cap \{3, 4, 5\}$ 2. _____

For problems 3 – 7, solve each linear inequality. Express the solution in (a) interval notation and (b) graph the interval on a number line.

3. $7(x - 2) \le 6(x - 2) + 3x$ 3a. _____

b.

4. $4 - 2(3 - 3x) < -3(x - 2) - (x - 12)$ 4a. _____

b.

5. $-9 \le 2x - 3 \le 5$ 5a. _____

b.

6. $3x - 4 < 2$ and $2(x - 5) > x - 15$ 6a. _____

b.

7. $11 - 3(x - 2) < 14$ or $-2x > 6$ 7a. _____

b.

Name _____   Date _____

For problems 8 –10, solve the absolute value inequality. Express the solution set in both (a) set-builder and (b) interval notation.

8. $|2x+4|-1 \le 5$

8a. _____

b. _____

9     $\left|\dfrac{4x-3}{2}\right| > 1$

9a _____

b. _____

10. $|x-2|+5 < 2$

10a. _____

b. _____

For problems 11 – 12, solve the absolute value equation.

11. $|3x-1|+3 = 4$

11. _____

12. $|4-x| = |2x-6|$

12. _____

For problems 13 – 14, graph each inequality in a rectangular coordinate system.

13. $-9x+3y \le -18$

13.

14. $y > -\dfrac{1}{2}x+3$

14.

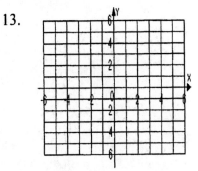

Name _____   Date _____

15. $-4x + 8y \le 24$ 15.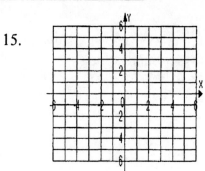
      $2x - y \ge -4$

16. $y < 4$ 16.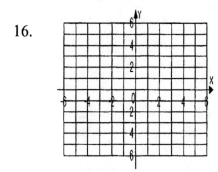
      $y > x + 2$

17. $x + y \le 5$ 17.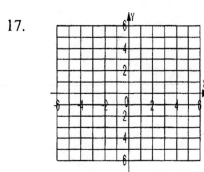
      $y \ge 2x$

18. $2x + 3y > 6$ 18.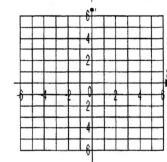
      $y < -x + 4$

19.   A local bank charges $10 per month plus 5¢ per   19. _____
     check. The local credit union charges $5 per month
     plus 7¢ a check. How many checks should be
     written each month to make the local bank a better
     deal?

20.   The formula $T = 0.01x + 56.7$ models the global mean   20. _____
     temperature, T, in degrees Fahrenheit, of Earth x years
     since 1905. For which range of years is the global
     mean temperature at least 57°F and at most 57.4°F?

Chapter 9 Test
Form D

Choose the correct answer.

For problems 1 – 10, solve the inequalities.

1. $-3x + 1 \leq -x - 7$
   a. $(4, \infty)$ b. $[-4. \infty)$ c. $[4, \infty)$ d. $(-4, \infty)$

2. $19x - 2x + 18 > 5x - (9 - 4x)$
   a. $\left\{ x \mid x < -\dfrac{27}{26} \right\}$ b. $\left\{ x \mid x < -\dfrac{27}{8} \right\}$ c. $\left\{ x \mid x > -\dfrac{27}{8} \right\}$ d. $\left\{ x \mid x > -\dfrac{27}{26} \right\}$

3. $2(x - 3) \geq x + 9$
   a. $(15, \infty)$ b. $[15, \infty)$ c. $(-\infty, 15)$ d. $(-\infty, 15]$

4. $-4 \leq -2x + 8 \leq 10$
   a. $\{x \mid -9 \leq x \leq -2\}$ b. $\{x \mid -6 \leq x \leq 1\}$
   c. $\{x \mid -1 \leq x \leq 6\}$ d. $\{x \mid 2 \leq x \leq 9\}$

5. $x + 1 \leq 5$ and $-9x < 27$

   a.   b.

   c.   d.

6. $x + 1 \leq 5$ and $-9x < 27$
   a. $[-3, 4]$ b. $(-3, 4)$ c. $(-\infty, -3) \cup (4, \infty)$ d. $(-3, 4]$

7. $4(2-x) > -3x + 5$ or $7 - 5(x-1) < 2(x-1)$

a.

b.

c.

d.

8.

$|4x - 7| < 3$

a. $\left(1, \dfrac{5}{2}\right)$ b. $\left[1, \dfrac{5}{2}\right]$ c. $\left(-1, -\dfrac{5}{2}\right)$ d. $\left[-1, -\dfrac{5}{2}\right]$

9. $|2x + 3| + 4 < 1$

a. $(-3, 0)$ b. $(0, -3)$ c. $\varnothing$ d. $(-\infty, \infty)$

10. $|4 - x| > 6$

a. $\{x \mid x < -2 \text{ or } x > 10\}$ b. $\{x \mid x < 10 \text{ or } x > -2\}$

c. $\{x \mid -2 < x < 10$ c. $\{x \mid x \text{ is a real number}\}$

For problems 11 – 13, solve the absolute vale equations.

11. $\left|\dfrac{4}{5}x + 5\right| + 8 = 11$

a. $\left\{-10, -\dfrac{5}{2}\right\}$ b. $\left\{-30, -\dfrac{5}{2}\right\}$ c. $\{10, 30\}$ d. $\left\{-\dfrac{32}{5}, -\dfrac{8}{5}\right\}$

12. $|x - 7| = |x + 3|$

a. $\varnothing$ b. $\{2, 5\}$ c. $\{2\}$ d. $\{-2, -5\}$

13. $\left|\dfrac{2x + 3}{4} + 7\right| = |3|$

a. $\left\{-\dfrac{19}{2}, \dfrac{13}{2}\right\}$ b. $\left\{-\dfrac{43}{2}, -\dfrac{19}{2}\right\}$ c. $\{x \mid x \text{ is a real number}\}$ d. $\varnothing$

14.   Graph $3x - y < -3$.

a.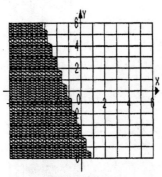

b.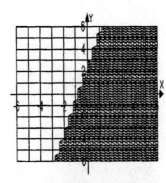

c.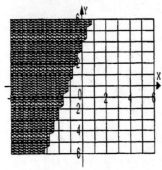

d.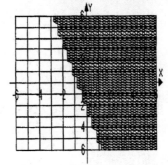

15.   Graph $7x - 21y > 21$.

a.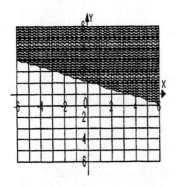

b.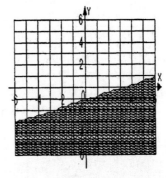

c.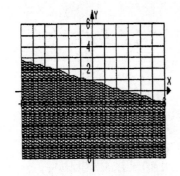

d.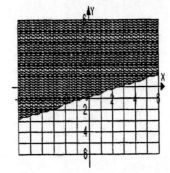

16.   Graph $y > 2x - 3$
        $y < 1$

a. 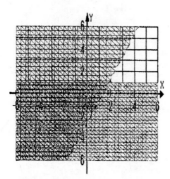   b.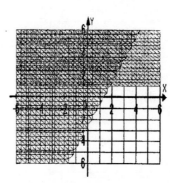

c. 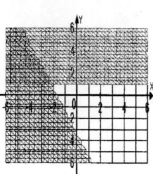   d.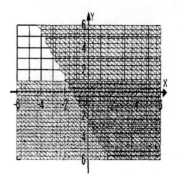

17.   Graph $2x + 3y \leq 6$
        $y \leq 1$

a. 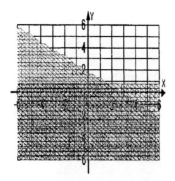   b.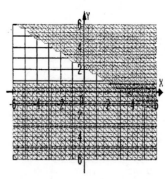

c. 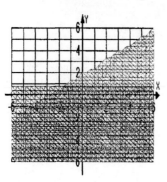   d.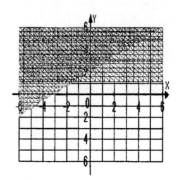

18. Find the minimum value of the objective function $z = 2x + 4y$, for the equations shown in the figure.

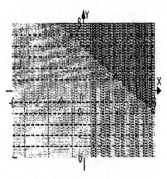

$$x + y \leq 4$$
$$y \geq -x + 2$$
$$y \geq 0$$
$$x \geq 0$$

a. 4   b. 2   c. 16   d. 0

19. The inequality $|T - 39| \leq 20$ describes the range of the monthly average temperature, T, in degrees Fahrenheit, for New City. Solve the inequality.

a. $(19, 59)$ b. $[19, 59]$ c. $(-\infty, 59]$ d. $[19, \infty)$

20. A student has made a 66, 68, and 77 on the first three tests in a course. One test remains. If the student wants to average greater than or equal to 70 and less than 80 (to make a C) in the course, what must be the range of the score on the fourth test.

a. $[69, 109)$ b. $[69, 109]$ c. $[-1, 29)$ d. $[-1, 29]$

Name _____   Date _____

Choose the correct answer.

For problems 1 – 10, solve the inequalities.

1. $6 - 4(x+1) \geq 2(1-x)$

    a.

        -6 -5 -4 -3 -2 -1 0 1 2 3 4 5 6

                         b.

                                -6 -5 -4 -3 -2 -1 0 1 2 3 4 5 6

    c.

        -6 -5 -4 -3 -2 -1 0 1 2 3 4 5 6

                         d.

                                -6 -5 -4 -3 -2 -1 0 1 2 3 4 5 6

                                No Solution

2. $3x - 7x + 10 > 9x - (5 - 6x)$

    a. $\left\{ x \mid x < \dfrac{15}{19} \right\}$ b. $\left\{ x \mid x < -\dfrac{15}{11} \right\}$ c. $\left\{ x \mid x > \dfrac{15}{19} \right\}$ d. $\left\{ x \mid x > -\dfrac{15}{11} \right\}$

3. $3(x-1) \leq 4x + 1$

    a.

        -6 -5 -4 -3 -2 -1 0 1 2 3 4 5 6

                         b.

                                -6 -5 -4 -3 -2 -1 0 1 2 3 4 5 6

    c.

        -6 -5 -4 -3 -2 -1 0 1 2 3 4 5 6

                         d.

                                -6 -5 -4 -3 -2 -1 0 1 2 3 4 5 6

4. $-10 \leq -2x + 6 \leq 8$
    a. $[-2, 7]$ b. $[-8, 1]$ c. $[-7, 2]$ d. $[-1, 8]$

5. $x + 6 \leq 7$ and $-8x < 16$
    a. $\{x \mid x < -2 \text{ or } x \geq 1\}$ b. $\{x \mid -2 < x \leq 1\}$
    c. $\{x \mid x \leq 1\}$ d. $\{x \mid x > -2\}$

6. $5 + (4 - 3x) < 0$ or $7(x + 2) < x + 2$
    a. $(-\infty, -2)$ b. $(-2, 3)$ c. $(-\infty, -2) \cup (3, \infty)$ d. $(3, \infty)$

7. $-8x \leq 16$ and $4(x-4) \geq 4$
     a. $[-2, 5]$ b. $[-2, \infty)$ c. $(-\infty, -2] \cup [5, \infty)$ d. $[5, \infty)$

8. $|3x - 6| \leq 9$
     a. $\{x \mid -1 < x < 5\}$ b. $\{x \mid x \leq -1 \text{ or } x \geq 5\}$
     c. $\{x \mid -1 \leq x \leq 5\}$ d. $\{x \mid x \text{ is a real number}\}$

9. $|2x + 3| - 4 > 1$
     a. $(-\infty, -1) \cup (4, \infty)$ b. $\{x \mid -1 < x < 4\}$
     c. $\emptyset$ d. $(-\infty, \infty)$

10. $\left|\dfrac{2x-1}{4}\right| > -3$
     a. $\left(-\dfrac{11}{2}, \dfrac{13}{2}\right)$ b. $\left(-\dfrac{11}{2}, \infty\right)$ c. $\emptyset$ d. $(-\infty, \infty)$

For problems 11 – 13, solve the absolute value equations.

11. $\left|\dfrac{2}{3}x + 7\right| + 8 = 10$
     a. $\left\{-\dfrac{75}{2}, -\dfrac{15}{2}\right\}$ b. $\left\{-\dfrac{27}{2}, -\dfrac{15}{2}\right\}$ c. $\left\{-6, -\dfrac{10}{3}\right\}$ d. $\left\{\dfrac{27}{2}, \dfrac{75}{2}\right\}$

12. $|x - 4| = |x - 2|$
     a. $\{3\}$ b. $\emptyset$
     c. $\{-3, 3\}$ d. $\{x \mid x \text{ is a real number}\}$

13. $\left|\dfrac{3x-2}{4}\right| + 2 = 1$
     a. $\{2\}$ b. $\left\{-\dfrac{2}{3}, 2\right\}$
     c. $\{x \mid x \text{ is a real number}\}$ d. $\emptyset$

14.   Graph $5x + 10y \leq 20$.

a.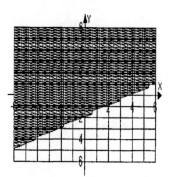

b.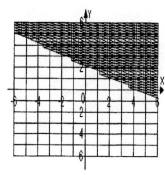

c.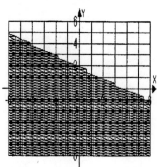

d.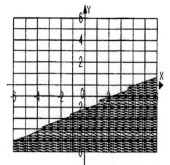

15.   Graph $2x - y > 6$

a.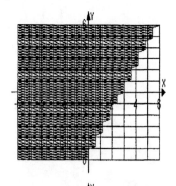

b.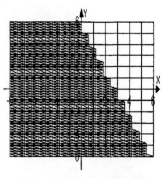

c.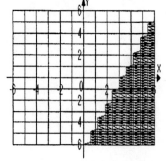

d.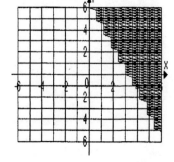

16. Graph $y \le -x + 2$
           $y \ge x$

a.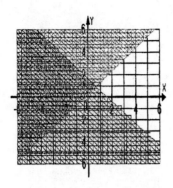

b.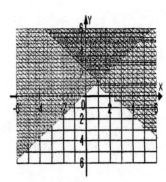

c.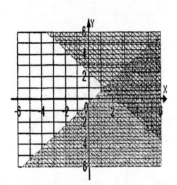

d.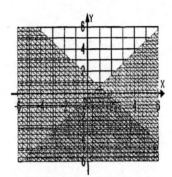

17. Graph $4x - y < 4$
           $x > -1$

a.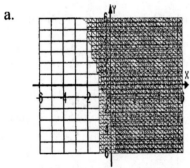

b.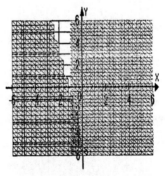

c.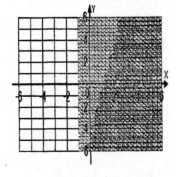

d.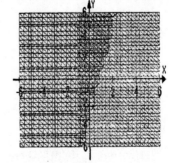

18.   Find the maximum value of the objective function $z = 3x + 2y$, for the equations shown
      in the graph below.

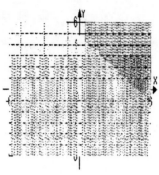

$$y \le 3$$
$$x \ge 0$$
$$y \ge 1$$
$$y \le -x + 5$$

a. 8   b. 14   c. 12   d. 0

19.   You can choose between two telephone companies. Company A has a monthly charge of
      $10 plus 5¢ a minute for each minute of long distance calls. Company B has a monthly
      charge of $8 plus 6¢ a minute for long distance calls. How many minutes must you use
      long distance to make Company A the better deal?

a. less than 200   b. less than 20   c. more than 200   d. more than 20

20.   The inequality $|T - 51| \le 15$ describes the range of monthly average temperature, T, in
      degrees Fahrenheit for North Central City. Solve the inequality to give the temperature
      range in interval form.

a. $(-\infty, 66]$ b. $[36, 66]$ c. $[-36, 66]$ d. $(36, 66)$

Name _____   Date _____

Chapter 9
Form F

Choose the correct answer.

For problems 1 – 10, solve the inequalities.

1. $7 - 3(2 - x) \le 4(3 - x) - 2x$

   a. $(-\infty, 2]$
   b. $[-2, \infty)$
   c. $\left[-\infty, \dfrac{11}{9}\right]$
   d. $\left(-\dfrac{11}{9}, \infty\right)$

2. $4x - (2x + 8) < 8x - (6 - 3x)$

   a. $\left(-\infty, -\dfrac{2}{9}\right)$
   b. $\left(-\infty, \dfrac{14}{3}\right)$
   c. $\left(\dfrac{14}{3}, \infty\right)$
   d. $\left(-\dfrac{2}{9}, \infty\right)$

3. $-6x + 2 < -4x + 6$

   a.

   b.

   c.

   d.

4. $-20 < 3x - 2 < 13$

   a. $\{x \mid x < -6 \text{ and } x > 5\}$
   b. $\{x \mid -6 < x < 5\}$
   c. $\left\{x \mid -\dfrac{22}{3} < x < \dfrac{11}{3}\right\}$
   d. $\left\{x \mid x > \dfrac{11}{3}\right\}$

5. $-2x + 3 \le -1 \text{ and } 4x + 1 < 3x + 5$

   a.

   b.

   c.

   d.

6. $6(x-2) \geq 3x-4$ or $8x-4 < 7(x-5)$

     a. $(-\infty,-1) \cup \left[\dfrac{8}{3},\infty\right)$ b. $(-\infty,-1) \cup \left(\dfrac{8}{3},\infty\right)$

     c. $(-\infty,-31) \cup \left(\dfrac{8}{3},\infty\right)$ d. $(-\infty,-31) \cup \left[\dfrac{8}{3},\infty\right)$

7. $4x-5 \leq 11$ and $-6x+2 \geq 2(x-11)$

     a. $(-\infty,3) \cup (-\infty,4]$ b. $(-\infty,3) \cup [4,\infty)$

     c. $(-\infty,3]$ d. $(-\infty, 4)$

8. $|3x+4| \geq 6$

     a. $\left(-\infty,-\dfrac{10}{3}\right] \cup \left[\dfrac{2}{3},\infty\right)$ b. $\left[-\dfrac{10}{3},\dfrac{2}{3}\right]$

     c. $(-\infty, \infty)$ d.   Ø

9. $|3x-2|+7 < 2$

     a. $(-\infty,-1) \cup \left(\dfrac{7}{3},\infty\right)$ b. $\left(-1,\dfrac{7}{3}\right)$

     c. $(-\infty, \infty)$ d.   Ø

10. $\left|\dfrac{4x-1}{6}\right| > -1$

     a. $\left(-\infty,-\dfrac{5}{4}\right) \cup \left(\dfrac{7}{4},\infty\right)$ b. $\left(-\dfrac{5}{4},\dfrac{7}{4}\right)$

     c. $(-\infty, \infty)$ d.   Ø

For problems 11 – 13, solve the absolute value equations.

11. $\left|\dfrac{1}{2}x-4\right|+2 = 4$

     a. {4}   b. {12}   c. {4, 12}   d. Ø

12. $|x-3| = |6-x|$

     a. $\left\{\dfrac{9}{2}\right\}$ b. {3, 6}

     c. $\{x \mid x$ is a real number$\}$ d. Ø

13. $\left|\dfrac{5x+1}{3}\right| - 4 = -3$

a. $\left\{-\dfrac{2}{5}, \dfrac{4}{5}\right\}$ b. $\left\{-\dfrac{4}{5}, \dfrac{2}{5}\right\}$

c. $\{x \mid x \text{ is a real number}\}$ d. $\varnothing$

14.   Graph $5x - 6y < 30$

a.

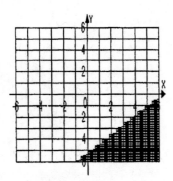

b.

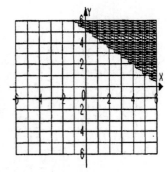

c.

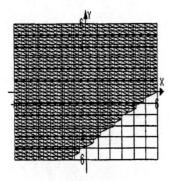

d.

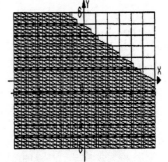

15.   Graph $y \geq 2x - 3$

a.

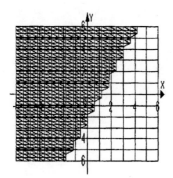

b.

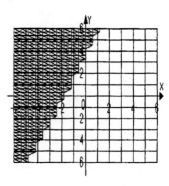

c.

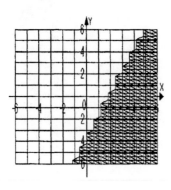

d.

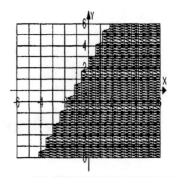

16.   Graph $y < -\dfrac{1}{2}x + 2$ and $y > 2x$.

a.

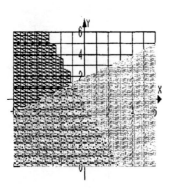

b.

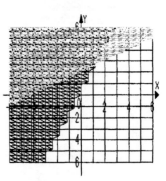

c.

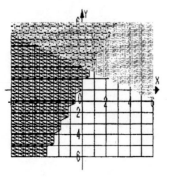

d.

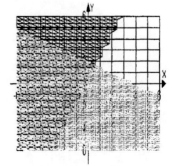

17.   Graph $8x - 4y < 4$
        $x > -2$

a.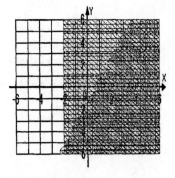

b.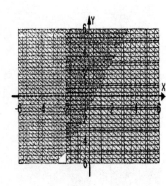

c.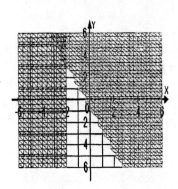

d.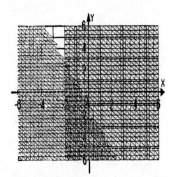

18.   Find the minimum value of the object function $z = 2x + 3y$, for the equations shown below.

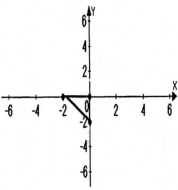

$$y \geq -x - 2$$
$$x \leq 0$$
$$y \leq 0$$

a. 0   b. −6   c. −4   d. $-\dfrac{9}{2}$

19.   A copy machine costs $1200 and has an estimated page cost of 2¢ for each page. Having a professional copy center make copies costs 5¢ per page. What is the minimum number of pages that you would need copied before buying the copy machine would be the better deal?

   a. 40,000   b. 4000   c. 17,143   d. 171,429

20.   A dairy produces whole milk and 2% milk. The dairy can produce no more than 150 gallons of milk products each day. It makes a profit of $2 per gallon on whole milk and a profit of $3 per gallon on 2% milk. It takes 30 minutes per gallon of whole milk and 5 minutes per gallon of 2% milk for processing. The dairy has available a maximum of 300 minutes for processing. Determine how many gallons of whole milk and 2% milk should be processed to maximize profit.

   a. 90 gallons whole; 60 gallons 2%   b. 60 gallons whole; 90 gallons 2%
   c. 100 gallons whole; 50 gallons 2%   d. 450 gallons 2%; 200 gallons whole

Chapter 10
Form A

1. For $f(x) = \sqrt{2-x}$, find   1a. _____
    (a) the domain of f, and (b) $f(-14)$.   b. _____

For problems 2 – 8, simplify each expression. Assume that all variables represent positive numbers.

2. $\sqrt{50a^{10}b^4}$ 2. _____

3. $\sqrt[4]{243x^8y^3}$ 3. _____

4. $8\sqrt{12} - 6\sqrt{75} + \sqrt{48}$ 4. _____

5. $4a\sqrt[4]{16ab^{13}} - 2b^2\sqrt[4]{a^5b^5}$ 5. _____

6. $\left(2\sqrt{3} + \sqrt{5}\right)^2$ 6. _____

7. $\left(3\sqrt{x} - 4\right)\left(4\sqrt{x} + 5\right)$ 7. _____

8. $\left(\sqrt{x} + 2\sqrt{y}\right)\left(\sqrt{x} - 2\sqrt{y}\right)$ 8. _____

For problems 9 – 11, rationalize the denominator and simplify. Assume that all variables represent positive numbers.

9. $\sqrt{\dfrac{9x^3}{5}}$ 9. _____

10. $\sqrt[3]{\dfrac{27y}{2x}}$ 10. _____

11. $\dfrac{3\sqrt{x} + 2}{\sqrt{x} + 3}$ 11. _____

Name _____   Date _____

For problems 12 – 16, perform the indicated operations. Assume that all variables represent positive numbers. Write answers in rational exponent form if rational exponents remain after simplifying.

12. $\dfrac{y^{\frac{2}{3}} y^{\frac{1}{4}}}{y^{\frac{5}{6}}}$ 12. _____

13. $\left(\dfrac{25x^4}{100x^8}\right)^{-\frac{1}{2}}$ 13. _____

14. $\left(9x^2 y^{\frac{2}{3}}\right)^{\frac{1}{2}} \left(4x^{\frac{3}{2}} y^{\frac{4}{3}}\right)^3$ 14. _____

15. $144^{\frac{3}{2}}$ 15. _____

16. $(-64)^{-\frac{4}{3}}$ 16. _____

For problems 17 – 22, perform the indicated operation. If answers are complex, write in $a + bi$ form.

17. $\sqrt{-121}$ 17. _____

18. $\sqrt{-72x^2}$ 18. _____

19. $6i(3 - 2i)$ 19. _____

20. $(2 - 3i)(3 - 4i)$ 20. _____

21. $\dfrac{4 - i}{5 + i}$ 21. _____

22. i^{47} 22. _____

Name _____   Date _____

For problems 23 – 25, solve the radical equation.

23. $\sqrt{2-x} = 6$ 23. _____

24. $\sqrt[3]{2x} + 3 = 6$ 24. _____

25. $\sqrt{3x+10} = x+4$ 25. _____

Chapter 10
Form B

For problems 1 – 2, simplify each expression. Assume that all variables represent real numbers.

1. $\sqrt[5]{-(x+y)^5}$ 1. _____

2. $\sqrt{4x^2y^2}$ 2. _____

For problems 3 – 9, simplify each expression. Assume that all variables represent positive numbers.

3. $\sqrt{192a^3b}$ 3. _____

4. $\sqrt[3]{-108x^4y^2}$ 4. _____

5. $xy\sqrt{147x^3} + \sqrt{12x^5y^2} - y\sqrt{27x^5}$ 5. _____

6. $\sqrt{6}\left(\sqrt{3} - \sqrt{2}\right)$ 6. _____

7. $\left(5\sqrt{3} + 3\right)\left(2\sqrt{3} - 1\right)$ 7. _____

8. $\left(3\sqrt{y} - 4\right)^2$ 8. _____

9. $\left(5\sqrt{x} + \sqrt{2}\right)\left(5\sqrt{x} - \sqrt{2}\right)$ 9. _____

For problems 10 – 12, rationalize the denominator and simplify. Assume that all variables represent positive numbers.

10. $\dfrac{\sqrt{48}}{\sqrt{4x}}$ 10. _____

Name _____   Date _____

11. $\sqrt[3]{\dfrac{3x}{5y^2}}$ 11. _____

12. $\dfrac{\sqrt{2}}{\sqrt{6}+\sqrt{3}}$ 12. _____

For problem 13, rationalize the numerator and simplify. Assume that all variables represent positive numbers.

13. $\dfrac{2\sqrt{x}+3}{2}$ 13. _____

For problems 14 – 16, perform the indicated operations. Assume that all variables represent positive numbers. Write answers in rational exponent form, if rational exponents remain after simplifying.

14. $81^{-\frac{3}{4}}$ 14. _____

15. $(-27)^{\frac{2}{3}}$ 15. _____

16. $\left(16x^3y^8\right)^{\frac{1}{4}}\left(8x^{-2}y^{-3}\right)^{\frac{1}{3}}$ 16. _____

For problems 17 – 22, perform the indicated operation. If answers are complex, write in $a+bi$ form. Assume that all variables represent positive numbers.

17. $\sqrt{-144}$ 17. _____

18. $\sqrt{-8}\cdot\sqrt{-5}$ 18. _____

19. $-6i(3-2i)$ 19. _____

20. $(4i-3)(5-2i)$ 20. _____

21. $\dfrac{7+i}{2-3i}$ 21. _____

22. i^{50} 22. _____

For problems 23 – 25, solve the radical equation.

23. $\sqrt{x+1}+2=\sqrt{x}$ 23. _____

24. $(2x-4)^{\frac{1}{3}}=4$ 24. _____

25. The formula $v=2\sqrt{6L}$ is used by police to estimate the   25. _____
speed of a car, v, in miles per hour, based on the length of its
skid marks, L, in feet, on dry pavement. How far will a car skid
at a speed of 72 miles per hour?

Name _____   Date _____

Chapter 10
Form C

1. For $f(x) = \sqrt{4 - 2x}$, find   1a. _____
    (a) the domain of f, and
    (b) $f(-10)$ b. _____

For problems 2 – 3, simplify each expression. Assume that all variables represent real numbers.

2. $\sqrt[4]{(3x+4)^2 (3x+4)^2}$ 2. _____

3. $\sqrt[5]{(6x)^5}$ 3. _____

For problems 4 – 9, simplify each expression. Assume that all variables represent positive numbers.

4. $\sqrt[3]{-500x^2 y^{13}}$ 4. _____

5. $4a\sqrt{28a^5 b^6} - 2ab\sqrt{63a^5 b^4} + 5b^2\sqrt{700a^7 b^2}$ 5. _____

6. $\sqrt{5x}\left(\sqrt{10x} - \sqrt{15x}\right)$ 6. _____

7. $\left(5 + \sqrt{6}\right)\left(5 - \sqrt{6}\right)$ 7. _____

8. $\left(3\sqrt{2x} - 4\right)\left(7\sqrt{2x} + 5\right)$ 8. _____

9. $\left(4\sqrt{3x} - 4\right)^2$ 9. _____

For problems 10 – 12, rationalize the denominator and simplify. Assume that all variables represent positive numbers.

10. $\dfrac{\sqrt{24x}}{\sqrt{5x^2}}$ 10. _____

11. $\sqrt[3]{\dfrac{3x^2}{4x}}$

11. _____

12. $\dfrac{\sqrt{5}-\sqrt{2}}{\sqrt{5}+\sqrt{2}}$

12. _____

For problem 13, rationalize the numerator and simplify. Assume that all variables represent positive numbers.

13. $\dfrac{\sqrt{3}+\sqrt{5}}{2}$

13. _____

For problems 14 – 16, perform the indicated operations. Assume that all variables represent positive numbers. Write answers in rational exponent form, if rational exponents remain after simplifying.

14. $\sqrt[4]{\sqrt{6561}}$

14. _____

15. $(-27)^{-\frac{4}{3}}$

15. _____

16. $\left(27x^{12}y^{-9}\right)^{\frac{1}{3}}\left(2x^{\frac{1}{4}}y^{\frac{1}{2}}\right)^{4}$

16. _____

For problems 17 – 22, perform the indicated operation. If answers are complex, write in $a+bi$ form. Assume that all variables represent positive numbers.

17. $\sqrt{-36x^2}$

17. _____

18. $\sqrt{-25}\cdot\sqrt{-36}$

18. _____

19. $(5-4i)(2+3i)$

19. _____

20. $\dfrac{3-i}{-2i}$

20. _____

21. $\dfrac{4i}{7-5i}$ 21. _____

22. i^{41} 22. _____

For problems 23 – 25, solve the radical equation.

23. $\sqrt[3]{1-x}+3=-2$ 23. _____

24. $(4x+1)^{\frac{1}{4}}=3$ 24. _____

25. The distance, d, measured in miles that an observer can   25. _____
     see from an observation tower is related to the height of the
     tower, h, in feet by the formula $d=1.4\sqrt{h}$. How tall must
     the tower be to see a distance of 8.4 miles?

Name _____   Date _____

Chapter 10
Form D

Choose the correct answer.

1. Find the domain of $f(x) = \sqrt{3-x}$.
   a. $[3, \infty)$
   b. $(-\infty, 3]$
   c. $(3, \infty)$
   d. $(-\infty, 3)$

2. Simplify $\sqrt{(9x)^2}$
   a. $9|x|$
   b. $9x$
   c. $-9x$
   d. $3x$

For problems 3 – 13, perform the indicated operations. Assume that all variables represent positive numbers.

3. $\sqrt{800x^{16}y^9}$
   a. $2x^4y^3\sqrt{100}$
   b. $2x^8y^4\sqrt{100y}$
   c. $20x^8y^4\sqrt{2y}$
   d. $20x^4y^3\sqrt{2}$

4. $\sqrt[3]{-64a^8b^{27}}$
   a. $-8a^2b^3$
   b. $-8a^2b^9\sqrt[3]{a^2}$
   c. $-4a^2b^3$
   d. $-4a^2b^9\sqrt[3]{a^2}$

5. $4x\sqrt{40x^2y^3} - 3x^2\sqrt{10y^3} + 5y\sqrt{90x^4y}$
   a. $6x^2y\sqrt{10y^3}$
   b. $28x^2y\sqrt{10y}$
   c. $20x^2y\sqrt{10y}$
   d. Cannot simplify

6. $\left(3 - 4\sqrt{2x}\right)^2$
   a. $9 + 32x$
   b. $9 - 24\sqrt{2x} + 32x$
   c. $9 + 24\sqrt{2x} + 32x$
   d. $9 + 64x$

7. $\left(5\sqrt{x} - 3\right)\left(5\sqrt{x} + 3\right)$
   a. $25x^2 - 9$
   b. $25x - 30\sqrt{x} - 9$
   c. $25x - 9$
   d. $25x + 30\sqrt{x} + 9$

8. $\left(4\sqrt{3} + \sqrt{6}\right)\left(2\sqrt{3} - \sqrt{6}\right)$
   a. $18 - 6\sqrt{2}$
   b. 18
   c. 36
   d. $36 - 2\sqrt{18}$

9. $\dfrac{y^{-\frac{1}{5}}y^{\frac{1}{2}}}{y^{\frac{2}{5}}}$
   a. $\dfrac{1}{y^{\frac{3}{10}}}$
   b. $y^{\frac{3}{10}}$
   c. $y^{\frac{1}{10}}$
   d. $\dfrac{1}{y^{-\frac{1}{10}}}$

Name _____   Date _____

10. $(32)^{-\frac{3}{5}}$

   a. $-\dfrac{1}{8}$ b. -8 c. $\dfrac{1}{8}$ d. 8

11. $81^{\frac{3}{4}}$

   a. 729 b. 27 c. $\dfrac{1}{27}$ d. $\dfrac{1}{729}$

12. $\left(\dfrac{16y^4}{81x^3}\right)^{-\frac{1}{4}}$

   a. $\dfrac{3x^{\frac{3}{4}}}{2y}$ b. $\dfrac{4y}{3x^{\frac{3}{4}}}$ c. $\dfrac{3x^{\frac{3}{4}}}{4y^1}$ d. $\dfrac{2x^{\frac{3}{4}}}{3y}$

13. $\left(2x^{-\frac{3}{2}}y^{-\frac{5}{2}}\right)^2\left(9x^4y^{-6}\right)^{\frac{1}{2}}$

   a. $\dfrac{12}{xy^8}$ b. $\dfrac{12y^{15}}{x^6}$ c. $\dfrac{36}{xy^8}$ d. $\dfrac{18y^{15}}{3y}$

For problems 14 – 16, rationalize the denominator.

14. $\sqrt{\dfrac{18x^2}{5}}$

   a. $9x\sqrt{2}$ b. $\dfrac{9x\sqrt{10}}{5}$ c. $3x\sqrt{2}$ d. $\dfrac{3x\sqrt{10}}{5}$

15. $\sqrt[3]{\dfrac{54}{2x}}$

   a. $3\sqrt[3]{4x}$ b. $\dfrac{3\sqrt[3]{x^2}}{x}$ c. $\dfrac{3\sqrt[3]{4x}}{2x}$ d. $3\sqrt[3]{2}$

16. $\dfrac{4\sqrt{x}-2}{\sqrt{x}+2}$

   a. $4+6\sqrt{x}$ b. $\dfrac{4x-10\sqrt{x}+4}{x-4}$ c. $4-10\sqrt{x}$ d. $\dfrac{4x+6\sqrt{x}-4}{x-4}$

Name _____   Date _____

For problems 17 – 22, perform the indicated operation. Assume that all variables represent positive numbers.

17. $\sqrt{-64}$
    a. –8   b. –8i   c. 8i   d. Cannot simplify

18. $\sqrt{-100x} \cdot \sqrt{-25x}$
    a. $50i\sqrt{x}$ b. $10i\sqrt{x}$ c. $50\sqrt{x}$ d. $-50x$

19. $-3i(2 - 4i)$
    a. $-6i - 12i^2$ b. $-6i + 12i^2$ c. $12 - 6i$ d. $-12 - 6i$

20. $(3 - 4i)(4 + 3i)$
    a. $12 - 12i^2$ b. 24   c. $24 - 7i$ d. $7 - i$

21. $\dfrac{3 - i}{4 - i}$

    a. $\dfrac{11}{15} + \dfrac{7}{15}i$ b. $\dfrac{11}{17} - \dfrac{6}{17}i$ c. $\dfrac{11}{17} + \dfrac{7}{17}i$ d. $\dfrac{4}{5} + \dfrac{2}{5}i$

22. i^{35}
    a. i b. $-i$ c. 1   d. –1

For problems 23 – 25, solve the radical equations.

23. $\sqrt{4 - x} = 6$
    a. {–32}   b. {32}   c. {8}   d. {–8}

24. $\sqrt{x + 5} = \sqrt{x} - 3$
    a. {–4}   b. $\left\{\dfrac{4}{9}\right\}$ c. {9}   d. Ø

25. $\sqrt[3]{2x - 3} + 4 = 6$
    a. Ø   b. $\left\{\dfrac{7}{2}\right\}$ c. $\left\{\dfrac{1003}{2}\right\}$ d. $\left\{\dfrac{11}{2}\right\}$

Chapter 10
Form E

Choose the correct answer.

1. Find the domain of $f(x) = \sqrt{4 - 2x}$.
    a. $(-\infty, 2)$ 　　　　 b. $(-\infty, 2]$ 　　　　 c. $[2, \infty)$ 　　　　 d. $(2, \infty)$

2. Simplify $\sqrt{(x+y)^2}$
    a. $|x + y|$ 　　　　 b. $x + y$ 　　　　 c. $\sqrt{x + y}$ 　　　　 d. $-(x + y)$

For problems 3 – 13, perform the indicated operations. Assume that all variables represent positive numbers.

3. $\sqrt[3]{-128x^{15}y^{27}}$
    a. $300a^4b^4\sqrt[3]{2x^{15}}$ 　　 b. $-8x^5y^9\sqrt[3]{2}$ 　　 c. $8x^5y^9\sqrt[3]{2}$ 　　 d. $-4x^5y^9\sqrt[3]{2}$

4. $\sqrt{600a^8b^9}$
    a. $300a^4b^4\sqrt{b}$ 　　 b. $300a^2b^3$ 　　 c. $10a^4b^4\sqrt{6b}$ 　　 d. $10b^3\sqrt{6a^8}$

5. $2x\sqrt[3]{48y^4} + 3y\sqrt[3]{162x^3y} - 4xy\sqrt[3]{384y}$
    a. $13xy\sqrt[3]{6y} - 4xy\sqrt[3]{384y}$ 　　　　 b. $-3xy\sqrt[3]{6y}$
    c. $27xy\sqrt[3]{6y}$ 　　　　 d. $xy\sqrt[3]{6y}$

6. $\left(5 - 2\sqrt{6}\right)^2$
    a. $1 - 20\sqrt{6}$ 　　 b. $25 + 4\sqrt{6}$ 　　 c. 49 　　 d. $49 - 20\sqrt{6}$

7. $2x\left(2\sqrt{x} - 4\sqrt{2}\right)$
    a. $4x - 8\sqrt{x}$ 　　 b. $2x\sqrt{2} - 8\sqrt{x}$ 　　 c. $4x - 8\sqrt{2}$ 　　 d. $4 - 12\sqrt{x} + 9x$

8. $\left(9 - \sqrt{3}\right)\left(9 + \sqrt{3}\right)$
    a. 78 　　 b. $84 - 18\sqrt{3}$ 　　 c. 84 　　 d. $2\sqrt{2x^2} - 4\sqrt{2}$

9. $\dfrac{\sqrt[6]{x^5}}{\sqrt[4]{x}}$
    a. $\sqrt{x^4}$ 　　 b. x^2 　　 c. $\sqrt[12]{x^7}$ 　　 d. $x\sqrt[12]{x}$

10. $(4)^{-\frac{3}{2}} + (-27)^{-\frac{2}{3}}$

   a. $\left\{\dfrac{1}{26}\right\}$ b. $\left\{\dfrac{2}{17}\right\}$ c. $\left\{\dfrac{17}{72}\right\}$ d. $\{12\}$

11. $\dfrac{x^{\frac{1}{3}} y^{-\frac{3}{4}}}{x^{-\frac{1}{4}}}$

   a. $x^{\frac{2}{3}}$ b. $\dfrac{1}{x^{\frac{2}{3}}}$ c. $x^{\frac{4}{3}}$ d. $-\dfrac{1}{x^{\frac{1}{6}}}$

12. $\left(16x^6 y^{36}\right)^{\frac{1}{2}} \left(2x^{\frac{1}{2}} y^{-\frac{3}{4}}\right)^4$

   a. $\dfrac{64x^6}{y^{54}}$ b. $20x^5 y^{15}$ c. $64x^5 y^{15}$ d. $64x^5 y^3$

For problems 13 – 14, rationalize the denominator.

13. $\sqrt[3]{\dfrac{x}{25y^2}}$

   a. $\dfrac{\sqrt[3]{5xy}}{25y}$ b. $\dfrac{\sqrt[3]{5xy}}{5y}$ c. $\dfrac{5\sqrt[3]{xy}}{y}$ d. $\dfrac{\sqrt[3]{5xy}}{25y^2}$

14. $\sqrt{\dfrac{5}{2\sqrt{5}-3}}$

   a. $\dfrac{5}{17}$ b. $\dfrac{10+3\sqrt{5}}{11}$ c. $\dfrac{7}{11}$ d. $\dfrac{10-3\sqrt{5}}{17}$

15. Rationalize the numerator $\sqrt{\dfrac{14x^3}{2x}}$

   a. $7x$ b. $\dfrac{7x}{\sqrt{7x}}$ c. $\dfrac{\sqrt{7}}{x}$ d. $\dfrac{7x}{\sqrt{7}}$

For problems 16 – 22, perform the indicated operation.

16. $-\sqrt{-50}$

   a. $5\sqrt{2}$ b. $-5\sqrt{2}i$ c. $-5\sqrt{2}$ d. $5\sqrt{2}i$

17. $(5+3i)-(2-4i)$

    a. $3-i$ b. $22-14i$ c. $3+7i$ d. -4

18. $\sqrt{-63}+\sqrt{-28}$

    a. $\sqrt{91}i$ b. $\sqrt{7}i$ c. $5\sqrt{7}i$ d. $-5\sqrt{7}i$

19. $(3+2i)(7-3i)$

    a. $21+5i$ b. $27+5i$ c. $21-i$ d. $21-9i$

20. $\dfrac{7+6i}{3+8i}$

    a. $-\dfrac{69}{73}-\dfrac{38}{73}i$ b. $-\dfrac{69}{73}+\dfrac{38}{73}i$ c. $\dfrac{69}{73}+\dfrac{38}{73}i$ d. $\dfrac{69}{73}-\dfrac{38}{73}i$

21. $\dfrac{3+i}{3i}$

    a. $-i$ b. $\dfrac{1-3i}{3}$ c. $3-i$ d. 1

22. i^{42}

    a. i b. $-i$ c. 1 d. -1

For problems 23 – 25, solve the radical equations.

23. $\sqrt{x+23}=x+11$

    a. $\{-7\}$ b. $\{-14,-7\}$ c. $\{-14\}$ d. $\varnothing$

24. $\sqrt{x-9}-\sqrt{x}=-1$

    a. $\{25\}$ b. $\{50\}$ c. $\{5\}$ d. $\varnothing$

25. $(3x+2)^{\frac{1}{3}}=2$

    a. $\{-2\}$ b. $\left\{\dfrac{4}{3}\right\}$ c. $\{2\}$ d. $\varnothing$

Name _____   Date _____

Chapter 10
Form F

Choose the correct answer.

1.　Find the domain of $f(x) = \sqrt{-8-2x}$.
　　a. $(-\infty, 4]$　　　　b. $(-\infty, -4]$　　　　c. $[-4, \infty)$　　　　d. $[4, \infty)$

For problems 3 – 13, perform the indicated operations. Assume that all variables represent positive numbers.

2.　$-\sqrt{\dfrac{49}{81}}$

　　a. $\dfrac{7}{9}$　　　　　　　　　　　　　　b. $-\dfrac{7}{9}$

　　c. $-\dfrac{5}{8}$　　　　　　　　　　　　　　d. Not a real number

3.　$16^{\frac{3}{2}}$

　　a. 192　　　　　b. 64　　　　　c. $\dfrac{1}{4}$　　　　　d. $\dfrac{1}{64}$

4.　$\left(\dfrac{1}{81}\right)^{-\frac{1}{4}}$

　　a. $\dfrac{1}{3}$　　　　b. $\dfrac{1}{9}$　　　　c. 9　　　　d. 3

5.　$\sqrt[3]{6x^4}\sqrt[3]{4x^2y^6}$
　　a. $\sqrt[3]{24x^8y^6}$　　b. $x^2y^2\sqrt[3]{24x^2}$　　c. $2x^2y^2\sqrt[3]{3}$　　d. $2x \cdot 2y^2\sqrt[3]{6}$

6.　$3\sqrt{2x} - 2\sqrt{4x} + 2\sqrt{18x}$
　　a. $9\sqrt{2x} - 4\sqrt{x}$　　b. $5\sqrt{2x}$　　c. $6\sqrt{2x} - 4\sqrt{x}$　　d. $3\sqrt{24x}$

7.　$\sqrt{6x}\left(7\sqrt{x} - 6\sqrt{6}\right)$
　　a. $42x - 36\sqrt{6}$　　b. $7x\sqrt{6} - 36\sqrt{x}$　　c. $7\sqrt{6x^2} - 6\sqrt{6}$　　d. $42x - 36\sqrt{x}$

8.　$\left(5\sqrt{x} - 2\sqrt{y}\right)^2$
　　a. $25x - 4y$　　　　　　　　b. $25 - 4y$
　　c. $25x - 20\sqrt{xy} + 4y$　　　　d. $5x - 10\sqrt{xy} + 4y$

T-226

9. $\left(5-\sqrt{3}\right)\left(5+\sqrt{3}\right)$

a. 22   b. $28-10\sqrt{3}$ c. $22-10\sqrt{3}$ d. 28

10. $a^{\frac{1}{2}}\left(a^{-\frac{2}{3}}\right)$

a. $a^{-\frac{1}{3}}$ b. $\dfrac{1}{a^{\frac{1}{6}}}$ c. $a^{\frac{1}{6}}$ d. $\dfrac{1}{a^{\frac{1}{3}}}$

11. $\dfrac{\sqrt[8]{x^7}}{\sqrt[4]{x^3}}$

a. $\sqrt[4]{x^4}$ b. x c. $\sqrt[8]{x}$ d. $\sqrt{x}$

12. $\sqrt{\dfrac{65x^9}{13x^3}}$

a. $5x^3$ b. $2x^3\sqrt{13}$ c. $x^3\sqrt{5}$ d. $52x^3$

13. $\left(4x^{-\frac{5}{2}}y^{-\frac{3}{2}}\right)^4\left(81x^8y^4\right)^{-\frac{1}{2}}$

a. $\dfrac{256}{9x^{14}y^8}$ b. $144x^3y^2$ c. $\dfrac{256}{9x^6y^4}$ d. $\dfrac{256x^{14}y^8}{9}$

For problems 14 – 15, rationalize the denominator.

14. $\sqrt[4]{\dfrac{x^3}{25y^5}}$

a. $\dfrac{\sqrt[4]{25x^3y^3}}{5y^2}$ b. $\dfrac{\sqrt[4]{25x^3y^3}}{25y^2}$ c. $\dfrac{\sqrt[4]{5x^3y^2}}{25y}$ d. $\dfrac{\sqrt[4]{5x^3y^2}}{25y^2}$

15. $\dfrac{\sqrt{5}-\sqrt{3}}{\sqrt{5}+\sqrt{3}}$

a. $\dfrac{1-\sqrt{15}}{8}$ b. $\dfrac{1}{4}$ c. $4-\sqrt{15}$ d. -1

For problems 16 – 22, perform the indicated operation.

16. $\sqrt{-80}$

a. $-4\sqrt{5}i$ b. $4\sqrt{5}i$ c. $-80i$ d. $80i$

17. $(4-5i)+(6+3i)-(8-6i)$

    a. $6-8i$ b. $2-8i$ c. $2+4i$ d. $18-8i$

18. $\sqrt{-288}-\sqrt{-98}$

    a. $5\sqrt{2}i$ b. $-5\sqrt{2}i$ c. $\sqrt{190}i$ d. $19\sqrt{2}i$

19. $(5-6i)(4+3i)$

    a. $6-18i$ b. $9-3i$ c. $38-9i$ d. $20-18i$

20. $\dfrac{5-3i}{2+9i}$

    a. $-\dfrac{1}{5}-\dfrac{3}{5}i$ b. $\dfrac{1}{5}+\dfrac{3}{5}i$ c. $\dfrac{1}{5}-\dfrac{3}{5}i$ d. $-\dfrac{1}{5}+\dfrac{3}{5}i$

21. $\sqrt{-81}\cdot\sqrt{-64}$

    a. $72i$ b. $-72i$ c. -72 d. 72

22. i^{43}

    a. i b. $-i$ c. 1 d. -1

For problems 23 – 24, solve the radical equations.

23. $\sqrt{x-2}=x-4$

    a. $\{3, 6\}$ b. $\varnothing$ c. $\{3\}$ d. $\{6\}$

24. $(5x-8)^{\frac{1}{4}}=(4x-1)^{\frac{1}{4}}$

    a. $\left\{\dfrac{7}{4}\right\}$ b. $\{1\}$ c. $\varnothing$ d. $\{7\}$

25. Oceanographers use the model $v=3\sqrt{d}$ to describe the velocity of a tsunami, a great sea wave produced by underwater earthquakes. In the model v represents the velocity, in feet per second, of a tsunami as it approaches land, and d is the depth of the water in feet. What is the depth of the water if the speed is 42 feet per second?

    a. 196 feet   b. 28 feet   c. 588 feet   d. 1764 feet

Name _____   Date _____

Cumulative Review 1 – 10
Form A

For problems 1 – 10, perform the indicated operations. If possible, simplify the answer.

1. $7 - 2 \cdot 3 + 4 \div 2$

1. _____

2. $9 + 2\left[x^2 + 3x - 4(x + 2)\right]$

2. _____

3. $\dfrac{(2x^4)^2(2x^{-3})^2}{4x^{-5}}$

3. _____

4. $(x + 3)(x^2 - 3x + 9)$

4. _____

5. $(2x - 5)^2$

5. _____

6. $\sqrt{24x^3 y^5}$

6. _____

7. $\dfrac{1}{2 + \sqrt{5}}$

7. _____

8. $\dfrac{\dfrac{1}{x^2} + \dfrac{1}{y}}{\dfrac{1}{x} - \dfrac{1}{y^2}}$

8. _____

9. $\dfrac{4}{x^2 - 25} + \dfrac{2}{x^2 + 4x - 5}$

9. _____

10.   If $g(x) = x^2 - x + 2$, find $g(-1)$.

10. _____

Name _____   Date _____

For problems 11 – 14, solve each equation.

11. $x^3 - 8$ 11. _____

12. $12x^3 y + 5x^2 y - 2xy$ 12. _____

13. $2y^2 - 8y + xy - 4x$ 13. _____

14. $4x^4 - 64$ 14. _____

For problems 15 – 19, solve each equation or system.

15. $3(x + 4) - 2x = 7x - 6$ 15. _____

16. $\dfrac{x}{2} - \dfrac{4x}{2x - 4} = -\dfrac{4}{x - 2}$ 16. _____

17. $\sqrt{x + 7} + 8 = 13$ 17. _____

18. $x + 2y = 9$ 18. _____
        $3x - 2y = -5$

19. $x + y + z = 6$ 19. _____
        $2x - 3y - z = -2$
        $3x + y - z = 4$

For problems 20 – 23, graph each equation or inequality.

20. $4x + 6y = 18$ 20.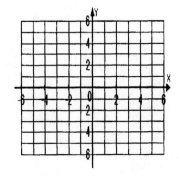

21. $3x - 2y \geq 6$ 21.

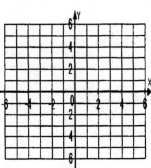

22. $y = -3$ 22.

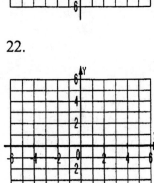

23. $y < 2x + 3$ 23.
        $3x - y < 4$

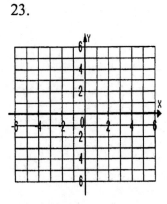

24.   Park rangers catch, tag, and then release 164 squirrels back   24. _____
        into a national park. One week later, they select a sample of
        250 squirrels, 82 of which are tagged. Assuming the ratio of
        tagged squirrels in the sample holds for all squirrels in the
        park, approximately how many squirrels are in the park?

25.   The sum of two numbers is 24. The larger number is three more   25. _____
        than twice the smaller number. Find the two numbers.

Name _____   Date _____

Cumulative Review 1 – 10
Form B

Choose the correct answer.

For problems 1 – 10, perform the indicated operations. If possible, simplify the answer.

1. $10 - 4(12 \div 2 \cdot 3)$
    a. 12   b. 2   c. −62   d. 108

2. $\sqrt{18x^4 y^5} + y^2 \sqrt{50x^4 y} - x\sqrt{32x^2 y^5}$
    a. $18x^2 y^2 \sqrt{2y}$ b. $4x^2 y^2 \sqrt{2y}$ c. $18\sqrt{2x^4 y^5}$ d. Cannot be simplified

3. $\dfrac{\left(5x^2\right)^{-2}\left(10x^3\right)}{2x^{-3}}$
    a. $\dfrac{2}{x^4}$ b. $2x^2$ c. $\dfrac{1}{5x^4}$ d. $\dfrac{x^2}{5}$

4. $-8x^2 y\left(2x^2 - 4x + 5\right)$
    a. $-16x^4 y + 32x^3 y - 40x^2 y$ b. $-16x^4 y + 32x^2 y - 40x^2 y$
    c. $-16x^4 y + 32x^3 y + 40x^2 y$ d. $-16x^4 y - 32x^2 y + 40x^2 y$

5. $\left(6x - 7y\right)^2$
    a. $12x^2 - 14y^2$ b. $36x^3 + 49y^2$
    c. $36x^2 - 84xy + 49y^2$ d. $36x^3 - 49y^2$

6. $\dfrac{4}{\sqrt{6} - 2}$
    a. $2\sqrt{6} + 4$ b. $2\sqrt{6} - 4$ c. $\sqrt{6} + 2$ d. $\sqrt{6} - 2$

7. $\dfrac{\dfrac{1}{3} - \dfrac{1}{x}}{\dfrac{1}{6} - \dfrac{1}{2x}}$

    a. $\dfrac{2x-2}{x}$ b. 2   c. 0   d. Undefined

8. $\dfrac{x^2 - 4}{x^2 + 5x + 6} \div \dfrac{x^2 + x - 6}{x^2 - 9}$

    a. -1 b. $\dfrac{x-3}{x+3}$ c. $\dfrac{(x-2)^2}{(x+3)(x-3)}$ d. $\dfrac{1}{(x+3)(x-3)}$

9. $\dfrac{2}{x} - \dfrac{3}{x-4}$

    a. $\dfrac{-5}{x-4}$ b. $\dfrac{1}{4}$ c. $\dfrac{-x-8}{x(x-4)}$ d. Cannot be

                                                     simplified

10. If $f(x) = -x^2 - 4$, find $f(-2)$

    a. -8 b. 0   c. -16 d. 16

For problems 11 – 14, factor completely.

11. $4x^2 + 20xy + 25y^2$

    a. $(2x + 5y)^2$ b. $(4x + 5y)(x + 5y)$ c. $(2x + 5y)(2x - 5y)$ d. Prime

12. $8y^2 - 27$

    a. $(2y - 3)^3$ b. $(2y - 3)(4y + 9)$

    c. $(2y - 3)(4y^2 - 6y + 9)$ d. $(2y - 3)(4y^2 + 6y + 9)$

13. $xy + 2x - 5y - 10$

    a. $(y + 2)(x - 5)$ b. $(x - 5)(y + 2)^2$ c. $(y + 2)(x + 5)$ d. Prime

14. $x^4 - 81$
   a. $(x^2 - 9)^2$
   b. $(x + 3)(x - 3)(x + 3)(x - 3)$
   c. $(x^2 + 9)(x^2 - 9)$
   d. $(x^2 + 9)(x + 3)(x - 3)$

For problems 15 – 20, solve each equation, inequality, or system of equations.

15. $-3x + 6 \le 6(x - 4)$
   a. $\left\{ x \mid x \ge \dfrac{10}{3} \right\}$
   b. $\left\{ x \mid x \le \dfrac{10}{3} \right\}$
   c. $\{ x \mid x \le -6 \}$
   d. $\{ x \mid x \ge 6 \}$

16. $\dfrac{7}{x + 2} = -\dfrac{4}{9}$
   a. $\left\{ \dfrac{55}{4} \right\}$
   b. $\left\{ -\dfrac{55}{4} \right\}$
   c. $\left\{ -\dfrac{71}{4} \right\}$
   d. No solution

17. $\sqrt{x + 4} - 6 = -8$
   a. $\{192\}$
   b. $\{8\}$
   c. $\{0\}$
   d. No solution

18. $x + 3y = -4$
    $3x\_2y = 2$
   a. $(8, -4)$
   b. $(2, -2)$
   c. $(-2, 2)$
   d. $(-4, 0)$

19. $5x^2 = 4x + 12$
   a. $\left\{ -\dfrac{6}{5}, 2 \right\}$
   b. $\{5, 12\}$
   c. $\{-6, 2\}$
   d. $\left\{ -\dfrac{2}{5}, 6 \right\}$

20. $3x + 4y = 6$
    $4x - 5y = 8$
   a. $(2, 0)$
   b. $(0, 6)$
   c. $(6, -3)$
   d. $\left(4, -\dfrac{3}{2} \right)$

Name _____   Date _____

For problems 21 – 23, graph each equation, inequality, or system of equations.

21. $2x - 3y = 6$

a.

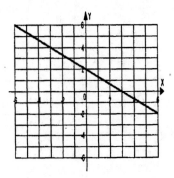

b.

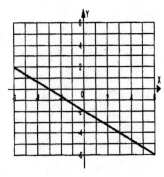

c.

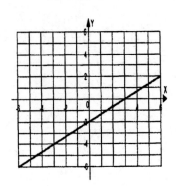

d.

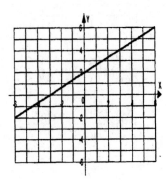

22. $x + y = -1$
$y = x - 3$

a.

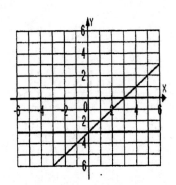

b.

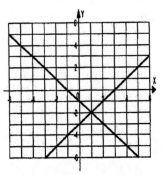

c.

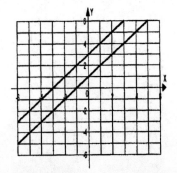

d.

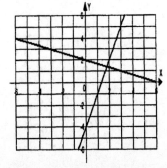

23. $y = x^2 - 4$

a.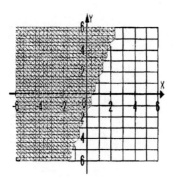

b.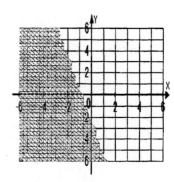

c.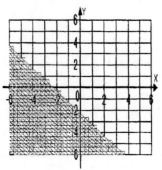

d.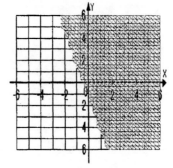

24.   Four times the sum of a number and 24 is 224. Find the number.
    a. 50   b. 32   c. 200   d. 2

25.   Find the slope of a line that passes through the points $(-3, -4)$ and $(5, 4)$.
    a. -1 b. 1   c. 0   d. Undefined

Chapter 11
Form A

1. Find the distance between (–2, –3) and (4, 6). If necessary, round   1. _____
   the answer to 2 decimal places.

2. Find the midpoint of the line-segment whose endpoints are   2. _____
   (–3, 6) and (–1, 8).

For problems 3 – 4, (a) what constant term completes the square for each binomial. Then (b) factor the resulting square trinomial.

3. $x^2 + 14x$ 3. _____

4. $x^2 - x$ 4. _____

5. Solve by completing the square $2x^2 - 6x + 2 = 0$.   5. _____

For problems 6 – 7, solve by the quadratic formula.

6. $3x^2 - 4x + 6 = 0$ 6. _____

7. $x^2 - 2x - 8 = 0$ 7. _____

8. Find the distance between (–2, –3) and (4, 6). If necessary, round   8. _____
   the answer to 2 decimals places.

9. Find the midpoint of the line-segment whose endpoints are   9. _____

For problems 10 – 11, write a quadratic equation in standard form with the given solution set.

10. $\left\{ -\dfrac{4}{3}, \dfrac{2}{5} \right\}$ 10. _____

11. $\{-4i, 4i\}$ 11. _____

For problems 12 – 16, solve using the method of your choice.

12. $(3x+2)^2 - 4 = 0$ 12. _____

13. $(x+1)(x-3) = 6$ 13. _____

14. $\dfrac{1}{x+1} + \dfrac{2}{x+2} = 4$ 14. _____

15. $x^4 - 6x^3 + 5 = 0$ 15. _____

16. $2x + x^{\frac{1}{2}} - 3 = 0$ 16. _____

For problems 17 – 20, solve each inequality. Express answers in interval form.

17. $x^2 - 2x - 24 < 0$ 17. _____

18. $x^2 - 4x \geq 0$ 18. _____

19. $\dfrac{x+8}{x-4} \leq 0$ 19. _____

20. $\dfrac{x-1}{x+3} \geq 2$ 20. _____

Name _____   Date _____

For problems 21 – 22, find the (a) vertex, (b) x-intercepts, (c) y-intercept, (d) axis of symmetry, and (e) graph the function. Round irrational numbers to the nearest hundredth.

21. $f(x) = -(x-2)^2 + 3$

21a. _____

b. _____

c. _____

d. _____

e.

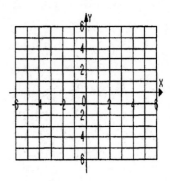

22. $f(x) = 2x^2 - 2x - 4$

22a. _____

b. _____

c. _____

d. _____

e.

23.   The number of inches that a young redwood tree grows per year can be modeled by $f(x) = 0.05x^2 + x + 1$, where x represents annual rainfall in inches, and $f(x)$ is the tree's annual growth, in inches. How many inches of rainfall produces the maximum annual growth in the tree?

23. _____

24. The distance h traveled in t seconds by an object dropped from a certain height is $h = 16t^2$. If an object is dropped from a height of 27 feet, how long will it take before the object hits the ground? Leave your answer in simplified radical form.

24. _____

25. A ball is thrown straight up from a rooftop 128 feet high with an initial speed of 40 feet per second. The function $s(t) = 16t^2 + 40t + 128$ models the ball's height above the ground, $s(t)$, in feet, t seconds after it was thrown. During which time period will the ball's height exceed that of the rooftop?

25. _____

Chapter 11
Form B

1. Find the distance between (–2, 4) and (6, –8). If necessary, round the answer to 2 decimal places.

   1. _____

2. Find the midpoint of the line-segment whose endpoints are (–5, 4) and (7, 8).

   2. _____

For problems 3 – 4, (a) what constant term completes the square for each binomial. Then (b) factor the resulting square trinomial.

3. $x^2 + 6x$

   3. _____

4. $x^2 + \dfrac{1}{3}x$

   4. _____

5. Solve by completing the square $3x^2 - 9x + 12 = 0$.

   5. _____

For problems 6 – 7, solve by the quadratic formula.

6. $4x^2 = -6x + 3$

   6. _____

7. $5x^2 + 11x = -2$

   7. _____

8. Find the distance between (–2, 4) and (6, –8). If necessary, round the answer to 2 decimal places.

   8. _____

9. Find the midpoint of the line-segment whose endpoints are (–5, 4) and (7, 8).

   9. _____

For problems 10 – 11, write a quadratic equation in standard form with the given solution set.

10. $\left\{ -\dfrac{1}{2}, \dfrac{3}{4} \right\}$

    10. _____

11. $\{-5i, 5i\}$ 11. _____

For problems 12 – 16, solve using the method of your choice.

12. $(x+4)(x+2) = 2$ 12. _____

13. $(2x-1)^2 + 4 = 0$ 13. _____

14. $\dfrac{3}{x-1} + \dfrac{1}{x+5} = -4$ 14. _____

15. $x^{\frac{2}{3}} - 7x^{\frac{1}{3}} + 12 = 0$ 15. _____

16. $8x^{-4} - 10x^{-2} = -2$ 16. _____

For problems 17 – 20, solve each inequality. Express answers in interval form.

17. $4x^2 - 9 \geq 0$ 17. _____

18. $x^2 - 6x + 5 < 0$ 18. _____

19. $\dfrac{x-3}{x+2} \leq 0$ 19. _____

20. $\dfrac{x+4}{x-1} > 1$ 20. _____

Name _____ Date _____

For problems 21 – 22, find the (a) vertex, (b) x-intercepts, (c) y-intercept, (d) axis of symmetry, and (e) graph the function. Round irrational numbers to the nearest hundredth.

21. $f(x) = -(x+1)^2 + 4$

21a. _____

b. _____

c. _____

d. _____

e.

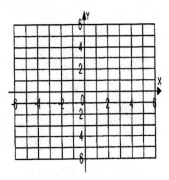

22. $f(x) = 3x^2 + 3x - 3$

22a. _____

b. _____

c. _____

d. _____

e.

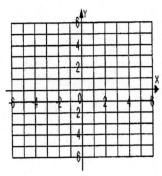

23. If the revenue is given by $R(x) = 180x - 0.06x^2$, find the value of x that yields the maximum revenue.

23. _____

24.   The perimeter of a rectangular concrete slab is 108 feet and   24. _____
        its area is 608 square feet. What is the length of the longer
        side of the slab?

25.   A baseball is hit by a batter. The function   25. _____
        $s(t) = -16t^2 + 140t + 3$ models the ball's height above the
        ground $s(t)$, in feet, t seconds after it was hit. During what time
        interval is the ball's height above 3 feet? Round answers to the
        nearest hundredth.

Name _____   Date _____

Chapter 11
Form C

For problems 1 – 2, (a) what constant term completes the square for each binomial. Then (b) factor the resulting square trinomial.

1. $x^2 + 10x$

1a _____

b. _____

2. $x^2 - 5x$

2a _____

b. _____

3. Find the distance between (–5, 0) and (4, –5). If necessary, round the answer to 2 decimal places.

3. _____

4. Find the midpoint of the line-segment whose endpoints are (5, 10) and (7, –6).

4. _____

For problems 5 – 6, write a quadratic equation in standard form with the given solution set.

5. $\left\{ -\dfrac{3}{4}, 5 \right\}$

5. _____

6. $\{ -6i, 6i \}$

6. _____

7. Solve by completing the square $3x^2 - 12x + 6 = 0$.

7. _____

For problems 8 – 13, solve each equation by the most appropriate method of your choice.

8. $(2x - 4)^2 = 16$

8. _____

9. $x^2 + 2x - 20 = 0$

9. _____

Name _____   Date _____

10. $3x^2 + 1 = -5x$ 10. _____

11. $(x-2)(x-4) = -4$ 11. _____

12. $4(x+2)^2 - 252 = 0$ 12. _____

13. $x^{-4} - 4x^{-2} + 3 = 0$ 13. _____

For problems 14 – 15, solve each inequality. Express answers in interval form.

14. $x^2 - 6x + 8 < 0$ 14. _____

15. $\dfrac{x+4}{x-2} \geq 2$ 15. _____

For problems 16 – 17, find the (a) vertex, (b) x-intercept, (c) y-intercept, (d) axis of symmetry, and (e) graph the function. Round irrational numbers to the nearest hundredth.

16. $f(x) = -3x^2 - x + 2$ 16a. _____

                                                        b. _____

                                                        c. _____

                                                        d. _____

                                                        e.

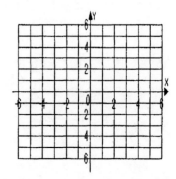

17. $f(x) = (x-2)^2 - 1$

17a. _____

b. _____

c. _____

d. _____

e.

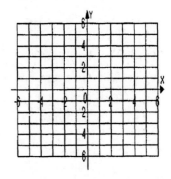

18.   A toy rocket is propelled directly upward from ground level with an initial velocity of 32 feet per second. The model $s(t) = -16t^2 + 32t$ describes the rocket's height above the ground $s(t)$, in feet, after t seconds. After how many seconds does the rocket reach its maximum height?

18. _____

19.   The distance h traveled in t seconds by an object dropped from a certain height is $h = 16t^2$. If an object is dropped from a height of 50 feet, how long will it take before the object hits the ground? Leave answer in simplified radical form.

19. _____

20.   Among all pairs of numbers whose difference is 4, find the values for the larger number so that the product is less than 0.

20. _____

Choose the correct answer.

1.   The trinomial that results from completing the square on the binomial $x^2 + 6x$ is
   a. $x^2 + 6x - 9$ b. $x^2 + 6x + 3$ c. $x^2 + 6x + 9$ d. $x^2 + 6x + 36$

2.   The trinomial that results from completing the square on the binomial $x^2 + 5x$ is
   a. $x^2 + 5x - 25$ b. $x^2 + 5x + 25$ c. $x^2 + 5x + \dfrac{5}{2}$ d. $x^2 + 5x + \dfrac{25}{4}$

3.   To use the process of completing the square on $2x^2 + 8x + 6 = 0$, the proper equation with the square completed is:
   a. $x^2 + 4x + 4 = -3 + 4$ b. $x^2 + 4x + 4 = 3 + 4$
   c. $x^2 + 4x - 16 = -3 - 16$ c. $x^2 + 4x + 16 = 3 + 16$

Choose the correct answer.

4.   Find the distance between (–2, 4) and (–3, –5).
   a. $\sqrt{82}$ b. $\sqrt{26}$ c. $4\sqrt{5}$ d. 5

5.   Find the midpoint of the line-segment whose endpoints are (–3, 4) and (–7, 6).
   a. (–10, 10)   b. (–5, 10)   c. (–10, 5)   d. (–5, 5)

6.   A quadratic equation with solutions $\left\{ -\dfrac{2}{3}, \dfrac{3}{4} \right\}$ is:
   a. $(3x - 2)(4x + 3) = 0$ b. $(2x - 3)(3x + 4) = 0$
   c. $(3x + 2)(4x - 3) = 0$ d. $(2x + 3)(3x - 4) = 0$

For problems 7 – 15, solve the equations with the most appropriate method of your choice.

7. $5x^2 - 27 = 0$
   a. $\left\{ \pm \dfrac{3\sqrt{3}}{5} \right\}$ b. $\left\{ \pm \dfrac{15\sqrt{3}}{\sqrt{5}} \right\}$ c. $\left\{ \pm \dfrac{3\sqrt{15}}{\sqrt{5}} \right\}$ d. $\left\{ \pm \dfrac{3\sqrt{15}}{5} \right\}$

8. $x^2 - 10x + 13 = 0$
   a. $\left\{ 5 \pm \sqrt{38} \right\}$ b. $\left\{ 5 \pm 3\sqrt{2} \right\}$ c. $\left\{ \pm \sqrt{7} \right\}$ d. $\left\{ 5 \pm 2\sqrt{3} \right\}$

9. $(x+2)(2x-3) = -8$

   a. $\left\{\dfrac{-1 \pm \sqrt{15}i}{4}\right\}$
   b. $\left\{\dfrac{1 \pm \sqrt{15}i}{4}\right\}$
   c. $\left\{\dfrac{-1 \pm \sqrt{17}}{4}\right\}$
   d. $\left\{\dfrac{1 \pm \sqrt{17}}{4}\right\}$

10. $4x^2 - 20x + 25 = -10$

   a. $\dfrac{-5 \pm \sqrt{10}}{2}$
   b. $\dfrac{5 \pm \sqrt{10}}{2}$
   c. $\dfrac{5 \pm \sqrt{10}i}{2}$
   d. $\dfrac{-5 \pm \sqrt{10}i}{2}$

11. $36(x-3)^2 - 7 = 0$

   a. $\left\{\dfrac{-18 \pm \sqrt{7}}{6}\right\}$
   b. $\left\{\dfrac{18 \pm \sqrt{7}}{6}\right\}$
   c. $\left\{\pm \dfrac{\sqrt{7}}{6}\right\}$
   d. $\left\{\dfrac{18 \pm 7}{6}\right\}$

12. $4x^2 + 4x = 5$

   a. $\left\{\dfrac{-1 \pm \sqrt{6}}{2}\right\}$
   b. $\left\{\dfrac{1 \pm \sqrt{6}}{2}\right\}$
   c. $\left\{\dfrac{-1 \pm 2\sqrt{6}}{2}\right\}$
   d. $\left\{\dfrac{1 \pm 2\sqrt{6}}{2}\right\}$

13. $x^4 + 2x^2 - 8 = 0$

   a. $\left\{\pm\sqrt{2}, \pm 2i\right\}$
   b. $\left\{\pm\sqrt{2}, \pm\sqrt{2}i\right\}$
   c. $\{\pm 2\}$
   d. $\left\{\pm 2, \pm\sqrt{2}\right\}$

14. $x^2 + 8x + 4 = 0$

   a. $\left\{4 \pm 2\sqrt{5}\right\}$
   b. $\left\{-4 \pm 2\sqrt{3}\right\}$
   c. $\left\{-4 \pm 2\sqrt{5}\right\}$
   d. $\left\{4 \pm 2\sqrt{3}\right\}$

15. $(x^2 - 2x)^2 - (x^2 - 2x) - 6 = 0$

   a. $\{3. -2\}$
   b. $\{1, -3, -1 \pm i\}$
   c. $\{-3, 2\}$
   d. $\{3, -1, 1 \pm i\}$

16. The solution of $-x^2 + 2x + 3 < 0$ is

   a. $(-\infty, -1) \cup (7, \infty)$
   b. $(-\infty, -3) \cup (1, \infty)$
   c. $(-1, 3)$
   d. $(-3, 1)$

17. The solution of $\dfrac{15}{x-6} \geq 15$ is

   a. $(-\infty, 6) \cup (7, \infty)$
   b. $(-6, 7]$
   c. $(-\infty, 3) \cup (6, \infty)$
   d. $[3, 6)$

18. The graph of $y = 2x^2 - 2x + 3$ has a vertex of _____ and opens _____.

    a. $\left(-\dfrac{1}{2}, \dfrac{9}{2}\right)$ b. $\left(-\dfrac{1}{2}, \dfrac{9}{2}\right)$ c. $\left(\dfrac{1}{2}, \dfrac{5}{2}\right)$ d. $\left(\dfrac{1}{2}, \dfrac{5}{2}\right)$

       downward   upward   upward   downward

19. The graph of $y = x^2 - 4x + 6$ has an axis of symmetry of

    a. $x = -2$ b. $x = 2$ c. $x = -4$ d. $x = 4$

20. The graph of $y = 2x^2 - 9x + 4$ has x-intercepts of

    a. $\left(-\dfrac{1}{2}, 0\right), (-4, 0)$ b. $\left(0, \dfrac{1}{2}\right), (0, 4)$ c. $\left(0, -\dfrac{1}{2}\right), (0, -4)$ d. $\left(\dfrac{1}{2}, 0\right), (4, 0)$

21. Find the equation of the graph.

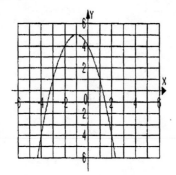

    a. $y = -x^2 - 2x + 4$ b. $y = -x^2 - 2x + 3$

    c. $y = -x^2 - 2x + 3$ d. $y = -x^2 - 2x + 2$

22. Find the equation of the graph.

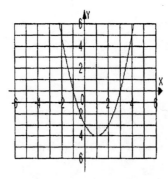

    a. $y = x^2 - 2x - 2$ b. $y = x^2 - 2x - 1$

    c. $y = x^2 - 2x - 3$ d. $y = x^2 - 2x + 3$

23. Macro Manufacturing estimates that its profit P, in hundred of dollars, after producing x thousand units can be expressed as $P(x) = -2x^2 + 8x + 3$. How many units must be produced to obtain the maximum profit?
   a. 2000 units   b. 200 units   c. 20 units   d. 2 units

24. The distance h traveled in t seconds by an object dropped from a certain height is $h = 16t^2$. If an object is dropped from a height of 24 feet, how long will it take before the object hits the ground?
   a. $2\sqrt{6}$ sec   b. $5\sqrt{6}$ sec   c. $\dfrac{\sqrt{6}}{2}$ sec   d. $\sqrt{6}$ sec

25. The volume of a box is 2,176 cubic feet. The width of the box is 8 feet and its height is 1 foot more than its length. Find the height of the box.
   a. 17 ft   b. 15 ft   c. 16 ft   d. 14 ft

Chapter 11
Form E

Choose the correct answer.

1, Find the distance between (–7, –8) and (–19, –4).
   a. $2\sqrt{205}$ b. 160   c. $4\sqrt{10}$ d. 38

2. Find the midpoint of the line segment whose endpoints are (6, 2) and (–8, –4).
   a. (1, 1)   b. (2, 2)   c. (–14, –2)   d. (–1, –1)

Choose the correct answer.

1. The trinomial that results from completing the square on the binomial $x^2 - 8x$ is
   a. $x^2 - 8x + 64$ b. $x^2 - 8x + 4$ c. $x^2 - 8x - 16$ d. $x^2 - 8x + 16$

2. The trinomial that results from completing the square on the binomial $x^2 + 7x$ is
   a. $x^2 + 7x + \dfrac{1}{2}$ b. $x^2 + 7x + \dfrac{49}{4}$ c. $x^2 + 7x + 14$ d. $x^2 + 7x + 49$

3. To use the process of completing the square on $3x^2 + 9x - 6 = 0$, the proper equation with the square completed is
   a. $x^2 + 3x + \dfrac{9}{4} = 2 + \dfrac{9}{4}$ b. $3x^2 + 9x + \dfrac{9}{4} = 6 + \dfrac{9}{4}$

   c. $x^2 + 3x + 9 = 2 + 9$ d. $3x^2 + 9x + \dfrac{81}{4} = 6 + \dfrac{81}{4}$

4. The value of the discriminant for $x^2 + 7x = -5$ is:
   a. 69   b. 29   c. 49   d. 18

5. The equation $4x^2 - 9x = 8$ has _____ answer(s).
   a. 2 rational   b. 2 imaginary   c. 2 irrational   d. 1 rational

6. A quadratic equation with solutions $\left\{-\dfrac{1}{4}, \dfrac{3}{4}\right\}$ is
   a. $(x - 4)(3x + 4) = 0$ b. $(4x - 1)(4x + 3) = 0$
   c. $(x + 4)(3x - 4) = 0$ d. $(4x + 1)(4x - 3) = 0$

Name _____   Date _____

For problems 7 – 14, solve the equations with the most appropriate method of your choice.

7. $7x^2 + 49 = 0$

    a. $\{\pm 7\}$ b. $\left\{\pm\sqrt{7i}\right\}$ c. $\left\{\pm\sqrt{7}\right\}$ d. $\{\pm 7i\}$

8. $3x^2 - 4x - 2 = 0$

    a. $\left\{\dfrac{2\pm\sqrt{2}i}{3}\right\}$ b. $\left\{\dfrac{2\pm 2\sqrt{10}}{3}\right\}$ c. $\left\{\dfrac{-2\pm\sqrt{10}}{3}\right\}$ d. $\left\{\dfrac{2\pm\sqrt{10}}{3}\right\}$

9. $(x+3)(x-4) = 12$

    a. $\left\{\dfrac{-1\pm\sqrt{97}}{2}\right\}$ b. $\{0, 1\}$ c. $\left\{\dfrac{1\pm 4\sqrt{2}i}{3}\right\}$ d. $\left\{1\pm 2\sqrt{2}i\right\}$

10. $2x^{-2} + 11x^{-1} + 5 = 0$

    a. $\left\{-5, -\dfrac{1}{2}\right\}$ b. $\left\{5, \dfrac{1}{2}\right\}$ c. $\left\{-2, -\dfrac{1}{5}\right\}$ d. $\left\{\dfrac{1}{5}, 2\right\}$

11. $x^4 + 8x^2 + 16 = 0$

    a. $\{-4\}$ b. $\{\pm 2\}$ c. $\{\pm 2i\}$ d. $\varnothing$

12. $2x(x-4) = 8$

    a. $\left\{4\pm 4\sqrt{2}\right\}$ b. $\left\{2\pm 2\sqrt{2}\right\}$ c. $\left\{2\pm 4\sqrt{2}\right\}$ d. $\{4,8\}$

13. $x^2 + 10x + 25 = -49$

    a. $\{-5\pm 7i\}$ b. $\{5\pm 7i\}$ c. $\{4,6\}$ d. $\{-6,-4\}$

14. $8x^2 - 5 = -18x$

    a. $\dfrac{-9\pm\sqrt{41}}{8}$ b. $\dfrac{9\pm\sqrt{41}i}{8}$ c. $\left\{-\dfrac{1}{4}, \dfrac{5}{2}\right\}$ d. $\left\{-\dfrac{5}{2}, \dfrac{1}{4}\right\}$

Name _____   Date _____

15.   Find the equation that corresponds to the graph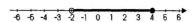

a. $(x-2)(x-4) \le 0$ b. $(x-2)(x+4) < 0$

c. $\dfrac{x-4}{x+2} \le 0$ d. $\dfrac{x-2}{x+4} < 0$

16.   The solution of $2x^2 - 9x \le 18$ is

a. $\left[-6, \dfrac{3}{2} \right]$ b. $\left[-\dfrac{3}{2}, 6 \right]$

c. $\left(-\infty, -6 \right] \cup \left[\dfrac{3}{2}, \infty \right)$ d. $\left(-\infty, -\dfrac{3}{2} \right] \cup \left[6, \infty \right)$

17.   The solution of $\dfrac{x+6}{x-3} \ge 2$ is

a. $(-\infty, -4) \cup (3, \infty)$ b. $(3, 12]$ c. $(-\infty, -6) \cup (3, \infty)$ d. $[3, 12)$

18.   The graph of $y = -3x^2 - 4x + 9$ has a vertex of _____ and opens _____.

a. $\left(-\dfrac{2}{3}, \dfrac{31}{3} \right)$ b. $\left(\dfrac{2}{3}, 5 \right)$ c. $\left(-\dfrac{2}{3}, \dfrac{31}{3} \right)$ d. $\left(\dfrac{2}{3}, 5 \right)$

  upward   downward   downward   upward

19.   The graph of $y = x^2 + 8 - 7x$ has an axis of symmetry of

a. $x = \dfrac{7}{2}$ b. $x = 4$ c. $x = -\dfrac{7}{2}$ d. $x = -4$

20.   The graph of $y = x^2 + 8 - 7x$ has x-intercepts of
a. $(0, 0.6)(0, 6.4)$ b. $(0.6, 0)(6.4, 0)$
c. $(0, -0.5)(0, 7.5)$ d. $(-0.5, 0)(7.5, 0)$

21.   Find the equation of the graph.

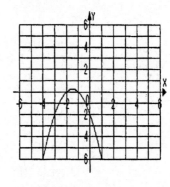

    a. $y = -x^2 + 3x - 2$ b. $y = x^2 + 3x + 2$

    c. $y = -x^2 - 3x + 2$ d. $y = -x^2 - 3x - 2$

22.   Find the equation of the graph.

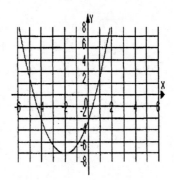

    a. $y = -x^2 - 4x + 3$ b. $y = x^2 - 4x - 3$

    c. $y = x^2 + 4x - 3$ d. $y = x^2 - 4x + 3$

23.   The revenue function $R(x) = 2000 + 100x - x^2$ represents the dollars received for selling x
       items. For what values of x will the revenue be a maximum?
       a. 20   b. 5   c. 100   d. 50

24.   In 2 years, an investment of \$3400 grows to \$3,677.44. Use the compound interest
       formula $A = P(1 + r)^t$ to find the annual interest rate.
       a. .01%   b. 4%   c. .4%   d. 40%

25.   A ball is thrown straight up from a rooftop 96 feet high with an initial speed of 80 feet
       per second. The function $s(t) = -16t^2 + 80t + 96$ models the ball's height above the
       ground $s(t)$, in feet, t seconds after it was thrown. During which time period will the
       ball's height exceed that of the rooftop?
       a. 0 to 5 sec   b. 1 to 5 sec   c. 6 to 16 sec   d. 2 to 3 sec

Name _____   Date _____

Choose the correct answer.

1.   The trinomial that results from completing the square on the binomial $x^2 - \dfrac{2}{3}x$ is

   a. $x^2 - \dfrac{2}{3}x + \dfrac{1}{9}$ b. $x^2 - \dfrac{2}{3}x + \dfrac{4}{3}$ c. $x^2 - \dfrac{2}{3}x + \dfrac{1}{6}$ d. $x^2 - \dfrac{2}{3}x + \dfrac{2}{81}$

2.   To use the process of completing the square on $4x^2 - 20x + 12 = 0$, the proper equation with the square completed is

   a. $x^2 - 5x + 25 = -3 + 25$ b. $x^2 - 5x + 25 = -3 - 25$

   c. $x^2 - 5x + \dfrac{25}{4} = -3 + \dfrac{25}{4}$ d. $x^2 - 5x + \dfrac{25}{4} = 3 + \dfrac{25}{4}$

Choose the correct answer.

3.   Find the distance between (–6, 12) and (–4, 3).

   a. $\sqrt{325}$ b. $5\sqrt{13}$ c. 5   d. $\sqrt{85}$

4.   Find the midpoint of the line segment whose endpoints are (4, 7) and (–6, 5).

   a. (6, –5)   b. (–2, 12)   c. $\left(\dfrac{11}{2}, -\dfrac{1}{2}\right)$ d. (–1, 6)

5.   Find the midpoint of the line segment whose endpoints are (4, 7) and (–6, 5).

   a. (6, –5)   b. (–2, 12)   c. $\left(\dfrac{11}{2}, -\dfrac{1}{2}\right)$ d. (–1, 6)

6.   A quadratic equation with solutions $\{-3i, 3i\}$ is

   a. $-x^2 = -9$ b. $x^2 - 9 = 0$
   c. $x^2 - 6x = -9$ d. $x^2 + 9 = 0$

For problems 7 – 14, solve the equations with the most appropriate method of your choice.

7. $2x^2 - 75 = 0$

   a. $\left\{\pm\dfrac{5\pm\sqrt{6}}{\sqrt{2}}\right\}$ b. $\left\{\pm\dfrac{6\sqrt{5}}{\sqrt{2}}\right\}$ c. $\left\{\pm\dfrac{5\sqrt{3}}{2}\right\}$ d. $\left\{\pm\dfrac{5\sqrt{6}}{2}\right\}$

8. $x(x-12) = -8$

    a. $\{-6 \pm 2\sqrt{7})$
    b. $\{6 \pm 2\sqrt{7})$
    c. $\{-6 \pm 2\sqrt{11})$
    d. $\{\pm\sqrt{34}$

9. $x^4 + 6x^2 - 27 = 0$

    a. $\{\pm 3, \pm\sqrt{3})$
    b. $\{\pm 3, \pm 3i)$
    c. $\{\pm 3 \pm \sqrt{3}i)$
    d. $\{\pm 3)$

10. $(x^2 + 4x)^2 - 25 = 0$

    a. $\{\pm 5\}$
    b. $\{\pm 5i\}$
    c. $\{5, -1, 2 \pm i\}$
    d. $\{-5, 1 - 2 \pm i\}$

11. $2x^2 - 6x - 3 = 0$

    a. $\left\{\dfrac{-3 \pm \sqrt{3}}{2}\right\}$
    b. $\left\{\dfrac{-3 \pm \sqrt{15}}{2}\right\}$
    c. $\left\{\dfrac{3 \pm \sqrt{15}}{2}\right\}$
    d. $\left\{\dfrac{3 \pm \sqrt{3}}{2}\right\}$

12. $4^2 - 1 = -2x$

    a. $\left\{\dfrac{-1 \pm \sqrt{5}}{4}\right\}$
    b. $\left\{\dfrac{1 \pm 2\sqrt{5}}{4}\right\}$
    c. $\left\{\dfrac{1 \pm \sqrt{5}}{4}\right\}$
    d. $\left\{\dfrac{-1 \pm 2\sqrt{5}}{4}\right\}$

13. $2x^2 - 4x + 9 = 0$

    a. $\left\{2 \pm \sqrt{14i}\right\}$
    b. $\left\{\dfrac{2 \pm \sqrt{14i}}{2}\right\}$
    c. $\{-1, 9\}$
    d. $\left\{\pm \dfrac{2i}{3}\right\}$

14. $25(x-1)^2 - 2 = 0$

    a. $\left\{\pm \dfrac{\sqrt{2}}{5}\right\}$
    b. $\left\{\dfrac{1 \pm \sqrt{2}}{5}\right\}$
    c. $\left\{\dfrac{-5 \pm \sqrt{2}}{5}\right\}$
    d. $\left\{\dfrac{5 \pm \sqrt{2}}{5}\right\}$

15.   Find the equation that corresponds to the graph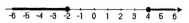

   a. $(x+2)(x-4) \geq 0$ b. $(x+2)(x-4) \leq 0$

   c. $\dfrac{x+2}{x-4} \geq 0$ d. $\dfrac{x-4}{x+2} \leq 0$

16.   Find the equation that corresponds to the graph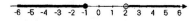

   a. $(x-1)(x+2) \leq 0$ b. $(x+1)(x-2) \leq 0$

   c. $\dfrac{x+1}{x-2} \leq 0$ d. $\dfrac{x-2}{x+1} \geq 0$

17.   The solution of $\dfrac{20}{x-7} \leq 5$ is

   a. $(-\infty, 7) \cup [11, \infty)$ b. $(7, 11]$ c. $[3, 7)$ d. $(-\infty, 3) \cup (7, \infty)$

18.   The graph of $y = -x^2 + 5x - 10$ has a vertex of _____ and opens _____.

   a. $\left(\dfrac{5}{2}, -\dfrac{15}{4}\right)$ b. $\left(-\dfrac{5}{2}, -\dfrac{115}{4}\right)$ c. $\left(\dfrac{5}{2}, -\dfrac{115}{4}\right)$ d. $\left(\dfrac{5}{2}, -\dfrac{15}{4}\right)$

        upward   downward   upward   downward

19.   The equation of the graph of _____ with an axis of symmetry of $x = -1$ is

   a. $y = x^2 - x + 1$ b. $y = 2x^2 + 4x - 6$ c. $y = x^2 - 2x + 3$ d. $y = 2x^2 - 4x + 3$

20.   The graph with x-intercepts of $(-1, 0)$ and $(2, 0)$ is

   a. $y = x^2 + x + 2$ b. $y = -x^2 - x - 2$ c. $y = x^2 - x - 2$ d. $y = x^2 + x - 2$

Name _____   Date _____

21.   Find the equation of the graph.

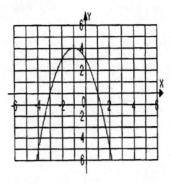

    a. $y = -x^2 + 2x + 3$ b. $y = -2x^2 + x - 6$

    c. $y = -x^2 - 2x + 3$ d. $y = -x^2 - 2x - 3$

22.   Find the equation of the graph.

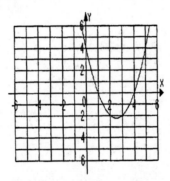

    a. $y = x^2 - 5x + 4$ b. $y = x^2 - 5x - 3$

    c. $y = x^2 + 5x + 4$ d. $y = x^2 - 5x - 4$

23.   The volume of a box is 4,104 cubic feet. The width of the box is 9 feet and its height is 5 feet more than its length. Find the height of the box.
    a. 25 ft   b. 24 ft   c. 19 ft   d. 14 ft

24.   Jafco Manufacturing estimates that its profit P, in hundreds of dollars, after producing x thousand units can be expressed $P(x) = -5x^2 + 30x - 3$. What is the maximum profit?
    a. $3000   b. $210.50   c. $360,300   d. $4,200

25.   In 2 years, an investment $2,700 grows to $2,920.32. Use the compound interest formula $A = P(1+r)^2$ to find the annual interest rate.
    a. 1.04%   b. .04%   c. 4%   d. 40%

Name _____   Date _____

Chapter 12
Form A

In Exercises 1 – 3, write each equation in its equivalent logarithmic form.

1.   Write $y = \log_4 x$ in equivalent exponential form.   1. _____

2. $\log_2 64 = x$ 2. _____

3. $2 = \log_3 x$ 3. _____

In Exercises 4 – 6, write each equation in its equivalent logarithmic form.

4.   Write $y = \left(\dfrac{3}{4}\right)^x$ in equivalent logarithmic form.   4. _____

5. $9^3 = 729$ 5. _____

6. $x^4 = 256$ 6. _____

In Exercises 7 – 9, use properties of logarithm to condense each logarithmic expression as much as possible. Write the expression as a single logarithm whose coefficient is 1.

7. $5\log_b x - 3\log_b y$ 7. _____

8. $\dfrac{1}{2}\ln x + 2\ln y$ 8. _____

9. $3\log x + 4\log y - 6\log z$ 9. _____

Exercises 10 –12, use properties of logarithm to expand each logarithmic expression as much as possible.

10. $\log_6 x^2 y^3$ 10. _____

11. $\ln\sqrt{\dfrac{x}{y}}$ 11. _____

12. $\log \dfrac{6}{x^5}$ 12. _____

13.   Find the domain of $f(x) = \log_4(x+2)$.   13. _____

14.   Evaluate $\log_6 100$ to four decimals places.   14. _____

For problems 15 – 18, solve each equation. If necessary round answers to 2 decimal places.

15. $2^{4x-3} = 32$ 15. _____

16. $e^{-2x} = 1.5$ 16. _____

17. $\log_5(x+1) = 2$ 17. _____

18. $\log x + \log(x - 21) = 2$ 18. _____

19.   Use the compound interest formula $A = P\left(1 + \dfrac{r}{n}\right)^{nt}$ to solve   19. _____

        this problem. If you invested \$5000 in an account which earns
        4% compounded quarterly, how long will it take for the money
        to grow to \$6874.70?

20.   The magnitude of an earthquake of intensity I is given by   20. _____

        $R = \log \dfrac{I}{I_\circ}$ where $I_\circ$ is the intensity of a barely felt zero-level

        earthquake. If an earthquake has an intensity of $10^{6.8}$ times the
        intensity of a zero-level earthquake, what is its magnitude on the
        Richter scale?

Chapter 12
Form B

In exercises 1 – 3, write each equation in its equivalent logarithmic form.

1.   Write $y = \log_6 (x + 2)$ in equivalent exponential form.   1. _____

2. $\log_3 81 = x$ 2. _____

3. $5 = \log_2 x$ 3. _____

In Exercises 4 – 6, write each equation in its equivalent logarithmic form.

4.   Write $y = \left(\dfrac{4}{3}\right)^{1-x}$ in equivalent logarithmic form.   4. _____

5. $4^3 = 64$ 5. _____

6. $x^5 = 243$ 6. _____

In exercises 7 – 9, use properties of logarithm to condense each logarithmic expression as much as possible. Write the expression as a single logarithm whose coefficient is 1.

7. $(x + 1)\log 4 + 13\log y - 2\log z$ 7. _____

8. $9\log_b x + 2\log_b y$ 8. _____

9. $2\ln x - 4\ln y - 3\ln z$ 9. _____

Exercises 10 –12, use properties of logarithm to expand each logarithmic expression as much as possible.

10. $\log_7 \sqrt[4]{xy}$ 10. _____

11. $\log_3 \sqrt{\dfrac{x^2}{y}}$ 11. _____

12. $\log \dfrac{4}{x^3}$ 12. _____

13. Find the domain of $f(x) = \log_3(6-x)$.   13. _____

14. Evaluate $\log_3 42$ to four decimals places.   14. _____

For problems 15 – 18, solve each equation. If necessary round answers to 2 decimal places.

15. $7^{x+1} = \dfrac{1}{49}$ 15. _____

16. $3e^{-4x} = 26$ 16. _____

17. $\log(2x+35) = 2$ 17. _____

18. $\log_2(x+3) + \log_2 x = 2$ 18. _____

19. Use the compound interest formula $A = P\left(1 + \dfrac{r}{n}\right)^{nt}$ to solve   19. _____
     this problem. If you invested $5000 in an account which earns
     5% compounded quarterly, how much is in your account after
     4 years? Round your answer to the nearest cent.

20. The magnitude of an earthquake of intensity I is given by   20. _____
     $R = \log \dfrac{I}{I_o}$ where I_o is the intensity of a barely felt zero-level
     earthquake. If an earthquake has an intensity of $10^{7.9}$ times the
     intensity of a zero-level earthquake, what is its magnitude on the
     Richter scale?

Chapter 12
Form C

In Exercises 1 – 3, write each equation in its equivalent logarithmic form.

1.   Write $y = \log_8 2 = x$ in equivalent exponential form.   1. _____

2. $\log_x 125 = 3$ 2. _____

3. $\log_6 x = 2$ 3. _____

In Exercises 4 – 6, write each equation in its equivalent logarithmic form.

4.   Write $y = \left(\dfrac{3}{4}\right)^{4x-4}$ in equivalent logarithmic form.   4. _____

5. $7^2 = 49$ 5. _____

6. $x^5 = 243$ 6. _____

In Exercises 7 – 9, use properties of logarithm to condense each logarithmic expression as much as possible. Write the expression as a single logarithm whose coefficient is 1.

7. $6 \ln y + 4 \ln z$ 7. _____

8. $3 \log x - 5 \log y - 6 \log z$ 8. _____

9. $3 \log x + \dfrac{1}{2} \log y$ 9. _____

Exercises 10 –12, use properties of logarithm to expand each logarithmic expression as much as possible.

10. $\ln \dfrac{x^3 y^4}{z^2}$ 10. _____

11. $\log \dfrac{3}{y^4}$ 11. _____

12. $\ln(7x)$ 12. _____

13.   Find the domain of $f(x) = \log_3(6-x)$.   13. _____

14.   Evaluate $\log_8 39$ to four decimals places.   14. _____

For problems 15 – 18, solve each equation. If necessary round answers to 2 decimal places.

15. $3^{5x-6} = 81$ 15. _____

16. $e^{7x} = 4$ 16. _____

17. $\log_{81}(x+3) = \dfrac{1}{2}$ 17. _____

18. $\log_6 x + \log_6(x+5) = 2$ 18. _____

19.   For this problem you may need to use one or both of these   19. _____

formulas: $A = P\left(1+\dfrac{r}{n}\right)^{nt}$ and $A = Pe^{rt}$ to solve this problem.

If you invested \$1000 in an account which earns 8.5% compounded semiannually, how much is in your account after 6 years? Round your answer to the nearest cent.

20.   A radioactive substance decays so that the amount A present   20. _____
at time t, in years, is $A = A_0 e^{-1.5t}$. Find the half-life (time for half to decay) of this substance. Round your answer to 2 decimals places.

Name _____   Date _____

Chapter 12
Form D

Choose the correct answer.

1.   Find the equation of the graph below.

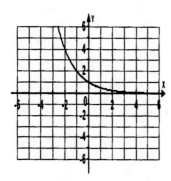

a. $f(x) = 2^x$ b. $f(x) = 2^{-x}$ c. $f(x) = -2^{-x}$ d. $f(x) = -2^{-x} + 3$

2.   Find the equation of the graph below.

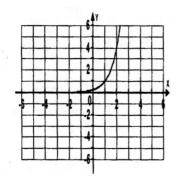

a. $f(x) = -4^x$ b. $f(x) = f^x$ c. $f(x) = 4^x - 1$ d. $y = 4^{(x-1)}$

3.   If the f and g were graphed in the same rectangular coordinate system. Describe how the graph of g relates to the graph of f.

$$f(x) = 3^x \text{ and } g(x) = 3^{x+1}$$

a. The graph of g is the graph of f shifted 1 unit to the left.
b. The graph of g is the graph of f shifted 1 unit to the right.
c. The graph of g is the graph of f shifted 1 unit up.
d. The graph of g is the graph of f shifted 1 unit down.

Name _____   Date _____

4. If the *f* and *g* were graphed in the same rectangular coordinate system. Describe how the graph of *g* relates to the graph of *f*.

$$f(x) = 4^x \text{ and } g(x) = 4^x - 2$$

a. The graph of *g* is the graph of *f* shifted 2 unit to the left.
b. The graph of *g* is the graph of *f* shifted 2 unit to the right.
c. The graph of *g* is the graph of *f* shifted 2 unit up.
d. The graph of *g* is the graph of *f* shifted 2 unit down.

5. Determine the point where the graph of *f* and *g* intersect in the same rectangular coordinate system.

$$f(x) = 3^x \text{ and } g(x) = 3^{-x}$$

a. $(0, 1)$ b. $(1, 0)$ c. $(3, 0)$ d. $(0, -3)$

6. Find the equation of the graph below.

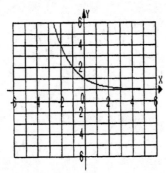

a. $y = \left(-\dfrac{1}{2}\right)^x$ b. $y = -\left(\dfrac{1}{2}\right)^x$ c. $y = 2^x$ d. $y = \left(\dfrac{1}{2}\right)^x$

7.. Graph $y = \log_2 x - 1$

a.

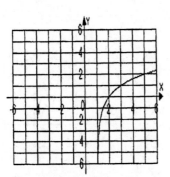

b.

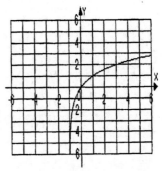

c.

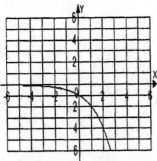

d.

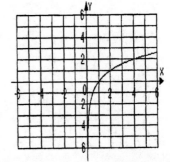

T-267

8. Write the equation $\log_{32} 64 = \dfrac{6}{5}$ in exponential form.

   a. $\left(\dfrac{6}{5}\right)^{32} = 64$.　　　b. $64^{\frac{5}{6}} = 32$　　　c. $64^{\frac{6}{5}} = 32$　　　d. $32^{\frac{6}{5}} = 64$

9. Write the equation $5^3 = 125$ in logarithmic form.
   a. $\log_{125} 5 = 3$　　　b. $\log_3 125 = 5$　　　c. $\log_5 125 = 3$　　　d. $\log_{\frac{1}{3}} 125 = 5$

10. Write the equation $5x = 8^y$ in logarithmic form.
   a. $y = \log_{5x} 8$　　　b. $y = \log_8 (5x)$　　　c. $5x = \log_8 y$　　　d. $y \log 8 = 5x$

11. Write $4 \log_b x + 5 \log_b y$ as a single logarithm.
   a. $20 \log_b (x + y)$　　　b. $\log_b (4x + 5y)$　　　c. $\log_b (x^4 y^5)$　　　d. $20 \log_b (xy)$

12. Use logarithms properties to expand the logarithmic expression $\log_7 \left(49x^6\right)$ as much as possible.
   a. $6 \log_7 (49x)$　　　b. $2 + 6 \log_7 x$　　　c. $2 + x \log_7 6$　　　d. $2 - 6 \log_7 x$

13. Find the value of $\log_7 14$.
   a. 2.0　　　　　　　b. 1.3562　　　　　　　c. 0.3010　　　　　　　d. 0.7376

For problems 14 – 17, solve each equation.

14. $2^{3x-8} = 256$

   a. $\{14\}$　　　　　　b. $\{4\}$　　　　　　c. $\{2\}$　　　　　　d. $\left\{\dfrac{8}{3}\right\}$

15. $e^{6.2x} = 3$
   a. $\{5.6435\}$　　　　　b. $\{0.1613\}$　　　　　c. $\{0.1772\}$　　　　　d. $\{2.0667\}$

16. $\log_8 x = \dfrac{4}{3}$

     a. $\{4\sqrt[3]{8}\}$ b. $\{5\sqrt{4}\}$ c. $\{8\}$ d. $\{16\}$

17. $\log_2 (x+7) - \log_2 x = 3$

     a. $\{-7\}$ b. $\{1\}$ c. $\{8\}$ d. $\{3\}$

18.   Find the domain of $f(x) = \log_4 (8 - x)$

     a. $(-8, \infty)$ b. $.(8, \infty)$ c. $.(-\infty, -8)$ d. $.(-\infty, 8)$

19.   In this problem, you need to use one or both of these formulas: $A = P\left(1 + \dfrac{r}{n}\right)^{nt}$ and

     $A = Pe^{rt}$. If you invested $1000 in an account which earns 7.5% compounded quarterly, how much is in your account after 5 years?

     a. $1,375   b. $1,449.95   c. $75   d. $375

20.   The number of bacteria present in a culture after t minutes is given by the formula $B = 10e^{kt}$. If there are 5519 bacteria present after 7 minutes, find k.

     a. 44.194   b. 1.052   c. 6.313   d. 0.902

Name _____   Date _____

Choose the correct answer.

1.   Find the equation of the graph below.

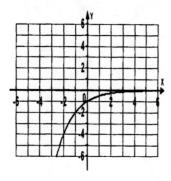

   a. $f(x) = 2^{-x}$ b. $f(x) = 2^{x-1}$ c. $f(x) = -2^{-x}$ d. $f(x) = -2^{x}$

2.   Find the equation of the graph below.

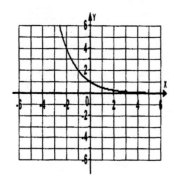

   a. $f(x) = 2^{-x}$ b. $f(x) = -2^{x}$ c. $f(x) = 2^{x-1}$ d. $y = 2^{x} - 1$

3.   If the f and g were graphed in the same rectangular coordinate system. Describe how the graph of g relates to the graph of f.

   $$f(x) = 5^{x} \text{ and } g(x) = 5^{x-1}$$

   a. The graph of g is the graph of f shifted 1 unit to the left.
   b. The graph of g is the graph of f shifted 1 unit to the right.
   c. The graph of g is the graph of f shifted 1 unit up.
   d. The graph of g is the graph of f shifted 1 unit down.

4.   If the *f* and *g* were graphed in the same rectangular coordinate system. Describe how the graph of *g* relates to the graph of *f*.

$$f(x) = 4^x \text{ and } g(x) = 4^x - 1$$

a. The graph of *g* is the graph of *f* shifted 1 unit to the left.
b. The graph of *g* is the graph of *f* shifted 1 unit to the right.
c. The graph of *g* is the graph of *f* shifted 1 unit up.
d. The graph of *g* is the graph of *f* shifted 1 unit down.

5.   Determine the point where the graph of *f* and *g* intersect in the same rectangular coordinate system.

$$f(x) = 3^{x+1} \text{ and } g(x) = 3^{-x+1}$$

a. (–3, 0)   b. (3, 0)   c. (0, 3)   d. (0, –3)

6.   Find the equation of the graph below.

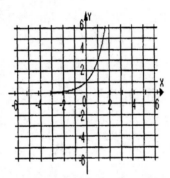

a. $y = -3^x$ b. $y = \dfrac{1}{3}^x$ c. $y = 3^{-x}$ d. $f(x) = 3^x$

7..   Graph $y = \log_4 (x+1)$

a.

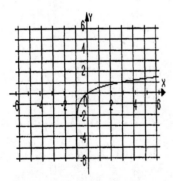

b.

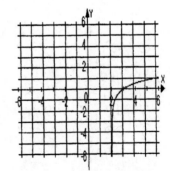

c.

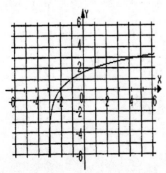

d.

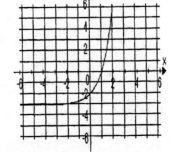

Name _____   Date _____

8. Write the equation $3^2 = 27$ in logarithmic form.

    a. $3 = \log_x 27$ b. $x = \log_{27} 3$ c. $x = \log_3 27$ d. $27 = \log_3 x$

9. Write the equation $x = \log_3 27$ in exponential form.

    a. $1^4 = y$ b. $10^y = 4$ c. $1^y = 4$ d. $10^4 = y$

10. Write the equation $x - 2 = 3^y$ in logarithmic form.

    a. $y = \log_{x-2} 3$ b. $y = \log_3 x - 2$ c. $y = \log_3 (x - 2)$ d. $x - 2 = \log_3 y$

11. Write $3 \log_4 x - 4 \log_4 y$ as a single logarithm.

    a. $x^3 y^4$ b. $\log_4 \dfrac{y^4}{x^3}$ c. $\log_4 x^3 y^4$ d. $\log_4 \dfrac{x^3}{y^4}$

12. Use logarithms properties to expand the logarithmic expression $\log_8 \left(64x^8\right)$ as much as possible.

    a. $\log_8 64 + \log_8 x^8$ b. $8 + \log_8 x^8$ c. $2 + x$ d. $\log_3 \dfrac{x^2}{y^3}$

13. Find the value of $\log_5 15$.

    a. 3   b. 1.6827   c. 0.4771   d. –0.4771

For problems 14 – 17, solve each equation.

14. $3^{1-2x} = \dfrac{1}{27}$

    a. {2}   b. {–2}   c. {–1}   d. {1}

15. $3e^{4.6x} = 2.3$

    a. {0.165}   b. {–0.058}   c. {–1.792}   d. {0.060}

16. $\log_3 x = \dfrac{7}{3}$

    a. {12.70}   b. {7}   c. {12.98}   d. {0.429}

17. $2\log x + \log 20 = 2$

a. $\{5\}$ b. $\left\{\dfrac{1}{20}\right\}$ c. $\left\{\pm\sqrt{5}\right\}$ d. $\left\{\sqrt{5}\right\}$

18. Find the domain of $f(x) = \log_3(6-2x)$.

a. $(-\infty, -3)$ b. $.(-\infty, 3)$ c. $(3, \infty)$ d. $(-3, \infty)$

19. In this problem, you need to use one or both of these formulas: $A = P\left(1+\dfrac{r}{n}\right)^{nt}$ and

$A = Pe^{rt}$. If the rate is 12.5%, find how long it takes for money to double, that is for $A = 2P$, with continuous compounding.

a. 2.77 yr.   b. 3.70 yr.   c. 11.08 yr.   d. 5.55 yr.

20. The number of a certain product that will be sold t years after the product is introduced is given by $S = 6900\ln(8t+6)$. How many of the product will be sold 8 years after the product is introduced? Round the answer to the nearest whole number.

a. 28,702   b. 29,315   c. 114,791   d. 28,721

Name _____   Date _____

Chapter 12
Form F

Determine the function notation for the graph illustrated.

1.

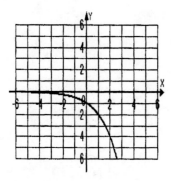

   a. $f(x) = -2^{-x}$ b. $f(x) = -2^{x}$ c. $f(x) = 2^{x} - 1$ d. $f(x) = -2^{x-1}$

2.

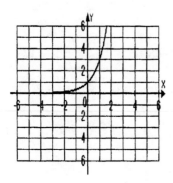

   a. $f(x) = -3^{x}$ b. $f(x) = 3^{x} - 1$ c. $f(x) = 3^{x}$ d. $f(x) = -3^{-x}$

3. $f(x) = 4x$ and $g(x) = 4^{x-1}$
   a. The graph of g is the graph of f shifted 1 unit to the left.
   b. The graph of g is the graph of f shifted 1 unit to the right.
   c. The graph of g is the graph of f shifted 1 unit up.
   d. The graph of g is the graph of f shifted 1 unit down.

4. $f(x) = 3x$ and $g(x) = 3^{x} + 2$
   a. The graph of g is the graph of f shifted 2 unit to the left.
   b. The graph of g is the graph of f shifted 2 unit to the right.
   c. The graph of g is the graph of f shifted 2 unit up.
   d. The graph of g is the graph of f shifted 2 unit down.

Name _____   Date _____

5. $f(x) = 5x$ and $g(x) = 5^{-x}$

     a. $(0, 1)$ b. $(1, 0)$ c. $(-1, 0)$ d. $(0, -1)$

6.   Find the equation of the graph below.

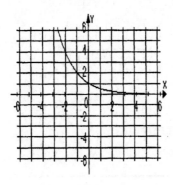

     a. $y = -2^x$ b. $y = 2^x$ c. $y = \left(\dfrac{1}{2}\right)^{-x}$ d. $y = \left(\dfrac{1}{2}\right)^{x}$

7..   Graph $y = \log_2 x + 2$.

     a.

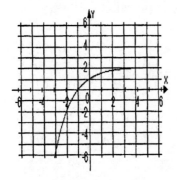

     b.

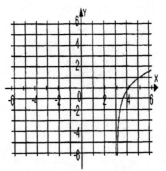

     c.

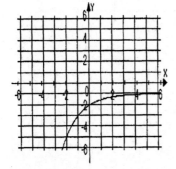

     d.

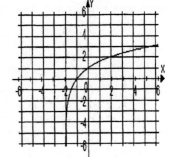

8. Write the equation $\log_{16} x = \dfrac{3}{8}$ in exponential form.

     a. $x^{\frac{3}{8}} = 16$ b. $16^{\frac{3}{8}} = x$ c. $\left(\dfrac{3}{8}\right)^{16} = x$ d. $x^{\frac{8}{3}} = 16$

9. Write the equation $4^2 = 16$ in logarithmic form.

     a. $\log_2 16 = 4$ b. $\log_{16} 2 = 4$ c. $\log_4 16 = 2$ d. $\log_{\frac{1}{2}} 16 = 4$

10. Write the equation $7x = 9^y$ in logarithmic form.

     a. $y = 7\log_x 9$ b. $y = \log_9 (7x)$ c. $7x = \log_y 9$ d. $7x = y\log 9$

11. Write $2\log_b x + 4\log_b y - lob_b z$ as a single logarithm.

     a. $\log_b (x^2 y^4 - z)$ b. $\log_b \dfrac{x^2 y^4}{z}$ c. $\log_b \dfrac{2x4y}{z}$ d. $\log_b \left(x^2 y^2 - \dfrac{1}{z}\right)$

12. Use logarithms properties to expand the logarithmic expression $\log_2 (8(x + y)^3)$ as much as possible.

     a. $3 + 3\log_2 (x + y)$ b. $3 + 3\log_2 x + 3\log_2 y$

     c. $\log_2 8 + 3\log_2 x + 3\log_2 y$ d. $3 + 3\log_2 x - \log_2 y$

13. Find the value of $\log_5 9$.

     a. 0.2553   b. 0.1908   c. 0.7325   d. 1.3652

For problems 14 – 17, solve each equation.

14. $2^{3x-11} = 128$

     a. {125}   b. {25}   c. {6}   d. {5}

15. $2e^{6.5x} = 12$

     a. {0.1538}   b. {3.6277}   c. {1.0833}   d. {0.2757}

16. $\log_{25} x = \dfrac{3}{2}$

   a. $\{125\}$
   b. $\{15\}$
   c. $\left\{5\sqrt{5}\right\}$
   d. $\left\{\sqrt[3]{25}\right\}$

17. $\log_3 (4x+15) - \log_3 x = 2$

   a. $\left\{-\dfrac{15}{4}\right\}$
   b. $\{2\}$
   c. $\{3\}$
   d. $\{9\}$

18. Find the domain of $f(x) = \log_5 (5x+10)$.

   a. $(3, \infty)$
   b. $(-2, \infty)$
   c. $(-\infty, 2)$
   d. $(-\infty, -2)$

19. The number of a certain product that will be sold t years after the product is introduced is given by $S = 2500 \ln(4t + 6)$. How many of the product will be sold 8 years after the product is introduced? Round the answer to the nearest whole number.

   a. 13,869
   b. 6937
   c. 6948
   d. 7728

20. The number of bacteria present in a culture after t minutes is given as $B(t) - 10e^{kt}$. If there are 3995 bacteria present after 3 minutes, find k.

   a. 1.997
   b. 17.971
   c. 2.995
   d. 5.99

Cumulative Review 1 – 12
Form A

For problems 1 – 8, perform the indicated operations.

1. $\dfrac{7 - 2[4 - 6^2]}{3 - 2^2}$

1. _____

2. $-\dfrac{18x^2 y^{-3}}{3^2 x^{-4} y^4}$

2. _____

3. $\dfrac{4x - 1}{x - 2} - \dfrac{3}{x^2 - 4}$

3. _____

4. $7y\sqrt{98x^2 y} - x\sqrt{18 y^3}$

4. _____

5. $\dfrac{3}{4 - \sqrt{2}}$

5. _____

6. $\sqrt[3]{\dfrac{4}{3x}}$

6. _____

7. $(x^2 - 4y)^2$

7. _____

8. $2(3 - 2x) - (2x + 3)$

8. _____

For problems 9 – 10, factor completely.

9. $8x^3 - 27$

9. _____

10. $x^3 + x^2 - 4x - 4$

10. _____

Name _____   Date _____

For problems 11 – 18, solve each equation, inequality, or system.

11. $4x - 3(x - 2) = 17x - 4$

11. _____

12. $\sqrt{2x + 3} + 4 = 6$

12. _____

13. $(5x + 6)^2 = -50$

13. _____

14. $3x^2 = 4x + 6 = 0$

14. _____

15. $\dfrac{2}{x - 3} - \dfrac{3}{x + 3} = \dfrac{12}{x^2 - 9}$

15. _____

16. $4x - 2 < 6$ and $-2x + 6 < 4$

16. _____

17. $2x + y + 4z = 12$
     $3x - 3y - 2z = 1$
     $x + 2y + 2z = 9$

17. _____

18. $x^2 + 2x - 15 \geq 0$

18. _____

19. Find the equation of the line passing through the points
     (2, 4) and (−1, 3).

19. _____

20. Solve for x: $\dfrac{2}{x} + 2y = 3z$

20. _____

Name _____   Date _____

21.   Find the domain of $f(x) = \dfrac{x-2}{x^2 + 6x + 8}$ 21. _____

22.   Write a quadratic equation whose solution set is $\left\{-3. \dfrac{1}{2}\right\}$.   22. _____

For problems 23 – 25, graph the function, equation, or inequality.

23. $y < 2x + 3$ 23.
       $y > -x - 3$

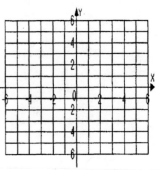

24. $f(x) = (x-2)^2 + 1$ 24.

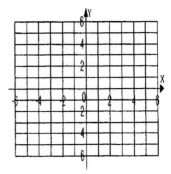

25. $y = 4$ 25.

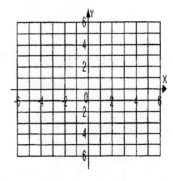

Name _____   Date _____

Cumulative Review 1 – 12
Form B

Choose the correct answer to each problem.

For problems 1 – 8, perform the indicated operations.

1. $8 \div 2 + \{3 \cdot 7 - [4 + (3 + 1)]\}$
    a. 18   b. 17   c. 19   d. 33

2. $(5r^6 pu^2)^2$
    a. $25r^{12}p^2u^4$ .b. $25r^8p^3u^4$ c. $-10r^8p^3u^4$ d. $-25r^{12}p^2u^4$

3. $\dfrac{10a^2 + 29a + 10}{2a^2 - 3a - 5} \cdot \dfrac{10a^2 - 25a}{4 - 25a^2}$

    a. $\dfrac{5a(2a-5)}{(2-5a)(a+1)}$ b. $\dfrac{(2a-5)(2a+5)}{(2-5a)(a+1)}$ c. $\dfrac{5a(2a+5)}{(2-5a)(a+1)}$ d. $\dfrac{5a}{(2-5a)(a+1)}$

4. Simplify $\dfrac{\dfrac{2}{x} + \dfrac{1}{4x}}{\dfrac{4}{3x} + \dfrac{3}{2x}}$

    a. $\dfrac{3}{12x^2}$ b. $\dfrac{1}{12x^2}$ c. $\dfrac{27}{34}$ d. $\dfrac{34}{27}$

5. $(256)^{\frac{3}{4}}$
    a. 192   b. 64   c. $\dfrac{1}{64}$ d. $\dfrac{1}{4}$

6. $(x - 5)(x^2 + 2x + 1)$
    a. $x^3 - 3x^2 - 9x - 5$ b. $x^3 - 3x^2 - 10x - 5$
    c. $x^2 + x - 5$ d. $x^3 + 2x^2 - 5$

7. $\sqrt{2x}\left(2\sqrt{x} - 4\sqrt{2}\right)$
    a. $4x - 8\sqrt{x}$ b. $2x\sqrt{2} - 8\sqrt{x}$ c. $4x - 8\sqrt{2}$ d. $2\sqrt{2x^2} - 4\sqrt{2}$

8.   Evaluate $(4j - k)^2$ for $j = 2$ and $k = 4$.
     a. 4   b. 144   c. 16   d. 80

For problems 9 – 10, factor completely.

9. $12u^2 - 5u - 25$
     a. $(4u + 5)(3u + 5)$ b. $(4u - 5)(3u + 5)$ c. $(4u - 5)(3u - 5)$ d. $(4u + 5)(3u - 5)$

10. $27u^3 - 64$
     a. $(3u - 4)^3$ b. $(3u + 4)(9u^2 - 12u + 16)$
     c. $(3u + 4)(9u^2 - 6)$ d. $(3u - 4)(9u^2 + 12u + 16)$

For problems 11 – 18, solve each equation, inequality, or system.

11. $-6(x - 6) = 36 - 6x$
     a. $\{-2\}$ b. $\{0\}$ c. All real numbers   d. No solution

12. $x^2 + 2x - 15 = 0$
     a. $\{3, 5\}$ b. $\{-5, 3\}$ c. $\{-5, -3\}$ d. $\{-3, 5\}$

13. $\dfrac{x}{x^2 - 16} + \dfrac{4}{x - 4} = \dfrac{1}{x + 4}$
     a. $\{-5\}$ b. $\varnothing$ c. $\{4\}$ d. $\{5\}$

14. $x^4 + 2x^2 - 8 = 0$
     a. $\left\{\pm \sqrt{2}, \pm 2i\right\}$ b. $\left\{\pm 2, , \pm \sqrt{2}i\right\}$ c. $\left\{\pm 2\right\}$ d. $\left\{\pm 2, , \pm \sqrt{2}\right\}$

15. $\sqrt{x + 23} = x + 11$
     a. $\{-7\}$ b. $\{-14, -7\}$ c. $\{-14\}$ d. $\varnothing$

16. $-10 \le -2x + 6 \le 8$
     a. $[-2, 7]$ b. $[-8, 1]$ c. $[-7, 2]$ d. $[-1, 8]$

17. $|x - 8| = |x - 6|$

    a. $\{7\}$ b. $\{8, 6\}$ c. $\{7, 1\}$ d. $\{1\}$

18. $x + 2y + z = 6$
$x + y - z = 7$
$11x + 17y + z = 8$

    a. $(8, -1, 0)$ b. Dependent   c. $(2, 3, -2)$ d. Inconsistent

19. Find the equation of the line passing through the points $(4, -2)$ and parallel to the line $y = 3x + 1$.

    a. $y = -3x + 14$ b. $y = 3x + 10$ c. $y = 3x - 14$ d. $y = -\dfrac{1}{3}x - \dfrac{2}{3}$

20. Solve $P = 2l + 2w$ for l.

    a. $l = \dfrac{P - 2w}{2}$ b. $l = \dfrac{P - w}{2}$ c. $l = P - w$ d. $l = 2P - w$

21. Use the discriminant to determine the number and type of solutions to $x^2 + 7x + 5 = 0$.

    a. 2 rational   b. 2 irrational   c. 1 rational   d. 2 imaginary

22. Find the vertex of the graph $f(x) = x^2 + 2x - 1$.

    a. $(1, 0)$ b. $(1, 2)$ c. $(-1, 0)$ d. $(-1, -2)$

23. The distance h traveled in t seconds by an object dropped from a certain height is $h = 16t^2$. If an object is dropped from a height of 63 feet, how long will it take before the object hits the ground?

    a. $\dfrac{3\sqrt{7}}{2}$ sec   b. $\dfrac{3\sqrt{7}}{4}$ sec   c. $3\sqrt{7}$ sec   d. $\dfrac{15\sqrt{7}}{2}$ sec

24.   Find the correct equation from the graph.   24.

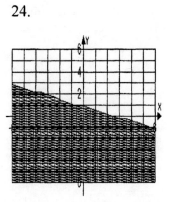

    a. $2x + 6y \leq 6$ b. $2x + 6y \geq 6$ c. $6x + 2y \leq 6$ d. $2x - 6y \geq 6$

25.   Find the correct equation from the graph.   25.

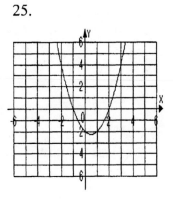

    a. $y = x^2 + x - 2$ b. $y = x^2 + 3x + 2$ c. $y = x^2 - x - 2$ d. $y = x^2 - x - 2$

Name _____   Date _____

Chapter 13
Form A

For problems 1 – 5, determine whether the equation represents a circle, an ellipse, a hyperbola, or a parabola.

1. $\dfrac{x^2}{4} + \dfrac{y^2}{9} = 1$ 1. _____

2. $y = 3x^2 - 4x + 7$ 2. _____

3. $(x + 2)^2 + (y - 3)^2 = 16$ 3. _____

4. $9(x - 1)^2 - 4(y + 3)^2 = 36$ 4. _____

5. $x = 4y^2 + 4y$ 5. _____

6.   Write the standard form of a circle with a center of $(2, -3)$ and radius 3.   6. _____

7.   Give the (a) center and (b) radius of $x^2 + y^2 + 6x - 4y + 4 = 0$.   7a. _____

                                                b. _____

8.   Give the vertex of $x = y^2 - 8y + 6$.   8. _____

9.   Give the axis of symmetry for $x = 3(y - 1)^2 + 8$.   9. _____

Name _____   Date _____

For problems 10 – 16, graph the conic section.

10. $(x-3)^2 + (y+1)^2 = 16$

10.

11. $y = -x^2 + 4x$

11.

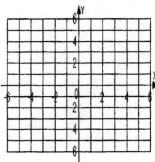

12. $4x^2 + 25y^2 = 100$

12.

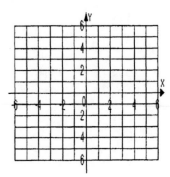

13. $9(x+2)^2 - (y+1)^2 = 9$

13.

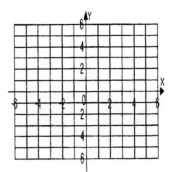

14. $x^2 + y^2 + 4x + 2y - 4 = 0$ 14.

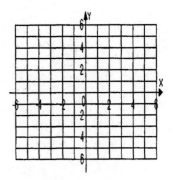

15. $36(x+1)^2 + 9y^2 = 36$ 15.

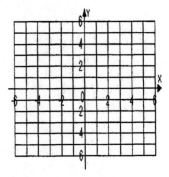

16. $x = (y+2)^2 - 1$ 16.

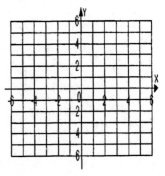

For problems 17 – 18, solve each system of equations.

17. $x^2 + y^2 = 1$ 17. _____
        $x + y = 2$

18. $x^2 + y^2 = 25$ 18. _____

        $49x^2 + 25y^2 = 1225$

19.   The cost C of manufacturing and selling x units of a product   19. _____
        is $C = 23x + 95$ and the corresponding revenue R is $R = x^2 - 40$.
        Find the break-even value of x.

20.   The sum of two numbers is 48. Their product is 551. Find the   20. _____
        two numbers.

Name _____   Date _____

Chapter 13
Form B

For problems 1 – 5, determine whether the equation represents a circle, an ellipse, a hyperbola, or a parabola.

1. $x = -y + 4y$ 1. _____

2. $9x^2 - 4y^2 = 36$ 2. _____

3. $2(x + 5)^2 + 4(y - 3)^2 = 4$ 3. _____

4. $y = x^2 - 2x$ 4. _____

5. $2x^2 + 2y^2 = 8$ 5. _____

6.   Write the standard form of a circle with a center of (4, 1) and radius 5.   6. _____

7.   Give the (a) center and (b) radius of $x^2 + y^2 - 2x + 4y = -1$.   7a. _____

                                                                       b. _____

8.   Give the vertex of $x = 2y^2 + 6y - 3$.   8. _____

9.   Give the axis of symmetry for $x = 4(y+1)^2 + 8$.   9. _____

For problems 10 – 16, graph the conic section.

10. $x = 3y^2 - 6y + 1$ 10.

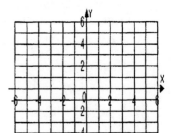

11. $\dfrac{x^2}{16} - \dfrac{y^2}{4} = 1$ 11.

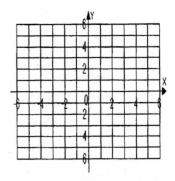

12. $25x^2 + 4(y+1)^2 = 100$ 12.

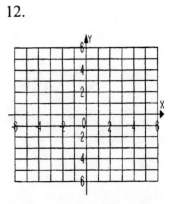

13. $8x^2 + 8y^2 = 32$

13.

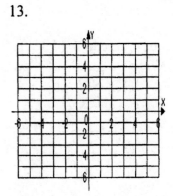

14. $y = (x+2)^2 + 4$

14.

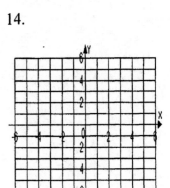

15. $4(y+1)^2 - (x+2)^2 = 4$

15.

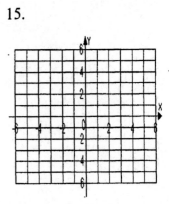

16. $x^2 + y^2 - 4y - 5 = 0$

16.

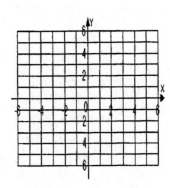

Name _____   Date _____

For problems 17 – 18, solve each system of equations.

17. $x^2 - 6y = -2$ 17. _____
       $x - y = 1$

18. $y = 2 - x^2$ 18. _____
       $2x^2 + y^2 = 3$

19.   The perimeter of a rectangle is 28 feet. The area of the   19. _____
       rectangle is 48 square feet. Find the dimensions of the
       rectangle.

20.   The cost C of manufacturing and selling x units of a product   20. _____
       is $C = 22x + 70$, and the corresponding revenue R is $R = x^2 - 65$.
       Find the break-even value of x.

Name _____   Date _____

Chapter 13
Form C

For problems 1 – 5, determine whether the equation represents a circle, ellipse, hyperbola, or parabola.

1. $16x^2 - 49y^2 = 784$ 1. _____

2. $y = -3x^2 + 5x$ 2. _____

3. $8(x-1)^2 + 16(y+3)^2 = 16$ 3. _____

4. $x - 4y = 2y^2$ 4. _____

5. $5x^2 + 5y^2 = 45$ 5. _____

6. Write the standard form of a circle with a center of $(0, 5)$ 6. _____
    and radius 6.

7. Give the (a) center and (b) radius of $x^2 + y^2 + 8x - 6y = -9$.   7a. _____

                                                              b. _____

8. Give the vertex of $x = -(y+3)^2 - 4$.   8. _____

9. Give the axis of symmetry for $x = 8y^2 - 24y + 8$.   9. _____

Name _____   Date _____

For problems 10 – 17, graph the conic section.

10. $16x^2 + 16y^2 = 64$

10.

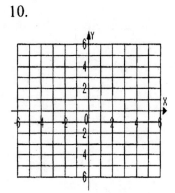

11. $\dfrac{y^2}{25} - \dfrac{x^2}{4} = 1$

11.

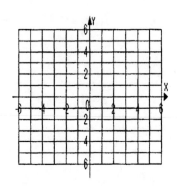

12. $y = 3x^2 - 6x$

12.

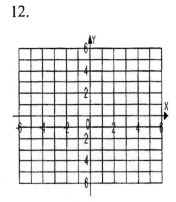

13. $4(x-1)^2 + 9(y-2)^2 = 36$

13.

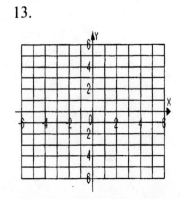

14. $(x+2)^2 + (y-5)^2 = 4$ 14.

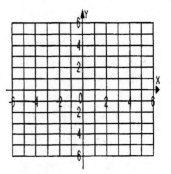

15. $x = (y-1)^2 - 2$ 15.

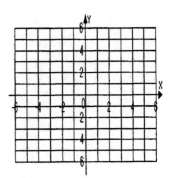

16. $x - 3 = (y+3)^2$ 16.

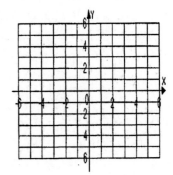

17. $x^2 + y^2 - 4x + 2y + 1 = 0$ 17.

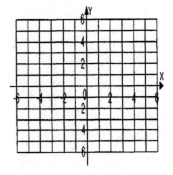

For problems 18 – 19, solve each system of equations.

18. $x^2 + y^2 = 121$

      $x + y = 22$

18. _____

19. $x^2 + y^2 = 16$

      $81x^2 + 16y^2 = 1296$

19. _____

20.   The product of two numbers is 270. Their sum is 33. Find the two numbers.

20. _____

Chapter 13
Form D

For problems 1 – 5, determine what conic section the equation represents.

1. $(x-2)^2 + (y+4)^2 = 16$

   a. circle　　　　b. ellipse　　　　c. hyperbola　　　　d. parabola

2. $y = 4x^2 + 2x - 9$

   a. circle　　　　b. ellipse　　　　c. hyperbola　　　　d. parabola

3. $x^2 - y^2 = 25$

   a. circle　　　　b. ellipse　　　　c. hyperbola　　　　d. parabola

4. $y^2 + x = 3y + 2$

   a. circle　　　　b. ellipse　　　　c. hyperbola　　　　d. parabola

5. $x^2 + 4y^2 = 16$

   a. circle　　　　b. ellipse　　　　c. hyperbola　　　　d. parabola

6. Write the standard form of a circle with a center of (–2, 1) and radius 4.

   a. $(x-2)^2 + (y-1)^2 = 16$　　　　b. $(x-2)^2 + (y-1)^2 = 4$

   b. $(x+2)^2 + (y-1)^2 = 16$　　　　d. $(x+2)^2 + (y-1)^2 = 4$

7. Give the radius of the circle with the equation $(x-4)^2 + (y+2)^2 = 4$.

   a. 2　　　　b. 4　　　　c. 8　　　　d. 16

Name _____   Date _____

8.   Give the center of the circle with the equation $4(x-3)^2 + 4(y+2)^2 = 16$.
      a. $(-3, 2)$ b. $(3, -2)$ c. $(-3, -2)$ d. $(3, 2)$

9.   Give the vertex of $x = (y+3)^2 - 1$.
      a. $(-3, 1)$ b. $(1, -3)$ c. $(-1, -3)$ d. $(-3, -1)$

10.   Which direction does the conic section in problem 9 open?
      a. up   b. down   c. right   d. left

11.   Give the axis of symmetry for $x = 3y^2 - 12y + 4$.
      a. $y = -2$ b. $y = 2$ c. $x = 2$ d. $x = -2$

12.   Graph $\dfrac{x^2}{4} + \dfrac{y^2}{9} = 1$.

      a.   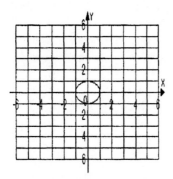   b.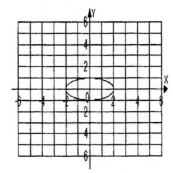

      c.   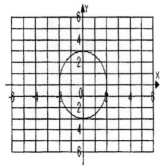   d.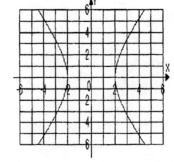

T-298

13.   Graph $4x^2 + 4y^2 = 16$.

a.   b.

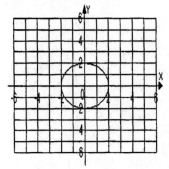   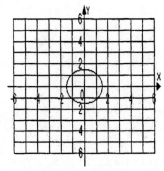

c.   d.

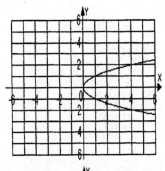   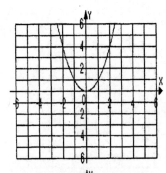

14.   Graph $y = x^2 - 2x + 1$.

a.   b.

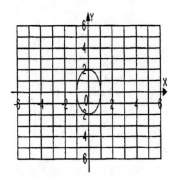   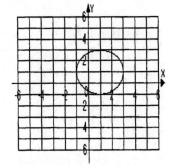

c.   d.

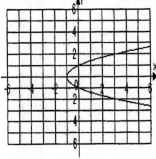   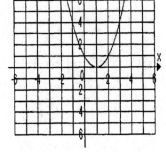

15.   Graph $4(y-1)^2 - (x+2)^2 = 4$.

a.

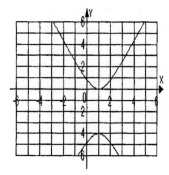

b.

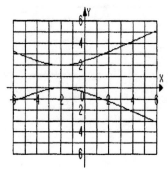

c.

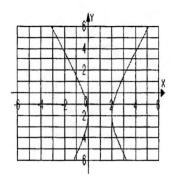

d.

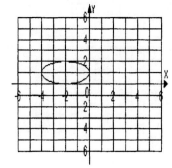

16.   Graph $x = -2(y+1)^2 - 3$.

a.

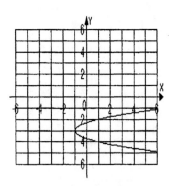

b.

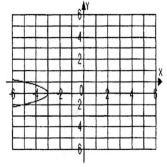

c.

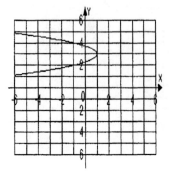

d.

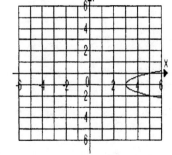

17.   Graph $(x-2)^2 + (y+2)^2 = 4$.

a.

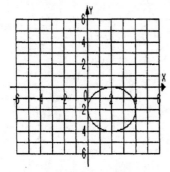

b.

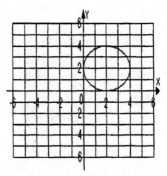

c.

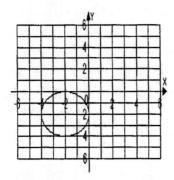

d.

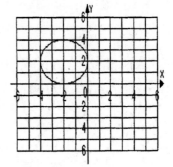

18.   Solve the system of equations.

$x^2 + y^2 = 64$

$x + y = 8$

a. $\{(0, -8),(-8, 0)\}$ b. $\{(0, 8),(8, 0)\}$

c. $\{(8, -8),(-8, -8)\}$ d. $\{(0, 0),(8, -8)\}$

19.   Solve the system of equations.

$x^2 + y^2 = 13$

$x^2 - 2y^2 = -14$

a. $\{(2, 3),(2, -3)\}$

b. $\left\{\left(1,2\sqrt{3}\right),\left(-1,2\sqrt{3}\right),\left(1,-2\sqrt{3}\right),\left(-1,-2\sqrt{3}\right)\right\}$

c. $\{(2, 3),(-2, 3),(2, -3),(-2, -3)\}$

d. $\{(-2, 3),(-2, -3)\}$

20.   The cost C of manufacturing and selling x units of a product is $C = 20x + 55$, and the corresponding revenue R is $R = x^2 - 70$. Find the break-even value of x.

    a. 30   b. 5   c. 25 or 5   d. 25

Name _____   Date _____

Chapter 13
Form E

For problems 1 – 5, determine what conic section the equation represents.

1. $x = 3y^2 - 4y$
     a. circle   b. ellipse   c. hyperbola   d. parabola

2. $x^2 + (y - 3)^2 = 25$
     a. circle   b. ellipse   c. hyperbola   d. parabola

3. $10x^2 + 10y^2 = 1$
     a. circle   b. ellipse   c. hyperbola   d. parabola

4. $4(x + 1)^2 + (y + 1)^2 = 4$
     a. circle   b. ellipse   c. hyperbola   d. parabola

5. $x^2 - y^2 = 16$
     a. circle   b. ellipse   c. hyperbola   d. parabola

6.   Write the standard form of a circle with a center of (3, –2) and radius 7.
     a. $(x - 3)^2 + (y + 2)^2 = 7$ b. $(x - 3)^2 + (y + 2)^2 = 49$
     b. $(x + 3)^2 + (y - 2)^2 = 7$ d. $(x + 3)^2 + (y - 2)^2 = 49$

7.   Give the center of the circle with the equation $(x - 1)^2 + (y + 7)^2 = 8$.
     a. (1, 7)   b. (–1, –7)   c. (–1, 7)   d. (1, –7)

8.   Give the radius of the circle with the equation $9(x - 2)^2 + 9(y - 1)^2 = 36$.
     a. 4   b. 2   c. 8   d. 16

9.   Give the vertex of $x = -2(y - 1)^2 + 3$.
     a. (3, –1)   b. (–3, 1)   c. (3, 1)   d. (–3, –1)

10. Which direction does the conic section in problem 9 open?
     a. up   b. down   c. right   d. left

11. Give the axis of symmetry for $x = 8y^2 - 12y + 4$.

   a. $x = -\dfrac{3}{4}$ b. $x = \dfrac{3}{4}$ c. $y = -\dfrac{3}{4}$ d. $y = \dfrac{3}{4}$

12. Choose the correct equation for the graph.

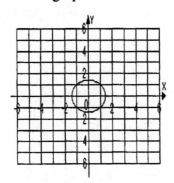

   a. $x^2 + y^2 = 16$ b. $4x^2 + 4y^2 = 1$ c. $x^2 + y^2 = 4$ d. $x^2 + y^2 = 2$

13. Choose the correct equation for the graph.

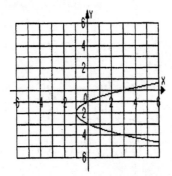

   a. $x = -(y+2)^2 + 1$ b. $x = -(y+2)^2 - 1$

   c. $x = -(y-2)^2 - 1$ d. $x = (y+2)^2 - 1$

14.   Choose the correct equation for the graph.

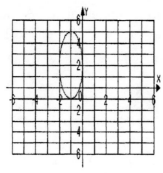

    a. $(x-1)^2 + (y+2)^2 = 9$ b. $9(x-1)^2 + (y+2)^2 = 9$

    c. $9(x+1)^2 + (y-2)^2 = 9$ d. $(x+1)^2 + (y-2)^2 = 9$

15.   Choose the correct equation for the graph.

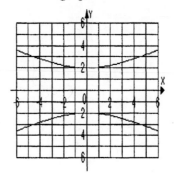

    a. $4x^2 - y^2 = 64$ b. $y^2 - 4x^2 = 16$

    c. $4y^2 + x^2 = 65$ d. $4y^2 - x^2 = 16$

16.   Choose the correct equation for the graph.

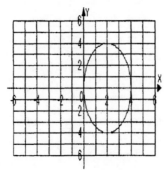

    a. $(x-2)^2 + 4y^2 = 16$ b. $(x+2)^2 + 4y^2 = 16$

    c. $4(x-2)^2 + y^2 = 16$ d. $4(x+2)^2 + y^2 = 16$

17.   Choose the correct equation for the graph

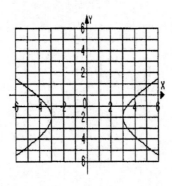

a. $4x^2 - 9(y+2)^2 = 36$ b. $4x^2 - 9(y-2)^2 = 36$

c. $9(y-2)^2 - 4x^2 = 36$ d. $9(y+2)^2 - 4x^2 = 36$

18.   Choose the correct equation for the graph.

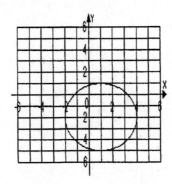

a. $x^2 + y^2 - 2x + 4y + 4 = 0$ b. $x^2 + y^2 - 2x + 4y - 4 = 0$

c. $x^2 + y^2 - 2x + 4y = 9$ d. $x^2 + y^2 + 2x - 4y + 4 = 0$

19.   The perimeter of a rectangle is 78 feet. The area of the same rectangle is 378 square feet. Find the length of the shortest side.

a. 14 ft   b. 18 ft   c. 21 ft   d. 4 ft

20.   The cost C of manufacturing and selling x units of a product is $C = 22x + 100$, and the corresponding revenue R is $R = x^2 - 35$. Find the break-even value of x.

a. 5   b. 32   c. 27   d. 27 or 5

Chapter 13
Form F

For problems 1 – 5, determine what conic section the equation represents.

1. $\dfrac{(x+2)^2}{25} + \dfrac{(y-3)^2}{16} = 1$

   a. circle   b. ellipse   c. hyperbola   d. parabola

2. $y = -3x^2 - 5$

   a. circle   b. ellipse   c. hyperbola   d. parabola

3. $y^2 - 3x + 2y = 0$

   a. circle   b. ellipse   c. hyperbola   d. parabola

4. $x^2 - y^2 = 4$

   a. circle   b. ellipse   c. hyperbola   d. parabola

5. $(x+2)^2 + y^2 = 12$

   a. circle   b. ellipse   c. hyperbola   d. parabola

6. Write the standard form of a circle with a center of $(8, 3)$ and passing through the point $(6, -3)$.

   a. $(x+8)^2 + (y-3)^2 = 81$ b. $(x-8)^2 + (y+3)^2 = 9$

   b. $(x-8)^2 + (y-3)^2 = 9$ d. $(x-8)^2 + (y+3)^2 = 81$

7. Give the center of the circle with the equation $x^2 + y^2 - 10x + 8y + 33 = 0$.

   a. $(-5, 4)$ b. $(5, -4)$ c. $(10, 4)$ d. $(10, 8)$

8. Give the radius of the circle with the equation given in problem 7.

   a. 4 b. 16 c. $2\sqrt{2}$ d. 8

9. Give the vertex of $y = -(x+1)^2 - 3$.

   a. $(3, -1)$ b. $(-3, -1)$ c. $(-1, -3)$ d. $(1, -3)$

10. Which direction does the conic section in problem 9 open?

    a. up   b. down   c. right   d. left

11. Give the axis of symmetry for $x = -4y^2 + 6y + 8$.

    a. $x = -\dfrac{3}{4}$ b. $x = \dfrac{3}{4}$ c. $y = -\dfrac{3}{4}$ d. $y = \dfrac{3}{4}$

Name _____   Date _____

12. Choose the correct equation for the graph.

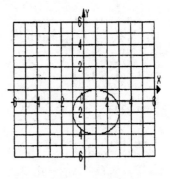

  a. $(x+1)^2 + (y-2)^2 = 4$
  b. $(x-1)^2 + (y+2)^2 = 2$
  c. $(x-1)^2 + (y+2)^2 = 4$
  d. $(x+1)^2 + (y-2)^2 = 2$

13. Choose the correct equation for the graph.

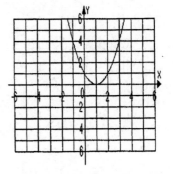

  a. $x = y^2 - 2y + 1$
  b. $x = y^2 + 2y + 1$
  c. $y = x^2 + 2x + 1$
  d. $y = x^2 - 2x + 1$

14. Choose the correct equation for the graph.

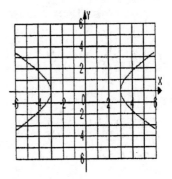

  a. $\dfrac{x^2}{4} + \dfrac{y^2}{9} = 1$

  b. $\dfrac{y^2}{9} + \dfrac{x^2}{4} = 1$

  c. $\dfrac{x^2}{9} - \dfrac{y^2}{4} = 1$

  d. $\dfrac{x^2}{4} - \dfrac{y^2}{9} = 1$

15. Choose the correct equation for the graph.

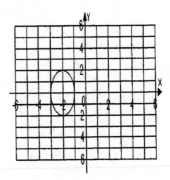

  a. $(x-2)^2 - \dfrac{y^2}{4} = 1$

  b. $16(x-2)^2 + 4y^2 = 16$

  c. $(x+2)^2 + \dfrac{y^2}{4} = 4$

  d. $16(x+2)^2 + 4y^2 = 16$

T-307

16.   Choose the correct equation for the graph.

    a. $(x+2)^2 - \dfrac{(y+1)^2}{4} = 1$

    b. $(y-2)^2 - 4(x-1)^2 = 4$

    c. $(y+2)^2 - \dfrac{(x+1)^2}{4} = 1$

    d. $4(y-2)^2 - (x-1)^2 = 4$

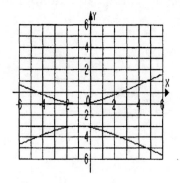

17.   Solve the system of equations.
    $x^2 + y^2 = 49$
    $x + y = 7$

    a. $\{(0, -7),(-7, 0)\}$ b. $\{(0, 0),(7, -7)\}$ c. $\{(0, 7),(7, 0)\}$ d. $\{(7, -7),(-7, -7)\}$

18.   Solve the system of equations.
    $x^2 + y^2 = 63$
    $x^2 - 3y^2 = 27$

    a. $\left\{\left(3\sqrt{6},3\right), \left(3\sqrt{6},-3\right)\right\}$
    c. $\left\{\left(-3\sqrt{6},3\right), \left(3\sqrt{6},-3\right)\right\}$

    b. $\left\{\left(3\sqrt{6},3\right), \left(3\sqrt{6},-3\right), \left(-3\sqrt{6},3\right), \left(-3\sqrt{6},-3\right)\right\}$
    d. $\left\{\left(1, \sqrt{62}\right), \left(1, -\sqrt{62}\right), \left(-1, \sqrt{62}\right), \left(-1, -\sqrt{62}\right)\right\}$

19.   The perimeter of a rectangle is 14 inches. The diagonal of the same rectangle is 5 inches. Find the length of the shortest side.

    a. 2 in   b. 4 in   c. 3 in   d. 6 in

20.   The sum of two numbers is 22. The sum of the squares of the two numbers is 274. Find the smaller of the two numbers.

    a. 7   b. 15   c. 9   d. 13

Name _____   Date _____

Chapter 14
Form A

For problems 1 – 2, write the first four terms of each sequence whose general term is given.

1. $a_n = \dfrac{n+2}{5}$ 1. _____

2. $a_n = (-1)^n (n^2 + 1)$ 2. _____

3. Find the indicated sum $\displaystyle\sum_{i=1}^{6} (i^2 - 4)$.   3. _____

4. Express the sum using summation notation. Use i for the index   4. _____
    of summation.
    $\dfrac{1}{4} + \dfrac{1}{16} + \dfrac{1}{64} + \ldots \dfrac{1}{65,536}$

5. Write the first four terms of the arithmetic sequence with   5. _____
    $a_1 = 10$ and $d = -4$.

6. For the arithmetic sequence 17, 21, 25, …, (a) find a formula   6. _____
    for the nth term. Then, (b) use the formula to find a_{14} .

7. Find the sum of the first 35 terms of the arithmetic sequence   7. _____
    6, 3, 0, –3, …

For problems 8 – 9, write the first four terms of each geometric sequence.

8. $a_1 = 10, r = -2$ 8. _____

9. $a_1 = 12, r = \dfrac{1}{4}$ 9. _____

Name _____   Date _____

For problems 10 – 11, use the formula for the nth term of a geometric sequence to find the indicated term.

10.   Find a_{12} when $a_1 = -2, r = -3$.   10. _____

11.   Find a_{15} when $a_1 = \dfrac{1}{4}, r = 2$.   11. _____

12.   For the geometric sequence $15, -5, \dfrac{5}{3} \ldots,$ 12a. _____

        (a) find a formula for the nth term. Then, (b) use the   b. _____
formula to find a_7.

13.   Find the sum of the first five terms for the geometric sequence   13. _____
$8, -24, 72, \ldots$

14.   Find the sum of the infinite geometric series $10 + 5 + \dfrac{5}{2} + \ldots$ 14. _____

15.   Express the repeating decimal $0.\overline{5}$ as a fraction in lowest terms.   15. _____

16.   Evaluate the given binomial coefficient $\dbinom{39}{4}$.   16. _____

For problems 17 – 18, use the Binomial Theorem to expand each binomial and express the result in simplified form.

17. $(2x + y)^4$ 17. _____

18.   The first three terms of $(2x - 4)^8$.   18. _____

19.   Find the 8th term of $(x - 2y)^{11}$.   19. _____

20.   A stack of firewood has 14 layers. The first layer has 40 pieces   20. _____
of wood. The second has 38 pieces of wood, the third has 36,
and so on. How many pieces of wood are in the stack?

Name _____   Date _____

Chapter 14
Form B

For problems 1 – 2, write the first four terms of each sequence whose general term is given.

1. $a_n = n^3 + 1$ 1. _____

2. $a_n = (-1)^{n+1}(n+3)$ 2. _____

3.   Find the indicated sum $\displaystyle\sum_{i=1}^{5}(3i+1)$.   3. _____

4.   Express the sum using summation notation. Use i for the index   4. _____
       of summation.
       $$1 + \frac{1}{4} + \frac{1}{9} + \dots \frac{1}{100}.$$

5.   Write the first four terms of the arithmetic sequence with   5. _____
       $a_1 = -8$ and $d = 5$.

6.   For the arithmetic sequence 15, 19, 23, ..., (a) find a formula   6. _____
       for the nth term. Then, (b) use the formula to find a_{24}.

7.   Find the sum of the first 35 terms of the arithmetic sequence   7. _____
       5, 0, −5, −10, ...

For problems 8 – 9, write the first four terms of each geometric sequence.

8. $a_1 = 8, r = 4$ 8. _____

9. $a_1 = -4, r = -\dfrac{1}{2}$ 9. _____

Name _____   Date _____

For problems 10 – 11, use the formula for the nth term of a geometric sequence to find the indicated term.

10.   Find a_7 when $a_1 = 3, r = 5$.   10. _____

11.   Find a_9 when $a_1 = 100, r = \dfrac{1}{2}$.   11. _____

12.   For the geometric sequence $20, -5, \dfrac{5}{4} \dots$,   12a. _____

         (a) find a formula for the nth term. Then, (b) use the   b. _____
         formula to find a_7.

13.   Find the sum of the first six terms for the geometric sequence   13. _____
         $-3, 6, -18, \dots$

14.   Find the sum of the infinite geometric series $4 + 2 + 1 + \dots$ 14. _____

15.   Express the repeating decimal $0.\overline{7}$ as a fraction in lowest terms.   15. _____

16.   Evaluate the given binomial coefficient $\dbinom{60}{5}$.   16. _____

For problems 17 – 18, use the Binomial Theorem to expand each binomial and express the result in simplified form.

17. $(j + 3k)^3$ 17. _____

18.   The first three terms of $(x - 2)^6$.   18. _____

19.   Find the 7th term of $(2x - y)^{12}$.   19. _____

20.   A club advertises that its membership has increased 20% each   20. _____
         year since it was formed with 10 charter members. How many
         members are there at the start of the 12th year?

Chapter 14
Form C

For problems 1 – 2, write the first four terms of each sequence whose general term is given.

1. $a_n = \dfrac{n(n-2)}{3}$

1. _____

2. $a_n = \dfrac{(-1)^{n+1}(n)}{n+1}$

2. _____

3. Find the indicated sum $\displaystyle\sum_{i=1}^{4}(3i^2+1)$.

3. _____

4. Express the sum using summation notation. Use i for the index of summation.
    $$\frac{1}{6}-\frac{1}{9}+\frac{1}{12}-\frac{1}{15}+\frac{1}{18}.$$

4. _____

5. Write the first four terms of the arithmetic sequence with $a_1 = 31$ and $d = -8$.

5. _____

6. For the arithmetic sequence 7, 4, 1, ..., (a) find a formula for the nth term. Then, (b) use the formula to find a_{10}.

6. _____

7. Find the sum of the first 42 terms of the arithmetic sequence 2, 5, 8, ...

7. _____

For problems 8 – 9, write the first four terms of each geometric sequence.

8. $a_1 = 22, r = -3$

8. _____

9. $a_1 = 6, r = \dfrac{1}{2}$

9. _____

Name _____   Date _____

For problems 10 – 11, use the formula for the nth term of a geometric sequence to find the indicated term.

10. Find a_5 when $a_1 = -16, r = -\dfrac{1}{2}$.

10. _____

11. Find a_9 when $a_1 = \dfrac{1}{2}, r = 6$.

11. _____

12. For the geometric sequence $\dfrac{1}{4}, \dfrac{1}{10}, \dfrac{1}{25}, \ldots,$

(a) find a formula for the nth term. Then, (b) use the formula to find a_8.

12a. _____

b. _____

13. Find the sum of the first five terms for the geometric sequence $9, -6, 4, -\dfrac{8}{3}, \ldots$

13. _____

14. Find the sum of the infinite geometric series $20 + 5 + \dfrac{5}{4} + \ldots$

14. _____

15. Express the repeating decimal $0.\overline{45}$ as a fraction in lowest terms.

15. _____

16. Evaluate the given binomial coefficient $\dbinom{29}{3}$.

16. _____

For problems 17 – 18, use the Binomial Theorem to expand each binomial and express the result in simplified form.

17. $(3x - y)^4$

17. _____

18. The first three terms of $(x - 3y)^7$.

18. _____

19. Find the 7th term of $(2x - 3y)^6$.

19. _____

20. A bricklayer is installing a brick pattern in a patio outside a new home. The first row has one brick, the second row has two bricks, and the third row has three bricks and so on. The longest row has 150 bricks. How many bricks will be needed?

20. _____

T-314

Name _____   Date _____

Chapter 14
Form D

Choose the correct answer.

1. Find a_{19} for the sequence $a_n = 6n - 4$.
   a. 19   b. 120   c. 110   d. 116

2. Find the general term, or nth term of the sequence: 2, 4, 8, 16, ...
   a. $a_n = n^2$ b. $a_n = 2n$ c. $a_n = 2^n$ d. $a_n = \dfrac{1}{2^n}$

3. Evaluate: $\displaystyle\sum_{i=1}^{4}\left(\dfrac{1}{4}\right)^{j}$
   a. $\dfrac{21}{64}$ b. $\dfrac{85}{64}$ c. $\dfrac{85}{4}$ d. $\dfrac{85}{256}$

4. Write as an indicated sum: $\displaystyle\sum_{i=1}^{5}\left(2i^2 + 1\right)$
   a. $5 + 17 + 37 + 65 + 101$ b. $3 + 9 + 19 + 33 + 51$
   c. $3 + 12 + 27 + 48 + 75$ d. $3 + 18 + 57 + 132 + 255$

5. Write the alternating series $\dfrac{1}{6} - \dfrac{1}{9} + \dfrac{1}{12} - \dfrac{1}{15} + \dfrac{1}{18}$ using summation notation with the summing index k starting at 1.
   a. $\displaystyle\sum_{k=1}^{6}\dfrac{(-1)^{k+1}}{3(k+1)}$ b. $\displaystyle\sum_{k=1}^{5}\dfrac{(-1)^{k+1}}{3(k+1)}$ c. $\displaystyle\sum_{k=1}^{6}\dfrac{(-1)^{k}}{3k+4}$ d. $\displaystyle\sum_{k=1}^{5}\dfrac{(-1)^{k}}{3(k+1)}$

6. Find a formula for the nth term of the arithmetic sequence: 14, 20, 26, 32, ...
   a. $a_n = 8 + 6n$ b. $a_n = 14 + 6n$ c. $a_n = 6 + 14n$ d. $a_n = 14 + 5n$

7. Find the 10th term of the sequence: 14, 20, 26, 32, ...
   a. 74   b. 80   c. 62   d. 68

8. Find a formula for the nth term of the arithmetic sequence: 9, 13, 17, 21, ...
   a. $a_n = 9x - 5$ b. $a_n = 4n - 13$ c. $a_n = 4n + 13$ d. $a_n = 4n + 5$

9. Find the eighth term of the sequence: 9, 13, 17, 21, ...
   a. 58   b. 15   c. 33   d. 41

10. Find the sum of the first 13 terms of the sequence: $-5, -1, 3, 7, \ldots$
    a. 247   b. 494   c. 251   d. 243

Name _____   Date _____

11. Find $\sum_{k=1}^{42}(-4k+7)$

    a. 3318   b. –3318   c. 161   d. –161

12. Find the common ratio of the geometric sequence: $\dfrac{3}{5}, \dfrac{12}{5}, \dfrac{48}{5}, \ldots$

    a. $-\dfrac{1}{4}$ b. 4   c. –4   d. $\dfrac{1}{4}$

13. Find the formula for the nth term of the geometric sequence: $\dfrac{2}{3}, \dfrac{4}{3}, \dfrac{8}{3}, \ldots$

    a. $a_n = \left(\dfrac{2}{3}\right)^{n-1}$ b. $a_n = 2\left(\dfrac{2}{3}\right)^{n-1}$ c. $a_n = \dfrac{2}{3}\cdot 2^{n-1}$ d. $a_n = 2^{n-1}$

14. Use the formula found in problem 13 to find the 6th term of the geometric sequence: $\dfrac{2}{3}, \dfrac{4}{3}, \dfrac{8}{3}, \ldots$

    a. $\dfrac{1023}{3}$ b. $\dfrac{128}{3}$ c. $\dfrac{64}{3}$ d. $\dfrac{256}{3}$

15. Find S_8 for the geometric sequence: 6, –18, 54, …

    a. –13,122   b. 8379   c. 39,366   d. –1458

16. Find $\sum_{i=1}^{10} 2(0.7)^i$

    a. about 1.4   b. about 0.03   c. about 0.97   d. about 4.5

17. Find the sum of the infinite geometric series: $12 + 3 + \dfrac{3}{4} + \dfrac{3}{16} + \ldots$

    a. $\dfrac{1023}{64}$ b. $\dfrac{255}{16}$ c. $\dfrac{271}{16}$ d. 16

18. Evaluate: $\begin{pmatrix} 21 \\ 18 \end{pmatrix}$

    a. 1330   b. 8379   c. 6   d. 150,822

19. Expand: $(3a-b)^4$

    a. $81a^4 + 12a^3b + 18a^2b^2 + 12ab^3 + b^4$ b. $81a^4 - 108a^3b + 54a^2b^2 - 12ab^3 + b^4$
    c. $81a^4 - 12a^3b + 18a^2b^2 - 12ab^3 + b^4$ d. $81a^4 + 108a^3b + 54a^2b^2 + 12ab^3 + b^4$

20. Find the 4th term in the expression of $(a-2)^6$.

    a. $360a^4$ b. $400a^2$ c. $120a$ d. $-160a^3$

Chapter 14
Form E

Choose the correct answer.

1. Find a_{21} for the sequence $a_n = 5n - 4$.
   a. 91   b. 96   c. 101   d. 106

2. Find the general term, or nth term of the sequence: 1, 8, 27, 64, ...
   a. $a_n = \dfrac{1}{3^n}$ b. $a_n = n^3$ c. $a_n = 3n$ d. $a_n = 3^n$

3. Evaluate: $\displaystyle\sum_{i=1}^{4}\left(\frac{1}{5}\right)^i$
   a. $\dfrac{156}{125}$ b. $\dfrac{156}{5}$ c. $\dfrac{31}{125}$ d. $\dfrac{156}{625}$

4. Write as an indicated sum: $\displaystyle\sum_{i=1}^{3}\left(3i^2 - 2\right)$
   a. $1 + 4 + 9$ b. $7 + 34 + 79$ c. $1 + 20 + 75$ d. $1 + 10 + 25$

5. Write the alternating series $\dfrac{1}{8} - \dfrac{1}{12} + \dfrac{1}{16} - \dfrac{1}{20} + \dfrac{1}{24}$ using summation notation with the summing index k starting at 1.
   a. $\displaystyle\sum_{k=1}^{5}\frac{(-1)^{k+1}}{4k+8}$ b. $\displaystyle\sum_{k=1}^{5}\frac{(-1)^{k}}{4(k+2)}$ c. $\displaystyle\sum_{k=1}^{5}\frac{(-1)^{k+1}}{4(k+2)}$ d. $\displaystyle\sum_{k=1}^{5}\frac{(-1)^{k+1}}{4(k+1)}$

6. Find a formula for the nth term of the arithmetic sequence: 9, 16, 23, 30, ...
   a. $a_n = 2 + 7n$ b. $a_n = 9 + 7n$ c. $a_n = 2 + 9n$ d. $a_n = 9 + 5n$

7. Find the 10th term of the sequence: 9, 16, 23, 30, ...
   a. 72   b. 63   c. 65   d. 79

8. Find a formula for the nth term of the arithmetic sequence: 4, 6, 8, 10, ...
   a. $a_n = 2n + 2$ b. $a_n = 2n + 6$ c. $a_n = 4n - 2$ d. $a_n = 2n - 6$

9. Find the ninth term of the sequence: 4, 6, 8, 10, ...
   a. 8   b. 16   c. 20   d. 26

10. Find the sum of the first 14 terms of the sequence: $-12, -8, -4, 0, ...$
    a. 192   b. 196   c. 392   d. 200

11. Find $\displaystyle\sum_{k=1}^{54}(-7k + 2)$
    a. 376   b. -376 c. $-10,287$ d. 10,287

12. Find the common ratio of the geometric sequence: $-2, -3, -\dfrac{9}{2}, \ldots$

   a. $-\dfrac{2}{3}$
   b. $\dfrac{2}{3}$
   c. $-\dfrac{3}{2}$
   d. $\dfrac{3}{2}$

13. Find the formula for the nth term of the geometric sequence: $2, 1, \dfrac{1}{2}, \ldots$

   a. $a_n = 2\left(\dfrac{1}{2}\right)^{n-1}$
   b. $a_n = \dfrac{1}{2} \cdot 2^{n-1}$
   c. $a_n = 2^{n-1}$
   d. $a_n = \left(\dfrac{1}{2}\right)^{n-1}$

14. Use the formula found in problem 13 to find the 6th term of the geometric sequence: $2, 1, \dfrac{1}{2}, \ldots$

   a. $\dfrac{1}{64}$
   b. $\dfrac{1}{32}$
   c. $\dfrac{1}{16}$
   d. $\dfrac{1}{8}$

15. Find S_7 for the geometric sequence: $7, -14, 28, \ldots$
   a. -301
   b. -224
   c. 77
   d. -147

16. Find $\displaystyle\sum_{i=1}^{10} 5(0.75)^i$
   a. about 0.94
   b. about 14.2
   c. about 5
   d. about 15

17. Find the sum of the infinite geometric series: $6 + 3 + \dfrac{3}{2} + \ldots$

   a. $\dfrac{45}{4}$
   b. $\dfrac{93}{8}$
   c. 12
   d. $\dfrac{49}{4}$

18. Evaluate: $\dbinom{26}{22}$

   a. 358,800
   b. 14,950
   c. 24
   d. 572

19. Expand: $(a - 2b)^4$
   a. $a^4 - 8a^3b + 24a^2b^2 - 32ab^3 + 16b^4$
   b. $a^4 + 8a^3b + 2334a^2b^2 + 32ab^3 + 16b^4$
   c. $a^4 - 8a^3b + 12a^2b^2 - 8ab^3 + 16b^4$
   d. $a^4 + 8a^3b + 12a^2b^2 + 8ab^3 + 16b^4$

20. Find the 4th term in the expression of $(a - 2)^8$.
   a. $-448a^5$
   b. $1680a^4$
   c. $336a^3$
   d. $1120a^4$

Chapter 14
Form F

Choose the correct answer.

1. Find a_{20} for the sequence $a_n = \dfrac{(-1)^{n+1}(n-1)}{n(n+2)}$.

   a. $\dfrac{18}{42}$ b. $-\dfrac{3}{7}$ c. $\dfrac{19}{440}$ d. $-\dfrac{19}{440}$

2. Find the general term, or nth term of the sequence $\dfrac{1}{3}, \dfrac{1}{2}, \dfrac{3}{5}, \dfrac{2}{3}, \ \ldots$

   a. $a_n = \dfrac{n+1}{3n+1}$ b. $a_n = \dfrac{n}{n+2}$ c. $a_n = \dfrac{1}{3}\left(\dfrac{3}{2}\right)^n$ d. $a_n = \dfrac{1}{3}\left(\dfrac{3}{2}\right)^{n-1}$

3. Give the formula for the nth term of the sequence $\dfrac{3}{4}, \dfrac{4}{5}, \dfrac{5}{6}, \dfrac{6}{7}, \ \ldots$

   a. $a_n = \dfrac{n+2}{n+3}$ b. $a_n = \dfrac{3}{4}\left(\dfrac{4}{15}\right)^{n-1}$ c. $a_n = \dfrac{3}{4}\left(\dfrac{4}{15}\right)^n$ d. $a_n = \dfrac{2n+1}{4n}$

4. Find the indicated sum: $\displaystyle\sum_{i=1}^{3}\left(2i^2 - 3\right)$.

   a. 50   b. 12   c. 54   d. 48

5. Express the sum using summation notation. $-\dfrac{1}{5} + \dfrac{1}{10} - \dfrac{1}{15} + \dfrac{1}{20} - \dfrac{1}{25}$

   a. $\displaystyle\sum_{i=1}^{5}\dfrac{(-1)^{i+1}}{5i}$ b. $\displaystyle\sum_{i=1}^{5}\dfrac{(-1)^{i-1}}{5i}$ c. $\displaystyle\sum_{i=1}^{5}\dfrac{(-1)}{5i}$ d. $\displaystyle\sum_{k=1}^{5}\left(-\dfrac{1}{5}\right)^i$

6. Write the first four terms of the arithmetic sequence with $a_1 = -4$ and $d = \dfrac{1}{2}$.

   a. $-4, -2, -1, -\dfrac{1}{2}$ b. $-4, 2, -1, \dfrac{1}{2}$ c. $-4, -\dfrac{7}{2}, -3, -\dfrac{5}{2}$ d. $-4, -\dfrac{9}{2}, -5, -\dfrac{11}{2}$

7. Find the sum of the first 40 terms of the sequence: 7, 12, 17, ...
   a. 4175   b. 4180   c. 4185   d. 4160

8. Give the formula for the nth term of the arithmetic sequence: 8, 12, 16, 20, ...

   a. $a_n = 8 + 2n$ b. $a_n = n + 4$ c. $a_n = 8\left(\dfrac{3}{2}\right)^{n-1}$ d. $a_n = 4n + 4$

9. Find $\displaystyle\sum_{i=1}^{47}(-3i + 11)$.

   a. -2867 b. 376   c. -2737 d. -122

Name _____   Date _____

10. Find a_6 when $a_1 = 12$ and $r = -\dfrac{1}{2}$.

   a. $\dfrac{3}{8}$ b. -6 c. $\dfrac{3}{16}$ d. $-\dfrac{3}{8}$

11. Find a_{10} when $a_1 = -10$ and $r = -2$.
   a. 20   b. 5120   c. 1280   d. 10,240

12. Find the formula for the nth term of the sequence $2, -\dfrac{2}{5}, \dfrac{2}{25}, \dots$

   a. $a_n = 2\left(-\dfrac{1}{5}\right)^{n-1}$ b. $a_n = 2\left(-\dfrac{1}{5}\right)^{n}$ c. $a_n = (-2)(-1)^{n+1}$ d. $a_n = (-2)\left(\dfrac{1}{5}\right)^{n-1}$

13. For the geometric sequence $-3, 6, -12, \dots$ find a_{12}.
   a. $-12{,}288$ b. -6144 c. 6144 d. $12{,}288$

14. Find the sum of the first five terms of the sequence $4, -12, 36, \dots$
   a. 256   b. 244   c. 976   d. 488

15. Find the sum of the infinite geometric series $8 + 2 + \dfrac{1}{2} + \dfrac{1}{8} + \dots$

   a. $\dfrac{3}{2}$ b. 6   c. $-\dfrac{8}{3}$ d. $\dfrac{32}{3}$

16. Evaluate the given binomial coefficient $\dbinom{22}{20}$.

   a. 2   b. 22   c. 231   d. 42

17. Expand the binomial $(x + 2y)^4$.
   a. $x^4 + 16y^4$
   b. $x^4 + 2x^3y + 4x^2y^2 + 8xy^3 + 16y^4$
   c. $x^4 + 40xy^3 + 24x^2y^2 + 16y^4$
   d. $x^4 + 8x^3y + 24x^2y^2 + 32xy^3 + 16y^4$

18. Find the first three terms of $(2x - 3y)^5$.
   a. $32x^5 - 240x^4y + 720x^3y^2$
   b. $32x^5 - 48x^4y + 72x^3y^2$
   c. $2x^5 - 30x^4y - 60x^3y^2$
   d. $2x^5 - 30x^4y + 60x^3y^2$

19. Find the 9th term of $(4x - 3y)^{12}$.
   a. $831{,}409{,}920x^4y^8$
   b. $8{,}916{,}100{,}450{,}000x^{12}y^{12}$
   c. $1{,}679{,}616x^4y^8$
   d. $7{,}077{,}888x^9y^3$

20. A new club begins at your school. Four people joined in one week one, 16 in week two, and 64 in week three. If the pattern continues, how many will join in week six?
   a. 4096   b. 2048   c. 1024   d. 512

Name _____   Date _____

Cumulative Review 1 – 14
Form A

Choose the correct answer to each problem.

For problems 1 – 13, perform the indicated operations.

1. $\dfrac{(26-27)^2+(-5)(-4)}{9-(18-6)}$ 1. _____

2. $-3(5x-2)+(6x+4)$ 2. _____

3. $\dfrac{(x^{12}y^3)(x^{-4}y^4)}{(x^0y^2)^5}$ 3. _____

4. For $f(x)=-3x^2+2x+5,$ find $f(-2)$.   4. _____

5. Divide the following: $\dfrac{x^3-1}{x-1}$.   5. _____

6. Subtract $8x^3-5x^2+3x-7$ from $2x^3+5x-3$.   6. _____

7. $(4x-3y)(2x+5y)$ 7. _____

8. $\dfrac{x-2}{x^2+2x-8}-\dfrac{x+4}{x^2-16}$ 8. _____

9. $\dfrac{2x^2-3x+2}{x+3}$ 9. _____

10. $\sqrt[3]{x}\sqrt[3]{x^2}$ 10. _____

11.   Rationalize the denominator $\dfrac{2\sqrt{x}}{\sqrt{x}+\sqrt{2}}$.

11. _____

12. $\sqrt{-98}$

12. _____

13.   Factor $x^3 + 8$.

13. _____

For problems 14 – 21, solve the equation, inequality, or system.

14. $4 - \dfrac{x}{3} = \dfrac{2(x+1)}{7}$

14. _____

15. $x + y = 6$
       $2x + 2y = 8$

15. _____

16. $-8 \le 2x - 8 \le 10$

16. _____

17. $3x^2 - 2x - 8 \le 0$

17. _____

18. $\dfrac{x}{x^2 - 16} + \dfrac{2}{x - 4} = \dfrac{1}{x + 4}$

18. _____

19. $\sqrt{x + 7} + \sqrt{x} = 5$

19. _____

20. $x^2 - 2x + 5 = 0$

20. _____

21. $\log_3 (x + 9) = 1$

21. _____

22.   For $f(x) = 5x + 2$, find $f^{-1}(x)$.

22. _____

Name _____   Date _____

For problems 23 – 24, graph the function, equation, or inequality.

23. $x + y \leq 4$
    $-2x + 4y \geq 8$

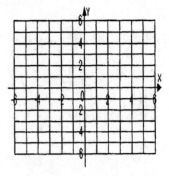

24. $x^2 + 9y^2 = 9$

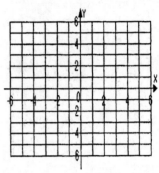

25. A radioactive substance decays so that the amount A present   25. _____
    at time t (years) is $A = A_0 e^{-1.5t}$. Find the half-life (time for half
    to decay) of this substance. Round the answer to the nearest
    thousandth.

Name _____   Date _____

Cumulative Review 1 – 14
Form B

Choose the correct answer to each problem.

For problems 1 – 9, perform the indicated operations.

1. $\left|-18\right|-\left(\left|6\right|-\left|-19\right|\right)$
    a. –5   b. 5   c. 31   d. –43

2. $(5.5\times10^{17})(2.1\times10^{-11})$
    a. 1.1765×10^{6} b. -1.176×10^{6} c. 1.176×10^{8} d. 1.176×10^{7}

3. Find $f(-2)$ for the function $f(x)=-x^{2}-2x+3$.
    a. 12   b. –18   c. –9   d. 2

4. Find the degree: $x^{5}+x^{2}y^{4}z^{6}-x^{4}$.
    a. 3   b. 11   c. 8   d. 7

5. $(x-5)(x^{2}+2x+1)$
    a. $x^{3}-3x^{2}-9x-5$ b. $x^{3}-3x^{2}-10x-5$
    c. $x^{2}+x-5$ d. $x^{3}+2x^{2}-5$

6. Subtract $8x^{3}-5x^{2}+3x-7$ from $2x^{3}+5x-3$.
    a. $3x^{3}-4x^{2}+2$ b. $3x^{3}+4x^{2}+2$
    c. $3x^{3}+2$ d. $3x^{3}-4x^{2}+2x$

7. $(4x-3y)(2x+5y)$
    a. $\dfrac{-1}{x^{2}+x-20}-\dfrac{x+5}{x^{2}-16}$ b. $\dfrac{-2x-9}{(x-5)(x+4)(x-4)}$
    c. $\dfrac{-2x-9}{(x+5)(x+4)(x-4)}$ d. $\dfrac{-1}{(x-5)(x+4)(x-4)}$

8. $\sqrt[3]{6x^{8}}\sqrt[3]{9xy^{6}}$
    a. $\sqrt[3]{54x^{8}y^{6}}$ b. $x^{2}y^{2}\sqrt[3]{54x^{2}}$ c. $3x^{3}y^{2}\sqrt[3]{6}$ d. $3x^{3}y^{2}\sqrt[3]{2}$

9. $(-2-3i)(-5+6i)$

    a. $-8+27i$ b. $28+3i$ c. $28-3i$ d. $-8+3i$

10. If $f(x)=x^5$ and $g(x)=-1-6x^2$, find $f\circ g$.

    a. $(-1-6x^2)^5$ b. $-1-6x^{10}$ c. $-x^5-6x^7$ d. $\dfrac{x^5}{-1-6x}$

11. Find the equation of the circle with a center at (2, 1) and radius of 2.

    a. $(x+2)^2+(y+1)^2=4$ b. $(x-2)^2+(y-1)^2=4$

    c. $(x+2)^2+(y+1)^2=2$ d. $(x+2)^2+(y+1)^2=4$

12. Find the equation of the line passing through the point (6, –3) and parallel to the line $y=5x-1$.

    a. $y=5x+21$ b. $y=-5x+33$ c. $y=5x-33$ d. $y=-\dfrac{1}{5}x-\dfrac{9}{5}$

For problems 13 – 19, solve the equation, inequality, or system.

13. $|6x+3|\le 9$

    a. $(-2, 1)$ b. $[-2, 1]$

    c. $(-\infty, -2]\cup[1, \infty)$ d. $(-\infty, -2)\cup(1, \infty)$

14. $x+2y+z=6$
    $x+y-z=7$
    $11x+17y+z=8$

    a. $(8, -1, 0)$ b. Dependent   c. $(2, 3, -2)$ d. Inconsistent

15. $x(x-3)=10$

    a. $\{-2, 5\}$ b. $\{-5, 2\}$ c. $\{2, 5\}$ d. $\{-5, -2\}$

16. $\dfrac{8}{x-6}+6=\dfrac{8}{x}$

    a. $\varnothing$ b. $\{-6\}$ c. $\{2, 4\}$ d. $\{-4, -2\}$

17. $\sqrt{x-9} = \sqrt{x-1}$

     a. {25}   b. {50}   c. {5}   d. Ø

18. $-x^2 + x < 0$

     a. $(-\infty, -1) \cup (0, \infty)$ b. $(-1, 0)$

     c. $(0, 1)$ d. a. $(-\infty, 0) \cup (1, \infty)$

19. $\log_4 x = \dfrac{5}{2}$

     a. $4\sqrt{2}$ b. $5\sqrt{4}$ c. 32   d. 10

20. Give the vertex of the parabola with the equation $x = (y+3)^2 - 1$.

     a. $(-3, 1)$ b. $(1, -3)$ c. $(-1, -3)$ d. $(-3, -1)$

21. Graph $3x + 4y = 12$.

a.
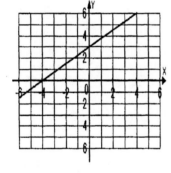

b.
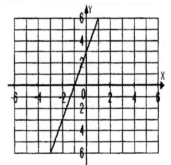

c.
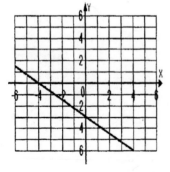

d.
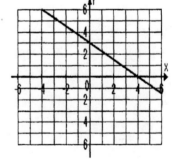

22.　Graph $(x-3)^2 + (y+2)^2 = 4$.

a.

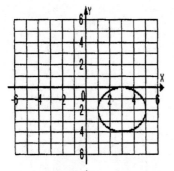

b.

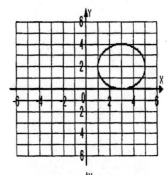

c.

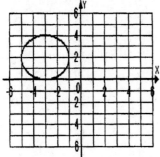

d.

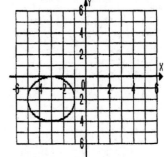

23.　Find the equation for the graph.

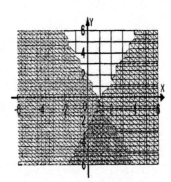

a.　$-4x + 2y \geq 4$
　　$-6x - 3y \geq -6$

b.　$-4x + 2y \leq -4$
　　$-6x - 3y \leq -6$

c.　$-4x + 2y \leq 4$
　　$-6x - 3y \leq -6$

d.　$-4x + 2y < 4$
　　$-6x - 3y > -6$

24.　The cost C of manufacturing and selling x units of a toy is $C = 20x + 55$ and the corresponding revenue R is $R = x^2 - 70$. Find the break-even value of x.
　　a. 30　　　　　　b. 5　　　　　　c. 5 or 25　　　　　　d. 25

25.　The distance h traveled in t seconds by an object dropped from a certain height is $h = 16t^2$. If an object is dropped from a height of 63 feet, how long will it take before the object hits the ground?

　　a. $\dfrac{3\sqrt{7}}{2}$ sec　　　b. $\dfrac{3\sqrt{7}}{4}$ sec　　　c. $3\sqrt{7}$ sec　　　d. $\dfrac{15\sqrt{7}}{2}$ sec

Name _____ Date _____

Final
Form A

For problems 1 – 9, perform the indicated operations. If possible, simplify the answer.

1. $\dfrac{14 - 6(-3 - 2)^2}{4^2 - 20 \div 5(2)}$

1. _____

2. $\dfrac{(3x^2)^3(2x^{-3})}{6x^3}$

2. _____

3. $\dfrac{10x^5 - 15x^3 + 5x^2}{-5x}$

3. _____

4. $\dfrac{4x^3 - 6x^2 + 4x - 8}{2x - 1}$

4. _____

5. $(x + 2)(x^2 - 4x + 6)$

5. _____

6. $(2x - 5y)^2$

6. _____

7. $\dfrac{3 + \dfrac{3}{x}}{4 + \dfrac{4}{x}}$

7. _____

For problems 8–9, perform the indicated operations and if possible, simplify.

8. $\dfrac{x + 2}{3x + 12} \cdot \dfrac{x^2 - 16}{x^2 - 3x - 10}$

8. _____

9. $\dfrac{x}{x + 4} - \dfrac{3}{x^2 + 10x + 24}$

9. _____

10. $\dfrac{y^2 - 4y + 3}{y^2 - 9} \div \dfrac{y^2 + 7y + 6}{y^2 + 3y - 18}$ 10. _____

11. $\sqrt{-128}$ 11. _____

12. $\sqrt{42x^3} \cdot \sqrt{14x}$ 12. _____

13. $(5 - i)(7 - 6i)$ 13. _____

14. $16^{\frac{1}{4}} \cdot 16^{\frac{-3}{4}}$ 14. _____

15. $\dfrac{5.2 \times 10^4}{1.3 \times 10^{-3}}$ 15. _____

Rationalize the denominator.

16. $\dfrac{4}{\sqrt{6} - 2}$ 16. _____

17. Write 10,700,000 in scientific notation.   17. _____

18. Solve $h = \dfrac{2A}{B + b}$ for B.   18. _____

19. Write as a single logarithm: $5\log_b x - 2\log_b y$.   19. _____

For problems 20 – 25. factor completely.

20. $4x^2 - 16$ 20. _____

21. $xy + y^2 - 4x - 4y$ 21. _____

22. $x^3 + 1$ 22. _____

23. $12x^2 - 23xy + 10y^2$ 23. _____

24. Factor $625x^4 - 81$.   24. _____

25. Factor $6x^3 + 40x^2 - 64x$.   25. _____

For problems 26 – 35, solve each equation, inequality, or system. Express irrational answers in simplified form and imaginary solutions in the form $a + bi$.

26. $7 - 5(x - 3) + 4 = 2 + 3(x + 4)$ 26. _____

27. $4(x - 2) \le 6(x + 5)$ 27. _____

28. $\dfrac{3x}{4} - \dfrac{1}{2} = \dfrac{x}{6} + \dfrac{2}{3}$ 28. _____

29. $5x^2 + 13x = 6$ 29. _____

30. $\dfrac{6}{x + 6} - \dfrac{2}{x - 2} = \dfrac{16}{x^2 + 4x - 12}$ 30. _____

31. $\sqrt{x - 1} = x - 1$ 31. _____

32. $(7x - 6)^2 = 48$ 32. _____

33. $|5x - 2| < 8$ 33. _____

34.　$x + 4y = 8$
　　　$2y - x = -2$

34. _____

35.　$2y - 3z = 12$
　　　$x + 2y - z = 0$
　　　$2x + 7y - 11z = 27$

35. _____

36.　Find the distance between the points (5, –6) and (–4, 6).

36. _____

For problems 29–35, graph the equation, inequality, or system.

37.　$y = -\dfrac{2}{3}x + 2$

37.

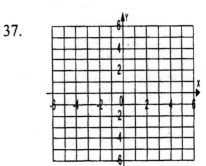

38.　$2x + 5y < 10$

38.

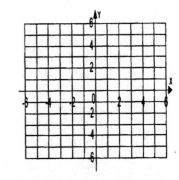

39.　$x = -4$

41.

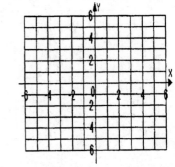

40. $y = x^2 - 2x - 3$

40.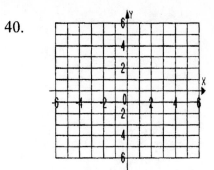

41. $x + 2y > 4$
        $3x - 6y < 6$

41.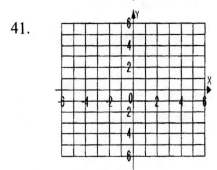

42. $f(x) = -2(x + 4)^2 - 1$

42.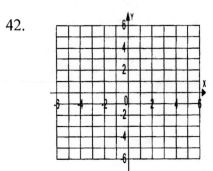

43. $x^2 - y^2 = 16$

43.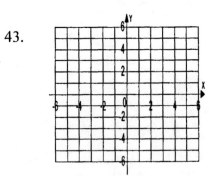

44. $(x - 2)^2 + (y - 3)^2 = 4$

44.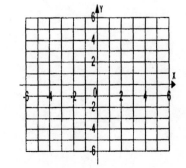

45. Write the slope-intercept form of the equation of the line   45. _____
     through (–4, 6) and parallel to the line whose equation
     is $3x - 4y = 12$.

46. For $f(x) = 3x - 5$, find $f^{-1}(x)$.   46. _____

47. Find the equation of the circle with center (–2, 4)   47. _____
     that passes through the point (–2, 8).

48. Find the sum of the first ten terms of the sequence   48. _____
     5, 7, 9, 11...

49. A breeder determines that a mouse population can be   49. _____
     approximated over a one year period with a function

     $f(t) = 40\left(\dfrac{5}{2}\right)^t$ where t is measured in years.

     Predict how many mice will be present after 5 years.
     Round to the nearest integer.

50. The formula $t = \dfrac{A - P}{Pr}$ describe the amount A that   50. _____

     an investment P is worth after t years of simple interest
     at rate r. If the investment rate is 6%, how much do you
     need to invest to have $1680 in 2 years?

Final
Form B

Choose the correct answer to each problem.

For problems 1 – 15, perform the indicated operations. If possible, simplify the answer.

1. $|-8 \div 2| + \{3 \cdot 7 - [4+)3 + 1)]\}$
     a. 18   b. 17   c. 9   d. 33

2. $(6x^2 y - 4x + 3) - (5x^2 y + 2x - 3)$
     a. $x^2 y - 2x$ b. $x^2 y - 6x + 6$ c. $x^2 y - 6x$ d. $11x^2 y - 2x$

3. $\sqrt{-240}$
     a. $-2\sqrt{30}$ b. $-4\sqrt{15}$
     c. $4\sqrt{15}i$ d. Cannot be simplified

4. $\dfrac{(8x)^2 (2x^0)^{-2}}{(4x^{-1})}$
     a. $2x$ b. $4x^3$ c. $256x^3$ d. $64x^3$

5. $\dfrac{12x^3 y^2 - 16x^2 y^2 - 20xy^3}{4xy}$
     a. $3x^2 y - 4xy - 5y^2$ b. $3x^2 y^2 - 4xy - 5xy$
     c. $3x^2 y - 4xy - 5xy^2$ d. $3x^4 y^3 - 4x^3 y^3 - 5x^2 y^4$

6. $\dfrac{4x^3 + 4x^2 - 8x + 3}{2x + 4}$
     a. $2x^2 + 2x - 1 + \dfrac{1}{2x + 4}$ b. $2x^2 + 2x + \dfrac{3}{2x + 4}$
     c. $2x^2 - 2x + 1 - \dfrac{1}{2x + 4}$ d. $2x^2 - 2x + \dfrac{3}{2x + 4}$

7. $\left(\sqrt{7}+3\sqrt{2}\right)\left(\sqrt{7}-\sqrt{2}\right)$

a. $13+2\sqrt{14}$ b. $1+2\sqrt{14}$ c. 61 d. 37

8. $4\sqrt{90x}-5\sqrt{10x}$

a. $-\sqrt{10x}$ b. $-\sqrt{90x}$ c. $7\sqrt{10x}$ d. $17\sqrt{10x}$

9. $\dfrac{7x-42}{4x^2-81}\cdot\dfrac{x^2-12x+36}{2x^2-3x-54}$

a. $\dfrac{2x+9}{x-6}$ b. $\dfrac{x-6}{2x-9}$ c. $\dfrac{7}{2x+9}$ d. $\dfrac{7}{2x-9}$

10. $\dfrac{x^2-4x+3}{x^2+3x-18}\div\dfrac{x^2-1}{x^2+10x+24}$

a. $\dfrac{(x+6)^2(x+4)}{(x-1)^2(x+1)}$ b. $\dfrac{(x-1)^2(x+1)}{(x+6)^2(x+4)}$

c. $\dfrac{x+1}{x+4}$ d. $\dfrac{x+4}{x+1}$

11. $\dfrac{x+1}{x+2}-\dfrac{x^2+1}{x^2-x-6}$

a. $\dfrac{-2x-2}{(x+2)(x-3)}$ b. $-\dfrac{2}{x-3}$

c. $\dfrac{-2x-4}{(x+2)(x-3)}$ d. $\dfrac{-4}{x-3}$

12. $(6x-5y)^2$

a. $36x^2-60xy+25y^2$ b. $36x^2-25y^2$

c. $36x^2+25y^2$ d. $12x-10y$

13. $(2x-7)(5x^2-6x+3)$

a. $10x^3-23x^2+48x-21$ b. $10x^3-23x^2-36x-21$

c. $10x^3-47x^2+48x-21$ d. $10x^3-47x^2-36x-21$

14. $81^{\frac{3}{4}}$

    a. $\dfrac{1}{27}$ b. -27 c. 27 d. $\dfrac{1}{3}$

15. $\dfrac{\sqrt{3}}{\sqrt{5}-2}$

    a. $\dfrac{\sqrt{15}-2\sqrt{3}}{21}$ b. $\sqrt{15}+2\sqrt{3}$ c. $\dfrac{\sqrt{15}-2\sqrt{3}}{3}$ d. $2\sqrt{18}$

16.   Rationalize the denominator and simplify $\dfrac{10}{4+3i}$.

    a. $\dfrac{8}{5}-\dfrac{6}{5}i$ b. $\dfrac{8}{5}+\dfrac{6}{5}i$ c. $\dfrac{14}{5}i$ d. $40-30i$

17.   Write as a single logarithm $7\log_b x - 4\log_b y$.

    a. $\log_b\left(\dfrac{x^7}{y^4}\right)$ b. $\log_b\left(x^7 y^4\right)$ c. $\log_b\left(\dfrac{7x}{4y}\right)$ d. $\log_b\left(28xy\right)$

18.   Solve $A = \dfrac{1}{2}bh$ for h.

    a. $h = 2Ab$ b. $h = \dfrac{b}{2A}$ c. $h = \dfrac{Ab}{2}$ d. $h = \dfrac{2A}{b}$

19.   Find the vertex of the graph of $x^2 - 8x + 11$.
    a. $(-4, 59)$ b. $(-4, -5)$ c. $(4, -5)$ d. $(4, 5)$

For problems 20 – 24, factor completely.

20. $4x^2 - 20x - 24$
    a. $4(x-6)(x+1)$ b. $4(x-3)(x+2)$ c. $4(x-2)(x+3)$ d. Prime

21. $4x^2 + 9$
    a. $(2x+3)^2$ b. $(2x-3)^2$ c. $(2x+3)(2x-3)$ d. Prime

22. $x^3 + 27y^3$
 a. $(x + 3y)(x^2 - 3xy + 9y^2)$ b. $(x + 3y)^3$
 c. $(x + 3y)(x^2 + 3xy + 3y^2)$ d. Prime

23. $6x^2 + x - 12$
 a. $(6x + 6)(x - 2)$ b. $(3x + 4)(2x + 3)$ c. $(3x - 4)(2x + 3)$ d. Prime

24. $12y - 8y^2 + 3x - 2xy$
 a. $(y - 4)(x + 3)$ b. $(3x - 2y)(1 - x)$
 c. $(4y + x)(3 - 2y)$ d. Prime

For problems 25 – 35, solve each equation, inequality, or system of equations.

25. $5x - 4(3 - 2x) = 2(3x - 2) + 6$
 a. $\left\{-\dfrac{16}{3}\right\}$ b. $\left\{-\dfrac{16}{9}\right\}$ c. $\{7\}$ d. $\{2\}$

26. $-5(x + 3) > (x + 1) + 2x$
 a. $\{x \mid x > 2\}$ b. $\{x \mid x > -2\}$ c. $\{x \mid x < -2\}$ d. $\{x \mid x < 2\}$

27. $\dfrac{x}{x + 4} = \dfrac{11}{x^2 - 16} + 2$
 a. $\{4, -4\}$ b. $\{3, -7\}$ c. $\{-7\}$ d. No solution

28. $x(x - 2) = 63$
 a. $\{-9, 7\}$ b. $\{-21, 3\}$ c. $\{-21, -3\}$ d. $\{-7, 9\}$

29. $2x^2 + 7 = 0$
 a. $\left\{\pm\dfrac{\sqrt{7}}{2}i\right\}$ b. $\left\{\pm\dfrac{\sqrt{14}}{2}i\right\}$ c. $\left\{\pm\sqrt{14}\right\}$ d. $\{2, 7\}$

Name _____   Date _____

30. $x - 7 = \sqrt{x - 5}$
    a. $\{9\}$ b. $\{6, 9\}$ c. $\{6\}$ d. $\{5\}$

31. $(5x - 3)^2 = -25$
    a. $\{3 \pm i\}$ b. $\left\{\dfrac{3 \pm 5i}{5}\right\}$ c. $\left\{\dfrac{-3 \pm 5i}{5}\right\}$ d. $\{-3 \pm i\}$

32. $3^{2x-10} = 81$
    a. $\{7\}$ b. $\{5\}$ c. $\{-3\}$ d. $\{3\}$

33. $\log_5(3x + 4) = 2$
    a. $\{5\}$ b. $\left\{-\dfrac{4}{3}\right\}$ c. $\left\{-\dfrac{2}{3}\right\}$ d. $\{7\}$

34. $x = 4y - 3$
     $3x - 12y = 9$
    a. $(-11, -2)$ b. $(11, -2)$ c. Dependent   d. Inconsistent

35. $|4x - 5| \geq 3$
    a. $\left(-\infty, \dfrac{1}{2}\right] \cup [2, \infty)$ b. $\left(-\infty, \dfrac{1}{2}\right] \cup (2, \infty)$ c. $\left[\dfrac{1}{2}, 2\right]$ d. $\left(\dfrac{1}{2}, 2\right)$

36. Give the coordinates of the vertex for $x = (y + 2)^2 - 3$.
    a. $(-2, -3)$ b. $(2, -3)$ c. $(-3, -2)$ d. $(3, -2)$

37. Find the x-intercept(s) of the graph of $y = -x^2 + 8x - 12$.
    a. $(0, -12)$ b. $(4, 4)$ c. $(2, 0), (6, 0)$ d. $(-2, 0), (6, 0)$

Name _____   Date _____

For problems 38 – 43, graph each equation, inequality, or system.

38. $-9x + 18y = 36$

a.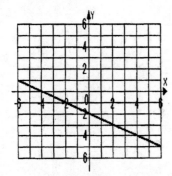

b.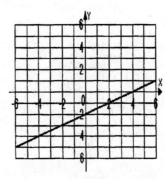

c.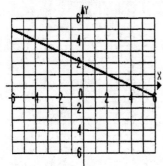

d.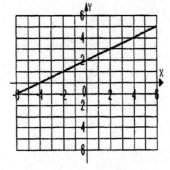

39. $y = -\dfrac{1}{2}x + 1$

a.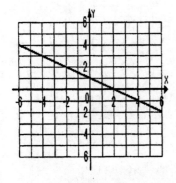

b.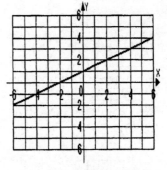

c.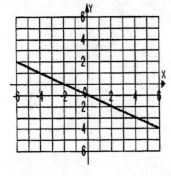

d.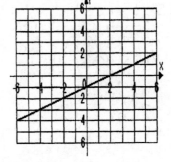

40. $y = x^2 = 5x + 4$

a.

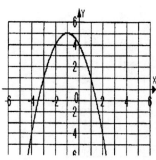

b.

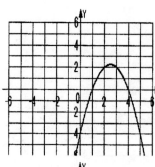

c.

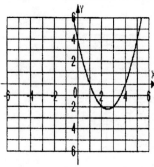

d.

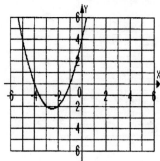

41. $2x - 3y < 6$

a.

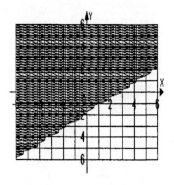

b.

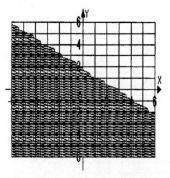

c.

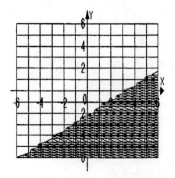

d.

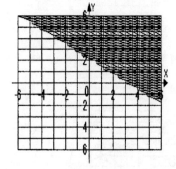

42.   Graph $y^2 - x^2 = 4$.

a.
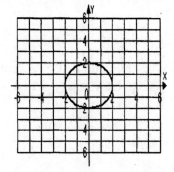

b.
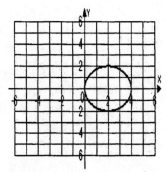

c.
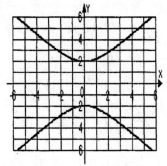

d.
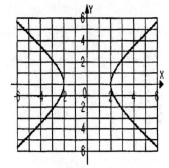

43.   Which equation corresponds to the graph?

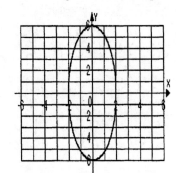

a. $\dfrac{x^2}{2} + \dfrac{y^2}{6} = 1$

b. $\dfrac{x^2}{6} + \dfrac{y^2}{2} = 1$

c. $\dfrac{x^2}{4} + \dfrac{y^2}{36} = 1$

d. $\dfrac{x^2}{36} + \dfrac{y^2}{4} = 1$

44.   Find the center and radius of $x^2 + y^2 + 6x + 2y - 26 = 0$.
   a. (3, 1); 6   b. (−3, −1); 36   c. (−3, −1); 6   d. (3, 1); 36

45.   Find the distance between (2, 5) and (−3, 6).

   a. $\sqrt{26}$ b. 26   c. 122   d. $\sqrt{122}$

46.   Find S_{12} for the sequence 2, 9, 16, 23, …

   a. 50   b. 586   c. 486   d. 412

Name _____   Date _____

47.   Find the 4th term of $(x - 2y)^5$.

     a. $80xy^4$ b. $-80x^2y^3$ c. $10x^2y^3$ d. $-10x^2y^3$

48.   An electronics store buys 7 televisions and 8 VCR's at a total cost of $5628. Another
store buys 5 of the same televisions and 8 of the same VCRs from the same wholesale
supplier at a total cost of $4564. Find the cost of one television.

     a. $532   b. $1064   c. $238   d. $437

49.   When a ball is thrown vertically upward, its height h, (in feet) above the ground after t
seconds is described by the mathematical model $h = -16t^2 + 96t + 80$. At what time is
the ball 103 feet above the ground?

     a. 1 sec and 183 sec   b. $\dfrac{1}{4}$ sec and $\dfrac{183}{4}$ sec

     c. 1 sec and 23 sec   d. $\dfrac{1}{4}$ sec and $\dfrac{23}{4}$ sec

50..   The wind is blowing at a steady rate of 10 miles per hour. It takes a truck 5 hours to
travel 120 miles west between two cities against the wind and then 120 miles back with
the wind. What is the speed of the truck in still air?

     a. 60 mph   b. 50 mph   c. 40 mph   d. 10 mph

Chapter 1 Answers

Form A

1. 10 2. $-\dfrac{7}{6}$ 3. -8 4. $\dfrac{3}{2}$ 5. -19 6. -25 7. -432 8. $\dfrac{6}{5}$ 9. $-4a-96$ 10. $20x-8$

11. $0, \sqrt{9}$ 12. Example; -3 13. $>$ 14. $\sqrt{3}$ 15. No 16. $6x-7=29$ 17. $3(x-8)$

18. -30 19. 18 20. $(3+5)+z$; $8+x$ 21. $2(4x)$; $8x$ 22. $72°$ 23. $\approx(4,7)$ After weeks there were 7 fish in the aquarium 24. 5 25. 22,037 ft.

Form B

1. -7 2. $-\dfrac{3}{20}$ 3. -6 4. $-\dfrac{48}{49}$ 5. 19 6. -9 7. 108 8. 4 9. $10x-1$ 10. $-4a+6$

11. $-\sqrt{29}, \pi$ 12. Example : $\dfrac{4}{5}$ 13. $<$ 14. $\dfrac{2}{3}$ 15. Yes 16. $x+8=2x-12$ 17. 0 18. 16

19. -2 20. $-28x+56y+7$ 21. $(5\cdot3)x$; $15x$ 22. 26% 23. 20

24. 30 birds. 25. 5211 ft

Form C

1. -56 2. $\dfrac{34}{33}$ 3. 18 4. $-\dfrac{12}{25}$ 5. -119 6. -64 7. 2000 8. 18 9. $12x+1$ 10. $-5x+3$

11. $-5, 0, 0.333..., \dfrac{9}{2}$ 12. 0 13. $>$ 14. 1.24 15. No 16. False 17. $x-10=3(x+2)$

18. -4 19. 82 20. $x+4-3$; $x+1$ 21. $(-2\cdot4)x$; $-8x$ 22. $35°$ 23. 252 24. 588 25. 846 ft.

Form D

1. b 2. a 3. d 4. a 5. b 6. c 7. c 8. a 9. a 10. d 11. a 12. c 13. a 14. b
15. b 16. c 17. d 18. d 19. c 20. c

Form E

1. a 2. d 3. b 4. d 5. a 6. d 7. c 8. c 9. b 10. a 11. c 12. d 13. a 14. b
15. b 16. a 17. a 18. a 19. d 20. b

Form F

1. c 2. b 3. c 4. d 5. b 6. b 7. a 8. d 9. c 10. b 11. c 12. a 13. b 14. a
15. c 16. a 17. d 18. b 19. d 20. b

Chapter 2 Answers

Form A

1. 3 2. 2 3. $\dfrac{5}{2}$ 4. -1 5. No solution 6. All real numbers

7. $\{x|x>-3\}$

8. $\{x|x \geq 4\}$

9. $\{x|x \text{ is a real number}\}$

10. $\{x|x > 1\}$

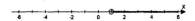

11. $\{x \mid x \le 5\}$ 12. $c = P - a - b$ 13. $b = \dfrac{2A}{h}$ 14. 11.25 15. 156.25% 16. 80 17. 671 and 673 18. 54 19. 20°, 80°, 80° 20. ≤ 7

Form B

1. 5 2. $-\dfrac{1}{3}$ 3. No solution 4. 1 5. $-\dfrac{17}{3}$ 6. All real numbers

7. $\{x|x \ge 1\}$ ⟨number line⟩ 8. No solution

9. $\{x|x > 2\}$ ⟨number line⟩ 10. $\{x|x < 3\}$ ⟨number line⟩

11. $\{x \mid x > 1\}$ 12. $y = \dfrac{6 - x}{2}$ 13. $r = \dfrac{A - P}{Pt}$ 14. 1000 15. 400 16. 6.25% 17. 17 18. $32 19. 72° 20. ≥ 76

Form C

1. $\dfrac{13}{2}$ 2. –2 3. $-\dfrac{6}{5}$ 4. –3 5. No solution 6. 3 7. All real numbers 8. 0 9. $\{x \mid x > 5\}$
10. No solution 11. $\{x \mid x \ge -2\}$

12. $x \le 2$ ⟨number line⟩ 13. $x > -3$ ⟨number line⟩

14. $\{x \mid x \ge -1\}$ 15. $h = \dfrac{2A}{b}$ 16. $x = \dfrac{-3y + 6}{2}$ 17. 2000 18. 2% 19. 14,040
20. $783 and $1330 21. 241 22. 3212 and 3214 23. $21,500 24. 148° 25. ≤ 140 min

Form D
1. a 2. d 3. b 4. c 5. a 6. a 7. a 8. c 9. a 10. d 11. c 12. d 13. a 14. b

15. d 16. d 17. c 18. b 19. a 20. c

Form E
1. d 2. c 3. b 4. d 5. c 6. c 7. d 8. b 9. c 10. a 11. c 12. c 13. a 14. a
15. b 16. c 17. b 18. a 19. b 20. a

Form F
1. d 2. d 3. b 4. a 5. c 6. c 7. a 8. d 9. d 10. c 11. a 12. d 13. c 14. d
15. b 16. a 17. c 18. d 19. d 20. c

Cumulative Review Chapters 1 – 2 Answers

Form A

1. -9 2. -5 3. 256 4. $\dfrac{2}{7}$ 5. $\dfrac{7}{6}$ 6. $26x-38$ 7. $4x^3+7x^2-4$

8. 15 9. $\{0, 1\}$ 10. Associative Property of Addition 11. $\dfrac{17}{6}$ 12. $\dfrac{60}{11}$ 13. No solution

14. $\{x \mid x \le 2\}$

15. $\{x \mid x > -2\}$ 16. No solution 17. $y = 6 - 2x$

18. $b = 2A - c$ 19. 300 20. 45 feet 21. 628 ft. 22. $\ge 40{,}000$ 23. 215 and 216 24. 83
25. 1638

Form B

1. b 2. b 3. d 4. c 5. a 6. d 7. b 8. c 9. a 10. d 11. d 12. c 13. a 14. b
15. d 16. b 17. b 18. d 19. b 20. c 21. c 22. d 23. a 24. b 25.c

Chapter 3 Answers

Form A

1. yes   2. $(0, -2)$; $(3, -1)$; $(6, 0)$

3.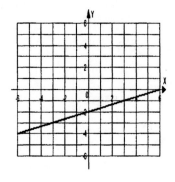

4.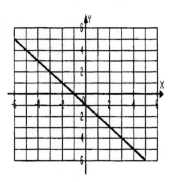

5a. $(-2, 0)$ b. $(0, 4)$ 6a. None b. $(0, 3)$ 7a. $(2, 0)$ b. $(0, -4)$

8.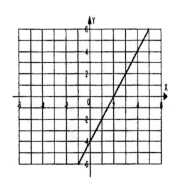

9.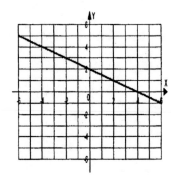

10.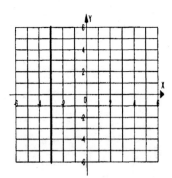

11a. 3 minutes b. 15ft 12a. $(0, 0)$

b. At time 0, the height was 0   13. $-\dfrac{5}{7}$

14. 0 15. Yes 16a. 2 b. $(0, -3)$

17.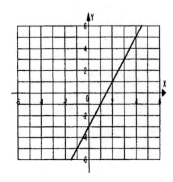

18a. $y - 3 = -3(x + 2)$ b. $y = -3x - 3$

19a. $m = \dfrac{1}{2}$ b. $m = -2$

20a. $y - 4 = 2(x - 1)$ b. $y = 2x + 2$

Form B

1. No 2. (–2, 3) ; (0, 4) ; (2, 5)

3.

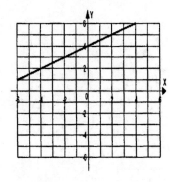

4.

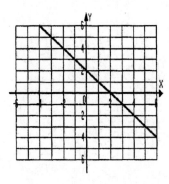

5a. (–1, 0) b. (0, –3) 6a. (3, 0) b. None 7a (2, 0) b. (0, 4)

8.

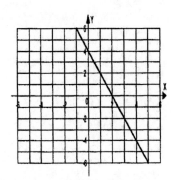

9.

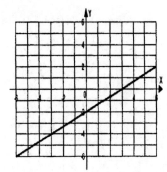

10.

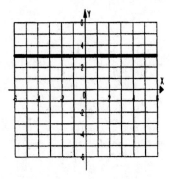

11a. 1 pm. b. 10 12a. (6, 0)
b. At 6 pm., there were no cars in the lot

13. $\dfrac{1}{11}$ 14. Undefined 15. No

16a. $\dfrac{8}{3}$ b. (0, –2)

17.

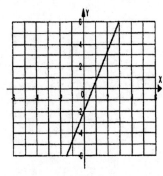

18a. $y + 2 = -2(x - 1)$ b. $y = -2x$

19a. $m = -\dfrac{2}{3}$ b. $m = \dfrac{3}{2}$

20a. $y - 6 = -\dfrac{3}{2}(x - 2)$ b. $y = -\dfrac{3}{2}x + 9$

Form C

1. Yes   2. $(0, 1)$; $\left(-2, -\dfrac{1}{3}\right)$; $(-6, -3)$

3.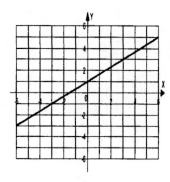

4.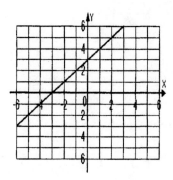

5a. $(-1, 0)$ b. $(0, 2)$ 6a. None   b. $(0, -4)$ 7a. $\left(\dfrac{5}{3}, 0\right)$ b. $\left(0, -\dfrac{5}{2}\right)$

8.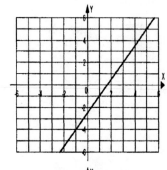

9.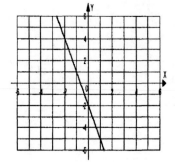

10.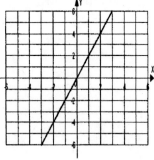

11.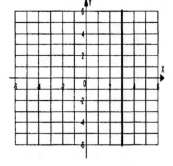

12.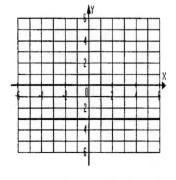

13. $-\dfrac{6}{7}$ 14. 0   15a. $\dfrac{5}{4}$ b. $(0, -2)$

16.

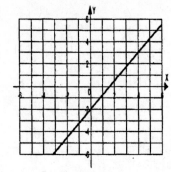

17. Yes   18a. $y - 0 = 1(x - 2)$ or $y - 3 = 1(x - 5)$ b. $y = x - 2$ 19. $y = 0.75x + 8$
20. A pizza with 2 toppings cost \$9.50   21a. $(0, 5)$

b. At time 0, the canary is at a height of 5 feet   22a. 2 minutes   b. 15 feet   23a. $m = \dfrac{2}{5}$

b. $m = -\dfrac{5}{2}$ 24a. $y - 5 = \dfrac{3}{2}(x - 2)$ b. $y = \dfrac{3}{2}x + 2$ 25a. $y - 1 = -9(x - 1)$ b. $y = -9x + 10$

Form D
1. c 2. a 3. b 4. c 5. c 6. d 7. a 8. a 9. c 10. d 11. d 12. d 13. a 14. d
15. b 16. a 17. b 18. c 19. c 20. d

Form E
1. b 2. d 3. a 4. d 5. a 6. a 7. c 8. c 9. d 10. a 11. d 12. a 13. a 14. d
15. b 16. d 17. a 18. a 19. b 20. d

Form F
1. a 2. d 3. d 4. b 5. c 6. d 7. b 8. a 9. b 10. c 11. a 12. a 13. c 14. c
15. a 16. a 17. c 18. b 19. c 20. c

Chapter 4 Answers

Form A
1. No 2. $(3, -1)$ 3. $(1, -2)$

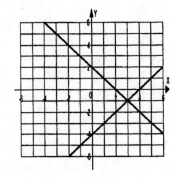   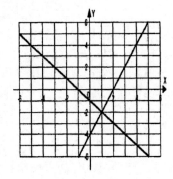

4. Infinite solutions

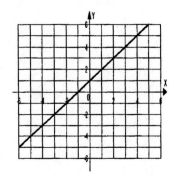

5. (–2, 1)

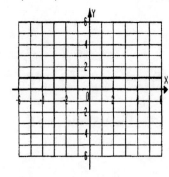

6. (2, –3) 7. (–1, –2) 8. (1, –4) 9. No solution 10. (1, 3) 11. (2 –2)

12. Infinite solutions 13. $\left(\dfrac{1}{2}, \dfrac{1}{2}\right)$ 14. $\left(3, -\dfrac{8}{3}\right)$ 15. (4, 6) 16. food $30 ; room $90

17. 80 adults ; 50 children 18. $5 19. (1, –2, –3) 20. (3, –2, –1)

Form B

1. Yes 2. (3, –2)

3. Parallel

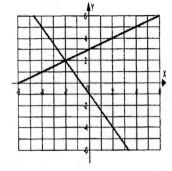

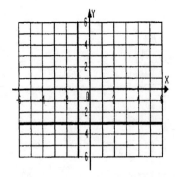

4. (–2, 2)

5. (–1, –3)

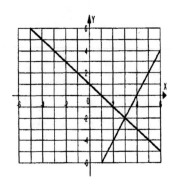

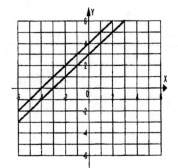

6. (5, –4) 7. (3, 2) 8. (7, 1) 9. Infinite solutions 10. (5, 0) 11. (2, 2) 12. No solution

13. $\left(3, -\dfrac{3}{2}\right)$ 14. (–2, –3) 15. (1, –2) 16. 20 televisions ; 200 radios 17. 30 and 100

18. $30 19. (3, –2, 1) 20. (1, 2 –3)

1. Yes   2. (–2, –1)   3. (1, 0)

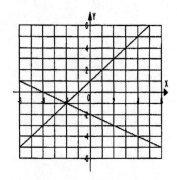
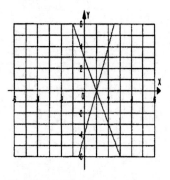

4.   Infinite solutions   5. (2, –3)

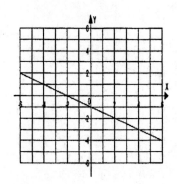
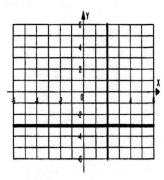

6. (1, –3)   7. (4, –16)   8. Infinite solutions   9. (4, 4)   10. (50, –10)   11. (3, 0)   12. (0, 5)
13. (4, –3)   14. No solution   15. (8, –3)   16. $16   17. jackets:$75 ; shirts: $25   18. 99; 85
19. (–4, 1, 3)   20. (2, 4, –3)

Form D

1. b   2. d   3. a   4. c   5. d   6. b   7. c   8. b   9. a   10. c   11. c   12. d   13. a   14. b
15. a   16. c   17. d   18. b   19. a   20. b

Form E

1. c   2. b   3. a   4. b   5. b   6. c   7. d   8. a   9. a   10. c   11. b   12. d   13. d   14. b
15. c   16. a   17. b   18. b   19. b   20. a

Form F

1. a   2. c   3. c   4. d   5. d   6. c   7. d   8. c   9. a   10. a   11. d   12. b   13. c   14. a
15. d   16. d   17. b   18. a   19. d   20. c

Cumulative Review Chapters 1 – 4 Answers

Form A

1. 4   2. $\dfrac{43}{4}$ 3. $6x - 19$ 4. $\{-1, 0, 6\}$ 5. $-\dfrac{9}{2}$ 6. 8   7. –3   8. $y = \dfrac{2}{3}x - 2$ 9. 882

10. $\{x \mid x > 3\}$

11. $\{x \mid x \geq -2\}$

12. $\dfrac{13}{2}$ hours   13. \$2360 at 6\% ; \$1640 at 5\%   14. $192\pi \text{ in}^2$ 15. $100°$ 16. $-\dfrac{5}{2}$

17a. $\dfrac{1}{2}$ b. $(0, -2)$ 18. $y = -4x + 2$

19.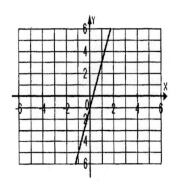

20.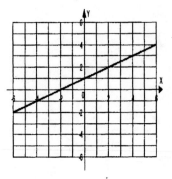

21.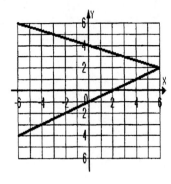

22. $\{(3, 1)\}$ 23. $\{(1, -2)\}$ 24. $\{(\square 2, -6)\}$
25. $\{(1, 2, 3)\}$

Form B

1. c 2. b 3. d 4. a 5. d 6. a 7. c 8. b 9. c 10. a 11. b 12. c 13. d 14. b
15. c 16. b 17. d 18. a 19. b 20. a 21. b 22. d 23. a 24. d 25. c

Chapter 5 Answers

Form A

1. binomial; degree 4 2. trinomial; degree 5 3. $7x^5 + 2x^3 + x^2 - 2x$ 4. $6x^2 - 5xy + 4y$

5. $-2x^3 + 3x^2 + 8x - 5$ 6. $14y^4 - 4y^3 + 14y^2 + y - 3$ 7. y^{11} 8. $6561y^{12}$ 9. 55 10. $\dfrac{63}{x^2}$

11. $75y^5$ 12. $\dfrac{25x^2}{4y^4}$ 13. $\dfrac{11}{18}$ 14. x^8 15. $-18x^6y^4+15x^5y^2-12x^2y^2$ 16. $10x^2+7x-12$

17. $9t^2-30t+25$ 18. $9a^2-16b^2$ 19. $5y^3-22y^2+23y-6$ 20. $3x^3-4x^2+2$

21. $x^2+2x-1+\dfrac{7}{3x-1}$ 22. 0.000214 23. 1.457×10^6 24. 5×10^7 25. $x^2+8x+15$

Form B

1. monomial ; degree 8 2. trinomial ; degree 7 3. $-7x^6+3x^5-x+5$ 4. $6x^5-7xy^3+4y^2$

5. $-6x^2+x+1$ 6. -59 7. $10y^6$ 8. $-64y^{15}$ 9. -5 10. $-72x^8$ 11. $\dfrac{81}{y^{20}}$ 12. y^{28}

13. $\dfrac{20}{x}$ 14. $-8x^5y^5+14x^4y^4+6x^3y^3$ 15. $6x^2-7x-20$ 16. $9y^2-48y+64$

17. $4a^2-9b^2$ 18. $125t^3-1$ 19. $5x^2y-3x+4$ 20. $2x^2+x-1-\dfrac{8}{4x-3}$ 21. 0.00178

22. 4.25×10^4 23. 1.728×10^{-10} 24. 6×10^{14} 25. 8.5×10^{-15} gram

Form C

1. trinomial; degree 11 2. binomial; degree 5 3. $\dfrac{13}{10}x^4-\dfrac{1}{2}x^3+\dfrac{3}{5}x^2-\dfrac{2}{3}$

4. $3x^4y^3-10x^3y^3+6x^2y^2$ 5. $6x^3+3x^2-x-1$ 6. 30 7. $\dfrac{x^3y^2}{64}$ 8. $81x^{16}y^{20}$ 9. 5

10. $\dfrac{108y^{18}}{x}$ 11. $\dfrac{25y^{10}}{x^{12}}$ 12. $\dfrac{y^2}{4x^3}$ 13. $8x^{14}$ 14. $-10x^5y^5+8x^4y^6-6x^4y^5$

15. $40x^2+9x-9$ 16. $25x^2+20xy+4y^2$ 17. t^4-25 18. $64y^3-27$ 19. $-8x+5y-10$

20. x^2+2x+4 21. $14,300,000$ 22. 1.59×10^{-5} 23. 1.536×10^{12} 24. 4×10^4

25. $2x^2+17x+21$

Form D

1. b 2. b 3. a 4. b 5. d 6. d 7. c 8. b 9. d 10. a 11. d 12. a 13. b 14. d
15. b 16. a 17. b 18. c 19. a 20. b 21. b 22. a 23. c 24. d 25. c

Form E

1. b 2. b 3. b 4. c 5. d 6. b 7. a 8. d 9. d 10. d 11. b 12. d 13. a 14. b
15. c 16. a 17. c 18. b 19. d 20. a 21. c 22. c 23. d 24. b 25.a

Form F

1. c 2. c 3. b 4. b 5. d 6. c 7. d 8. a 9. c 10. c 11. b 12. d 13. a 14. b
15. b 16. a 17. b 18. d 19. b 20. c 21. a 22. a 23. a 24. d 25. c

Chapter 6 Answers

Form A

1. $(x-4)(x+3)$ 2. $x(x+8)(x-8)$ 3. $3(2x-y)^2$ 4. $2(3x+1)(4x-5)$ 5. Prime
6. $(2x-5)(4x^2+10x+25)$ 7. $x^2(y^2-6)(y+1)$ 8. $(6x+5)(2x-1)$
9. $(x^2+25)(x+5)(x-5)$ 10. $xy(x+1)^2$ 11. $4x(x^2-2)$ 12. $(x+6)(x-1)$
13. $(y-4)(y+5)(y-5)$ 14. $-9, -4$ 15. $-\dfrac{1}{3}, \dfrac{5}{4}$ 16. $-\dfrac{5}{3}, \dfrac{5}{3}$ 17. $-2, 6$ 18. $1, \dfrac{9}{2}$
19. 5 sec   20. width 9 ft.; length 15 ft.

Form B

1. $(x+3)(x+1)$ 2. $(x+5)(x+2)(x-2)$ 3. $2xy(3x+y)$ 4. $4(2x-3y)^2$
5. $(4x-3)(16x^2+12x+9)$ 6. Prime   7. $(8x-1)(2x+3)$ 8. $x^2(x-7)(x+2)$ 9. $(7y+1)^2$
10. $(y^2-8)(y+4)$ 11. $5(x-8)(x+3)$ 12. $(9x^2+4)(3x+2)(3x-2)$
13. $2y^2(3y+4)(3y-5)$ 14. 4   15. $-10, 5$ 16. $-\dfrac{4}{5}, \dfrac{4}{5}$ 17. $-\dfrac{31}{12}, 3$ 18. $-3, -1$
19. width 7 ft; length 23 ft   20. 3 sec

Form C

1. $x(x+3)(x-3)$ 2. $(x-12)(x+9)$ 3. $2x^2y(5x+2y)^2$ 4. $3x^2y^3(1-7xy)$
5. $(2y+1)(y+3)(y-3)$ 6. $(5x+2)(5x-2)$ 7. $2(4x^2+9)(2x+3)(2x-3)$
8. $(8x+5)(4x-9)$ 9. $(2x-5)(4x^2+10x+25)$ 10. $9(x-4)^2$ 11. $(x-7)(x+1)$
12. $(y^2-5)(y+4)$ 13. Prime   14. $-5, 5$ 15. $-2, 10$ 16. $-\dfrac{3}{2}$ 17. $-\dfrac{2}{3}, \dfrac{1}{2}$ 18. $-6, 5$
19. $\dfrac{9}{8}$ sec   20. width 8 ft.; length 12 ft.

Form D

1. a 2. b 3. b 4. a 5. c 6. b 7. d 8. c 9. c 10. c 11. b 12. a 13. c 14. c
15. b 16. b 17. c 18. d 19. b 20. a

Form E

1. c 2. b 3. c 4. a 5. b 6. c 7. a 8. a 9. c 10. b 11. d 12. c 13. a 14. c
15. c 16. b 17. b 18. a 19. d 20. c

Form F

1. b 2. d 3. b 4. b 5. a 6. a 7. b 8. b 9. c 10. a 11. c 12. b 13. d 14. a
15. d 16. c 17. a 18. d 19. b 20. c

Cumulative Review 1–6 Answers

Form A

1. $-35x - 56$ 2. $\dfrac{8}{3}$ 3. $\dfrac{18}{x^8}$ 4. $3x^3 + x^2 - x$ 5. $2x^5 - 4x^3 + 3$ 6. $x^2 - 5x + 25$

7. $12x^3y - 8x^2y - 6xy^3$ 8. $49x^2 + 28xy + 4y^2$ 9. -8 10. $\dfrac{19}{10}$ 11. $\{x \mid x > -16\}$

12. $(5, 1)$ 13. No solution

14. $(-1, 2)$

15. Infinite solutions

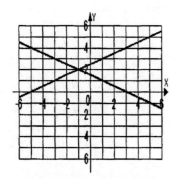

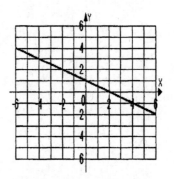

16.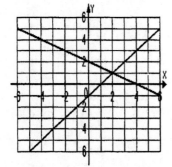

17.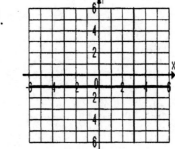

18. $\dfrac{3}{4}$ 19. $(0, -3)$ 20. $m = 0$ 21. $y + 1 = -2(x - 4)$ 22. \$247.00 23. 4 24. 16π ft

25. 9 and 33

Form B

1. a 2. c 3. d 4. b 5. d 6. a 7. b 8. a 9. a 10. d 11. b 12. c 13. a 14. c
15. b 16. c 17. a 18. a 19. b 20. b 21. c 22. b 23. b 24. d 25. a

Chapter 7 Answers

Form A

1. -5 2. $-1, -5$ 3. $\dfrac{8x^3}{3}$ 4. $\dfrac{x-1}{x-5}$ 5. $-2x - 7$ 6. $\dfrac{3x}{x-4}$ 7. $\dfrac{4}{y-1}$ 8. $\dfrac{x-2}{(x+1)(x+2)}$

9. $\dfrac{x(2x-3)}{(x-4)(x+2)}$ 10. $\dfrac{2x+1}{2x-1}$ 11. $\dfrac{2(3y-5)}{y-5}$ 12. $\dfrac{x+13}{(x+3)(x-3)(x-2)}$ 13. $\dfrac{y-x}{y}$

14. $\dfrac{2x}{x-2}$ 15. 10   16. –8   17. $s = \dfrac{Ra}{a-R}$ 18. $\dfrac{10}{3}$ ohms   19. 24 mph   20. 4 feet

Form B

1. Defined for all real numbers   2. –4, 4   3. $\dfrac{3}{x^4}$ 4. $\dfrac{1}{x^2+2x+4}$ 5. –3   6. $\dfrac{x(x-6)}{2}$

7. $\dfrac{2y+5}{(y-2)(y+2)}$ 8. $\dfrac{27}{x}$ 9. $\dfrac{x+5}{x+6}$ 10. 1   11. $\dfrac{-7y+12}{2y(y+4)}$ 12. $\dfrac{x+1}{(x+3)(x-2)}$

13. $\dfrac{4(3-2x)}{x}$ 14. $\dfrac{x(xy-1)}{y(xy+1)}$ 15. 10   16. 0   17. $p = \dfrac{qf}{q-f}$ 18. $\dfrac{20}{9}$ hours

19. Car 40 mph; train 80 mph   20. $\dfrac{15}{2}$ ohms

Form C

1. 6   2. –2, 2   3. $\dfrac{3}{x^3}$ 4. $\dfrac{1}{x+3}$ 5. $-\dfrac{x+y}{4}$ 6. $\dfrac{1}{x}$ 7. $\dfrac{1}{x+3}$ 8. $\dfrac{x-7}{x-6}$ 9. $\dfrac{32}{(x+y)^2}$

10. 1   11. $\dfrac{x^2+3x-15}{x(x-5)}$ 12. $\dfrac{1}{2(x-1)}$ 13. $\dfrac{6+2y}{y}$ 14. $\dfrac{x}{2(2x+1)}$ 15. –5, 5

16. No solution, 4 does not check   17. $E = I(R+r)$ 18. $\dfrac{4}{3}$ hours   19. 440 mph

20. 36 cc

Form D

1. b   2. b   3. c   4. b   5. a   6. d   7. c   8. a   9. d   10. c   11. c   12. b   13. a   14. b
15. c   16. a   17. c   18. b   19. d   20. a

Form E

1. b   2. c   3. b   4. a   5. b   6. a   7. d   8. c   9. b   10. b   11. a   12. c   13. d   14. a
15. b   16. b   17. a   18. a   19. c   20. d

Form F

1. a   2. a   3. a   4. d   5. a   6. d   7. b   8. b   9. a   10. c   11. d   12. d   13. c   14. c
15. c   16. b   17. d   18. d   19. c   20. a

Chapter 8 Answers

Form A

1a. Function   b. $\{2, 5, 7\}$ c. $\{1, 7, 8\}$ 2a. 1   b. –5   c. 16   3a. 1   b. 17   c. 31
4. Not a function   5. A function

6a. $\{x \mid -5 < x \le 2\}$ b.

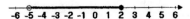

7a. $\{x \mid x < 8\}$ b.

8. 0 9. 4 10. $\{x \mid x \text{ is a real number}\}$ 11. $\{x \mid x \text{ is a real number and } x \neq -5\}$ 12. $2a + 9$

13. –5 14. –1 15. 18 16. $\{x \mid x \text{ is a real number and } x \neq -\frac{1}{2}\}$ 17. 24 18. $6x$ 19. inverses

20. not inverses

Form B

1a. Function b. $\{-2, 3, 4\}$ c. $\{-2, 3, 4\}$ 2a. –5 b. –11 c. 3 3a. 2 b 24 c. 52
4. Function 5. not a function

6a. $\{x \mid x > 4\}$ b.

7a. $\{x \mid x - 3 \leq x < 6\}$ b.

8. 2 9. 0 10. $\{x \mid x \text{ is a real number and } x \neq -4\}$ 11. $\{x \mid x \text{ is a real number}\}$ 12. 10
13. $-a + 1$ 14. –1 15. –10 16. $\{x \mid x \text{ is a real number}\}$ 17. 33 18. $12x + 5$ 19. inverses
20. not inverses

Form C

1a. Function b. $\{-2, 3, 4\}$ c. $\{-6, -2, 3\}$ 2a. Not a function b. $\{2\}$ c. $\{6, 7, 8\}$
3a. –4 b. –9 c. 11 4a. –6 b. –4 c. 21 5. Function 6. Not a function

7a. $\{x \mid 2 < x \leq 5\}$ b.

8a. $\{x \mid x \leq -3\}$ b.

9a. $\{x \mid x \geq 6\}$ b.

10. 1 11. –2 12. –5 13. $\{x \mid x \text{ is a real number}\}$ 14. $\{x \mid x \text{ is a real number and } x \neq -7\}$
15. 18 16. $2a + 4$ 17. 80 18. 9 19. $\{x \mid x \text{ is a real number and } x \neq -1\}$ 20. $3x - 14$ 21. 12
22. $\sqrt{x} + 5$ 23. inverses 24. inverses 25. not inverses

Form D

1. c 2. a 3. d 4. c 5. b 6. c 7. d 8. b 9. c 10. d 11. a 12. c 13. b 14. d 15. d 16. a 17. c 18. b 19. a 20. d

Form E

1. c 2. d 3. a 4. a 5. c 6. c 7. d 8. a 9. c 10. d 11. a 12. a 13. c 14. d 15. b 16. c 17. d 18. b 19. d 20. b

Form F

1. d 2. a 3. a 4. b 5. b 6. a 7. d 8. b 9. b 10. a 11. d 12. a 13. c 14. c 15. c 16. d 17. a 18. a 19. b 20. d

Cumulative Review 1 – 8 Answers

Form A

1. -2 2. $\dfrac{x^2 - 6x + 2}{x(x-2)}$ 3. $-8x^5 + 2x^2 - 6$ 4. $x + 10 + \dfrac{34}{x-3}$ 5. $-6x^{11}$ 6. $2x^6 + 6x^5 - 8x^4$

7. $9x^2 - 24xy + 16y^2$ 8. $x - 6$ 9. $(x^2 + 9)(x + 3)(x - 3)$ 10. $7x^2 y(1 - 2xy)$

11. $(2x - 5)(3x + 2)$ 12. 3 13. $\{x \mid x \ge 5\}$ 14. $-3, -2$ 15. $-\dfrac{7}{3}, 6$ 16. $(14, -8)$

17. $(14, 10)$

18.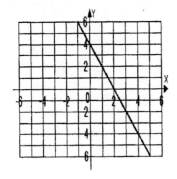

19.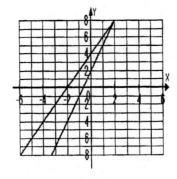

20. $122°$ 21. 65 22. 13 ft. 23. 600% 24. $2T - b = a$ 25. $122°$

Form B

1. a 2. d 3. d 4. c 5. c 6. c 7. b 8. a 9. c 10. d 11. b 12. d 13. c 14. a 15. d 16. c 17. d 18. c 19. b 20. b 21. a 22. b 23. d 24. b 25. a

Chapter 9 Answers

Form A

1. $\{a, e\}$ 2. $\{a, b, c, d, e, i, o, u\}$

3a. $(-1, \infty)$

b.

T-358

4a. $(-\infty, 2]$ **b.**

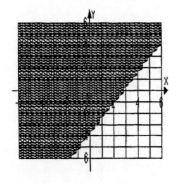

5a. $(-2, 1]$ **b.**

6a. $(-\infty, 1] \cup [2, \infty)$ **b.**

7a. $\varnothing$ **b.**

8a. $\{x \mid -\dfrac{1}{2} \le x \le 2\}$ **b.** $\left[-\dfrac{1}{2}, 2\right]$ **9a.** $\{x \mid x < -\dfrac{13}{2} \text{ or } x > \dfrac{11}{2}\}$ **b.** $\left(-\infty, -\dfrac{13}{2}\right) \cup \left(\dfrac{11}{2}, \infty\right)$

10a. $\{x \mid x \text{ is a real number}\}$ **b.** $(-\infty, \infty)$ **11.** $\{-1, 2\}$ **12.** $\left\{\dfrac{1}{2}, 3\right\}$

13.

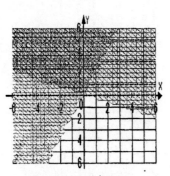

14.

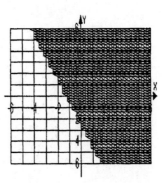

15.

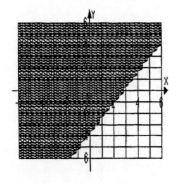

16.

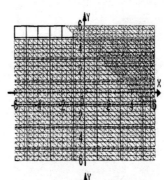

17.

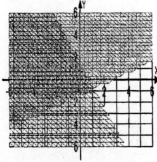

18.

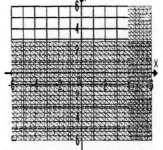

19. [56, 106)　　　20a. 1 horse, 12 cows　b. $6800

Form B

1. {2, 4, 6, 8}　2. {1, 2, 3, 4, 5, 6, 7, 8, 10}

3a. $(-1, \infty)$　　　b. 　-6 -5 -4 -3 -2 -1 0 1 2 3 4 5 6

4a. $(-\infty, 3]$　　　b. 　-6 -5 -4 -3 -2 -1 0 1 2 3 4 5 6

5a. $(-4, -2]$　　　b. 　-6 -5 -4 -3 -2 -1 0 1 2 3 4 5 6

6a. $(-\infty, 2) \cup (4, \infty)$　　　b. 　-6 -5 -4 -3 -2 -1 0 1 2 3 4 5 6

7a. $(-\infty, \infty)$　　　b. 　-6 -5 -4 -3 -2 -1 0 1 2 3 4 5 6

8a. $\left\{ x \mid x \leq \dfrac{1}{2} \text{ or } x > 2 \right\}$　b. $\left(-\infty, \dfrac{1}{2} \right] \cup [2, \infty)$　9a. $\left\{ x \mid -\dfrac{7}{2} < x < \dfrac{9}{2} \right\}$　b. $\left(-\dfrac{7}{2}, \dfrac{9}{2} \right)$　10a. Ø

b. Ø　11. $\left\{ -\dfrac{4}{7}, 2 \right\}$　12. $\left\{ -\dfrac{2}{3}, 8 \right\}$

13.

14.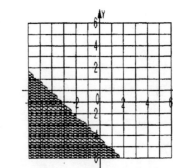

15.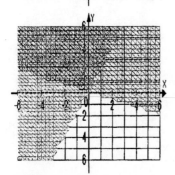

16.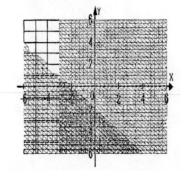

17.　18.

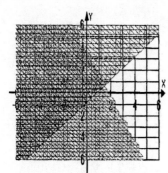 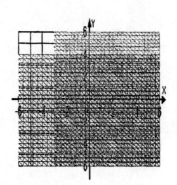

19.　The monthly average temperature is between 52° and 92° F.
20a.　40 plain, 200 logo　b.　$1160

Form C

1. {4}　　　　　　　　2. {2, 3, 4, 5}

3a. [−1, ∞)　　　　b.
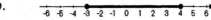

4a. (−∞, 2)　　　　b.
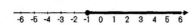

5a. [−3, 4]　　　　b.

6a. (−5, 2)　　　　b.

7a. (−∞, −3) ∪ (1, ∞)　　b.

8a. $\{x \mid -5 \le x \le 1\}$　b. [−5,1]　9a. $\left\{ x \mid x < \dfrac{1}{4} \text{ or } x > \dfrac{5}{4} \right\}$　b. $\left(-\infty, \dfrac{1}{4} \right) \cup \left(\dfrac{5}{4}, \infty \right)$　10a. Ø

b. Ø　11. $\left\{ 0, \dfrac{2}{3} \right\}$　12. $\left\{ 2, \dfrac{10}{3} \right\}$

13.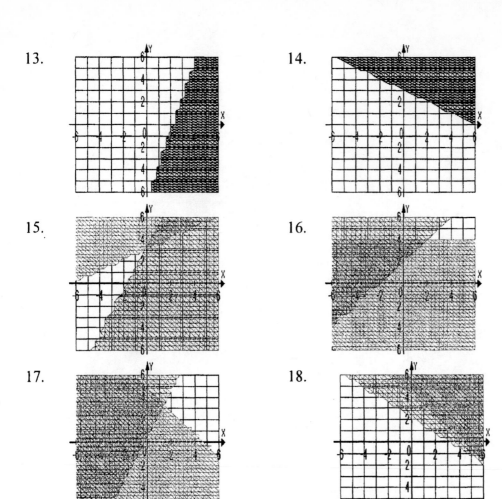

14.

15.

16.

17.

18.

19.   More than 250 checks per month   20. [2035, 2155]

Form D

1. c 2. c 3. b 4. c 5. b 6. d 7. c 8. a 9. c 10. a 11. a 12. c 13. d 14. c
15. b 16. a 17. a 18. a 19. b 20. a

Form E

1. b 2. a 3. a 4. d 5. b 6. c 7. d 8. c 9. a 10. d 11. b 12. a 13. d 14. c
15. c 16. a 17. d 18. b 19. c 20. b

Form F

1. c 2. d 3. d 4. b 5. a 6. d 7. c 8. a 9. d 10. c 11. c 12. a 13. b 14. c
15. a 16. d 17. b 18. b 19. a 20. b

Chapter 10 Answers

Form A

1a. $\left(-\infty, 2\right]$ b. 4   2. $5a^5 b^2 \sqrt{2}$ 3. $3x^2 \sqrt[4]{3y^3}$ 4. $-10\sqrt{3}$ 5. $6ab^3 \sqrt[4]{ab}$ 6. $17 + 4\sqrt{15}$

7. $12x - \sqrt{x} - 20$ 8. $x - 4y$ 9. $\dfrac{3x\sqrt{5x}}{5}$ 10. $\dfrac{3\sqrt[3]{4x^2 y}}{2x}$ 11. $\dfrac{3x - 7\sqrt{x} - 6}{x - 9}$ 12. $y^{\frac{11}{12}}$

13. $2x^2$ 14. $192x^{\frac{11}{2}} y^{\frac{13}{3}}$ 15. $1{,}728$ 16. $\dfrac{1}{256}$ 17. $11i$ 18. $6x\sqrt{2}\,i$ 19. $12 + 18i$

20. $-6 - 17i$ 21. $\dfrac{19}{26} - \dfrac{9}{26} i$ 22. $-i$ 23. $\{-34\}$ 24. $\left\{\dfrac{27}{2}\right\}$ 25. $\{-3, -2\}$

Form B

1. $-(x - y)$ 2. $2xy$ 3. $8a\sqrt{3ab}$ 4. $-3x\sqrt[3]{4xy^2}$ 5. $6x^2 y\sqrt{3x}$ 6. $3\sqrt{2} - 2\sqrt{3}$

7. $27 + \sqrt{3}$ 8. $9y - 24\sqrt{y} + 16$ 9. $25x - 2$ 10. $\dfrac{2\sqrt{3x}}{x}$ 11. $\dfrac{\sqrt[3]{75xy}}{5y}$ 12. $\dfrac{2\sqrt{3} - \sqrt{6}}{3}$

13. $\dfrac{4x - 9}{4\sqrt{x} - 6}$ 14. $\dfrac{1}{27}$ 15. 9 16. $4x^{\frac{1}{12}} y$ 17. $12i$ 18. $-2\sqrt{10}$ 19. $-12 - 18i$

20. $-7 + 26i$ 21. $\dfrac{11}{13} + \dfrac{23}{13} i$ 22. -1 23. $\varnothing$ 24. $\{34\}$ 25. 216 feet

Form C

1a. $(-\infty, 2]$ b. $2\sqrt{6}$ 2. $3x + 4$ 3. $6x$ 4. $-5y^4\sqrt{4x^2 y}$ 5. $52a^3 b^3\sqrt{7a}$ 6. $5x\sqrt{2} - 5x\sqrt{3}$

7. 19 8. $42x - 13\sqrt{2x} - 20$ 9. $48x - 32\sqrt{3x} + 16$ 10. $\dfrac{2\sqrt{30x}}{5x}$ 11. $\dfrac{\sqrt[3]{6x}}{2}$ 12. $\dfrac{7 - 2\sqrt{10}}{3}$

13. $-\dfrac{1}{\sqrt{3} - \sqrt{5}}$ 14. 3 15. $\dfrac{1}{81}$ 16. $\dfrac{48x^5}{4}$ 17. $6xi$ 18. -30 19. $22 + 7i$ 20. $\dfrac{1}{2} + \dfrac{3}{2} i$

21. $-\dfrac{10}{37} + \dfrac{14}{37} i$ 22. i 23. 126 24. $\{20\}$ 25. 36 feet

Form D

1. b 2. a 3. c 4. d 5. c 6. b 7. c 8. a 9. d 10. c 11. b 12. a 13. a 14. d
15. b 16. b 17. c 18. d 19. d 20. c 21. c 22. b 23. a 24. d 25. d

Form E

1. b 2. a 3. d 4. c 5. b 6. d 7. b 8. a 9. c 10. c 11. d 12. c 13. b 14. b
15. d 16. b 17. c 18. c 19. b 20. d 21. b 22. d 23. a 24. a 25. c

Form F

1. b 2. b 3. b 4. d 5. c 6. a 7. b 8. c 9. a 10. b 11. c 12. c 13. a 14. a
15. c 16. b 17. c 18. a 19. c 20. a 21. c 22. b 23. d 24. d 25. a

Cumulative Review 1 – 10 Answers

Form A

1. 3   2. $2x^2 - 2x - 7$ 3. $4x^7$ 4. $x^3 + 27$ 5. $4x^2 - 20x + 25$ 6. $2xy^2\sqrt{6xy}$

7. $-2 \pm \sqrt{5}$ 8. $\dfrac{x(y + x^2)}{x(y^2 - x)}$ 9. $\dfrac{2(x - 7)}{(x + 5)(x - 5)(x - 1)}$ 10. 4   11. $(x - 2)(x^2 + 2x + 4)$

12. $xy(3x + 2)(4x - 1)$ 13. $(y - 4)(2y + x)$ 14. $4(x^2 + 4)(x + 2)(x - 2)$ 15. $\{3\}$

16. $\{4, 2\}$ 17. 18   18. $\dfrac{4 \pm 3\sqrt{3}i}{7}$ 19. $\dfrac{5 \pm \sqrt{65}}{4}$

20. 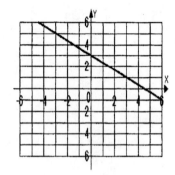   21.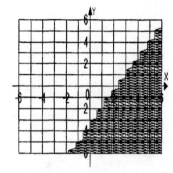

22. 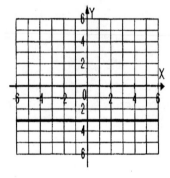   23.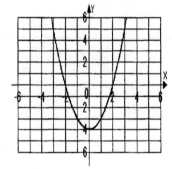

24. 500   25. 7 and 17

Form B

1. c   2. b   3. d   4. a   5. c   6. a   7. b   8. b   9. c   10. a   11. a   12. d   13. a   14. d
15. a   16. c   17. d   18. b   19. a   20. a   21. c   22. b   23. c   24. b   25. b

Chapter 11 Answers

Form A

1. $\left\{\dfrac{3 \pm 3\sqrt{2}}{2}\right\}$ 2. $\{-4 \pm 3i\}$ 3a. 4   b. $(x - 2)^2$ 4a. $\dfrac{1}{4}$ b. $\left(x - \dfrac{1}{2}\right)^2$ 5. $\dfrac{3 \pm \sqrt{5}}{6}$

6. $\left\{\dfrac{2 \pm \sqrt{14}i}{3}\right\}$ 7. $\{-2, 4\}$ 8. 10.82   9. $(-2, 7)$ 10. $8x^2 - 2x - 3 = 0$ 11. $x^2 + 49 = 0$

12. $\left\{-\frac{4}{3},0\right\}$ 13. $\left\{1\pm\sqrt{10}\right\}$ 14. $\left\{\frac{-9\pm\sqrt{7}i}{8}\right\}$ 15. $\left\{\pm\sqrt{5},\pm1\right\}$ 16. $\{1\}$ 17. $(-4,6)$

18. $(-\infty,0]\cup[5,\infty)$ 19. $[-8,4)$

20. $[-7,-3)$ 21a. $(-4,-1)$ b. None c. $(0,-17)$ d. $x=-4$

e.

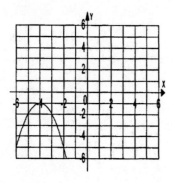

22a. $\left(\frac{1}{2},-\frac{9}{2}\right)$ b. $(-1,0),(2,0)$ c. $(0,-4)$ d. $x=\frac{1}{2}$ e.

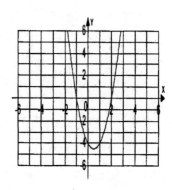

23. 10 in. 24. $\sqrt{2}\sec$ 25. $\left(0,\frac{5}{2}\right)$

Form B

1. $\left\{\frac{1\pm2\sqrt{5}}{4}\right\}$ 2. $\left\{3\pm2\sqrt{2}i\right\}$ 3a. 25 b. $(x+5)^2$ 4a. $\frac{1}{144}$ b. $\left(x-\frac{1}{12}\right)^2$ 5. $\frac{3\pm\sqrt{7}i}{2}$

6. $\left\{\frac{-3\pm\sqrt{21}}{4}\right\}$ 7. $\left\{-\frac{1}{5},-2\right\}$ 8. 14.42 0. $(1,6)$ 10. $40x^2+x-6=0$ 11. $x^2+9=0$

12. $\left\{1\pm\sqrt{10}\right\}$ 13. $\left\{\frac{1\pm2i}{2}\right\}$ 14. $\left\{\frac{-5\pm\sqrt{31}}{2}\right\}$ 15. $\{27,64\}$ 16. $\{\pm1,\pm2\}$ 17. $\left(-\infty,-\frac{3}{2}\right]\cup\left[\frac{3}{2},\infty\right)$

18. $(1,5)$ 19. $(-3,5]$ 20. $(1,\infty)$

21a. $(-2,-3)$ b. $(-3.73,0)$ c. $(-0.27,0)$ d. $x=-2$

e.

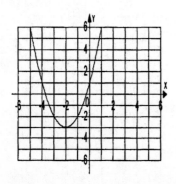

22a. $\left(-\dfrac{1}{2}, -\dfrac{15}{4}\right)$ b. $(-1.61, 0), (0.62, 0)$ c. $(0, -3)$ d. $x = -\dfrac{1}{2}$

e. 2

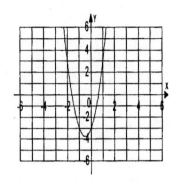

23. 1500 24. 38 ft 25. $(0, 8.74)$

Form C

1a. 49 b. $(x+7)^2$ 2a. $\dfrac{9}{4}$ b. $\left(x - \dfrac{3}{2}\right)^2$ 3. 10.30 4. $(6, 2)$ 5. $4x^2 - 17x - 15 = 0$

6. $x^2 + 100 = 0$ 7. $\left\{2 \pm \sqrt{2}\right\}$ 8. $\{0, 4\}$ 9. $\left\{-1 \pm \sqrt{21}\right\}$ 10. $\dfrac{-5 \pm \sqrt{13}}{6}$ 11. $\left\{3 \pm \sqrt{3}\,i\right\}$

12. $\left\{-2 \pm 3\sqrt{7}\right\}$ 13. $\left\{\pm 1, \pm\dfrac{\sqrt{3}}{3}\right\}$ 14. $(2, 4)$ 15. $(2, 8]$ 16a. $\left(-\dfrac{1}{6}, \dfrac{25}{12}\right)$ b. $(-1, 0)\left(\dfrac{2}{3}, 0\right)$

c. $(0, 2)$ d. $x = -\dfrac{1}{6}$

e.

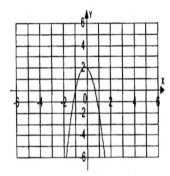

17a. $(4, 2)$ b. $(2.59, 0), (5.41, 0)$ c. $(0, -14)$ d. $x = 4$ e.

18. 1 sec 19. $\dfrac{5\sqrt{3}}{4}$ sec 20. $(0, 4)$

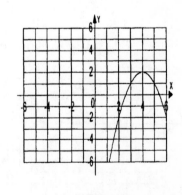

Form D

1. c 2. b 3. a 4. a 5. d 6. c 7. d 8. d 9. a 10. c 11. b 12. a 13. a 14. b

15. d 16. a 17. b 18. c 19. a 20. d 21. b 22. b 23. a 24. a 25. a

Form E

1. d 2. b 3. a 4. c 5. d 6. a 7. b 8. d 9. a 10. c 11. c 12. b 13. a 14. d
15. c 16. b 17. d 18. c 19. a 20. b 21. b 22. a 23. d 24. d 25. a

Form F

1. c 2. c 3. d 4. d 5. c 6. b 7. d 8. b 9. b 10. d 11. c 12. a 13. b 14. d
15. a 16. c 17. a 18. d 19. d 20. c 21. b 22. d 23. b 24. d 25. c

Chapter 12 Answers

Form A

1. $4^y = 8$ 2. $2^x = 64$ 3. $3^2 = x$ 4. $\log_{\frac{3}{4}} y = x$ 5. $\log_9 729 = 3$ 6. $\log_x 256 = 4$

7. $\log_b \dfrac{x^5}{y^3}$ 8. $\ln \sqrt{x} y^2$ 9. $\log \dfrac{x^3 y^4}{z^6}$ 10. $2\log_6 x + 3\log_b y$ 11. $\dfrac{1}{2}\ln x = \dfrac{1}{2}\ln y$

12. $\log 6 - 5\log x$ 13. $(-2, \infty)$ 14. 2.7782 15. {2} 16. {-0.20} 17. {24} 18. {25}
19. 8 years 20. 6.8

Form B

1. $6^y = (x+2)$ 2. $3^x = 81$ 3. $2^5 = x$ 4. $\log_{\frac{4}{3}} y = (1-x)$ 5. $\log_4 64 = 3$ 6. $\log_x 243 = 5$

7. $\log \dfrac{4^{(x+1)} y^{13}}{z^2}$ 8. $\log_b x^9 y^2$ 9. $\ln \dfrac{x^2}{y^4 z^3}$ 10. $\dfrac{1}{4}\log_7 x + \dfrac{1}{4}\log_7 y$ 11. $\dfrac{2}{3}\log x = \dfrac{1}{3}\log y$

12. $\log 4 - 3\log x$ 13. $(-\infty, 6)$ 14. 3.4022 15. (–3} 16. {-0.54} 17. {32.5} 18. {1}
19. $6099.45 20. 7.9

Form C

1. $8^x = 2$ 2. $x^3 = 125$ 3. $6^2 = x$ 4. $\log_{\frac{3}{4}} y = (4x-4)$ 5. $\log_7 49 = 2$ 6. $\log_x 243 = 5$

7. $\ln y^6 z^4$ 8. $\log \dfrac{x^3}{y^5 z^6}$ 9. $\log x\sqrt[3]{y}$ 10. $3\ln x + 4\ln y - 2\ln z$ 11. $\log 3 - 4\log y$

12. $\ln 7 + \ln x$ 13. $(-\infty, 0)$ 14. 1.7618 15. {2} 16. {0.20} 17. {6}
18. {4} –9 does not check 19. $1,647.83 20. 0.46 year

Form D

1. b 2. d 3. a 4. d 5. a 6. d 7. a 8. d 9. c 10. b 11. c 12. b 13. b 14. b
15. c 16. d 17. b 18. d 19. b 20. d

Form E

1. c 2. a 3. b 4. d 5. c 6 d 7. a 8. c 9. b 10. c 11. d 12. d 13. b 14. a
15. b 16. c 17. d 18. b 19. d 20. b

Form F

1. b 2. c 3. b 4. c 5. a 6. d 7. d 8. b 9. c 10. b 11. b 12. a 13. d 14. c
15. d 16. a 17. c 18. b 19. d 20. a

Cumulative Review Chapters 1–12 Answers

Form A

1. -71 2. $-\dfrac{2x^6}{y^7}$ 3. $\dfrac{4x^2+7x-5}{(x+2)(x-2)}$ 4. $46xy\sqrt{2y}$ 5. $\dfrac{12+3\sqrt{2}}{14}$ 6. $\dfrac{\sqrt[3]{36x^2}}{3x}$

7. $x^4-8x^2y+16y^2$ 8. $-6x+3$ 9. $(2x-3)(4x^2+6x+9)$ 10. $(x+2)(x-2)(x+1)$

11. $\left\{\dfrac{5}{8}\right\}$ 12. $\left\{\dfrac{1}{2}\right\}$ 13. $\left\{\dfrac{-6\pm5\sqrt{2}i}{5}\right\}$ 14. $\left\{\dfrac{2\pm\sqrt{14}i}{3}\right\}$ 15. $\varnothing$; 3 does not check 16. $(1,2)$

17. $(3,2,1)$ 18. $(-\infty,-5)\cup(3,\infty)$ 19. $y=\dfrac{1}{2}x+\dfrac{11}{2}$ 20. $x=\dfrac{2}{3z-2y}$

21. $\{x \mid x \neq -4 \text{ and } x \neq 2\}$ 22. $3x^2+10x-8=0$

23.

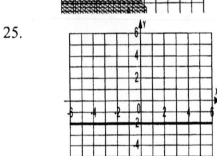

24.

25.

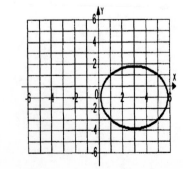

Form B

1. b 2. a 3. c 4. c 5. a 6. a 7. b 8. c 9. d 10. d 11. c 12. b 13. a 14. a
15. a 16. d 17. a 18. d 19. a 20. a 21 b 22. d 23. b 24. c 25. a

Chapter 13 Answers

Form A

1. ellipse 2. parabola 3. circle 4. hyperbola 5. parabola 6. $(x-2)^2+(y+3)^2=9$
7a. $(-3,2)$ b. 3 8. $(-10,4)$ 9. $y=1$

10.

11.

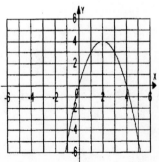

12.

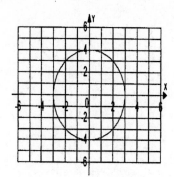

13.

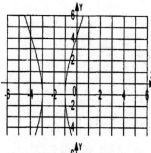

14.

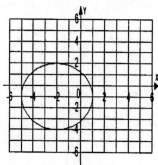

15.

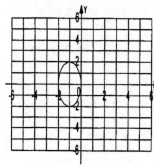

16.

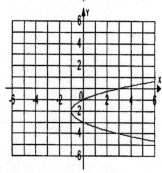

17. Ø **18.** (5, 0),(–5, 0) **19.** 28 **20.** 19 and 29

Form B

1. parabola 2. hyperbola 3. ellipse 4. parabola 5. circle 6. $(x-4)^2 + (x-1)^2 = 25$

7a. (1, –2) b. 2 8. $\left(-\dfrac{15}{2}, -\dfrac{3}{2}\right)$ 9. $y = -1$

10.

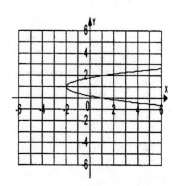

11.

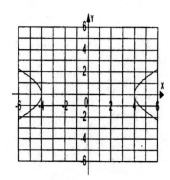

12.

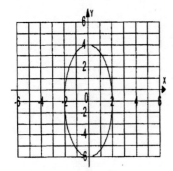

13.

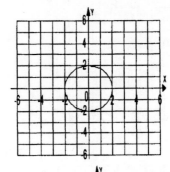

14.

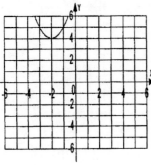

15.

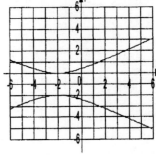

16.

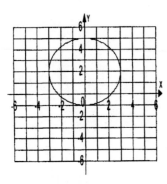

17. (2, 1), (4, 3) 18. (1, 1), (–1, 1) 19. 6 ft x 8 ft
20. 27

Form C

1. hyperbola 2. parabola 3. ellipse 4. parabola 5. circle 6. $x^2 + (y-5)^2 = 36$

7a. (–4, 3) b. 4 8. (–4, –3) 9. $\frac{3}{2}$

10.

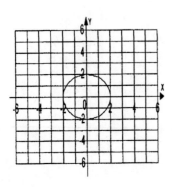

11.

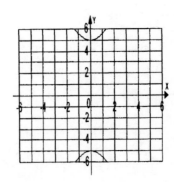

12.
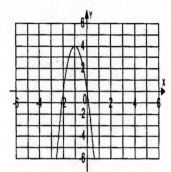

13.
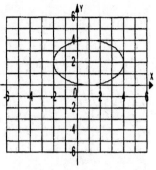

14.
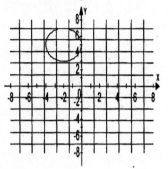

15.
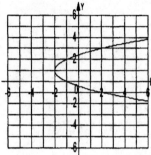

16.
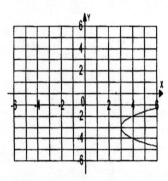

17.
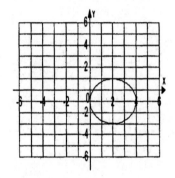

18. Ø   19. (4,0),(–4,0)   20. 15 and 18

Form D

1. a 2. d 3. c 4. d 5. b 6. c 7. a 8. b 9. c 10. c 11. b 12. c 13. a 14. d
15. b 16. b 17. a 18. b 19. c 20. d

Form E

1. d 2. a 3. a 4. b 5. c 6. b 7. d 8. b 9. c 10. d 11. d 12. d 13. d 14. c
15. d 16. c 17. a 18. b 19. b 20. c

Form F

1. b 2. d 3. d 4. c 5. a 6. c 7. b 8. c 9. c 10. b 11. d 12. c 13. d 14. c
15. d 16. c 17. c 18. b 19. c 20. a

Chapter 14 Answers

Form A

1. $\frac{3}{5}, \frac{4}{5}, 1, \frac{6}{5}$ 2. $-2, 5, -10, 17$ 3. 67 4. $\sum_{i=1}^{8} \frac{1}{4^i}$ 5. $10, 6, 2, -2$ 6a. $a_n = 4n + 13$ b. 69

7. -1575 8. $10, -20, 40, -80$ 9. $12, 3, \dfrac{3}{4}, \dfrac{3}{16}$ 10. $354,294$ 11. 4096 12a. $a_n = 15\left(-\dfrac{1}{3}\right)^{n-1}$

b. $\dfrac{5}{243}$ 13. 488 14. 20 15. $\dfrac{5}{9}$ 16. $82,251$ 17. $16x^4 + 32x^3 y + 24x^2 y^2 + 8xy^3 + y^4$

18. $256x^8 - 4096x^7 + 28,672x^6$ 19. $-42,240x^4 y^7$ 20. 378

Form B

1. $2, 9, 28, 65$ 2. $4, -5, 6, -7$ 3. 50 4. $\displaystyle\sum_{i=1}^{10} \dfrac{1}{i^2}$ 5. $-8, -3, 2, 7$ 6a. $a_n = 4n + 11$ b. 107

7. -2800 8. $8, 32, 128, 512$ 9. $-4, 2, -1, \dfrac{1}{2}$ 10. $46,875$ 11. $\dfrac{25}{64}$ 12a. $a_n = 20\left(-\dfrac{1}{4}\right)^{n-1}$

b. $-\dfrac{5}{4096}$ 13. 363 14. 8 15. $\dfrac{7}{9}$ 16. $5,461,512$ 17. $j^3 + 9j^2 k + 27 jk^2 + 27k^3$

18. $x^6 - 12x^5 + 60x^4$ 19. $59,136x^6 y^6$ 20. 74

Form C

1. $-\dfrac{1}{3}, 0, 1, \dfrac{8}{3}$ 2. $\dfrac{1}{2}, -\dfrac{2}{3}, \dfrac{3}{4}, -\dfrac{4}{5}$ 3. 94 4. $\displaystyle\sum_{i=1}^{5} \dfrac{(-1)^{i+1}}{3(i+1)}$ 5. $31, 23, 15, 7$ 6a. $a_n = 10 - 3n$

b. -20 7. 2667 8. $22, -66, 198, -594$ 9. $6, 3, \dfrac{3}{2}, \dfrac{3}{4}$ 10. 1 11. $839,808$

12a. $a_n = \dfrac{1}{4}\left(\dfrac{2}{5}\right)^{n-1}$ b. $\dfrac{32}{78125}$ 13. $\dfrac{55}{9}$ 14. $\dfrac{80}{3}$ 15. $\dfrac{5}{11}$ 16. 3654

17. $81x^4 - 108x^3 y + 54x^2 y^2 - 12xy^3 + y^4$ 18. $x^7 - 21x^6 y + 189x^5 y^2 - 945x^4 y^3$ 19. $729y^6$

20. $11,325$

Form D

1. c 2. d 3. d 4. b 5. b 6. a 7. d 8. d 9. b 10. a 11. b 12. b 13. c 14. c
15. a 16. d 17. d 18. a 19. b 20. d

Form E

1. c 2. b 3. d 4. d 5. d 6. a 7. a 8. a 9. c 10. b 11. c 12. d 13. a 14. c
15. a 16. b 17. c 18. b 19. a 20. a

Form F

1. d 2. b 3. a 4. d 5. c 6. b 7. b 8. d 9. a 10. b 11. b 12. b 13. a 14. a
15. d 16. c 17. d 18. a 19. a 20. d

Cumulative Review Chapters 1–14 Answers

Form A

1. -7 2. $20x + 24$ 3. $\dfrac{x^8}{y^3}$ 4. -11 5. $x^2 + x + 1$ 6. $-3x + 5x^2 - x + 6$ 7. $18x^2 + 15x - 7$

8. $\dfrac{-8}{(x+4)(x-4)}$ 9. $2x-9+\dfrac{29}{x+3}$ 10. x^2 11. $\dfrac{2x-2\sqrt{2x}}{x-2}$ 12. $7\sqrt{2}i$ 13. $(x-5)(x^2+5x+25)$

14. $\{6\}$ 15. $\varnothing$ 16. $[0,9]$ 17. $\left[-\dfrac{4}{3},2\right]$ 18. $\{-6\}$ 19. $\left\{\dfrac{81}{25}\right\}$ 20. $\{1\pm2i\}$ 21. $\{-6\}$ 22. $f^{-1}(x)=\dfrac{x-2}{5}$

23.

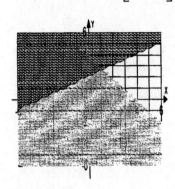

24.

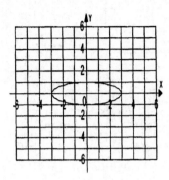

25. 0.462 year

Form B

1. c 2. d 3. a 4. a 5. a 6. b 7. c 8. d 9. c 10. a 11. b 12. c 13. b 14. d 15. a
16. c 17. a 18. d 19. c 20. c 21. d 22. c 23 d 24. d 25. b

Final Answers

Form A

1. -17 2. 9 3. $-2x^4+3x^2-x$ 4. $2x^2-2x+1-\dfrac{7}{2x-1}$ 5. $x^3-2x^2-2x+12$

6. $4x^2-20xy+25y^2$ 7. $\dfrac{3}{4}$ 8. $\dfrac{x-4}{3(x-5)}$ 9. $\dfrac{x^2+6x-3}{(x+4)(x+6)}$ 10. $\dfrac{(y-3)(y-1)}{(y+3)(y+1)}$ 11. $8\sqrt{2}i$

12. $14x^2\sqrt{3}$ 13. $41-23i$ 14. $\dfrac{1}{4}$ 15. 4×10^7 16. $2\sqrt{6}+4$ 17. 1.07×10^7 18. $B=\dfrac{2A-bh}{h}$

19. $\log_b\dfrac{x^5}{y^2}$ 20. $4(x+2)(x-2)$ 21. $(x+y)(y-4)$ 22. $(x+1)(x^2-x+1)$ 23. $(3x-2y)(4x-5y)$

24. $(25x^2+9)(5x+3)(5x-3)$ 25. $2x(3x-4)(x+8)$ 26. $\left\{\dfrac{3}{2}\right\}$ 27. $\{x\,|\,x\geq-19\}$ 28. $\{2\}$

29. $\left\{-3,\dfrac{2}{5}\right\}$ 30. No solution; 2 does not check 31. $\{1,2\}$ 32. $\left\{\dfrac{6\pm4\sqrt{3}}{7}\right\}$ 33. $\left(-\dfrac{6}{5},2\right)$

34. $(4,1)$ 35. $(-8,3,-2)$ 36. 15

37.

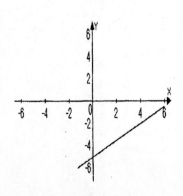

38.

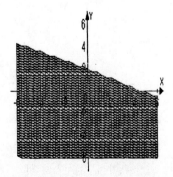

39.

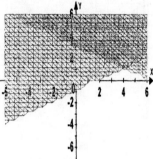

40.

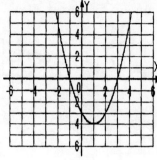

41.

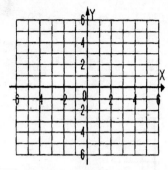

42.

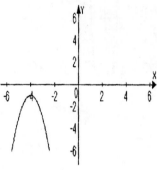

43.

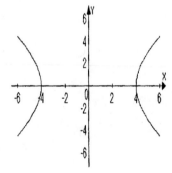

44.

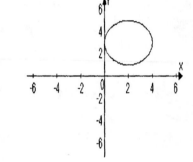

45. $y = \dfrac{3}{4}x + 9$ 46. $f^{-1}(x) = \dfrac{x+5}{3}$ 47. $(x+2)^2 + (y-4)^2 = 16$ 48. 140

49. 3906   50. $1500

Form B

1. b 2. b 3. c 4. b 5. a 6. d 7. b 8. c 9. d 10. d 11. b 12. a 13. c 14. c
15. b 16. a 17. a 18. d 19. c 20. a 21. d 22. a 23. c 24. c 25. d 26. c 27. b
28. d 29. b 30. a 31. b 32. d 33. d 34. d 35. a 36. c 37. c 38. d 39. a 40. c
41. a 42. c 43. c 44. c 45. a 46. c 47. b 48. a 49. d 50. b